Second Edition

Taken From

Intermediate Algebra, Fourth Edition
by John Tobey and Jeffrey Slater

Custom Edition for Hostos Community College

Jeffrey Slater
John Tobey

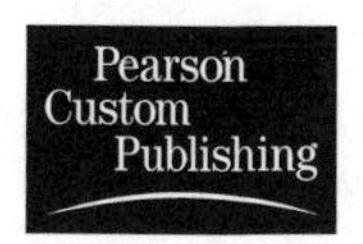

Taken from:

Intermediate Algebra, Fourth Edition
by John Tobey and Jeffrey Slater

A Pearson Education Company
Upper Saddle River, New Jersey 07458

This special edition published in cooperation with Pearson Custom Publishing.

Printed in the United States of America

10 9 8 7 6 5 4 3 2

Please visit our web site at www.pearsoncustom.com

ISBN 0–536–70055–9

BA 995657

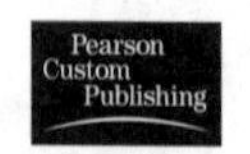

PEARSON CUSTOM PUBLISHING
75 Arlington Street, Suite 300, Boston, MA 02116
A Pearson Education Company

CONTENTS

Chapter 7

Rational Exponents and Radicals 109

Chapter 8

Quadratic Equations and Inequalities 173

Chapter 9

The Conic Sections 235

Chapter 5

Polynomials

Equations can be used to simulate aircraft flights and are especially helpful for determining the locations of missing aircraft. In the United States, planes are tracked continuously by a number of radar sites. Could you estimate the path of an airplane that has disappeared from the radar screen and is missing? Turn to the Putting Your Skills to Work exercises on page 302 to find out.

Pretest Chapter 5

1. ______

2. ______

3. ______

4. ______

5. ______

6. ______

7. ______

8. ______

9. ______

10. ______

11. ______

12. ______

13. ______

14. ______

15. ______

If you are familiar with the topics in this chapter, take this test now. Check your answers with those in the back of the book. If an answer is wrong or you can't do an exercise, study the appropriate section of the chapter.

If you are not familiar with the topics in this chapter, don't take this test now. Instead, study the examples, work the practice exercises, and then take the test.

This test will help you identify those concepts that you have mastered and those that need more study.

Follow the directions. Simplify all answers.

Section 5.1

Simplify.

1. $(5x^2 - 3x + 2) + (-3x^2 - 5x - 8) - (x^2 + 3x - 10)$

2. $(x^2 - 3x - 4)(2x - 3)$

3. $(5a - 8)(a - 7)$

4. $(2y - 3)(2y + 3)$

5. $(3x^2 + 4)^2$

6. Evaluate the polynomial function $p(x) = 2x^3 - 5x^2 - 6x + 1$ for $p(-3)$.

Sections 5.2 and 5.3

Simplify.

7. $(25x^3y^2 - 30x^2y^3 - 50x^2y^2) \div 5x^2y^2$

8. $(3y^3 - 5y^2 + 2y - 1) \div (y - 2)$

9. $(2x^4 + 9x^3 + 8x^2 - 9x - 10) \div (2x + 5)$

Section 5.4

Factor completely.

10. $24a^3b^2 + 36a^4b^2 - 60a^3b^3$

11. $3x(4x - 3y) - 2(4x - 3y)$

12. $10wx + 6xz - 15yz - 25wy$

Section 5.5

Factor.

13. $x^2 - 7xy + 10y^2$

14. $4y^2 - 4y - 15$

15. $28x^2 - 19xy + 3y^2$

Section 5.6

Factor.

16. $36x^2 - 60xy + 25y^2$

16. ______

17. $121x^2 - 1$

17. ______

18. $8x^3 - y^3$

18. ______

19. $64x^3 + 27$

19. ______

Section 5.7

Factor if possible. Indicate the prime expressions.

20. $x^3y^3 - 27y^6$

20. ______

21. $2x^3 - 2x^2 - 24x$

21. ______

22. $2x^2 + 8x - 3$

22. ______

23. $81a^3 + 126a^2y + 49ay^2$

23. ______

Section 5.8

Solve by factoring.

24. $12x^2 + x - 6 = 0$

24. ______

25. $3x^2 + 5x = 7x^2 - 2x$

25. ______

26. $(x + 5)(x - 3) = 2x + 1$

26. ______

▲ **27.** The area of a rectangle is 52 square meters. The length of the rectangle is 1 meter longer than three times its width. Find the length and width of the rectangle.

27. ______

5.1 Introduction to Polynomials and Polynomial Functions: Addition, Subtraction, and Multiplication

Student Learning Objectives

After studying this section, you will be able to:

1. Identify types and degrees of polynomials.
2. Evaluate a polynomial function.
3. Add and subtract polynomials.
4. Multiply polynomials.
5. Multiply two binomials by FOIL.
6. Multiply two binomials $(a + b)(a - b)$.
7. Multiply two binomials $(a - b)^2$ or $(a + b)^2$.

SSM PH TUTOR CENTER CD & VIDEO MATH PRO WEB

1 *Identifying Types and Degrees of Polynomials*

A **polynomial** is an algebraic expression of one or more terms. A **term** is a number, a variable raised to a nonnegative integer power, or a product of numbers and variables raised to nonnegative integer powers. There must be no division by a variable. Three types of polynomials that you will see often are **monomials, binomials**, and **trinomials.**

1. A **monomial** has *one* term.
2. A **binomial** has *two* terms.
3. A **trinomial** has *three* terms.

Here are some examples of polynomials.

Number of Variables	Monomials	Binomials	Trinomials	Other Polynomials
One Variable	$8x^3$	$2y^2 + 3y$	$5x^2 + 2x - 6$	$x^4 + 2x^3 - x^2 + 9$
Two Variables	$6x^2y$	$3x^2 - 5y^3$	$8x^2 + 5xy - 3y^2$	$x^3y + 5xy^2 + 3xy - 7y^5$
Three Variables	$12uvw^3$	$11a^2b + 5c^2$	$4a^2b^4 + 7c^4 - 2a^5$	$3c^2 + 4c - 8d + 2e - e^2$

The following are *not* polynomials.

$$2x^{-3} + 5x^2 - 3 \qquad 4ab^{\frac{1}{2}} \qquad \frac{2}{x} + \frac{3}{y}$$

To Think About Give a reason each expression is not a polynomial.

Polynomials are also classified by degree. The **degree of a term** is the sum of the exponents of its variables. The **degree of a polynomial** is the degree of the highest-degree term in the polynomial. If the polynomial has no variable, then it has degree zero.

EXAMPLE 1 Name the type of polynomial and give its degree.

(a) $5x^6 + 3x^2 + 2$ **(b)** $7x + 6$

(c) $5x^2y + 3xy^3 + 6xy$ **(d)** $7x^4y^5$

(a) This is a trinomial of degree 6.

(b) This is a binomial of degree 1. Remember that if a variable has no exponent, the exponent is understood to be 1.

(c) This is a trinomial of degree 4.

(d) This is a monomial of degree 9.

Practice Problem 1 State the type of polynomial and give its degree.

(a) $3x^5 - 6x^4 + x^2$ **(b)** $5x^2 + 2$

(c) $3ab + 5a^2b^2 - 6a^4b$ **(d)** $16x^4y^6$

Some polynomials contain only one variable. A **polynomial in *x*** is an expression of the form

$$a_nx^n + a_{n-1}x^{n-1} + a_{n-2}x^{n-2} + \cdots + a_0$$

where n is a nonnegative integer and the constants $a_n, a_{n-1}, a_{n-2}, \ldots, a_0$ are real numbers. We usually write polynomials in **descending order** of the variable. That is, the exponents on the variables decrease from left to right. For example, the polynomial $4x^5 - 2x^3 + 6x^2 + 5x - 8$ is written in descending order.

2 Evaluating Polynomial Functions

A **polynomial function** is a function that is defined by a polynomial.
For example,

$$p(x) = 5x^2 - 3x + 6 \quad \text{and} \quad p(x) = 2x^5 - 3x^3 + 8x - 15$$

are both polynomial functions.

To evaluate a polynomial function, we use the skills developed in Section 3.5.

EXAMPLE 2 Evaluate the polynomial function $p(x) = -3x^3 + 2x^2 - 5x + 6$ for **(a)** $p(-3)$ and **(b)** $p(6)$.

(a) $p(-3) = -3(-3)^3 + 2(-3)^2 - 5(-3) + 6$
$= -3(-27) + 2(9) - 5(-3) + 6$
$= 81 + 18 + 15 + 6$
$= 120$

(b) $p(6) = -3(6)^3 + 2(6)^2 - 5(6) + 6$
$= -3(216) + 2(36) - 5(6) + 6$
$= -648 + 72 - 30 + 6$
$= -600$

Practice Problem 2 Evaluate the polynomial function $p(x) = 2x^4 - 3x^3 + 6x - 8$ for **(a)** $p(-2)$ **(b)** $p(5)$.

3 Adding and Subtracting Polynomials

We can add and subtract polynomials by combining like terms as we learned in Section 1.5.

EXAMPLE 3 Add: $(5x^2 - 3x - 8) + (-3x^2 - 7x + 9)$

$5x^2 - 3x - 8 - 3x^2 - 7x + 9$ We remove the parentheses and combine like terms.
$= 2x^2 - 10x + 1$

Practice Problem 3 Add: $(-7x^2 + 5x - 9) + (2x^2 - 3x + 5)$

To subtract real numbers, we add the opposite of the second number to the first. Thus, for real numbers a and b, we have $a - (+b) = a + (-b)$. Similarly for polynomials, to subtract polynomials we add the opposite of the second polynomial to the first.

EXAMPLE 4 Subtract: $(-5x^2 - 19x + 15) - (3x^2 - 4x + 13)$

$(-5x^2 - 19x + 15) + (-3x^2 + 4x - 13)$ We add the opposite of the second polynomial to the first polynomial.
$= -8x^2 - 15x + 2$

Practice Problem 4 Subtract: $(2x^2 - 14x + 9) - (-3x^2 + 10x + 7)$

4 Multiplying Polynomials

The distributive property is the basis for multiplying polynomials. Recall that

$$a(b + c) = ab + ac.$$

We can use this property to multiply a polynomial by a monomial.

$$3xy(5x^3 + 2x^2 - 4x + 1) = 3xy(5x^3) + 3xy(2x^2) - 3xy(4x) + 3xy(1)$$
$$= 15x^4y + 6x^3y - 12x^2y + 3xy$$

A similar procedure can be used to multiply two binomials.

$$\begin{aligned}(3x+5)(6x+7) &= (3x+5)6x + (3x+5)7 \quad \text{We use the distributive property again.}\\ &= (3x)(6x) + (5)(6x) + (3x)(7) + (5)(7)\\ &= 18x^2 + 30x + 21x + 35\\ &= 18x^2 + 51x + 35\end{aligned}$$

A popular method for multiplying two binomials, called the **FOIL method**, will be introduced in Example 7.

The multiplication of a binomial and a trinomial is more involved. One way to multiply two polynomials is to write them vertically, as we do when multiplying two- and three-digit numbers. We then multiply them in the usual way.

EXAMPLE 5 Multiply: $(4x^2 - 2x + 3)(-3x + 4)$

$$\begin{array}{rrrrl} & 4x^2 & -\ 2x & +\ 3 & \\ & & -\ 3x & +\ 4 & \\ \hline & 16x^2 & -\ 8x & +\ 12 & \quad \text{Multiply } (4x^2 - 2x + 3)(+4). \\ -12x^3 & +\ 6x^2 & -\ 9x & & \quad \text{Multiply } (4x^2 - 2x + 3)(-3x). \\ \hline -12x^3 & +\ 22x^2 & -\ 17x & +\ 12 & \quad \text{Add the two products.} \end{array}$$

Practice Problem 5 Multiply: $(2x^2 - 3x + 1)(x^2 - 5x)$

Another way to multiply polynomials is to multiply horizontally. We redo Example 5 in the following example.

EXAMPLE 6 Multiply in a horizontal fashion $(4x^2 - 2x + 3)(-3x + 4)$.

By the distributive law, we have the following:

$$\begin{aligned}(4x^2 - 2x + 3)(-3x + 4) &= (4x^2 - 2x + 3)(-3x) + (4x^2 - 2x + 3)(4)\\ &= -12x^3 + 6x^2 - 9x + 16x^2 - 8x + 12\\ &= -12x^3 + 22x^2 - 17x + 12\end{aligned}$$

In actual practice you will find that you can do some of these steps mentally.

Practice Problem 6 Multiply in a horizontal fashion $(2x^2 - 3x + 1)(x^2 - 5x)$.

5 Multiplying Two Binomials by FOIL

The FOIL method for multiplying two binomials has been developed to help you keep track of the order of the terms to be multiplied. The acronym FOIL means the following:

F	**First**
O	**Outer**
I	**Inner**
L	**Last**

That is, we multiply the first terms, then the outer terms, then the inner terms, and finally, the last terms.

EXAMPLE 7 Multiply: $(5x + 2)(7x - 3)$

First Last — First + Outer + Inner + Last

$$\begin{aligned}(5x + 2)(7x - 3) &= 35x^2 - 15x + 14x - 6\\ &= 35x^2 - x - 6\end{aligned}$$

Inner

Outer

Practice Problem 7 Multiply: $(7x + 3)(2x - 5)$

EXAMPLE 8 Multiply: $(7x^2 - 8)(2x - 3)$

First Last

$$(7x^2 - 8)(2x - 3) = 14x^3 - 21x^2 - 16x + 24$$

Inner

Outer

Note that in this case we were not able to combine the inner and outer products.

Practice Problem 8 Multiply: $(5a - 2b)(3c - 4d)$

6 Multiplying $(a + b)(a - b)$

Products of the form $(a + b)(a - b)$ deserve special attention.

$$(a + b)(a - b) = a^2 - ab + ab - b^2 = a^2 - b^2$$

Notice that the middle terms, $-ab$ and $+ab$, when combined equal zero. The product is the difference of two squares, $a^2 - b^2$. This is always true when you multiply binomials of the form $(a + b)(a - b)$. You should memorize the following formula.

$$(a + b)(a - b) = a^2 - b^2 \qquad (3.1)$$

EXAMPLE 9 Multiply: $(2a - 9b)(2a + 9b)$

$$\begin{aligned}(2a - 9b)(2a + 9b) &= (2a)^2 - (9b)^2 \\ &= 4a^2 - 81b^2\end{aligned}$$

Of course, we could have used the FOIL method, but recognizing the special product allowed us to save time.

Practice Problem 9 Multiply: $(7x - 2y)(7x + 2y)$

7 Multiplying $(a - b)^2$ or $(a + b)^2$

Another special product is the square of a binomial.

$$(a - b)^2 = (a - b)(a - b) = a^2 - ab - ab + b^2 = a^2 - 2ab + b^2$$

Once you understand the pattern, you should memorize these two formulas.

$$(a - b)^2 = a^2 - 2ab + b^2 \qquad (3.2)$$

$$(a + b)^2 = a^2 + 2ab + b^2 \qquad (3.3)$$

This procedure is also called **expanding a binomial.** *Note*: $(a - b)^2 \neq a^2 - b^2$ and $(a + b)^2 \neq a^2 + b^2$.

EXAMPLE 10 Multiply (that is, expand the binomials).

(a) $(5a - 8b)^2$ **(b)** $(3u + 11v^2)^2$

(a) $(5a - 8b)^2 = (5a)^2 - 2(5a)(8b) + (8b)^2$
$= 25a^2 - 80ab + 64b^2$

(b) Here $a = 3u$ and $b = 11v^2$.

$$\begin{aligned}(3u + 11v^2)^2 &= (3u)^2 + 2(3u)(11v^2) + (11v^2)^2 \\ &= 9u^2 + 66uv^2 + 121v^4\end{aligned}$$

Practice Problem 10 Multiply.

(a) $(4u + 5v)^2$ **(b)** $(7x^2 - 3y^2)^2$

5.1 Exercises

Name the type of polynomial and give its degree.

1. $26x^3y - 35$

2. $12a + 15ab - 16$

3. $17x^3y^5z$

4. $\frac{1}{2}xy^4 + \frac{1}{3}x^2y^5$

5. $\frac{3}{5}m^3n - \frac{2}{5}mn + \frac{1}{5}n^8$

6. $-27ab^3cd$

Simplify the following polynomials.

7. $(x^2 + 3x - 2) + (-2x^2 - 5x + 1) + (x^2 - x - 5)$

8. $(2x^2 - 5x - 1) + (3x^2 - 7x + 3) + (-5x^2 + x + 1)$

9. $(4x^3 - 6x^2 - 3x + 5.5) - (2x^3 + 3x^2 - 5x - 8.3)$

10. $(3x^3 + 2x^2 - 8x - 9.2) - (-5x^3 + x^2 - x - 12.7)$

11. $(5a^3 - 2a^2 - 6a + 8) + (5a + 6) - (-a^2 - a + 2)$

12. $(a^4 - a) + (6a^3 + 5a^2 + 2a - 4) - (a^3 - 8)$

13. $\left(\frac{1}{2}x^2 - 7x\right) + \left(\frac{1}{3}x^2 + \frac{1}{4}x\right)$

14. $\left(\frac{1}{5}x^2 + 9x\right) + \left(\frac{4}{5}x^2 - \frac{1}{6}x\right)$

15. $(2.3x^3 - 5.6x^2 - 2) - (5.5x^3 - 7.4x^2 + 2)$

16. $(5.9x^3 + 3.4x^2 - 7) - (2.9x^3 - 9.6x^2 + 3)$

For the polynomial function $p(x) = 5x^2 - 9x - 12$ *find the following:*

17. $p(3)$

18. $p(-4)$

For the polynomial function $g(x) = -2x^3 - 3x^2 + 5x + 8$ *find the following:*

19. $g(-2)$

20. $g(5)$

For the polynomial function $h(x) = 2x^4 - x^3 + 2x^2 - 4x - 3$ *find the following:*

21. $h(-1)$

22. $h(3)$

Multiply.

23. $2x(3x^2 - 5x + 1)$

24. $-5x(x^2 - 6x - 2)$

25. $-\frac{1}{3}xy(2x - 6y + 15)$

26. $\frac{3}{5}xy^3(x - 10y + 4)$

27. $(6x + 7)(x + 1)$

28. $(2x - 4)(9x - 5)$

29. $(5w + 2d)(3a - 4b)$

30. $(7a + 8b)(5d - 8w)$

31. $(3x - 2y)(-4x + y)$

32. $(-9x - 5y)(3a + 2y)$

33. $(7r - s^2)(-4a - 11s^2)$

34. $(-3r - 2s^2)(5r - 6s^2)$

35. $(2x - 3)(x^2 - x + 1)$

36. $(4x + 1)(2x^2 + x + 1)$

37. $(3x^2 - 2xy - 6y^2)(2x - y)$

38. $(5x^2 + 3xy - 7y^2)(3x - 2y)$

39. $\left(\frac{3}{2}x^2 - x + 1\right)(x^2 + 2x - 6)$

40. $\left(\frac{2}{3}x^2 + 5x - 2\right)(2x^2 - 3x + 9)$ **41.** $(5a^3 - 3a^2 + 2a - 4)(a - 3)$ **42.** $(2b^3 - 5b^2 - 4b + 1)(2b - 1)$

43. $(r^2 + 3rs - 2s^2)(3r^2 - 4rs - 2s^2)$

44. $(m^2 - 6mp + 2p^2)(2m^2 - 4mp + 3p^2)$

Multiply mentally.

45. $(5x - 8y)(5x + 8y)$

46. $(2a - 7b)(2a + 7b)$

47. $(5a - 2b)^2$

48. $(6a + 5b)^2$

49. $(7m - 1)^2$

50. $(5r + 3)^2$

51. $\left(\frac{1}{2}x^2 - 1\right)\left(\frac{1}{2}x^2 + 1\right)$

52. $\left(1 - \frac{2}{3}x^3\right)\left(1 + \frac{2}{3}x^3\right)$

53. $(2a^2b^2 - 3)^2$

54. $(3x^2 - 5y^2)^2$

55. $(0.6x - 0.5y^2)(0.6x + 0.5y^2)$

56. $(0.8x + 0.9y^2)(0.8x - 0.9y^2)$

First multiply any two binomials in the exercise; then multiply the result by the third binomial.

57. $(x + 2)(x - 3)(2x - 5)$

58. $(x - 6)(x + 2)(3x + 2)$

59. $(a + 3)(2 - a)(4 - 3a)$

60. $(6 - 5a)(a + 1)(2 - 3a)$

Applications

▲ **61.** The area of the base of a rectangular box measures $2x^2 + 5x + 8$ cm^2. The height of the box measures $3x + 5$ cm. Find the volume of the box.

▲ **62.** A rectangular garden has $3n^2 + 4n + 7$ flowers planted in each row. The garden has $2n + 5$ rows. Find the number of flowers in the garden.

The concentration of a certain antimalaria medication, in parts per million after time t, in hours, is given by the polynomial $p(t) = -0.03t^2 + 78$.

63. Find the concentration after 3 hours.

64. Find the concentration after 30 hours.

65. Find the concentration after 50 hours.

66. Find the concentration after 50.9 hours.

Cumulative Review Problems

67. Evaluate $\frac{3(2)^2 - 6}{5(-2) - (-1)}$.

68. Evaluate $4(3^2 - 4) + 5 \cdot 12 \div 10$.

69. An American Airlines jet is cruising at an altitude of 31,000 feet on an approach to Logan Airport. The tower instructs the jet to descend to 8000 feet for the final approach. The plane is descending at a rate of 2500 feet per minute. How long will it take the jet to reach the 8000-foot altitude?

70. A certain company produces small "reminder" notepads. Each pad has eighty square 2″ × 2″ sheets. One day at the factory, eighty thousand reminder notepads were produced. Unfortunately, due to mechanical error, every fifth page of every notepad was defective. How many total pages were defective?

5.2 Division of Polynomials

Student Learning Objectives

After studying this section, you will be able to:

 1 Divide a polynomial by a monomial.

 2 Divide a polynomial by a polynomial.

1 Dividing a Polynomial by a Monomial

The easiest type of polynomial division occurs when the divisor is a monomial. We perform this type of division just as if we were dividing numbers. First we write the indicated division as the sum of separate fractions, and then we reduce each fraction (if possible).

EXAMPLE 1 Divide: $(15x^3 - 10x^2 + 40x) \div 5x$

$$\frac{15x^3 - 10x^2 + 40x}{5x} = \frac{15x^3}{5x} - \frac{10x^2}{5x} + \frac{40x}{5x}$$
$$= 3x^2 - 2x + 8$$

Practice Problem 1 Divide: $(-16x^4 + 16x^3 + 8x^2 + 64x) \div 8x$

2 Dividing a Polynomial by a Polynomial

When we divide polynomials by binomials or trinomials, we perform long division. This is much like the long division method for dividing numbers. The polynomials must be in descending order.

First we write the problem in the form of long division.

$$2x + 3\overline{)6x^2 + 17x + 12}$$

The divisor is $2x + 3$; the dividend is $6x^2 + 17x + 12$. Now we divide the first term of the dividend $(6x^2)$ by the first term of the divisor $(2x)$.

$$\begin{array}{r} \boxed{3x} \\ 2x + 3\overline{)6x^2 + 17x + 12} \end{array} \qquad \boxed{6x^2 \div 2x = 3x}$$

Now we multiply $3x$ (the first term of the quotient) by the divisor $2x + 3$.

$$\begin{array}{r} 3x \\ 2x + 3\overline{)6x^2 + 17x + 12} \\ 6x^2 + 9x \end{array} \leftarrow \boxed{\text{The product of } 3x(2x + 3).}$$

Next, just as in long division with numbers, we subtract and bring down the next monomial.

$$\begin{array}{r} 3x \\ 2x + 3\overline{)6x^2 + 17x + 12} \\ 6x^2 + 9x \\ \hline 8x + 12 \end{array} \quad \begin{array}{l} \boxed{\text{Subtract } 6x^2 + 9x \text{ from } 6x^2 + 17x.} \\ \leftarrow \boxed{\text{Bring down the next monomial.}} \end{array}$$

Now we divide the first term of this binomial $(8x)$ by the first term of the divisor $(2x)$.

$$\begin{array}{r} 3x + \boxed{4} \\ 2x + 3\overline{)6x^2 + 17x + 12} \\ 6x^2 + 9x \\ \hline 8x + 12 \\ 8x + 12 \\ \hline 0 \end{array} \quad \begin{array}{l} \boxed{8x \div 2x = 4} \\ \\ \\ \leftarrow \boxed{\text{The product of } 4(2x + 3).} \end{array}$$

Note that we then multiplied $(2x + 3)(4)$ and subtracted, just as we did before. We continue this process until the remainder is zero. Thus, we find that

$$\frac{6x^2 + 17x + 12}{2x + 3} = 3x + 4.$$

Graphing Calculator

Verifying Answers When Dividing Polynomials

One way to verify that the division was performed correctly is to graph $y_1 = 3x + 4$ and $y_2 = \frac{6x^2 + 17x + 12}{2x + 3}$.

If the graphs appear to coincide, then we have an independent verification that

$$\frac{6x^2 + 17x + 12}{2x + 3} = 3x + 4.$$

Dividing a Polynomial by a Binomial or Trinomial

1. Write the division problem in long division form. Write both polynomials in descending order; write missing terms with a coefficient of zero.
2. Divide the *first* term of the divisor into the first term of the dividend. The result is the first term of the quotient.
3. Multiply the first term of the quotient by *every* term in the divisor.
4. Write the product under the dividend (align like terms) and subtract.
5. Treat this difference as a new dividend. Repeat steps 2 through 4. Continue until the remainder is zero or a polynomial of lower degree than the *first term* of the divisor.
6. If there is a remainder, write it as the numerator of a fraction with the divisor as the denominator. Add this fraction to the quotient.

EXAMPLE 2 Divide: $(6x^3 + 7x^2 + 3) \div (3x - 1)$

There is no x-term in the dividend, so we write $0x$.

$$\begin{array}{r} 2x^2 + 3x + 1 \\ 3x - 1 \overline{)6x^3 + 7x^2 + 0x + 3} \\ \underline{6x^3 - 2x^2} \qquad\qquad \\ 9x^2 + 0x \qquad \\ \underline{9x^2 - 3x} \qquad \\ 3x + 3 \\ \underline{3x - 1} \\ 4 \end{array}$$

Note that we calculate $7x^2 - (-2x^2)$ to obtain $9x^2$.

Note that we calculate $0x - (-3x)$ to obtain $3x$.

The quotient is $2x^2 + 3x + 1$ with a remainder of 4. We may write this as

$$2x^2 + 3x + 1 + \frac{4}{3x - 1}$$

Check:

$$(3x - 1)(2x^2 + 3x + 1) + 4 \stackrel{?}{=} 6x^3 + 7x^2 + 3$$
$$6x^3 + 7x^2 - 0x - 1 + 4 \stackrel{?}{=} 6x^3 + 7x^2 + 3$$
$$6x^3 + 7x^2 + 3 = 6x^3 + 7x^2 + 3 \quad \checkmark$$

Practice Problem 2 Divide: $(14x + 8x^2 - 14) \div (-3 + 4x)$

EXAMPLE 3 Divide $\dfrac{64x^3 - 125}{4x - 5}$.

This fraction is equivalent to the problem $(64x^3 - 125) \div (4x - 5)$.

Note that two terms are missing in the dividend. We write them with zero coefficients.

$$\begin{array}{r} 16x^2 + 20x + 25 \\ 4x - 5 \overline{)64x^3 + 0x^2 + 0x - 125} \\ \underline{64x^3 - 80x^2} \qquad\qquad\qquad \\ 80x^2 + 0x \qquad\quad \\ \underline{80x^2 - 100x} \qquad\quad \\ 100x - 125 \\ \underline{100x - 125} \\ 0 \end{array}$$

Note that $0x^2 - (-80x^2) = 80x^2$.

Note that $0x - (-100x) = 100x$.

The quotient is $16x^2 + 20x + 25$.

Check: Verify that $(4x - 5)(16x^2 + 20x + 25) = 64x^3 - 125$.

Practice Problem 3 Divide: $(8x^3 + 27) \div (2x + 3)$

EXAMPLE 4 Divide: $(7x^3 - 10x - 7x^2 + 2x^4 + 8) \div (2x^2 + x - 2)$

Arrange the dividend in descending order before dividing.

$2x^4 \div 2x^2 = x^2$

$$
\begin{array}{r}
x^2 + 3x - 4 \\
2x^2 + x - 2 \overline{\smash{)}\, 2x^4 + 7x^3 - 7x^2 - 10x + 8} \\
\underline{2x^4 + x^3 - 2x^2} \qquad\qquad \\
6x^3 - 5x^2 - 10x \qquad \\
\underline{6x^3 + 3x^2 - 6x} \qquad \\
-8x^2 - 4x + 8 \\
\underline{-8x^2 - 4x + 8} \\
0
\end{array}
$$

Note that $(7x^3 - 7x^2) - (x^3 - 2x^2) = 7x^3 - 7x^2 - x^3 + 2x^2$.

Note that $(-5x^2 - 10x) - (3x^2 - 6x) = -5x^2 - 10x - 3x^2 + 6x$.

The quotient is $x^2 + 3x - 4$.

Check: Verify that $(2x^2 + x - 2)(x^2 + 3x - 4) = 2x^4 + 7x^3 - 7x^2 - 10x + 8$.

Practice Problem 4 Divide: $(x^4 - 3x^3 + 3x + 4) \div (x^2 - 1)$

Developing Your Study Skills

Taking Notes In Class

An important part of studying mathematics is taking notes. In order to take meaningful notes, you must be an active listener. Keep your mind on what the instructor is saying, and be ready with questions whenever you do not understand something.

If you have previewed the lesson material, you will be prepared to take good notes. The important concepts will seem somewhat familiar. You will have a better idea of what needs to be written down. If you frantically try to write all that the instructor says or copy all the examples done in class, you may find your notes to be nearly worthless when you are home alone. You may find that you are unable to make sense of what you have written.

Write down *important* ideas and examples as the instructor lectures, making sure that you are listening and following the logic. Include any helpful hints or suggestions that your instructor gives you or refers to in your text. You will be amazed at how easily these are forgotten if they are not written down.

Successful note taking requires active listening and processing. Stay alert in class. You will realize the advantages of taking your own notes over copying those of someone else.

5.2 Exercises

Divide.

1. $(24x^2 - 8x - 44) \div 4$

2. $(18x^2 - 63x + 81) \div 9$

3. $(27x^4 - 9x^3 + 63x^2) \div 9x$

4. $(22x^4 + 33x^3 - 121x^2) \div 11x$

5. $\dfrac{4x^3 - 2x^2 + 5x}{2x}$

6. $\dfrac{4w^3 + 8w^2 - w}{4w}$

7. $\dfrac{18a^3b^2 + 12a^2b^2 - 4ab^2}{2ab^2}$

8. $\dfrac{25m^5n - 10m^4n + 15m^3n}{5m^3n}$

Divide. Check your answers for Exercises 9–14.

9. $(15x^2 + 23x + 4) \div (5x + 1)$

10. $(12x^2 + 11x + 2) \div (4x + 1)$

11. $(28x^2 - 29x + 6) \div (4x - 3)$

12. $(30x^2 - 17x + 2) \div (5x - 2)$

13. $(x^3 - x^2 + 11x - 1) \div (x + 1)$

14. $(x^3 + 2x^2 - 3x + 2) \div (x + 1)$

15. $(2x^3 - x^2 - 7) \div (x - 2)$

16. $(4x^3 - 6x - 11) \div (2x - 4)$

17. $\dfrac{8x^3 - 14x^2 - 17x + 5}{2x - 5}$

18. $\dfrac{9x^3 + 9x^2 - 10x - 6}{3x + 2}$

19. $\dfrac{2x^4 - x^3 + 16x^2 - 4}{2x - 1}$

20. $\dfrac{9x^4 - 13x^2 - 19x + 15}{3x - 4}$

21. $\dfrac{6t^4 - 5t^3 - 8t^2 + 16t - 8}{3t^2 + 2t - 4}$

22. $\dfrac{2t^4 + 5t^3 - 11t^2 - 20t + 12}{t^2 + t - 6}$

Applications

▲ **23.** For the space station an engineer has designed a new rectangular solar panel that has an area of $18x^3 - 21x^2 + 11x - 2$ square meters. The length of the solar panel is $6x^2 - 5x + 2$ meters. What is the width of the solar panel?

▲ **24.** For the space station an engineer has designed a new rectangular solar panel that has an area of $8x^3 + 22x^2 - 29x + 6$ square meters. The length of the solar panel is $2x^2 + 7x - 2$ meters. What is the width of the solar panel?

Optional Graphing Calculator Problems

If you have a graphing calculator, verify the following:

25. $\dfrac{2x^2 - x - 10}{2x - 5} = x + 2$

26. $\dfrac{4x^3 + 12x^2 + 7x - 3}{2x + 3} = 2x^2 + 3x - 1$

Cumulative Review Problems

Solve for x.

27. $3x + 4(3x - 5) = -x + 12$

28. $9x - 2x + 8 = 4x + 38$

29. $2(x + 5) - 3y = 5x - (2 - y)$

30. $\dfrac{2x + 4}{3} - \dfrac{y}{2} = x - 2y + 1$

To Think About

Sylvia likes Coca-Cola, but she doesn't like root beer or grape soda. Curt likes 7-Up and root beer but not orange soda. Fritz likes ginger ale and Coca-Cola, but does not like grape soda or 7-Up.

31. If one person likes grape soda, who is it?

32. If one person likes orange soda, who could it be?

5.3 Synthetic Division

1 Using Synthetic Division to Divide Polynomials

Student Learning Objectives

After studying this section, you will be able to:

 1 Use synthetic division to divide polynomials.

When dividing a polynomial by a binomial of the form $x + b$ you may find a procedure known as **synthetic division** quite efficient. Notice the following division exercises. The right-hand problem is the same as the left, but without the variables.

$$
\begin{array}{r|l}
 & 3x^2 - 2x + 2 \\
\hline
x + 3 & 3x^3 + 7x^2 - 4x + 3 \\
 & \underline{3x^3 + 9x^2} \\
 & \quad -2x^2 - 4x \\
 & \quad \underline{-2x^2 - 6x} \\
 & \qquad\quad 2x + 3 \\
 & \qquad\quad \underline{2x + 6} \\
 & \qquad\qquad -3
\end{array}
\qquad\qquad
\begin{array}{r|l}
 & 3 \;\; -2 \;\; 2 \\
\hline
1 + 3 & 3 \;\; 7 \;\; -4 \;\; 3 \\
 & \underline{3 \;\; 9} \\
 & \;\; -2 \;\; -4 \\
 & \;\; \underline{-2 \;\; -6} \\
 & \qquad 2 \;\; 3 \\
 & \qquad \underline{2 \;\; 6} \\
 & \qquad\;\; -3
\end{array}
$$

Eliminating the variables makes synthetic division efficient, and we can make the procedure simpler yet. Note that the colored numbers (3, −2, and 2) appear twice in the previous example, once in the quotient and again in the subtraction. Synthetic division makes it possible to write each number only once. Also, in synthetic division we change the subtraction that division otherwise requires to addition. We do this by dropping the 1, which is the coefficient of x in the divisor, and taking the opposite of the second number in the divisor. In our first example, this means dropping the 1 and changing 3 to −3. The following steps detail synthetic division.

Step 1

Divisor, without the 1 and opposite sign	$\begin{array}{r|rrrr} -3 & 3 & 7 & -4 & 3 \\ & & & & \\ \hline & 3 & & & \end{array}$	Dividend, without variables

Step 2

$$
\begin{array}{r|rrrr}
-3 & 3 & 7 & -4 & 3 \\
 & & -9 & & \\
\hline
 & 3 & -2 & &
\end{array}
$$

Multiply $(-3)(3) = -9$ and add $7 + (-9) = -2$.

Step 3

$$
\begin{array}{r|rrrr}
-3 & 3 & 7 & -4 & 3 \\
 & & -9 & 6 & \\
\hline
 & 3 & -2 & 2 &
\end{array}
$$

Multiply $(-3)(-2) = 6$ and add $-4 + 6 = 2$.

Step 4

$$
\begin{array}{r|rrrr}
-3 & 3 & 7 & -4 & 3 \\
 & & -9 & 6 & -6 \\
\hline
 & 3 & -2 & 2 & \boxed{-3}
\end{array}
$$

Multiply $(-3)(2) = -6$ and add $3 + (-6) = -3$.

$3x^2 - 2x + 2 +$ remainder of -3

Replace the variables in descending order. The degree of the quotient should be one less than the degree of the dividend.

The result is read from the bottom row. Our answer is $3x^2 - 2x + 2 + \dfrac{-3}{x + 3}$.

EXAMPLE 1 Divide by synthetic division: $(3x^3 - x^2 + 4x + 8) \div (x + 2)$

$$\begin{array}{r|rrrr} -2 & 3 & -1 & 4 & 8 \\ & & -6 & 14 & -36 \\ \hline & 3 & -7 & 18 & \boxed{-28} \end{array}$$

The quotient is $3x^2 - 7x + 18 + \dfrac{-28}{x + 2}$.

Practice Problem 1 Divide by synthetic division:
$(x^3 - 3x^2 + 4x - 5) \div (x + 3)$

When a term is missing in the sequence of descending powers of x, we use a zero to indicate the coefficient of that term.

EXAMPLE 2 Divide by synthetic division: $(3x^4 - 21x^3 + 31x^2 - 25) \div (x - 5)$

Since $b = -5$, we use 5 as the divisor for synthetic division.

$$\begin{array}{r|rrrrr} 5 & 3 & -21 & 31 & 0 & -25 \\ & & 15 & -30 & 5 & 25 \\ \hline & 3 & -6 & 1 & 5 & \boxed{0} \end{array}$$

Note that the remainder is zero.

The quotient is $3x^3 - 6x^2 + x + 5$.

Practice Problem 2 Divide by synthetic division:
$(2x^4 - x^2 + 5x - 12) \div (x - 3)$.

EXAMPLE 3 Divide by synthetic division: $(3x^4 - 4x^3 + 8x^2 - 5x - 5) \div (x - 2)$

$$\begin{array}{r|rrrrr} 2 & 3 & -4 & 8 & -5 & -5 \\ & & 6 & 4 & 24 & 38 \\ \hline & 3 & 2 & 12 & 19 & \boxed{33} \end{array}$$

The quotient is $3x^3 + 2x^2 + 12x + 19 + \dfrac{33}{x - 2}$.

Practice Problem 3 Divide by synthetic division:
$(2x^4 - 9x^3 + 5x^2 + 13x - 3) \div (x - 3)$

5.3 Exercises

Divide by synthetic division.

1. $(2x^2 - 11x - 8) \div (x - 6)$

2. $(2x^2 - 15x - 23) \div (x - 9)$

3. $(3x^3 + x^2 - x + 4) \div (x + 1)$

4. $(3x^3 + 10x^2 + 6x - 4) \div (x + 2)$

5. $(x^3 + 7x^2 + 17x + 15) \div (x + 3)$

6. $(3x^3 - x^2 + 4x + 8) \div (x + 2)$

7. $(8x^3 - 30x^2 - 55x + 27) \div (x - 5)$

8. $(4x^3 + x^2 - 3x - 1) \div (x - 1)$

9. $(x^3 - 2x^2 + 8) \div (x + 2)$

10. $(2x^3 + 7x^2 - 5) \div (x + 3)$

11. $(6x^4 + 13x^3 + 35x - 24) \div (x + 3)$

12. $(3x^4 - 25x^2 - 18) \div (x - 3)$

13. $(x^4 - 6x^3 + x^2 - 9) \div (x + 1)$

14. $(x^4 - 3x^3 - 11x^2 + 3x + 10) \div (x - 5)$

15. $(3x^5 + x - 1) \div (x + 1)$

16. $(2x^4 - x + 3) \div (x - 2)$

17. $(2x^5 + x^4 - 11x^3 + 13x^2 - x - 8) \div (x - 1)$

18. $(3x^5 - 5x^3 + 13x^2 + 6x + 10) \div (x + 2)$

19. $(x^6 - 4) \div (x + 1)$

20. $(x^6 - 5x^3 + x^2 + 12) \div (x + 1)$

21. $(x^3 + 2.5x^2 - 3.6x + 5.4) \div (x - 1.2)$

22. $(x^3 - 4.2x^2 - 8.8x + 3.7) \div (x + 1.8)$

23. When the quotient $(x^4 + 3x^3 - 2x^2 + bx + 5) \div (x + 3)$ is simplified, there is no remainder. What is the value of b?

24. When the quotient $(2x^4 + 12x^3 + ax^2 - 5x + 75) \div (x + 5)$ is simplified, there is no remainder. What is the value of a?

To Think About

How do we use synthetic division when the divisor is in the form $ax + b$? We divide the divisor by a to get $x + \frac{b}{a}$. Then, after performing the synthetic division, we divide each term of the result by a. The number that is the remainder does not change. To divide $(2x^3 + 7x^2 - 5x - 4) \div (2x + 1)$, we would use $-\frac{1}{2}\,\big|\;2\quad 7\quad -5\quad -4$ and then divide each term of the result by 2.

In Exercises 25 and 26, divide by synthetic division.

25. $(2x^3 - 3x^2 + 6x + 4) \div (2x + 1)$

26. $(4x^3 - 6x^2 + 6) \div (2x + 3)$

27. When the divisor is of the form $ax + b$, why does the method discussed above work? What are we really doing when we divide the divisor and the quotient by the value a?

28. Why do we not have to divide the remainder by a when using this method?

Cumulative Review Problems

A total of 21 people were killed and 150 people injured in the Great Boston Molasses Flood in January 1919. A molasses storage tank burst and spilled 2 million gallons of molasses through the streets of Boston.

29. How many cubic feet of molasses were contained in the 2-million-gallon molasses tank? (Use 1 gallon $\approx$ 0.134 cubic feet.)

▲ **30.** At one point the moving flood of molasses appeared as a huge cylindrically shaped object with a radius of 200 feet. At that point how deep was the molasses? (Round to the nearest tenth.)

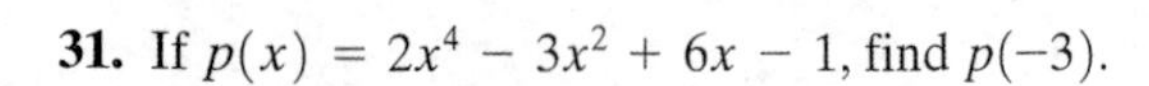

31. If $p(x) = 2x^4 - 3x^2 + 6x - 1$, find $p(-3)$.

5.4 Removing Common Factors; Factoring by Grouping

We learned to multiply polynomials in Section 5.1. When two or more algebraic expressions (monomials, binomials, and so on) are multiplied, each expression is called a **factor**.

In the rest of this chapter, we will learn how to find the factors of a polynomial. **Factoring** is the opposite of multiplication and is an extremely important mathematical technique.

Student Learning Objectives

After studying this section, you will be able to:

1. Factor out the greatest common factor from a polynomial.
2. Factor a polynomial by the grouping method.

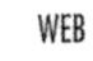

SSM PH TUTOR CENTER   CD & VIDEO   MATH PRO   WEB

1 *Factoring Out the Greatest Common Factor*

To factor out a common factor, we make use of the distributive property.

$$ab + ac = a(b + c)$$

The **greatest common factor** is simply the largest factor that is common to all terms of the expression. It must contain

1. The largest possible common factor of the numerical coefficients and
2. The largest possible common variable factor

EXAMPLE 1 Factor out the greatest common factor.

(a) $7x^2 - 14x$ **(b)** $40a^3 - 20a^2$

(a) $7x^2 - 14x = 7x(x - 2)$
Be careful. The greatest common factor is $7x$, not 7.

(b) $40a^3 - 20a^2 = 20a^2(2a - 1)$
The greatest common factor is $20a^2$.

Suppose we had written $10a(4a^2 - 2a)$ or $10a(2a)(2a - 1)$ as our answer. Although we have factored the expression, we have not found the *greatest* common factor.

Practice Problem 1 Factor out the greatest common factor.

(a) $19x^3 - 38x^2$ **(b)** $100a^4 - 50a^2$

EXAMPLE 2 Factor out the greatest common factor.

(a) $9x^2 - 18xy - 15y^2$ **(b)** $4a^3 - 12a^2b^2 - 8ab^3 + 6ab$

(a) $9x^2 - 18xy - 15y^2 = 3(3x^2 - 6xy - 5y^2)$
The greatest common factor is 3.

(b) $4a^3 - 12a^2b^2 - 8ab^3 + 6ab = 2a(2a^2 - 6ab^2 - 4b^3 + 3b)$
The greatest common factor is $2a$.

Practice Problem 2 Factor out the greatest common factor.

(a) $21x^3 - 18x^2y + 24xy^2$
(b) $12xy^2 - 14x^2y + 20x^2y^2 + 36x^3y$

How do you know whether you have factored correctly? You can do two things to verify your answer.

1. Examine the polynomial in the parentheses. Its terms should not have any remaining common factors.
2. Multiply the two factors. You should obtain the original expression.

In each of the remaining examples, you will be asked to **factor** a polynomial—i.e., to find the factors that, when multiplied, give the polynomial as a product. For each of these examples, this will require you to factor out the greatest common factor.

EXAMPLE 3 Factor $6x^3 - 9x^2y - 6x^2y^2$. Check your answer.

$$6x^3 - 9x^2y - 6x^2y^2 = 3x^2(2x - 3y - 2y^2)$$

Check:

1. $(2x - 3y - 2y^2)$ has no common factors. If it did, we would know that we had not factored out the *greatest* common factor.
2. Multiply the two factors.

$$3x^2(2x - 3y - 2y^2) = 6x^3 - 9x^2y - 6x^2y^2$$

Observe that we do obtain the original polynomial.

Practice Problem 3 Factor $9a^3 - 12a^2b^2 - 15a^4$. Check your answer.

The greatest common factor need not be a monomial. It may be a binomial or even a trinomial. For example, note the following:

$$5a(x + 3) + 2(x + 3) = (x + 3)(5a + 2)$$
$$5a(x + 4y) + 2(x + 4y) = (x + 4y)(5a + 2)$$

The common factors are binomials.

EXAMPLE 4 Factor.

(a) $2x(x + 5) - 3(x + 5)$ **(b)** $5a(a + b) - 2b(a + b) - 1(a + b)$

The common factor is $x + 5$.

(a) $2x(x + 5) - 3(x + 5) = (x + 5)(2x - 3)$

(b) $5a(a + b) - 2b(a + b) - 1(a + b) = (a + b)(5a - 2b - 1)$

The common factor is $a + b$.

Practice Problem 4 Factor $7x(x + 2y) - 8y(x + 2y) - (x + 2y)$.

2 *Factoring by Grouping*

Because the common factors in Example 4 were grouped inside parentheses, it was easy to pick them out. However, this rarely happens, so we have to learn how to manipulate expressions to find the greatest common factor.

Polynomials of four terms can often be factored by the method of Example 4(a). However, the parentheses are not always present in the original problem. When they are not present, we look for a way to remove a common factor from the first two terms. We then factor out a common factor from the first two terms and a common factor from the second two terms. Then we can find the greatest common factor of the original expression.

EXAMPLE 5 Factor $ax + 2ay + 2bx + 4by$.

Remove the greatest common factor (a) from the first two terms.

$$ax + 2ay + 2bx + 4by = a(x + 2y) + 2b(x + 2y)$$

Remove the greatest common factor ($2b$) from the last two terms.

Now we can see that $(x + 2y)$ is a common factor.

$$a(x + 2y) + 2b(x + 2y) = (x + 2y)(a + 2b)$$

Practice Problem 5 Factor $bx + 5by + 2wx + 10wy$.

EXAMPLE 6 Factor $2x^2 - 18y - 12x + 3xy$.

First write the polynomial in this order: $2x^2 - 12x + 3xy - 18y$

Remove the greatest common factor ($2x$) from the first two terms.

$$2x^2 - 12x + 3xy - 18y = 2x(x - 6) + 3y(x - 6) = (x - 6)(2x + 3y)$$

Remove the greatest common factor ($3y$) from the last two terms.

Practice Problem 6 Factor $5x^2 - 12y + 4xy - 15x$.

If a problem can be factored by this method, we must rearrange the order of the four terms whenever necessary so that the first two terms do have a common factor.

EXAMPLE 7 Factor $xy - 6 + 3x - 2y$.

$xy + 3x - 2y - 6$	Rearrange the terms so that the first two terms have a common factor and the last two terms have a common factor.
$= x(y + 3) - 2(y + 3)$	Factor out a common factor of x from the first two terms and -2 from the second two terms.
$= (y + 3)(x - 2)$	Factor out the common binomial factor $y + 3$.

Practice Problem 7 Factor $xy - 12 - 4x + 3y$.

EXAMPLE 8 Factor $2x^3 + 21 - 7x^2 - 6x$. Check your answer by multiplication.

$2x^3 - 7x^2 - 6x + 21$	Rearrange the terms.
$= x^2(2x - 7) - 3(2x - 7)$	Factor out a common factor from each group of two terms.
$= (2x - 7)(x^2 - 3)$	Factor out the common binomial factor $2x - 7$.

Check:

$(2x - 7)(x^2 - 3) = 2x^3 - 6x - 7x^2 + 21$	Multiply the two binomials.
$= 2x^3 + 21 - 7x^2 - 6x$	Rearrange the terms.

The product is identical to the original expression.

Practice Problem 8 Factor $2x^3 - 15 - 10x + 3x^2$.

Developing Your Study Skills

Reading the Textbook

Your homework time each day should begin with a careful reading of the section(s) assigned in your textbook. Usually, much time and effort have gone into the selection of a particular text, and your instructor has decided that this is the book that will help you become successful in this mathematics class. Textbooks are expensive, but they can be a wise investment if you take advantage of them by reading them.

Reading a mathematics textbook is unlike reading the types of books that you may find in your literature, history, psychology, or sociology courses. Mathematics texts are technical books that provide you with exercises to practice. Learning from a mathematics text requires slow and careful reading of each word, which takes time and effort.

Begin reading your textbook with a paper and pencil in hand. As you come across a new definition or concept, underline it in the text and/or write it down in your notebook. Whenever you encounter an unfamiliar term, look it up and make a note of it. When you come to an example, work through it step-by-step. Be sure to read each word and to follow directions carefully.

Notice the helpful hints the author provides. They guide you to correct solutions and prevent you from making errors. Take advantage of these pieces of expert advice.

Be sure that you understand what you are reading. Make a note of any of the things that you do not understand, and ask your instructor about them. Do not hurry through the material. Learning mathematics takes time.

5.4 Exercises

Factor. (Be sure to factor out the greatest common factor.)

1. $-30 - 15y$

2. $16x - 16$

3. $xy - 3x^2y$

4. $7a^2 - 14a$

5. $3c^2x^3 - 9cx - 6c$

6. $5a^2b^4 + 15ab - 30a$

7. $2x^3 - 8x^2 + 12x$

8. $3x^4 - 6x^3 + 9x^2$

9. $9a^2b^2 - 36ab + 45ab^2$

10. $-12x^2y - 18xy + 6x$

11. $12xy^3 - 24x^3y^2 + 36x^2y^4 - 60x^4y^3$

12. $15a^3b^3 + 6a^4b^3 - 9a^2b^3 + 30a^5b^3$

13. $3x(x + y) - 2(x + y)$

14. $5a(a + 3b) + 4(a + 3b)$

15. $5b(a - 3b) + 8(-3b + a)$

16. $4y(x - 5y) - 3(-5y + x)$

17. $3x(a + 5b) + (a + 5b)$

Hint: Is the expression in the first parentheses equal to the expression in the second parentheses in exercises 15 and 16?

18. $2w(s - 3t) - (s - 3t)$

19. $2a^2(3x - y) - 5b^3(3x - y)$

20. $7a^3(5a + 4) - 2(5a + 4)$

21. $3x(5x + y) - 8y(5x + y) - (5x + y)$

22. $4w(y - 8x) + 5z(y - 8x) + (y - 8x)$

23. $x^3 + 5x^2 + 3x + 15$

24. $x^3 + 8x^2 + 2x + 16$

25. $8x + 8 - 5xy - 5y$

26. $by + b - 3xy - 3x$

27. $7ax - 7ay + x - y$

28. $12bx - 15by + 4x - 5y$

29. $yz^2 - 15 - 3z^2 + 5y$

30. $ad^4 - 4ab - d^4 + 4b$

31. $40x^2 + 18by^2 - 15xb - 48xy^2$

32. $18ax - 6bx + 9ay^2 - 3by^2$

Applications

33. The total number of oranges stacked in a pile of x rows is given by the polynomial $\frac{1}{3}x^3 + \frac{1}{2}x^2 + \frac{1}{6}x$. Write this polynomial in factored form.

▲ **34.** The volume of the box pictured below is given by the polynomial $4x^3 + 2x^2 - 6x$. Write this polynomial in factored form.

$x - 1$

$2x$

$2x + 3$

Cumulative Review Problems

Graph the equations in 35 and 36.

35. $6x - 2y = -12$

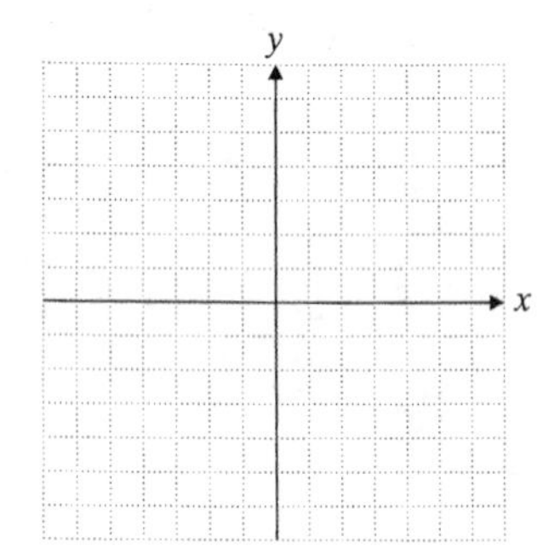

36. $y = \frac{2}{3}x - 2$

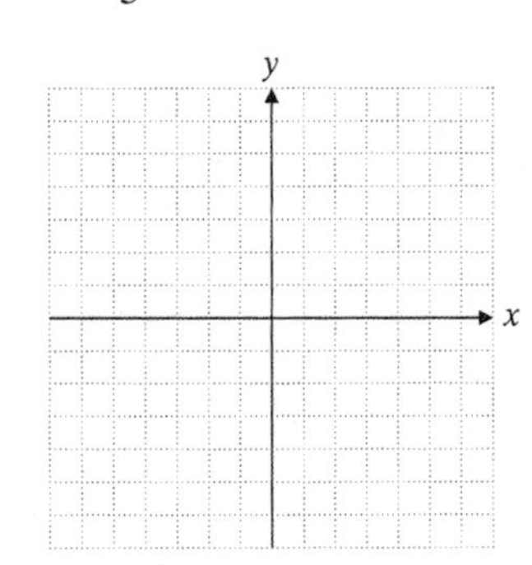

37. Find the slope of the line passing through $(6, -1)$ and $(2, 3)$.

38. Find the slope and y-intercept of $2y + 6x = -3$.

39. A student scored 82 on a test that had only 5-point fill-in questions and 4-point multiple-choice questions. The student had 4 fill-in questions wrong. The maximum possible score on the test was 102 points. If the entire test had 22 questions, how many multiple-choice questions did the student answer correctly?

40. Reynaldo swims in a lap pool that is 50 meters long. He wants to swim at least 1 mile each day. How many laps (up and down the distance of the pool) will he have to swim to reach his goal of 1 mile per day? (Use 1 mile = 1.61 kilometers.)

5.5 Factoring Trinomials

 *Factoring Trinomials of the Form $x^2 + bx + c$*

Student Learning Objectives

After studying this section, you will be able to:

 Factor trinomials of the form $x^2 + bx + c$.

 Factor trinomials of the form $ax^2 + bx + c$.

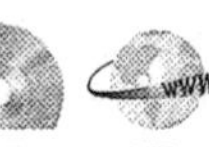

If we multiply $(x + 4)(x + 5)$, we obtain $x^2 + 9x + 20$. But suppose that we already have the polynomial $x^2 + 9x + 20$ and need to factor it. In other words, suppose we need to find the expressions that, when multiplied, give us the polynomial. Let's use this example to find a general procedure.

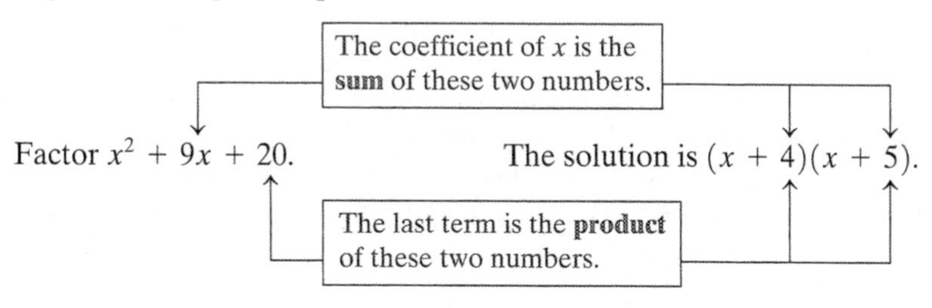

Factoring Trinomials of the Form $x^2 + bx + c$

1. The answer has the form $(x + m)(x + n)$, where m and n are real numbers.
2. The numbers m and n are chosen so that
   (a) $m \cdot n = c$ and
   (b) $m + n = b$.

If the last term of the trinomial is positive and the middle term is negative, the two numbers m and n will be negative numbers.

EXAMPLE 1 Factor $x^2 - 14x + 24$.

We want to find two numbers whose product is 24 and whose sum is −14. They will both be negative numbers.

Factor Pairs of 24	*Sum of the Factors*
$(-24)(-1)$	$-24 - 1 = -25$
$(-12)(-2)$	$-12 - 2 = -14$ ✓
$(-6)(-4)$	$-6 - 4 = -10$
$(-8)(-3)$	$-8 - 3 = -11$

The numbers whose product is 24 and whose sum is −14 are −12 and −2. Thus,

$$x^2 - 14x + 24 = (x - 12)(x - 2).$$

Practice Problem 1 Factor $x^2 - 10x + 21$.

If the last term of the trinomial is negative, the two numbers m and n will be opposite in sign.

EXAMPLE 2 Factor $x^2 + 11x - 26$.

We want to find two numbers whose product is −26 and whose sum is 11. One number will be positive and the other negative.

Factor Pairs of −26	*Sum of the Factors*
$(-26)(1)$	$-26 + 1 = -25$
$(26)(-1)$	$26 - 1 = 25$
$(-13)(2)$	$-13 + 2 = -11$
$(13)(-2)$	$13 - 2 = 11$ ✓

The numbers whose product is -26 and whose sum is 11 are -2 and 13. Thus,

$$x^2 + 11x - 26 = (x + 13)(x - 2).$$

Practice Problem 2 Factor $x^2 - 13x - 48$.

Sometimes we can make a substitution that makes a polynomial easier to factor as shown in the following example.

EXAMPLE 3 Factor $x^4 - 2x^2 - 24$.

We need to recognize that we can write this as $(x^2)^2 - 2(x^2) - 24$. We can make this polynomial easier to factor if we substitute y for x^2. Then we have $y^2 + (-2)y + (-24)$. So the factors will be $(y + m)(y + n)$. The two numbers whose product is -24 and whose sum is -2 are -6 and 4. Therefore, we have $(y - 6)(y + 4)$. But $y = x^2$, so our answer is

$$x^4 - 2x^2 - 24 = (x^2 - 6)(x^2 + 4).$$

Practice Problem 3 Factor $x^4 + 9x^2 + 8$.

Facts about Signs

Suppose $x^2 + bx + c = (x + m)(x + n)$. We know certain facts about m and n.

1. m and n have the same sign if c is positive. (*Note:* We did *not* say that they will have the same sign as c.)
   (a) They are positive if b is positive.
   (b) They are negative if b is negative.
2. m and n have opposite signs if c is negative. The larger number is positive if b is positive and negative if b is negative.

If you understand these sign facts, continue on to Example 4. If not, review Examples 1 through 3.

EXAMPLE 4 Factor.

(a) $y^2 + 5y - 36$
(b) $x^4 - 4x^2 - 12$

(a) $y^2 + 5y - 36 = (y + 9)(y - 4)$ The larger number (9) is positive because b (5) is positive.

(b) $x^4 - 4x^2 - 12 = (x^2 - 6)(x^2 + 2)$ The larger number (6) is negative because b (-4) is negative.

Practice Problem 4 Factor.

(a) $a^2 + 2a - 48$ **(b)** $x^4 + 2x^2 - 15$

Does the order in which we write the factors make any difference? In other words, is it true that $x^2 + bx + c = (x + n)(x + m)$? Since multiplication is commutative,

$$x^2 + bx + c = (x + n)(x + m) = (x + m)(x + n).$$

The order of the factors is not important.

We can also factor trinomials that have more than one variable.

EXAMPLE 5 Factor.

(a) $x^2 - 21xy + 20y^2$ **(b)** $x^2 + 4xy - 21y^2$

(a) $x^2 - 21xy + 20y^2 = (x - 20y)(x - y)$

The last terms in each factor contain the variable y.

(b) $x^2 + 4xy - 21y^2 = (x + 7y)(x - 3y)$

Practice Problem 5 Factor.

(a) $x^2 - 16xy + 15y^2$ **(b)** $x^2 + xy - 42y^2$

If the terms of a trinomial have a common factor, you should remove the greatest common factor from the terms first. Then you will be able to follow the factoring procedure we have used in the previous examples.

EXAMPLE 6 Factor $3x^2 - 30x + 48$.

The factor 3 is common to all three terms of the polynomial. Factoring out the 3 gives us the following:

$$3x^2 - 30x + 48 = 3(x^2 - 10x + 16)$$

Now we continue to factor the trinomial in the usual fashion.

$$3(x^2 - 10x + 16) = 3(x - 8)(x - 2)$$

Practice Problem 6 Factor $4x^2 - 44x + 72$.

2 Factoring Trinomials of the Form ax^2+bx+c

Grouping Number Method

One way to factor a trinomial $ax^2 + bx + c$ is to write it as four terms and factor it by grouping as we did in Section 5.4. For example, the trinomial $2x^2 + 11x + 12$ can be written as $2x^2 + 3x + 8x + 12$.

$$2x^2 + 3x + 8x + 12 = x(2x + 3) + 4(2x + 3)$$
$$= (2x + 3)(x + 4)$$

We can factor all factorable trinomials of the form $ax^2 + bx + c$ in this way. Use the following procedure.

Grouping Number Method for Factoring Trinomials of the Form $ax^2 + bx + c$

1. Obtain the grouping number ac.
2. Find the factor pair of the grouping number whose sum is b.
3. Use those two factors to write bx as the sum of two terms.
4. Factor by grouping.

EXAMPLE 7 Factor $2x^2 + 19x + 24$.

1. The grouping number is $(2)(24) = 48$.
2. The factor pairs of 48 are as follows:

$48 \cdot 1$ $\quad$ $12 \cdot 4$
$24 \cdot 2$ $\quad$ $8 \cdot 6$
$16 \cdot 3$

We want the factor pair of 48 whose sum is 19. Therefore, we select the factors 16 and 3.

3. We use the numbers 16 and 3 to write $19x$ as the sum of $16x$ and $3x$.

$$2x^2 + 19x + 24 = 2x^2 + 16x + 3x + 24$$

4. Factor by grouping.

$$\begin{aligned} 2x^2 + 16x + 3x + 24 &= 2x(x + 8) + 3(x + 8) \\ &= (x + 8)(2x + 3) \end{aligned}$$

Practice Problem 7 Factor $3x^2 + 2x - 8$.

EXAMPLE 8 Factor $6x^2 + 7x - 5$.

1. The grouping number is -30.
2. We want the factor pair of -30 whose sum is 7.

$$\begin{aligned} -30 &= (-30)(1) & -30 &= (5)(-6) \\ &= (30)(-1) & &= (-5)(6) \\ &= (15)(-2) & &= (3)(-10) \\ &= (-15)(2) & &= (-3)(10) \end{aligned}$$

3. Since $-3 + 10 = 7$, use -3 and 10 to write $6x^2 + 7x - 5$ with four terms.

$$6x^2 + 7x - 5 = 6x^2 - 3x + 10x - 5$$

4. Factor by grouping.

$$\begin{aligned} 6x^2 - 3x + 10x - 5 &= 3x(2x - 1) + 5(2x - 1) \\ &= (2x - 1)(3x + 5) \end{aligned}$$

Practice Problem 8 Factor $10x^2 - 9x + 2$.

If the three terms have a common factor, then prior to using the four-step grouping number procedure, we first factor out the greatest common factor from the terms of the trinomial.

EXAMPLE 9 Factor $6x^3 - 26x^2 + 24x$.

First we factor out the greatest common factor $2x$ from each term.

$$6x^3 - 26x^2 + 24x = 2x(3x^2 - 13x + 12)$$

Next we follow the four steps to factor $3x^2 - 13x + 12$.

1. The grouping number is 36.
2. We want the factor pair of 36 whose sum is -13. The two factors are -4 and -9.
3. We use -4 and -9 to write $3x^2 - 13x + 12$ with four terms.

$$3x^2 - 13x + 12 = 3x^2 - 4x - 9x + 12$$

4. Factor by grouping. Remember that we first factored out the factor $2x$. This factor must be part of the answer.

$$\begin{aligned} 2x(3x^2 - 4x - 9x + 12) &= 2x[x(3x - 4) - 3(3x - 4)] \\ &= 2x(3x - 4)(x - 3) \end{aligned}$$

Practice Problem 9 Factor $9x^3 - 15x^2 - 6x$.

Trial-and-Error Method

Another way to factor trinomials of the form $ax^2 + bx + c$ is by trial and error. This method has an advantage if the grouping number is large and we would have to list many factors. In the trial-and-error method, we try different values and see which ones can be multiplied out to obtain the original expression.

If the last term is negative, there are many more sign possibilities.

EXAMPLE 10 Factor by trial and error $10x^2 - 49x - 5$.

The first terms in the factors could be $(10x)$ and (x) or $(5x)$ and $(2x)$. The second terms could be $(+1)$ and (-5) or (-1) and $(+5)$. We list all the possibilities and look for one that will yield a middle term of $-49x$.

Possible Factors	*Middle Term of Product*
$(2x - 1)(5x + 5)$	$+5x$
$(2x + 1)(5x - 5)$	$-5x$
$(2x + 5)(5x - 1)$	$+23x$
$(2x - 5)(5x + 1)$	$-23x$
$(10x - 5)(x + 1)$	$+5x$
$(10x + 5)(x - 1)$	$-5x$
$(10x - 1)(x + 5)$	$+49x$
$(10x + 1)(x - 5)$	$-49x$

Thus,

$$10x^2 - 49x - 5 = (10x + 1)(x - 5)$$

As a check, it is always a good idea to multiply the two binomials to see whether you obtain the original expression.

$$\begin{aligned}(10x + 1)(x - 5) &= 10x^2 - 50x + 1x - 5.\\ &= 10x^2 - 49x - 5\end{aligned}$$

Practice Problem 10 Factor by trial and error $8x^2 - 6x - 5$.

EXAMPLE 11 Factor by trial and error $6x^4 + x^2 - 12$.

The first term of each factor must contain x^2. Suppose that we try the following:

Possible Factors	*Middle Term of Product*
$(2x^2 - 3)(3x^2 + 4)$	$-x^2$

The middle term we get is $-x^2$, but we need its opposite, x^2. In this case, we just need to reverse the signs of -3 and 4. Do you see why? Therefore,

$$6x^4 + x^2 - 12 = (2x^2 + 3)(3x^2 - 4).$$

Practice Problem 11 Factor by trial and error $6x^4 + 13x^2 - 5$.

Developing Your Study Skills

Keep Trying

You may be one of those students who has had much difficulty with mathematics in the past and who is sure that you cannot do well in this course. Perhaps you are thinking, "I have never been any good at mathematics" or "I have always hated mathematics" or "Math scares me" or "I have not had any math for so long that I have forgotten it all." You may even have picked up on the label "math anxiety" and attached it to yourself. That is most unfortunate, and it is time for you to reprogram your thinking. Replace those negative thoughts with more positive ones. You need to say things like, "I will give this math class my best shot" or "I can learn mathematics if I work at it" or "I will try to do better than I have done in previous math classes." You will be pleasantly surprised at the difference a positive attitude makes!

We live in a highly technical world, and you cannot afford to give up on the study of mathematics. Dropping mathematics may prevent you from entering certain career fields that you find interesting. You may not have to take math courses at as high a level as calculus, but such courses as finite math, college algebra, and trigonometry may be necessary. Learning mathematics can open new doors for you.

Learning mathematics is a process that takes time and effort. You will find that regular study and daily practice are necessary to strengthen your skills and to help you grow academically. This process will lead you toward success in mathematics. Then, as you become more successful, your confidence in your ability to do mathematics will grow.

5.5 Exercises

Factor each polynomial.

1. $x^2 + 3x - 28$
2. $x^2 - 9x - 22$
3. $x^2 + x - 30$
4. $x^2 - x - 6$
5. $x^2 + 10x + 24$
6. $x^2 - 3x - 18$
7. $a^2 + 4a - 45$
8. $a^2 + 17a + 60$
9. $x^2 - 9xy + 20y^2$
10. $x^2 - 6xy - 27y^2$
11. $x^2 - 15xy + 14y^2$
12. $x^2 + 10xy + 9y^2$
13. $x^4 - 3x^2 - 40$
14. $x^4 + 6x^2 + 5$
15. $x^4 + 16x^2y^2 + 63y^4$
16. $x^4 - 6x^2 - 55$

Factor out the greatest common factor from the terms of the trinomial. Then factor the remaining trinomial.

17. $2x^2 + 26x + 44$
18. $2x^2 + 30x + 52$
19. $x^3 + x^2 - 20x$
20. $x^3 - 4x^2 - 45x$

Factor each polynomial. You may use the grouping number method or the trial-and-error method.

21. $30x^2 - x - 1$
22. $6x^2 + x - 1$
23. $6x^2 - 7x - 5$
24. $5x^2 - 13x - 28$
25. $3a^2 - 8a + 5$
26. $6a^2 + 11a + 3$
27. $8a^2 + 14a - 9$
28. $3a^2 - 20a + 12$
29. $2x^2 + 13x + 15$
30. $5x^2 - 8x - 4$
31. $3x^4 - 8x^2 - 3$
32. $6x^4 + 7x^2 - 5$
33. $6x^2 + 35xy + 11y^2$
34. $5x^2 + 12xy + 7y^2$
35. $7x^2 + 11xy - 6y^2$
36. $4x^2 - 13xy + 3y^2$

Factor out the greatest common factor from the terms of the trinomial. Then factor the remaining trinomial.

37. $4x^3 + 4x^2 - 15x$
38. $8x^3 + 6x^2 - 9x$
39. $12x^3 + 66x^2 + 30x$
40. $15x^3 - 50x^2 - 40x$

Mixed Practice

Factor each polynomial.

41. $x^2 - 2x - 63$
42. $x^2 + 6x - 40$
43. $6x^2 + x - 2$
44. $5x^2 + 17x + 6$
45. $x^2 - 20x + 51$
46. $x^2 - 20x + 99$
47. $15x^2 + x - 2$
48. $12x^2 - 5x - 3$
49. $2x^2 + 4x - 96$
50. $3x^2 + 9x - 84$
51. $18x^2 + 21x + 6$
52. $24x^2 + 26x + 6$
53. $7x^3 - 28x^2 - 35x$
54. $9x^3 - 27x^2 - 90x$
55. $6x^3 + 26x^2 - 20x$
56. $12x^3 - 14x^2 + 4x$

57. $3x^4 - 2x^2 - 5$

58. $6x^4 - 13x^2 - 5$

59. $7x^2 - 22xy + 3y^2$

60. $10x^2 - 17xy + 6y^2$

61. $x^6 - 10x^3 - 39$

62. $x^6 - 3x^3 - 70$

63. $4x^3y + 2x^2y - 2xy$

64. $9x^3y + 24x^2y - 9xy$

Applications

▲ **65.** A plan has been made in northern Maine to replace trees harvested by paper mills. The proposed planting zone is in the shape of a giant rectangle with an area of $30x^2 + 19x - 5$ square feet. Use your factoring skills to determine a possible configuration of the number of rows of trees and the number of trees to be placed in each row.

▲ **66.** A plan has been made in northern Washington to replace trees harvested by paper mills. The proposed planting zone is in the shape of a giant rectangle with an area of $12x^2 + 20x - 25$ square feet. Use your factoring skills to determine a possible configuration of the number of rows of trees and the number of trees to be placed in each row.

Cumulative Review Problems

67. Find the area of a circle of radius 3 inches.

68. Solve for b: $A = \frac{1}{2}(2a + 5b)$

69. A state college campus has a paved road called a "loop" that encircles the entire campus. There are two very steep hills at each end of the loop.

(a) Find the slope (pitch) of the hill that rises 48 yards vertically over a horizontal distance of 156 yards.

(b) Does this hill violate the city ordinance requiring all roads to have a slope that does not exceed 30%?

70. Graph $6x + 4y = -12$.

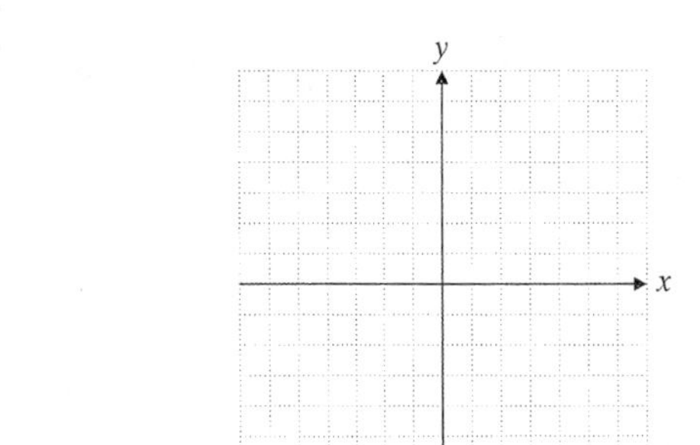

71. John and Carolyn Ciukaj have opened a new bicycle shop in Beverly. They want to have at least 120 bicycle racks and bicycle helmets in stock. Their wholesale cost for bicycle racks averages around \$60 and for bicycle helmets around \$70. They have available \$7950 in capital to pay for bicycle racks and bicycle helmets. How many of each should they stock?

72. A large commercial jetliner flies from Atlanta to San Francisco. The jetliner can carry a total of 184 passengers. There are two types of seats on the aircraft: first class and coach. The number of coach seats is sixteen more than six times the number of first class seats. How many of each type of seat are there on the airplane?

5.6 Special Cases of Factoring

Student Learning Objectives

After studying this section, you will be able to:

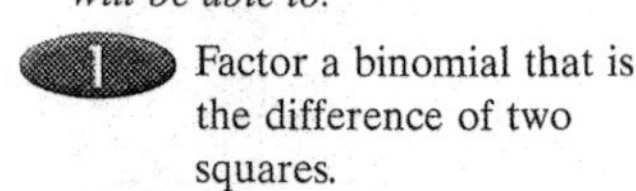
1. Factor a binomial that is the difference of two squares.

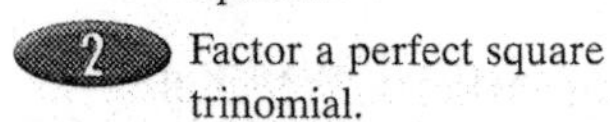
2. Factor a perfect square trinomial.

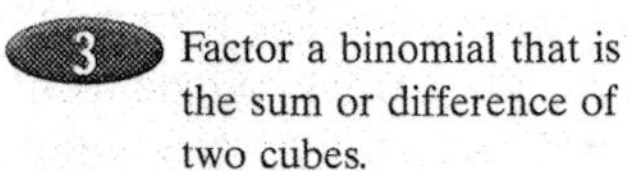
3. Factor a binomial that is the sum or difference of two cubes.

1 *Difference of Two Squares*

Recall the special product formula (3.1): $(a + b)(a - b) = a^2 - b^2$. We can use it now as a factoring formula.

Factoring the Difference of Two Squares

$$a^2 - b^2 = (a + b)(a - b)$$

EXAMPLE 1 Factor $x^2 - 16$.

In this case $a = x$ and $b = 4$ in the formula.

$$\begin{array}{ccccc} a^2 & - & b^2 & = & (a + b)(a - b) \\ \downarrow & & \downarrow & & \downarrow \quad \downarrow \quad \downarrow \quad \downarrow \\ (x)^2 & - & (4)^2 & = & (x + 4)(x - 4) \end{array}$$

Practice Problem 1 Factor $x^2 - 9$.

EXAMPLE 2 Factor $25x^2 - 36$.

In each case we will use the formula $a^2 - b^2 = (a + b)(a - b)$.

$$25x^2 - 36 = (5x)^2 - (6)^2 = (5x + 6)(5x - 6)$$

Practice Problem 2 Factor $64x^2 - 121y^2$.

EXAMPLE 3 Factor $100w^4 - 9z^4$.

$$100w^4 - 9z^4 = (10w^2)^2 - (3z^2)^2 = (10w^2 + 3z^2)(10w^2 - 3z^2)$$

Practice Problem 3 Factor $49x^2 - 25y^4$.

Whenever possible, a common factor should be factored out in the first step. Then the formula can be applied.

EXAMPLE 4 Factor $75x^2 - 3$.

We factor out a common factor of 3 from each term.

$$\begin{aligned} 75x^2 - 3 &= 3(25x^2 - 1) \\ &= 3(5x + 1)(5x - 1) \end{aligned}$$

Practice Problem 4 Factor $7x^2 - 28$.

2 *Perfect Square Trinomials*

Recall the formulas for squaring a binomial.

$$(a - b)^2 = a^2 - 2ab + b^2 \qquad (3.2)$$
$$(a + b)^2 = a^2 + 2ab + b^2 \qquad (3.3)$$

We can use these formulas to factor a perfect square trinomial.

Perfect Square Factoring Formulas

$$a^2 - 2ab + b^2 = (a - b)^2$$
$$a^2 + 2ab + b^2 = (a + b)^2$$

Recognizing these special cases will save you a lot of time when factoring. How can we recognize a perfect square trinomial?

1. The first and last terms are perfect squares. (The numerical values are 1, 4, 9, 16, 25, 36, . . . , and the variables have an exponent that is an even whole number.)
2. The middle term is twice the product of the values that, when squared, give the first and last terms.

EXAMPLE 5 Factor $25x^2 - 20x + 4$.

Is this trinomial a perfect square? Yes.

1. The first and last terms are perfect squares.

$$25x^2 - 20x + 4 = (5x)^2 - 20x + (2)^2$$

2. The middle term is twice the product of the value $5x$ and the value 2. In other words, $2(5x)(2) = 20x$.

$$(5x)^2 - 2(5x)(2) + (2)^2 = (5x - 2)^2$$

Therefore, we can use the formula $a^2 - 2ab + b^2 = (a - b)^2$. Thus,

$$\begin{array}{ccccccc} a^2 & - & 2ab & + b^2 & = (a & - & b)^2 \\ \downarrow & & \downarrow & \downarrow & \downarrow & & \downarrow \\ 25x^2 & - & 20x & + 4 & = (5x & - & 2)^2. \end{array}$$

Practice Problem 5 Factor $9x^2 - 30x + 25$.

EXAMPLE 6 Factor $16x^2 - 24x + 9$.

1. The first and last terms are perfect squares: $16x^2 = (4x)^2$ and $9 = (3)^2$.
2. The middle term is twice the product $(4x)(3)$. Therefore, we have the following:

$$\begin{aligned} a^2 - 2ab + b^2 &= (a - b)^2 \\ 16x^2 - 24x + 9 &= (4x)^2 - 2(4x)(3) + (3)^2 \\ 16x^2 - 24x + 9 &= (4x - 3)^2 \end{aligned}$$

Practice Problem 6 Factor $25x^2 - 70x + 49$.

EXAMPLE 7 Factor $200x^2 + 360x + 162$.

First we factor out the common factor of 2.

$$\begin{aligned} 200x^2 + 360x + 162 &= 2(100x^2 + 180x + 81) \\ a^2 + 2ab + b^2 &= (a + b)^2 \\ 2[100x^2 + 180x + 81] &= 2[(10x)^2 + (2)(10x)(9) + (9)^2] \\ &= 2(10x + 9)^2 \end{aligned}$$

Practice Problem 7 Factor $242x^2 + 88x + 8$.

EXAMPLE 8 Factor.

(a) $x^4 + 14x^2 + 49$ **(b)** $9x^4 + 30x^2y^2 + 25y^4$

(a) $x^4 + 14x^2 + 49 = (x^2)^2 + 2(x^2)(7) + (7)^2$
$= (x^2 + 7)^2$

(b) $9x^4 + 30x^2y^2 + 25y^4 = (3x^2)^2 + 2(3x^2)(5y^2) + (5y^2)^2$
$= (3x^2 + 5y^2)^2$

Practice Problem 8 Factor. **(a)** $49x^4 + 28x^2 + 4$
(b) $36x^4 + 84x^2y^2 + 49y^4$

3 Sum or Difference of Two Cubes

There are also special formulas for factoring cubic binomials. We see that the factors of $x^3 + 27$ are $(x + 3)(x^2 - 3x + 9)$, and that the factors of $x^3 - 64$ are $(x - 4)(x^2 + 4x + 16)$. Therefore, we can generalize this pattern and derive the following factoring formulas.

Sum and Difference of Cubes Factoring Formulas

$$a^3 + b^3 = (a + b)(a^2 - ab + b^2)$$
$$a^3 - b^3 = (a - b)(a^2 + ab + b^2)$$

EXAMPLE 9 Factor $125x^3 + y^3$.

Here $a = 5x$ and $b = y$.

$$a^3 + b^3 = (a + b)(a^2 - ab + b^2)$$
$$\downarrow \quad \downarrow \quad \downarrow \quad \downarrow \quad \downarrow$$
$$125x^3 + y^3 = (5x)^3 + (y)^3 = (5x + y)(25x^2 - 5xy + y^2)$$

Practice Problem 9 Factor $8x^3 + 125y^3$.

EXAMPLE 10 Factor $64x^3 - 27$.

Here $a = 4x$ and $b = 3$.

$$a^3 - b^3 = (a - b)(a^2 + ab + b^2)$$
$$\downarrow \quad \downarrow \quad \downarrow \quad \downarrow \quad \downarrow$$
$$64x^3 - 27 = (4x)^3 - (3)^3 = (4x - 3)(16x^2 + 12x + 9)$$

Practice Problem 10 Factor $64x^3 - 125y^3$.

EXAMPLE 11 Factor $125w^3 - 8z^6$.

Here $a = 5w$ and $b = 2z^2$.

$$a^3 - b^3 = (a - b)(a^2 + ab + b^2)$$
$$\downarrow \quad \downarrow \quad \downarrow \quad \downarrow \quad \downarrow$$
$$125w^3 - 8z^6 = (5w)^3 - (2z^2)^3 = (5w - 2z^2)(25w^2 + 10wz^2 + 4z^4)$$

Practice Problem 11 Factor $27w^3 - 125z^6$.

EXAMPLE 12 Factor $250x^3 - 2$.

First we must factor out the common factor of 2.

$$250x^3 - 2 = 2(125x^3 - 1)$$
$$= 2(5x - 1)\underbrace{(25x^2 + 5x + 1)}$$

↑

Note that this trinomial cannot be factored.

Practice Problem 12 Factor $54x^3 - 16$.

What should you do if a polynomial is the difference of two cubes *and* the difference of two squares? Usually, it's easier to use the difference of two squares formula first. Then apply the difference of two cubes formula.

EXAMPLE 13 Factor $x^6 - y^6$.

We can write this binomial as $(x^2)^3 - (y^2)^3$ or as $(x^3)^2 - (y^3)^2$. Therefore, we can use either the difference of two cubes formula or the difference of two squares formula. It's usually better to use the difference of two squares formula first, so we'll do that.

$$x^6 - y^6 = (x^3)^2 - (y^3)^2$$

Here $a = x^3$ and $b = y^3$. Therefore,

$$(x^3)^2 - (y^3)^2 = (x^3 + y^3)(x^3 - y^3).$$

Now we use the sum of two cubes formula for the first factor and the difference of two cubes formula for the second factor.

$$x^3 + y^3 = (x + y)(x^2 - xy + y^2)$$
$$x^3 - y^3 = (x - y)(x^2 + xy + y^2)$$

Hence,

$$x^6 - y^6 = (x + y)(x^2 - xy + y^2)(x - y)(x^2 + xy + y^2).$$

Practice Problem 13 Factor $64a^6 - 1$.

You'll see these special cases of factoring often. You should memorize the following formulas.

Special Cases of Factoring

Difference of Two Squares

$$a^2 - b^2 = (a + b)(a - b)$$

Perfect Square Trinomial

$$a^2 - 2ab + b^2 = (a - b)^2$$
$$a^2 + 2ab + b^2 = (a + b)^2$$

Sum and Difference of Cubes

$$a^3 + b^3 = (a + b)(a^2 - ab + b^2)$$
$$a^3 - b^3 = (a - b)(a^2 + ab + b^2)$$

5.6 Exercises

Use the difference of two squares formula to factor. Be sure to factor out any common factors.

1. $16x^2 - 81$ **2.** $64x^2 - 49$ **3.** $64x^2 - 1$ **4.** $81x^2 - 1$

5. $81x^4 - 1$ **6.** $16x^4 - 1$ **7.** $49m^2 - 9n^2$ **8.** $36x^2 - 25y^2$

9. $1 - 81x^2y^2$ **10.** $1 - 49x^2y^2$ **11.** $100y^2 - 81$ **12.** $49y^2 - 144$

13. $32x^2 - 18$ **14.** $50x^2 - 8$ **15.** $5x - 20x^3$ **16.** $49x^3 - 36x$

Use the perfect square trinomial formulas to factor. Be sure to factor out any common factors.

17. $49x^2 - 14x + 1$ **18.** $9x^2 - 6x + 1$ **19.** $16y^2 - 8y + 1$ **20.** $100y^2 - 20y + 1$

21. $81w^2 + 36wt + 4t^2$ **22.** $25w^2 + 20wt + 4t^2$ **23.** $36x^2 - 60xy + 25y^2$ **24.** $64x^2 - 48xy + 9y^2$

25. $8x^2 + 24x + 18$ **26.** $128x^2 + 32x + 2$ **27.** $3x^3 - 24x^2 + 48x$ **28.** $50x^3 - 20x^2 + 2x$

Use the sum and difference of cubes formulas to factor. Be sure to factor out any common factors.

29. $8x^3 + 27$ **30.** $64x^3 + 27$ **31.** $x^3 + 125$ **32.** $x^3 + 64$

33. $64x^3 - 1$ **34.** $125x^3 - 1$ **35.** $125x^3 - 8$ **36.** $27x^3 - 64$

37. $1 - 27x^3$ **38.** $1 - 8x^3$ **39.** $64x^3 + 125$ **40.** $27x^3 + 125$

41. $64s^6 + t^6$ **42.** $125s^6 + t^6$ **43.** $6y^3 - 6$ **44.** $80y^3 - 10$

45. $3x^3 - 24$ **46.** $54y^2 - 2$ **47.** $x^5 - 8x^2y^3$ **48.** $x^5 - 27x^2y^3$

Mixed Practice

Factor by the methods of this section.

49. $25w^6 - 1$

50. $x^8 - 1$

51. $8w^6 + 8w^3 + 2$

52. $18w^4 + 24w^2 + 8$

53. $24a^3 - 3b^3$

54. $54w^3 + 250$

55. $125m^3 + 8n^3$

56. $64z^3 - 27w^3$

57. $9x^2 - 100y^2$

58. $49 - 64a^2b^2$

59. $4w^2 - 20wz + 25z^2$

60. $9x^2y^2 + 24xy + 16$

61. $36a^2 - 81b^2$

62. $400x^4 - 36y^2$

63. $64x^5 + x^2y^3z^3$

64. $w^4z^3 - 8wy^3$

65. $81x^4 - 36x^2 + 4$

66. $121 + 66y^2 + 9y^4$

67. $16x^4 - 81y^4$

68. $256x^4 - 1$

Try to factor the following four exercises by using the formulas for the perfect square trinomial. Why can't the formulas be used? Then factor each exercise correctly using an appropriate method.

69. $25x^2 + 25x + 4$

70. $16x^2 + 40x + 9$

71. $4x^2 - 15x + 9$

72. $36x^2 - 65x + 25$

Applications

▲ **73.** Find the area of a maple cabinet surface that is constructed as a large square with sides of $4x$ feet and has a square cut out region whose sides are y feet. Factor the expression.

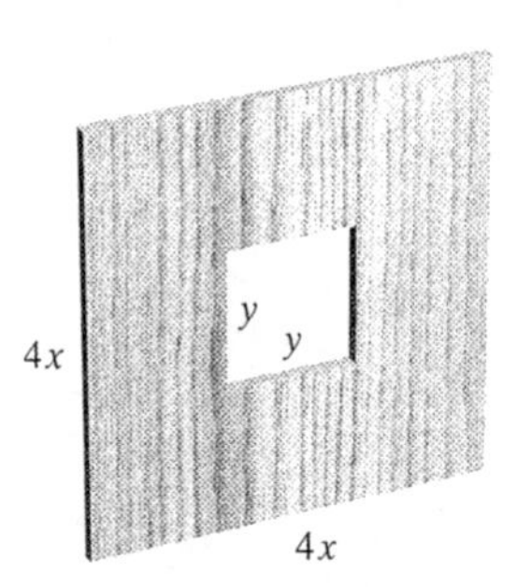

▲ **74.** A copper base for a lamp consists of a large circle of radius $2y$ inches with a cut out area in the center of radius x inches. Write an expression for the area of this copper base. Write your answer in factored form.

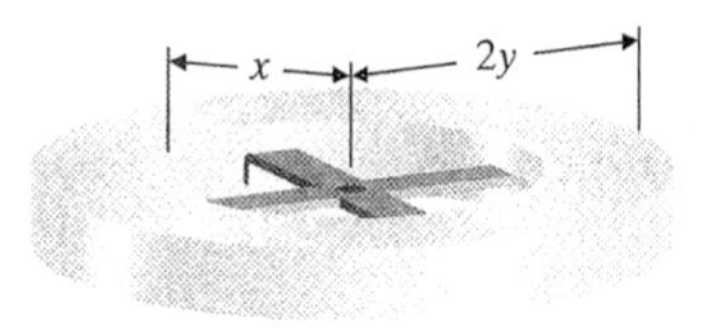

Cumulative Review Problems

75. The average beginning annual salary y offered to a student graduating with a bachelor's degree in marketing can be approximated by the equation $y = 1200x + 27{,}000$, where x is the number of years since 1996. The average beginning annual salary y offered to a student graduating with a bachelor's degree in mathematics can be approximated by the equation $y = 3200x + 29{,}000$, where x in the number of years since 1996. If this trend continues, in what year will a student graduating with a bachelor's degree in math be offered $12,000 more per year than a student graduating with a bachelor's degree in marketing? *Source:* U.S. Census Bureau.

76. Belinda invested $4000 in mutual funds. In 1 year she earned $482. Part was invested at 14% simple interest and the remainder at 11% simple interest. How much did she invest at each rate?

▲ **77.** A triangular circuit board has a perimeter of 66 centimeters. The first side is two-thirds as long as the second side. The third side is 14 centimeters shorter than the second side. Find the length of each side.

78. Three friends each bought a portable compact disc player. The total for the three purchases was $858. Melinda paid $110 more than Hector. Alice paid $86 less than Hector. How much did each person pay?

5.7 Factoring a Polynomial Completely

1 Factoring Factorable Polynomials

Student Learning Objectives

After studying this section, you will be able to:

Factor any factorable polynomial.

Recognize polynomials that are prime.

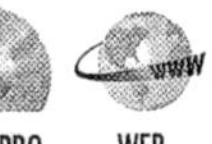

Not all polynomials have the convenient form of one of the special formulas. Most do not. The following procedure will help you handle these common cases. You must practice this procedure until you can *recognize the various forms* and *determine which factoring method to use.*

Completely Factoring a Polynomial

1. Check for a common factor. Factor out the greatest common factor (if there is one) before doing anything else.

2. (a) If the remaining polynomial has two terms, try to factor it as one of the following.
- **(1)** The difference of two squares: $a^2 - b^2 = (a + b)(a - b)$
- **(2)** The difference of two cubes: $a^3 - b^3 = (a - b)(a^2 + ab + b^2)$
- **(3)** The sum of two cubes: $a^3 + b^3 = (a + b)(a^2 - ab + b^2)$

(b) If the remaining polynomial has three terms, try to factor it as one of the following.
- **(1)** A perfect square trinomial: $a^2 + 2ab + b^2 = (a + b)^2$ or $a^2 - 2ab + b^2 = (a - b)^2$
- **(2)** A general trinomial of the form $x^2 + bx + c$ or the form $ax^2 + bx + c$

(c) If the remaining polynomial has four terms, try to factor by grouping.

3. Check to see whether the factors can be factored further.

EXAMPLE 1 Factor completely.

(a) $2x^2 - 18$ **(b)** $27x^4 - 8x$ **(c)** $27x^2 + 36xy + 12y^2$

(d) $2x^2 - 100x + 98$ **(e)** $6x^3 + 11x^2 - 10x$ **(f)** $5ax + 5ay - 20x - 20y$

(a) $2x^2 - 18 = 2(x^2 - 9)$ Factor out the common factor.
$= 2(x + 3)(x - 3)$ Use $a^2 - b^2 = (a + b)(a - b)$.

(b) $27x^4 - 8x = x(27x^3 - 8)$ Factor out the common factor.
$= x(3x - 2)(9x^2 + 6x + 4)$ Use $a^3 - b^3 = (a - b)(a^2 + ab + b^2)$.

(c) $27x^2 + 36xy + 12y^2 = 3(9x^2 + 12xy + 4y^2)$ Factor out the common factor.
$= 3(3x + 2y)^2$ Use $(a + b)^2 = a^2 + 2ab + b^2$.

(d) $2x^2 - 100x + 98 = 2(x^2 - 50x + 49)$ Factor out the common factor.
$= 2(x - 49)(x - 1)$ The trinomial has the form $x^2 + bx + c$.

(e) $6x^3 + 11x^2 - 10x = x(6x^2 + 11x - 10)$ Factor out the common factor.
$= x(3x - 2)(2x + 5)$ The trinomial has the form $ax^2 + bx + c$.

(f) $5ax + 5ay - 20x - 20y = 5(ax + ay - 4x - 4y)$ Factor out the common factor.

$= 5[a(x + y) - 4(x + y)]$ Factor by grouping.
$= 5(x + y)(a - 4)$

Practice Problem 1 Factor completely.

(a) $7x^5 + 56x^2$ **(b)** $125x^2 + 50xy + 5y^2$ **(c)** $12x^2 - 75$

(d) $3x^2 - 39x + 126$ **(e)** $6ax + 6ay + 18bx + 18by$ **(f)** $6x^3 - x^2 - 12x$

2 Recognizing Polynomials That Are Prime

Can all polynomials be factored? No. Many polynomials cannot be factored. If a polynomial cannot be factored, it is said to be **prime**.

EXAMPLE 2 If possible, factor $6x^2 + 10x + 3$.

The trinomial has the form $ax^2 + bx + c$. The grouping number is 18. If the trinomial can be factored, we must find two numbers whose product is 18 and whose sum is 10.

Factor Pairs of 18	*Sum of the Factors*
(18)(1)	19
(6)(3)	9
(9)(2)	11

There are no numbers meeting the necessary conditions. Thus, the polynomial is prime. (If you use the trial-and-error method, try all the possible factors and show that none of them has a product with a middle term of $10x$.)

Practice Problem 2 If possible, factor $3x^2 - 10x + 4$.

EXAMPLE 3 If possible, factor $25x^2 + 49$.

Unless there is a common factor that can be factored out, binomials of the form $a^2 + b^2$ cannot be factored. Therefore, $25x^2 + 49$ is prime.

Practice Problem 3 If possible, factor $16x^2 + 81$.

5.7 Exercises

Verbal and Writing Skills

1. In any factoring problem the first step is _______________________________.

2. If $x^2 + bx + c = (x + e)(x + f)$ and c is positive and b is negative, what can you say about the signs of e and of f?

Mixed Practice

Factor, if possible. Be sure to factor completely.

3. $3xy - 6yz$

4. $x^2 - 4x - 77$

5. $3x^2 - 8x + 5$

6. $ax - 2xy + 3aw - 6wy$

7. $8x^3 - 125y^3$

8. $27x^3 + 64y^3$

9. $x^2 + 2xy - xz$

10. $x^2 + 16$

11. $3x^2 - x - 1$

12. $x^3 - 11x^2 + 30x$

13. $6x^2 - 23x - 4$

14. $25x^2 - 40x + 16$

15. $3x^2 - 3x - xy + y$

16. $xb - x - yb + y$

17. $81a^4 - 1$

18. $1 - 16x^4$

19. $2x^5 - 16x^3 - 18x$

20. $8a^3b - 50ab^3$

21. $6x^3 - 9x^2 - 15x$

22. $3x^2 + 2xy - 7y^2$

23. $4x^2 - 8x - 6$

24. $10x^2 + 5x + 5$

25. $y^2 - 5y + 7$

26. $2a^6 + 20a^5b + 50a^4b^2$

27. $6a^2 - 6a - 36$

28. $9a^2 + 18a - 72$

29. $64 + 49y^2$

30. $5x^4 - 13x^2 - 6$

31. $2x^4 - 3x^2 - 5$

32. $50x^2y^2 - 32y^2$

33. $12x^2 + 11x - 2$

34. $49x^8 + 14x^5 + x^2$

35. $4x^4 + 20x^2y^4 + 25y^8$

36. $81x^4z^6 - 25y^8$

Applications

A cattle pen is constructed with solid wood walls. The pen is divided into four rectangular compartments. Each compartment is x feet long and y feet wide. The walls are $x - 10$ feet high.

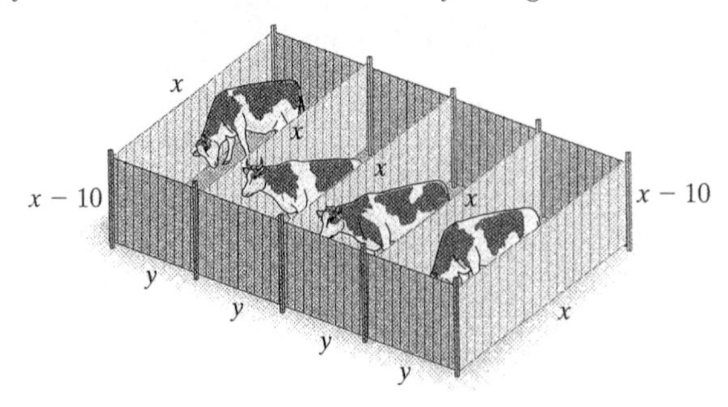

▲ **37.** Find the total surface area of the walls used in the cattle pen. Express the answer in factored form and in the form with the factors multiplied.

▲ **38.** The rancher who owns the cattle pen wants to increase the length x by 3 feet. Find the new total surface area of the walls that would be used in this enlarged cattle pen. Express the answer in factored form and in the form with the factors multiplied.

Cumulative Review Problems

Solve the following inequalities.

39. $3x - 2 \leq -5 + 2(x - 3)$

40. $|2 + 5x - 3| < 2$

41. $\left|\frac{1}{3}(5 - 4x)\right| > 4$

42. $x - 4 \geq 7$ or $4x + 1 \leq 17$

Use the bar graph at the right to answer the following.

43. What was the average value of the net receipts for a 2-year period for the Republican Party?

44. What was the average percent of increase from one 2-year period to the next for the Democratic Party? (*Hint:* First find the percents of increase from 1985–86 to 1989–90, from 1989–90 to 1993–94, and from 1993–94 to 1997–98. Then average the three values.)

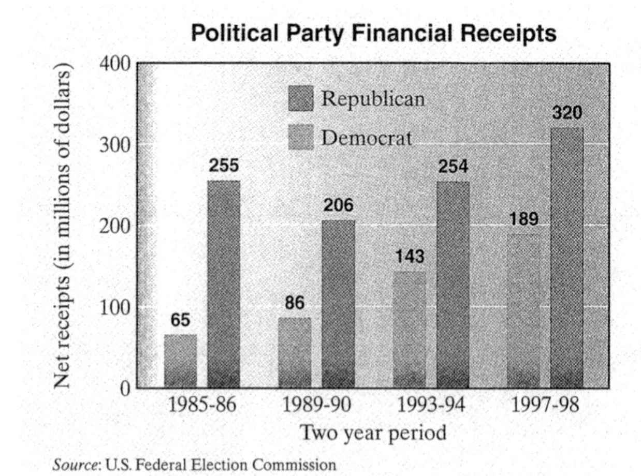

Source: U.S. Federal Election Commission

45. Assuming the average percent of increase obtained in Exercise 44, was unchanged after the 2001–2002 period, what would be the expected net receipts for the Democratic party in the 2001–2002 period?

46. If the percent of increase from 1997–98 to 2001–2002 was the same as that from 1993–94 to 1997–98, what would be the expected net receipts for the Democratic Party in the 2001–2002 period?

5.8 Solving Equations and Applications Using Polynomials

Student Learning Objectives

After studying this section, you will be able to:

Factor to find the roots of a quadratic equation.

Solve applied exercises that involve a factorable quadratic equation.

1 *Factoring to Find the Roots of a Quadratic Equation*

Up until now, we have solved only first-degree equations. In this section we will solve quadratic, or second-degree, equations.

Definition

A second-degree equation of the form $ax^2 + bx + c = 0$, where a, b, c are real numbers and $a \neq 0$, is a **quadratic equation**. $ax^2 + bx + c = 0$ is the **standard form** of a quadratic equation.

Before solving a quadratic equation, we will first write the equation in standard form. Although it is not necessary that a, b, and c be integers, the equation is usually written this way.

The key to solving quadratic equations by factoring is called the **zero factor property**. When we multiply two real numbers, the resulting product will be zero if one or both of the factors is zero. Thus, if the product of two real numbers is zero, at least one of the factors must be zero. We state this property of real numbers formally.

Zero Factor Property

For all real numbers a and b,

$$\text{if } a \cdot b = 0, \text{ then } a = 0, b = 0, \text{ or both} = 0.$$

EXAMPLE 1 Solve the equation $x^2 + 15x = 100$.

When we say "solve the equation" or "find the roots," we mean "find the values of x that satisfy the equation."

$$x^2 + 15x - 100 = 0 \quad \text{Subtract 100 from both sides so that one side is 0.}$$

$$(x + 20)(x - 5) = 0 \quad \text{Factor the trinomial.}$$

$$x + 20 = 0 \quad \text{or} \quad x - 5 = 0 \quad \text{Set each factor equal to 0.}$$

$$x = -20 \qquad x = 5 \quad \text{Solve each equation.}$$

Check: Use the *original* equation $x^2 + 15x = 100$.

$$x = -20: \quad (-20)^2 + 15(-20) \stackrel{?}{=} 100$$

$$400 - 300 \stackrel{?}{=} 100$$

$$100 = 100 \checkmark$$

$$x = 5: \quad (5)^2 + 15(5) \stackrel{?}{=} 100$$

$$25 + 75 \stackrel{?}{=} 100$$

$$100 = 100 \checkmark$$

Thus, 5 and -20 are both roots of the quadratic equation $x^2 + 15x = 100$.

Practice Problem 1 Find the roots of $x^2 + x = 56$.

For convenience, we list the steps we have employed to solve the quadratic equation.

1. Rewrite the quadratic equation in standard form (so that one side of the equation is 0) and, if possible, *factor* the quadratic expression.
2. Set each factor equal to zero.
3. Solve the resulting equations to find both roots. (A quadratic equation has two roots.)
4. Check your solutions.

It is extremely important to remember that when you are placing the quadratic equation in standard form, one side of the equation must be zero. Several algebraic operations may be necessary to obtain that desired result before you can factor the polynomial.

EXAMPLE 2 Find the roots of $6x^2 + 4 = 7(x + 1)$.

$6x^2 + 4 = 7x + 7$ Apply the distributive property.

$6x^2 - 7x - 3 = 0$ Rewrite the equation in standard form.

$(2x - 3)(3x + 1) = 0$ Factor the trinomial.

$2x - 3 = 0 \quad \text{or} \quad 3x + 1 = 0$ Set each factor equal to 0.

$2x = 3 \qquad 3x = -1$ Solve the equations.

$x = \frac{3}{2} \qquad x = -\frac{1}{3}$

Check: Use the *original* equation $6x^2 + 4 = 7(x + 1)$.

$$x = \frac{3}{2}: \quad 6\left(\frac{3}{2}\right)^2 + 4 \stackrel{?}{=} 7\left(\frac{3}{2} + 1\right)$$
$$6\left(\frac{9}{4}\right) + 4 \stackrel{?}{=} 7\left(\frac{5}{2}\right)$$
$$\frac{27}{2} + 4 \stackrel{?}{=} \frac{35}{2}$$
$$\frac{27}{2} + \frac{8}{2} \stackrel{?}{=} \frac{35}{2}$$
$$\frac{35}{2} = \frac{35}{2} \quad ✓$$

It checks, so $\frac{3}{2}$ is a root. Verify that $-\frac{1}{3}$ is also a root.

If you are using a calculator to check your roots, you can complete the check more rapidly using the decimal values 1.5 and −0.33333333. The latter value is approximate, so some round-off error is expected.

Practice Problem 2 Find the roots of $12x^2 - 11x + 2 = 0$.

EXAMPLE 3 Find the roots of $3x^2 - 5x = 0$.

$3x^2 - 5x = 0$ The equation is already in standard form.

$x(3x - 5) = 0$ Factor.

$x = 0 \quad \text{or} \quad 3x - 5 = 0$ Set each factor equal to 0.

$3x = 5$

$x = \frac{5}{3}$

Check: Verify that 0 and $\frac{5}{3}$ are roots of $3x^2 - 5x = 0$.

Practice Problem 3 Find the roots of $7x^2 - 14x = 0$.

EXAMPLE 4 Solve $9x(x - 1) = 3x - 4$.

$9x^2 - 9x = 3x - 4$ Remove parentheses.

$9x^2 - 9x - 3x + 4 = 0$ Get 0 on one side.

$9x^2 - 12x + 4 = 0$ Combine like terms.

$(3x - 2)^2 = 0$ Factor.

$3x - 2 = 0 \quad \text{or} \quad 3x - 2 = 0$

$3x = 2 \qquad 3x = 2$

$x = \frac{2}{3} \qquad x = \frac{2}{3}$

We obtain one solution twice. This value is called a **double root**.

Graphing Calculator

Finding Roots

Not all quadratic equations are as easy to factor as the one in Example 2. Suppose you are asked to find the roots of

$10x(x + 1) = 83x + 12{,}012.$

This can be written in the form

$10x^2 - 73x - 12{,}012 = 0$

and factored to obtain the following:

$(5x + 156)(2x - 77) = 0$

$x = -\frac{156}{5}$ *and* $x = \frac{77}{2}$

In decimal form the solutions are −31.2 and 38.5.

However, you can use the graphing calculator to graph

$y = 10x^2 - 73x - 12{,}012.$

By setting an appropriate viewing window and then using the Zoom and Trace features of your calculator, you can find the two places where $y = 0$.

Some calculators have a command that will find the zeros (roots) of a graph.

In a similar fashion graph each equation using the form $y = ax^2 + bx + c$ and use the graph to find the roots.

(a)
$10x^2 - 189x - 12{,}834 = 0$

(b)
$10x(x + 2) = 11{,}011 - 193x$

Practice Problem 4 Solve $16x(x - 2) = 8x - 25$.

The zero factor property can be extended to a polynomial equation of degree greater than 2. In the following example, we will find the three roots of a third-degree polynomial equation.

EXAMPLE 5 Solve $2x^3 = 24x - 8x^2$.

$2x^3 + 8x^2 - 24x = 0$			Get 0 on one side of the equation.
$2x(x^2 + 4x - 12) = 0$			Factor out the common factor $2x$.
$2x(x + 6)(x - 2) = 0$			Factor the trinomial.
$2x = 0$	$x + 6 = 0$	$x - 2 = 0$	Zero factor property.
$x = 0$	$x = -6$	$x = 2$	Solve for x.

The solutions are 0, −6, and 2.

Practice Problem 5 Solve $3x^3 + 6x^2 = 45x$.

2 Solving Applied Exercises That Involve a Factorable Quadratic Equation

Some applied exercises lead to a factorable quadratic equation. Using the methods developed in this section, we can solve these types of exercises.

EXAMPLE 6 A racing sailboat has a triangular sail. Find the base and altitude of the triangular sail that has an area of 35 square meters and a base that is 3 meters shorter than the altitude.

1. ***Understand the problem.***
   We draw a sketch and recall the formula for the area of a triangle.

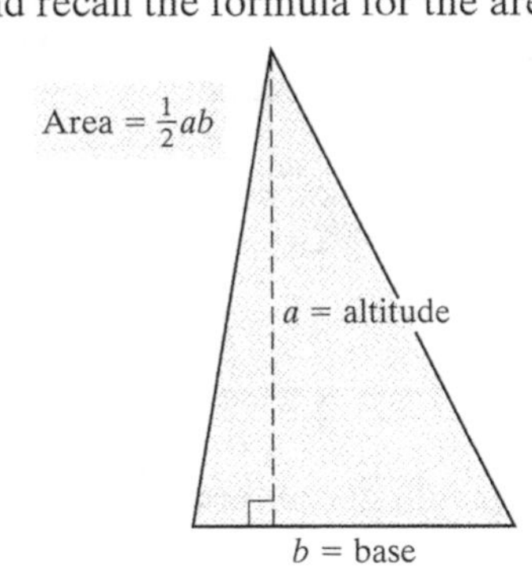

Let x = the length of the altitude in meters.
Then $x - 3$ = the length of the base in meters.

2. ***Write an equation.***

$$A = \frac{1}{2}ab$$

$$35 = \frac{1}{2}x(x - 3)$$ Replace A (area) by 35, a (altitude) by x, and b (base) by $x - 3$.

3. ***Solve the equation and state the answer.***

$70 = x(x - 3)$ Multiply each side by 2.

$70 = x^2 - 3x$ Remove parentheses.

$0 = x^2 - 3x - 70$ Subtract 70 from each side.

$0 = (x - 10)(x + 7)$

$x = 10 \quad or \quad x = -7$

The altitude of a triangle must be a positive number, so we disregard −7. Thus,

$$\text{altitude} = x = 10 \text{ meters and}$$
$$\text{base} = x - 3 = 7 \text{ meters.}$$

The altitude of the triangular sail measures 10 meters, and the base of the sail measures 7 meters.

4. ***Check.***

Is the base 3 meters shorter than the altitude?

$$10 - 3 = 7 \ \checkmark$$

Is the area of the triangle 35 square meters?

$$A = \frac{1}{2}ab$$

$$A = \frac{1}{2}(10)(7) = 5(7) = 35 \ \checkmark$$

Practice Problem 6 A racing sailboat has a triangular sail. Find the base and the altitude of the triangular sail if the area is 52 square feet and the altitude is 5 feet longer than the base.

EXAMPLE 7 A car manufacturer uses a square panel that holds fuses. The square panel that is used this year has an area that is 72 square centimeters greater than the area of the square panel used last year. The length of each side of the new panel is 3 centimeters more than double the length of last year's panel. Find the dimensions of each panel.

1. ***Understand the problem.***

We draw a sketch of each square panel and recall that the area of each panel is obtained by squaring its side.

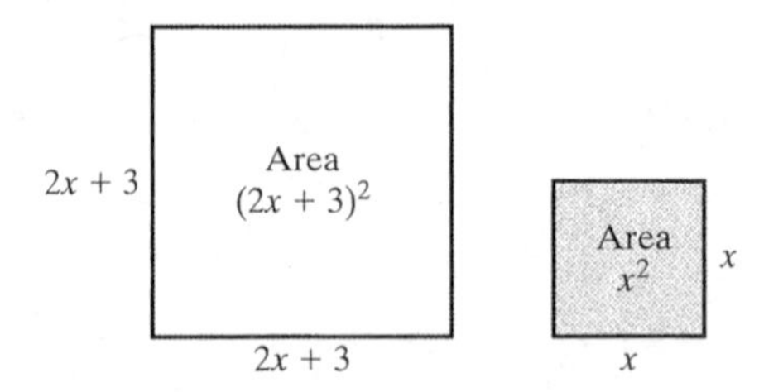

Let x = the length in centimeters of last year's panel.

Then $2x + 3$ = the length in centimeters of this year's panel.

The area of this year's panel is 72 square centimeters greater than the area of last year's panel.

2. ***Write an equation.***

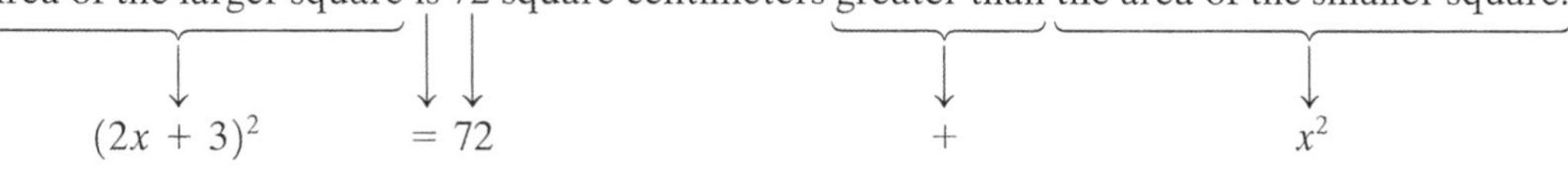

$$(2x + 3)^2 \quad = 72 \quad + \quad x^2$$

3. ***Solve the equation and state the answer.***

$4x^2 + 12x + 9 = 72 + x^2$ Remove parentheses.

$4x^2 + 12x + 9 - x^2 - 72 = 0$ Get 0 on one side of the equation.

$3x^2 + 12x - 63 = 0$ Simplify.

$3(x^2 + 4x - 21) = 0$ Factor out the common factor of 3.

$3(x + 7)(x - 3) = 0$ Factor the trinomial.

$x + 7 = 0 \qquad x - 3 = 0$ Use the zero factor property.

$x = -7 \qquad x = 3$ Solve for x.

A fuse box cannot measure −7 centimeters, so we reject the negative answer. We use $x = 3$; then $2x + 3 = 2(3) + 3 = 6 + 3 = 9$.

Thus, the old fuse panel measured 3 centimeters on a side. The new fuse panel measures 9 centimeters on a side.

4. ***Check.***
Verify that each answer is correct.

Practice Problem 7 Last year Grandpa Jones had a small square garden. This year he has a square garden that is 112 square feet larger in area. Each side of the new garden is 2 feet longer than triple each side of the old garden. Find the dimensions of each garden.

Developing Your Study Skills

Getting Help

Getting the right kind of help at the right time can be a key ingredient in being successful in mathematics. Even if you have gone to class on a regular basis, taken careful notes, methodically read your textbook, and diligently done your homework—all of which means making every effort possible to learn the mathematics—you may find that you are still having difficulty. If this is the case, then you need to seek help. Make an appointment with your instructor to find out what help is available to you. The instructor, tutoring services, a mathematics lab, videotapes, and computer software may be among the resources you can draw on.

Once you discover the resources available in your school, you need to take advantage of them. Do not put it off, or you will find yourself getting behind. You cannot afford that. When studying mathematics, you must keep up with your work.

5.8 Exercises

Find all the roots and check your answers.

1. $x^2 - 13x = -36$

2. $x^2 - x = 2$

3. $5x^2 - 6x = 0$

4. $3x^2 + 5x = 0$

5. $3x^2 - x - 2 = 0$

6. $2x^2 - 9x + 7 = 0$

7. $3x^2 - 2x - 8 = 0$

8. $4x^2 - 13x + 3 = 0$

9. $8x^2 - 3 = 2x$

10. $4x^2 - 15 = 4x$

11. $8x^2 = 11x - 3$

12. $5x^2 = 11x - 2$

13. $x^2 + \frac{5}{3}x = \frac{2}{3}x$

14. $x^2 - \frac{5}{2}x = \frac{x}{2}$

15. $2x^2 + 3x = -14x^2 + 5x$

16. $5x^2 - 2x = x^2 - 8x$

17. $x^3 + 5x^2 + 6x = 0$

18. $x^3 + 11x^2 + 18x = 0$

19. $x^3 = x^2 + 20x$

20. $x^3 = 2x^2 + 24x$

21. $3x^3 - 10x = 17x$

22. $5x^3 - 8x = 12x$

23. $3x^3 + 15x^2 = 42x$

24. $2x^3 + 6x^2 = 20x$

25. $\frac{7x^2 - 3}{2} = 2x$

26. $\frac{3x^2 + 3x}{2} = \frac{2}{3}$

27. $2(x + 3) = -3x + 2(x^2 - 3)$

28. $2(x^2 - 4) - 3x = 4x - 11$

29. $7x^2 + 6 = 2x^2 + 2(4x + 3)$

30. $11x^2 - 3x + 1 = 2(x^2 - 5x) + 1$

To Think About

31. The equation $x^2 + bx - 12 = 0$ has a solution of -4. What is the value of b? What is the other solution to the equation?

32. The equation $2x^2 - 3x + c = 0$ has a solution of $-\frac{1}{2}$. What is the value of c? What is the other solution to the equation?

Applications

Solve the following applied exercises.

▲ **33.** The area of the triangular logo on a laptop computer is 87 square millimeters. The altitude of the logo is 5 millimeters longer than 4 times the base. Find the measurements of the altitude and the base.

▲ **34.** The local child care center has big, colorful geometric designs in its carpet. A bright orange triangle has an area of 242 square centimeters. The altitude of the orange triangle is 22 centimeters longer than twice its base. Find the length of the altitude and the length of the base.

▲ **35.** During halftime at the Super Bowl, one of the performers will sing on a triangular platform that measures 119 square yards. The base of the triangular stage is 6 yards longer than four times the length of the altitude. What are the dimensions of the triangular stage?

▲ **36.** The area of a triangular neon billboard advertising the local mall is 104 square feet. The base of the triangle is 2 feet longer than triple the length of the altitude.
(a) What are the dimensions of the triangular billboard in feet?
(b) What are the dimensions of the triangular billboard in yards?

▲ **37.** The area of a rectangular desk telephone is 896 square centimeters. The length of the rectangular telephone is 4 centimeters longer than its width.
(a) What are the length and width, in centimeters, of the desk telephone?
(b) What are the length and width, in millimeters, of the desk telephone?

▲ **38.** The area of a rectangular mouse pad is 480 square centimeters. Its length is 16 centimeters shorter than twice its width.
(a) What are the length and width of the mouse pad in centimeters?
(b) What are the length and width of the mouse pad in millimeters?

▲ **39.** The backstage dressing room of the most famous circus in the world is in the shape of a square. The area of the square dressing room in square feet is 165 more than its perimeter in feet. Find the length of the side.

▲ **40.** A rare square Turkish rug, belonging to the family of President John F. Kennedy, was auctioned off. The area of the Turkish rug in square feet is 96 more than its perimeter in feet. Find the length in feet of the side.

▲ **41.** The volume of a rectangular solid can be written as $V = LWH$, where L is the length of the solid, W is the width, and H is the height. A box of cereal has a width of 2 inches. Its height is 2 inches longer than its length. If the volume of the box is 198 cubic inches, what are the length and height of the box?

▲ **42.** The volume of a rectangular solid can be written as $V = LWH$, where L is the length of the solid, W is the width, and H is the height. The North Shore Community College catalog is $\frac{1}{2}$ inch wide. Its height is 3 inches longer than its length. The volume of the catalog is 27 cubic inches. What are the height and length of the catalog?

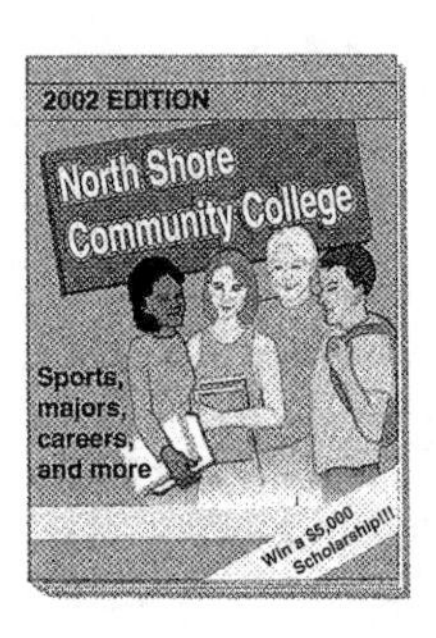

▲ **43.** In the northern Atlantic Ocean, a certain fishing area is in the shape of a rectangle. The length of the rectangle is 7 miles longer than double its width. The area of this rectangle is 85 square miles. What are the dimensions of this rectangle?

▲ **44.** In planning for the first trip to the moon, NASA surveyed a rectangular area of 54 square miles. The length of the rectangle was 3 miles less than double the width. What were the dimensions of this potential landing area?

▲ **45.** Media One has a square target that receives signal transmissions from a television tower. They recently enlarged the square target so that its area is 176 square centimeters more than the area of the old target. The new target is a square and has a side that is 1 cm longer than double the side of the old target. What are the dimensions of the old and the new targets?

▲ **46.** The Parad family has a square vegetable garden. They increased the size of the garden so that the new, larger square garden is 84 square feet larger than the old garden. The new garden has a side that is 2 feet longer than double the length of the side of the old garden. What are the dimensions of the old and the new gardens?

A manufacturer finds that the profit in dollars for manufacturing n units is $P = 2n^2 - 19n - 10$. *(Assume that n is a positive integer.) Use this formula for Exercises 47–50.*

47. How many units are produced when the profit is \$410?

48. How many units are produced when the profit is \$0?

49. How many units are produced when there is a loss of \$52 $(P = -52)$?

50. How many units are produced when there is a loss of \$34 $(P = -34)$?

The number N of mutual funds in the United States can be approximated by the equation $N = 28x^2 + 80x + 560$, *where x is the number of years since 1980. Use this equation to solve Exercises 51–54.*

Source: U.S. Bureau of Economic Analysis.

51. Approximately how many mutual funds were there in the year 2000?

52. Approximately how many mutual funds were there in the year 1998?

53. In what year were there 668 mutual funds?

54. In what year were there 832 mutual funds?

Cumulative Review Problems

Simplify. Do not leave negative exponents in your answers.

55. $(2x^3y^2)^3(5xy^2)^2$

56. $\dfrac{(2a^3b^2)^3}{16a^5b^8}$

57. $(-3x^{-2}y^4z)^{-2}$

58. $\left(\dfrac{5xy^{-2}}{2x^{-3}y}\right)^3$

Putting Your Skills to Work

Locating a Downed Aircraft

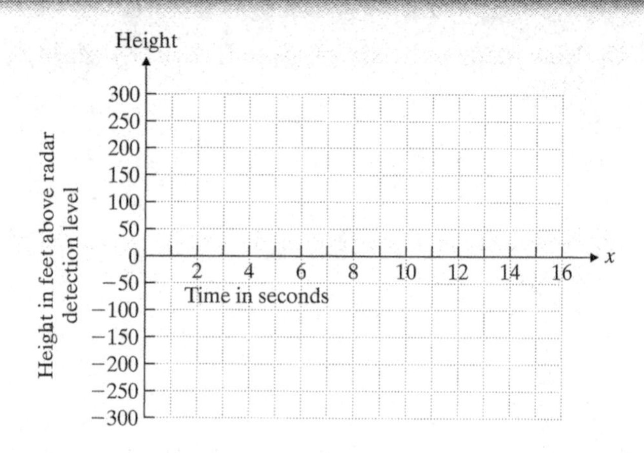

When a plane crashes, every effort is made to locate it. Often the most important clue is where the aircraft was when it disappeared from the radar screen. Once this is determined, estimates can be made as to the location of the aircraft. Sometimes when a plane is descending out of control, it drops below the minimum altitude needed to be detected by radar, only to rise again briefly before it finally crashes.

Suppose the height h of an aircraft above the minimum radar-detection level is given by the equation $y = -x^3 + 23x^2 - 130x$, where x is the number of seconds since the aircraft first dropped off the radar screen and h is measured in feet. See whether you can determine the following.

Problems for Individual Investigation and Analysis

1. Factor the equation. Determine the values of x where $y = 0$.

2. Find the values of y when $x = 2, 4, 6, 8, 11, 12$, and 14. Use these values along with the values obtained in Exercise 1 to graph the equation.

Problems for Group Investigation and Cooperative Learning

3. Find the values of y when $x = -3, -2$ and -1. What is the significance of positive y-values for negative values of x?

4. Suppose the equation represents an airplane that will impact the ground when it is 1000 feet below the level of radar detection. Find the values of y when $x = 18$, 19, and 20. How many seconds after the plane disappears from the radar will the plane impact the ground?

Internet Connections

Netsite:  http://www.prenhall.com/tobey_intermediate 

Site: Federal Aviation Administration

5. Describe five air traffic control factors that could trigger a special written notification to pilots, navigators, and flight engineers.

6. In each of the years 1996, 1997, and 1998, find the level of air fatalities in the U.S. transportation system as a percent of highway fatalities. What do you think this comparison proves?

Math in the Media

Media Literacy Tips

We receive information daily from a number of media sources—radio, newspapers, television, and on-line content providers. It's important to be able to use math skills to understand the data presented. But using your math skills alone is not enough. You also need to be able to interpret the message in context of the article.

The media can be very persuasive when promoting a viewpoint. There are many factors to consider when evaluating the article. Following are a few tips that may help you to filter out the "hype" and focus on the meaning.

1. Consider the source. Who is the author? Does he or she have a particular platform that may influence the message?
2. Look for the key points. Has anything been done to either attract attention to certain issues and facts or distract the reader from them?
3. Be alert for key omissions. Sometimes what is left unsaid is the most compelling statement.
4. Consider the supporting information. Does the author support his or her argument with facts, opinions, both? How is math used to support the argument?

EXERCISES

1. Locate an article or news feature that interests you. Read the article and write down your responses to each of the 4 tips above.
2. What response do you think the author is trying to elicit?
3. Suppose you read an article with the following information: "Data released yesterday by the FBI indicates that the number of murders committed in the United States has decreased by 33.7% in the last five years. The murder rate for 1998 was 6.3% per 100,000 inhabitants. This rate is the lowest the rate has been since 1979. What a wonderful improvement. Truly the United States is becoming a safe place to live." What concerns or objections would you raise concerning this article?

Chapter 5 Organizer

Topic	Procedure	Examples
Adding and subtracting polynomials, p. 255.	Combine like terms following the rules of signs.	$(5x^2 - 6x - 8) + (-2x^2 - 5x + 3) = 3x^2 - 11x - 5$ $(3a^2 - 2ab - 5b^2) - (-7a^2 + 6ab - b^2)$ $= (3a^2 - 2ab - 5b^2) + (7a^2 - 6ab + b^2)$ $= 10a^2 - 8ab - 4b^2$
Multiplying polynomials, p. 255.	**1.** Multiply each term of the first polynomial by each term of the second polynomial. **2.** Combine like terms.	$2x^2(3x^2 - 5x - 6) = 6x^4 - 10x^3 - 12x^2$ $(3x + 4)(2x - 7) = 6x^2 - 21x + 8x - 28$ $= 6x^2 - 13x - 28$ $(x - 3)(x^2 + 5x + 8)$ $= x^3 + 5x^2 + 8x - 3x^2 - 15x - 24$ $= x^3 + 2x^2 - 7x - 24$
Division of a polynomial by a monomial, p. 260.	**1.** Write the division as the sum of separate fractions. **2.** If possible, reduce the separate fractions.	$(16x^3 - 24x^2 + 56x) \div (-8x)$ $= \frac{16x^3}{-8x} + \frac{-24x^2}{-8x} + \frac{56x}{-8x}$ $= -2x^2 + 3x - 7$
Dividing a polynomial by a binomial or a trinomial, p. 261.	**1.** Write the division exercise in long division form. Write both polynomials in descending order; write any missing terms with a coefficient of zero. **2.** Divide the *first* term of the divisor into the first term of the dividend. The result is the first term of the quotient. **3.** Multiply the first term of the quotient by *every* term in the divisor. **4.** Write this product under the dividend (align like terms) and subtract. **5.** Treat this difference as a new dividend. Repeat steps 2 to 4. Continue until the remainder is zero or is a polynomial of lower degree than the *first term* of the divisor. **6.** If there is a remainder, write it as the numerator of a fraction with the divisor as the denominator. Add this fraction to the quotient.	Divide $(6x^3 + 5x^2 - 2x + 1) \div (3x + 1)$. $\begin{array}{r} 2x^2 + x - 1 \\ 3x + 1 \overline{)\, 6x^3 + 5x^2 - 2x + 1} \\ \underline{6x^3 + 2x^2} \qquad\qquad \\ 3x^2 - 2x \qquad \\ \underline{3x^2 + x} \qquad\; \\ -3x + 1 \\ \underline{-3x - 1} \\ 2 \end{array}$ The quotient is $2x^2 + x - 1 + \frac{2}{3x + 1}$.
Synthetic division, p. 265.	Synthetic division can be used if the divisor is in the form $(x + b)$. **1.** Write the coefficients of the terms in descending order of the dividend. Write any missing terms with a coefficient of zero. **2.** The divisor will be of the form $x + b$. Write down the opposite of b to the left. **3.** Bring down the first coefficient to the bottom row. **4.** Multiply the coefficient in the bottom row by the opposite of b and add it to the coefficient above it in the top row. Write the result in the second row. **5.** Add the values in the top and second rows and place the result in the bottom row. **6.** Repeat steps 3 and 4 until the bottom row is filled.	Divide $(3x^5 - 2x^3 + x^2 - x + 7) \div (x + 2)$. $\begin{array}{r\|rrrrrr} -2 & 3 & 0 & -2 & 1 & -1 & 7 \\ & & -6 & 12 & -20 & 38 & -74 \\ \hline & 3 & -6 & 10 & -19 & 37 & -67 \end{array}$ The quotient is $3x^4 - 6x^3 + 10x^2 - 19x + 37 + \frac{-67}{x + 2}$.

Topic	Procedure	Examples
Factoring out a common factor, p. 269.	Remove the greatest common factor from each term. Many factoring problems are two steps, of which this is the first.	$5x^3 - 25x^2 - 10x = 5x(x^2 - 5x - 2)$ $20a^3b^2 - 40a^4b^3 + 30a^3b^3 = 10a^3b^2(2 - 4ab + 3b)$
Factoring the difference of two squares, p. 282.	$a^2 - b^2 = (a + b)(a - b)$	$9x^2 - 1 = (3x + 1)(3x - 1)$ $8x^2 - 50 = 2(4x^2 - 25) = 2(2x + 5)(2x - 5)$
Factoring a perfect square trinomial, p. 283.	$a^2 + 2ab + b^2 = (a + b)^2$ $a^2 - 2ab + b^2 = (a - b)^2$	$16x^2 + 40x + 25 = (4x + 5)^2$ $18x^2 + 120xy + 200y^2 = 2(9x^2 + 60xy + 100y^2)$ $= 2(3x + 10y)^2$ $4x^2 - 36x + 81 = (2x - 9)^2$ $25a^3 - 10a^2b + ab^2 = a(25a^2 - 10ab + b^2)$ $= a(5a - b)^2$
Factoring the sum and difference of two cubes, p. 284.	$a^3 + b^3 = (a + b)(a^2 - ab + b^2)$ $a^3 - b^3 = (a - b)(a^2 + ab + b^2)$	$8x^3 + 27 = (2x + 3)(4x^2 - 6x + 9)$ $250x^3 + 2y^3 = 2(125x^3 + y^3)$ $= 2(5x + y)(25x^2 - 5xy + y^2)$ $27x^3 - 64 = (3x - 4)(9x^2 + 12x + 16)$ $125y^4 - 8y = y(125y^3 - 8)$ $= y(5y - 2)(25y^2 + 10y + 4)$
Factoring trinomials of the form $x^2 + bx + c$, p. 275.	The factors will be of the form $(x + m)(x + n)$, where $m \cdot n = c$ and $m + n = b$.	$x^2 - 7x + 12 = (x - 4)(x - 3)$ $3x^2 - 36x + 60 = 3(x^2 - 12x + 20)$ $= 3(x - 2)(x - 10)$ $x^2 + 2x - 15 = (x + 5)(x - 3)$ $2x^2 - 44x - 96 = 2(x^2 - 22x - 48)$ $= 2(x - 24)(x + 2)$
Factoring trinomials of the form $ax^2 + bx + c$, p. 277.	Use the trial-and-error method or the grouping number method.	$2x^2 + 7x + 3 = (2x + 1)(x + 3)$ $8x^2 - 26x + 6 = 2(4x^2 - 13x + 3)$ $= 2(4x - 1)(x - 3)$ $7x^2 + 20x - 3 = (7x - 1)(x + 3)$ $5x^3 - 18x^2 - 8x = x(5x^2 - 18x - 8)$ $= x(5x + 2)(x - 4)$
Factoring by grouping, p. 271.	**1.** Make sure that the first two terms have a common factor and the last two terms have a common factor; otherwise, regroup the terms. **2.** Factor out the common factor in each group. **3.** Factor out the common binomial factor.	$6xy - 8y + 3xw - 4w$ $= 2y(3x - 4) + w(3x - 4)$ $= (3x - 4)(2y + w)$
Solving a quadratic equation by factoring, p. 293.	**1.** Rewrite the equation in standard form. **2.** Factor, if possible. **3.** Set each factor equal to 0. **4.** Solve each of the resulting equations.	Solve $(x + 3)(x - 2) = 5(x + 3)$. $x^2 - 2x + 3x - 6 = 5x + 15$ $x^2 + x - 6 = 5x + 15$ $x^2 + x - 5x - 6 - 15 = 0$ $x^2 - 4x - 21 = 0$ $(x - 7)(x + 3) = 0$ $x - 7 = 0 \quad x + 3 = 0$ $x = 7 \quad x = -3$

Chapter 5 Review Problems

Perform the indicated operations.

1. $(x^2 - 3x + 5) + (-2x^2 - 7x + 8)$

2. $(-4x^2y - 7xy + y) + (5x^2y + 2xy - 9y)$

3. $(-6x^2 + 7xy - 3y^2) - (5x^2 - 3xy - 9y^2)$

4. $(-13x^2 + 9x - 14) - (-2x^2 - 6x + 1)$

5. $(7x - 2) + (5 - 3x) + (2 - 2x)$

6. $(5x - 2x^2 - x^3) - (2x - 3 + 5x^2)$

For the polynomial function $p(x) = 3x^3 - 2x^2 - 6x + 1$ *find the following.*

7. $p(-4)$

8. $p(3)$

For the polynomial function $g(x) = -2x^4 + x^3 - 5x - 2$ *find the following.*

9. $g(2)$

10. $g(-3)$

For the polynomial function $h(x) = -x^3 - 6x^2 + 12x - 4$ *find the following.*

11. $h(3)$

12. $h(-2)$

Multiply.

13. $3xy(x^2 - xy + y^2)$

14. $(3x^2 + 1)(2x - 1)$

15. $(5x^2 + 3)^2$

16. $(x - 3)(2x - 5)(x + 2)$

17. $(x^2 - 3x + 1)(-2x^2 + x - 2)$

18. $(3x - 5)(3x^2 + 2x - 4)$

Divide.

19. $(25x^3y - 15x^2y - 100xy) \div (-5xy)$

20. $(12x^2 - 16x - 4) \div (3x + 2)$

21. $(2x^3 - 7x^2 + 2x + 8) \div (x - 2)$

22. $(3y^3 - 2y + 5) \div (y - 3)$

23. $(15a^4 - 3a^3 + 4a^2 + 4) \div (3a^2 - 1)$

24. $(x^4 - x^3 - 7x^2 - 7x - 2) \div (x^2 - 3x - 2)$

25. $(2x^4 - 13x^3 + 16x^2 - 9x + 20) \div (x - 5)$

26. $(3x^4 + 5x^3 - x^2 + x - 2) \div (x + 2)$

Factor, if possible. Be sure to factor completely.

27. $5x^2 - 11x + 2$

28. $9x^2 - 121$

29. $36x^2 + 25$

30. $x^2 - 8wy + 4xw - 2xy$

31. $x^3 + 8x^2 + 12x$

32. $2x^2 - 7x - 3$

33. $x^2 + 6xy - 27y^2$

34. $27x^4 - x$

35. $21a^2 + 20ab + 4b^2$

36. $-3a^3b^3 + 2a^2b^4 - a^2b^3$

37. $a^4b^4 + a^3b^4 - 6a^2b^4$

38. $3x^4 - 5x^2 - 2$

39. $9a^2b + 15ab - 14b$

40. $2x^4 + 7x^2 - 6$

41. $12x^2 + 12x + 3$

42. $4y^4 - 13y^3 + 9y^2$

43. $y^4 + 2y^3 - 35y^2$

44. $4x^2y^2 - 12x^2y - 8x^2$

45. $3x^4 - 7x^2 - 6$

46. $a^2 + 5ab^3 + 4b^6$

47. $3x^2 - 12 - 8x + 2x^3$

48. $2x^4 - 12x^2 - 54$

49. $8a + 8b - 4bx - 4ax$

50. $8x^4 + 34x^2y^2 + 21y^4$

51. $4x^3 + 10x^2 - 6x$

52. $2a^2x - 15ax + 7x$

53. $16x^4y^2 - 56x^2y + 49$

54. $128x^3y - 2xy$

55. $5xb - 28y + 4by - 35x$

56. $27abc^2 - 12ab$

Solve the following equations.

57. $5x^2 - 9x - 2 = 0$

58. $2x^2 - 11x + 12 = 0$

59. $(2x - 1)(3x - 5) = 20$

60. $7x^2 = 21x$

61. $x^3 + 7x^2 = -12x$

62. $3x^2 + 14x + 3 = -1 + 4(x + 1)$

Use a quadratic equation to solve each of the following exercises.

▲ **63.** The area of a triangle is 77 square meters. The altitude of the triangle is 3 meters longer than the base of the triangle. Find the base and the altitude of the triangle.

▲ **64.** A rectangular park has an area of 40 square miles. The length of the rectangle is 2 miles less than triple the width. Find the dimensions of the park.

▲ **65.** A square sound insulator is constructed for a restaurant. It does not provide enough insulation, so a larger square is constructed. The larger square has 24 square yards more insulation. The side of the larger square is 3 yards longer than double the side of the smaller square. Find the dimensions of each square.

66. The hourly profit in dollars made by a scientific calculator manufacturing plant is given by the equation $P = 3x^2 - 7x - 10$, where x is the number of calculators assembled in 1 hour. Find the number of calculators that should be made in 1 hour if the hourly profit is to be \$30.

Developing Your Study Skills

Exam Time: Taking the Exam

Allow yourself plenty of time to get to your exam. You may even find it helpful to arrive a little early in order to collect your thoughts and ready yourself. This will help you feel more relaxed.

After you receive your exam, you will find it helpful to do the following.

1. Take two or three moderately deep breaths. Inhale; then exhale slowly. You will feel your entire body begin to relax.
2. Write down on the back of the exam any formulas or ideas that you need to remember.
3. Look over the entire test quickly in order to pace yourself and use your time wisely. Notice how many points each exercise is worth. Spend more time on items of greater worth.
4. Read directions carefully and be sure to answer all questions clearly. Keep your work neat and easy to read.
5. Ask your instructor about anything that is not clear to you.
6. Work the exercises and answer the questions that are easiest for you first. Then go back to the more difficult ones.
7. Do not get bogged down on one exercise for too long because it may jeopardize your chances of finishing other exercises. Leave the tough exercise and go back to it when you have time later.
8. Check your work. This will help you catch minor errors.
9. Stay calm if others leave before you do. You are entitled to use the full amount of allotted time.

Chapter 5 Test

Combine.

1. $(3x^2y - 2xy^2 - 6) + (5 + 2xy^2 - 7x^2y)$

2. $(5a^2 - 3) - (2 + 5a) - (4a - 3)$

Multiply.

3. $-2x(x + 3y - 4)$

4. $(2x - 3y^2)^2$

5. $(x^2 + 6x - 2)(x^2 - 3x - 4)$

Divide.

6. $(-15x^3 - 12x^2 + 21x) \div (-3x)$

7. $(2x^4 - 7x^3 + 7x^2 - 9x + 10) \div (2x - 5)$

8. $(x^3 - x^2 - 5x + 2) \div (x + 2)$

9. $(x^4 + x^3 - x - 3) \div (x + 1)$

10. $(2x^5 - 7x^4 - 15x^2 - x + 5) \div (x - 4)$

Factor, if possible.

11. $121x^2 - 25y^2$

12. $9x^2 + 30xy + 25y^2$

13. $x^3 - 26x^2 + 48x$

14. $24x^2 + 10x - 4$

15. $4x^3y + 8x^2y^2 + 4x^2y$

16. $x^2 - 6wy + 3xy - 2wx$

17. $2x^2 - 3x + 2$

1. ______

2. ______

3. ______

4. ______

5. ______

6. ______

7. ______

8. ______

9. ______

10. ______

11. ______

12. ______

13. ______

14. ______

15. ______

16. ______

17. ______

18. ____________

19. ____________

20. ____________

21. ____________

22. ____________

23. ____________

24. ____________

25. ____________

26. ____________

27. ____________

28. ____________

29. ____________

30. ____________

31. ____________

32. ____________

18. $3x^4 + 36x^3 + 60x^2$

19. $18x^2 + 3x - 15$

20. $25x^2y^4 - 16y^4$

21. $54a^4 - 16a$

22. $9x^5 - 6x^3y + xy^2$

23. $3x^4 + 17x^2 + 10$

24. $x^2 - 8xy + 12y^2$

25. $3x - 10ay + 6y - 5ax$

26. $16x^4 - 1$

Evaluate the following if $p(x) = -2x^3 - x^2 + 6x - 10$.

27. $p(2)$

28. $p(-3)$

Solve the following equations.

29. $x^2 = 5x + 14$

30. $3x^2 - 11x - 4 = 0$

31. $7x^2 + 6x = 8x$

Use a quadratic equation to solve the following exercise.

▲ **32.** The area of a triangular road sign is 70 square inches. The altitude of the triangle is 4 inches less than the base of the triangle. Find the altitude and the base of the triangle.

Cumulative Test for Chapters 1–5

Approximately one half of this test covers the content of Chapters 1–4. The remainder covers the content of Chapter 5.

1. What property is illustrated by the equation $3(5 \cdot 2) = (3 \cdot 5)2$?

2. Evaluate $\dfrac{2 + 6(-2)}{(2 - 4)^3 + 3}$.

3. Evaluate $2\sqrt{16} + 3\sqrt{49}$.

4. Solve for x: $5x + 7y = 2$

5. Solve for x. $2(3x - 1) - 4 = 2x - (6 - x)$

6. Find the slope of the line passing through $(-2, -3)$ and $(1, 5)$.

7. Graph $y = -\dfrac{2}{3}x + 4$.

8. Graph the region $3x - 4y \geq -12$.

y

x

y

x

9. Solve the inequality. $-3(x + 2) < 5x - 2(4 + x)$

▲ 10. What are the dimensions of a rectangle with a perimeter of 46 meters if the length is 5 meters longer than twice the width?

11. Combine $(2a^2 - 3ab + 4b^2) - (-3a^2 + 6ab - 8b^2)$.

Multiply and simplify your answer.

12. $-3xy^2(2x + 3y - 5xy)$

13. $(5x - 2)(2x^2 - 3x - 4)$

1. __________
2. __________
3. __________
4. __________
5. __________
6. __________
7. __________
8. __________
9. __________
10. __________
11. __________
12. __________
13. __________

14. ______

15. ______

16. ______

17. ______

18. ______

19. ______

20. ______

21. ______

22. ______

23. ______

24. ______

25. ______

26. ______

27. ______

28. ______

Divide.

14. $(-21x^3 + 14x^2 - 28x) \div (7x)$

15. $(2x^3 - 3x^2 + 3x - 4) \div (x - 2)$

Factor, if possible.

16. $2x^3 - 10x^2$

17. $64x^2 - 49$

18. $9x^3 - 24x^2 + 16x$

19. $25x^2 + 60x + 36$

20. $3x^2 - 15x - 42$

21. $2x^2 + 24x + 40$

22. $16x^2 + 9$

23. $6x^3 + 11x^2 + 3x$

24. $27x^4 + 64x$

25. $14mn + 7n + 10mp + 5p$

Solve for x.

26. $3x^2 - 4x - 4 = 0$

27. $x^2 + 11x = 26$

▲ **28.** A hospital has paved a triangular parking lot for emergency helicopter landings. The area of the triangle is 68 square meters. The altitude of the triangle is 1 meter longer than double the base of the triangle. Find the altitude and the base of this triangular region.

Chapter 6

Rational Expressions and Equations

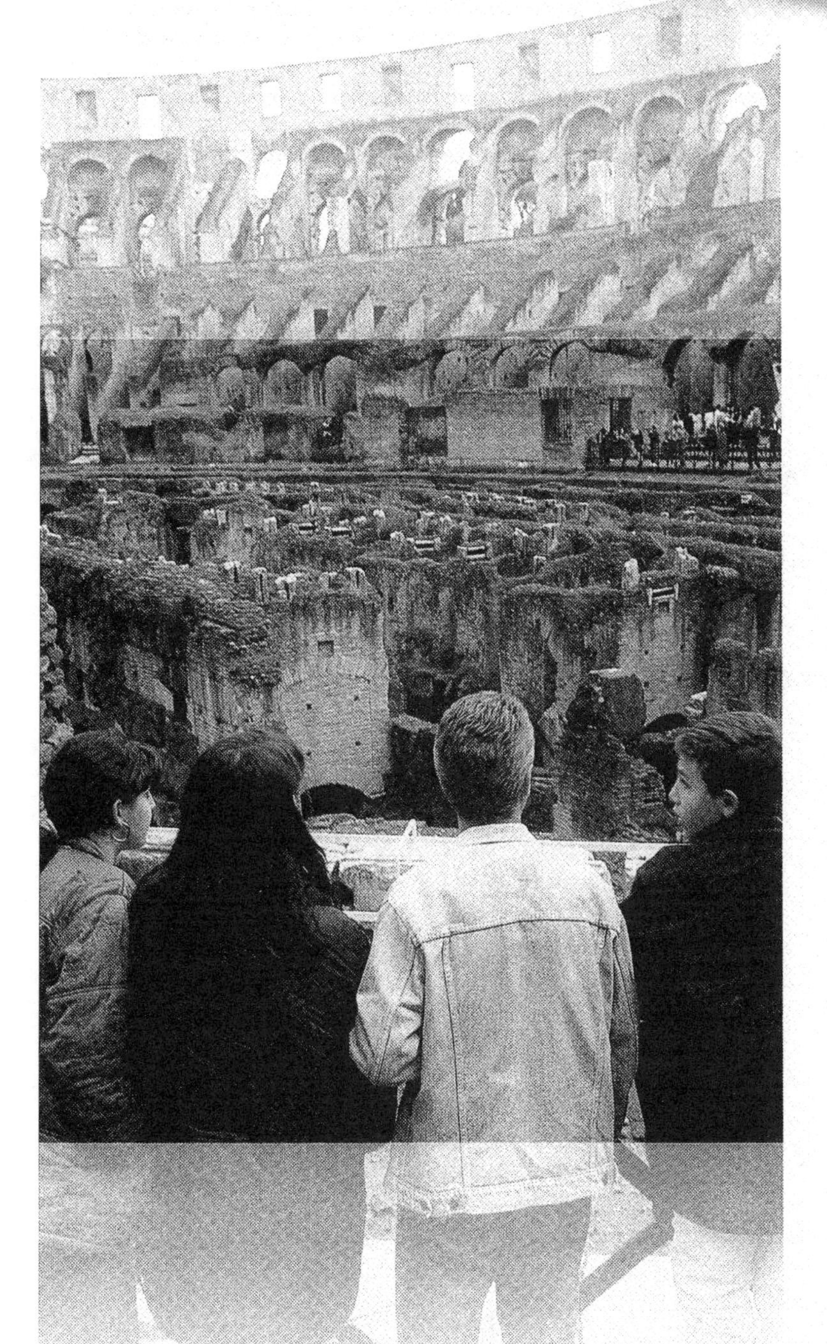

Traveling to foreign countries requires that U.S. dollars be exchanged for the local currencies of those countries. Although visiting Europe has become simpler with the introduction of Eurodollars, at the present time they are used only on a limited scale. Tourists still require French francs, Italian lire, and Spanish pesetas in those countries. Do you think you could use your mathematical skills to keep a record of your travel budget? Could you keep a record for exchanging U.S. dollars for foreign currency? Turn to the Putting Your Skills to Work exercises on page 348 to find out.

Pretest Chapter 6

1. ____________

2. ____________

3. ____________

4. ____________

5. ____________

6. ____________

7. ____________

8. ____________

9. ____________

10. ____________

11. ____________

12. ____________

13. ____________

14. ____________

15. ____________

If you are familiar with the topics in this chapter, take this test now. Check your answers with those in the back of the book. If an answer is wrong or you can't do an exercise, study the appropriate section of the chapter.

If you are not familiar with the topics in this chapter, don't take this test now. Instead, study the examples, work the practice exercises, and then take the test.

This test will help you to identify those concepts that you have mastered and those that need more study.

Section 6.1

Simplify.

1. $\dfrac{49x^2 - 9y^2}{7x^2 + 4xy - 3y^2}$

2. $\dfrac{2x^3 - 5x^2 - 3x}{x^3 - 8x^2 + 15x}$

3. $\dfrac{2a^2 + 5a + 3}{a^2 + a + 1} \cdot \dfrac{a^3 - 1}{2a^2 + a - 3} \cdot \dfrac{6a - 30}{3a + 3}$

4. $\dfrac{5x^3y^2}{x^2y + 10xy^2 + 25y^3} \div \dfrac{2x^4y^5}{3x^3 - 75xy^2}$

Section 6.2

Add or subtract. Simplify your answers.

5. $\dfrac{x}{3x - 6} - \dfrac{4}{3x}$

6. $\dfrac{2}{x + 5} + \dfrac{3}{x - 5} + \dfrac{7x}{x^2 - 25}$

7. $\dfrac{y + 1}{y^2 + y - 12} - \dfrac{y - 3}{y^2 + 7y + 12}$

Section 6.3

Simplify.

8. $\dfrac{\dfrac{1}{12x} + \dfrac{5}{3x}}{\dfrac{2}{3x^2}}$

9. $\dfrac{\dfrac{x}{4x^2 - 1}}{3 - \dfrac{2}{2x + 1}}$

Section 6.4

Solve for the variable and check your solutions. If there is no solution, say so.

10. $\dfrac{3}{y + 5} - \dfrac{1}{y - 5} = \dfrac{5}{y^2 - 25}$

11. $\dfrac{1}{6y} - \dfrac{4}{9} = \dfrac{4}{9y} - \dfrac{1}{2}$

Section 6.5

Solve for the variable indicated.

12. $\dfrac{d_1}{d_2} = \dfrac{w_1}{w_2}$ for d_2

13. $I = \dfrac{nE}{nr + R}$ for n

Set up a proportion and use it to find the desired quantity.

▲ **14.** A house 49 feet tall casts a shadow 14 feet long. At the same time a nearby flagpole casts a 9-foot shadow. How tall is the flagpole?

15. A drawing on a 3-by-5-inch card is projected onto a wall. A $\frac{3}{4}$-inch line on the card is 2 feet long on the wall. What are the dimensions of the outline of the card on the wall?

6.1 Rational Expressions and Functions: Simplifying, Multiplying, and Dividing

1 Simplifying a Rational Expression or Function

You may recall from Chapter 1 that a *rational number* is an exact quotient $\frac{a}{b}$ of two numbers a and b with $b \neq 0$. A **rational expression** is an expression of the form $\frac{P}{Q}$, where P and Q are polynomials and Q is not zero. For example,

$$\frac{7}{x + 2} \quad \text{and} \quad \frac{x + 5}{x - 3}$$

are rational expressions. Since the denominator cannot equal zero, the first expression is undefined if $x + 2 = 0$. This occurs when $x = -2$. We say that x can be any real number except -2. Look at the second expression. When is this expression undefined? Why? For what values of x is the expression defined? Note that the numerator can be zero because any fraction $\frac{0}{a}$ $(a \neq 0)$ is just 0.

A function defined by a rational expression is a **rational function**. The domain of a rational function is the set of values that can be used to replace the variable. Thus, the domain of $f(x) = \frac{7}{x + 2}$ is all real numbers except -2. The domain of $g(x) = \frac{x + 5}{x - 3}$ is all real numbers except 3.

EXAMPLE 1 Find the domain of the function $f(x) = \frac{x - 7}{x^2 + 8x - 20}$.

The domain will be all real numbers except those that make the denominator equal to zero. What value(s) will make the denominator equal to zero? We determine this by solving the equation $x^2 + 8x - 20 = 0$.

$(x + 10)(x - 2) = 0$		Factor.
$x + 10 = 0$ or	$x - 2 = 0$	Use the zero factor property.
$x = -10$	$x = 2$	Solve for x.

The domain of $y = f(x)$ is all real numbers except -10 and 2.

Practical Problem 1 Find the domain of $f(x) = \frac{4x + 3}{x^2 - 9x - 22}$.

We have learned that we can simplify fractions (or reduce them to lowest terms) by factoring the numerator and denominator into prime factors and dividing by the common factors. For example,

$$\frac{15}{25} = \frac{3 \cdot \cancel{5}}{5 \cdot \cancel{5}} = \frac{3}{5}.$$

We can do this by using the **basic rule of fractions**.

Basic Rule of Fractions

For any polynomials a, b, and c,

$$\frac{ac}{bc} = \frac{a}{b}, \quad \text{where } b \text{ and } c \neq 0.$$

Student Learning Objectives

After studying this section, you will be able to:

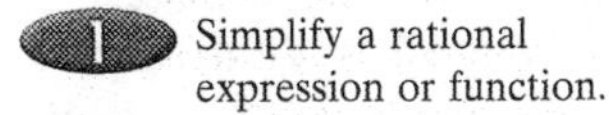

1. Simplify a rational expression or function.

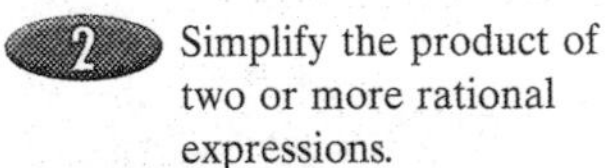

2. Simplify the product of two or more rational expressions.

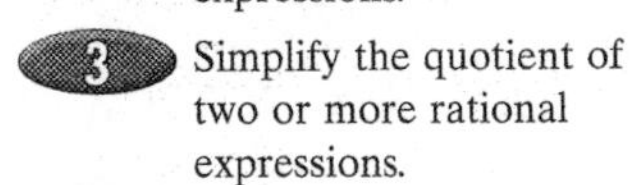

3. Simplify the quotient of two or more rational expressions.

SSM | PH TUTOR CENTER | CD & VIDEO | MATH PRO | WEB

Graphing Calculator

Finding Domains

To find the domain in Example 1, graph $y = \frac{x - 7}{x^2 + 8x - 20}$ on a graphing calculator. Since graphing calculators try to connect the points in a graph, it may not be easy to see where the expression is not defined.

Display:

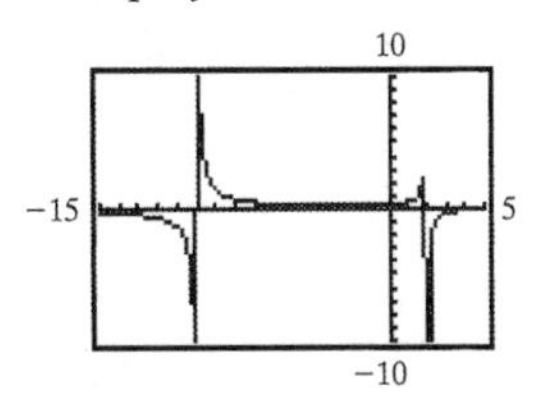

Since the domain will be values except those that make the denominator equal to zero, we can graph $y = x^2 + 8x - 20$ in order to identify the values that are not in the domain.

Display:

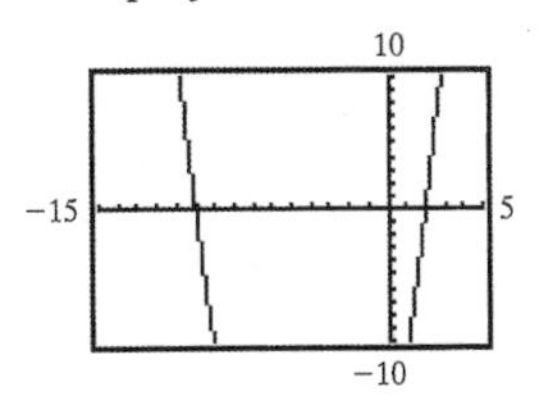

(continues on next page)

(continued)

Use the Zoom and Trace features or the zero command to find where $y = 0$.

Try to find the domain of the following function. Round any values where the function is not defined to the nearest tenth.

$$y = \frac{x + 9}{2.1x^2 + 5.2x - 3.1}$$

What we are doing is factoring out a common factor of 1 $\left(\frac{c}{c} = 1\right)$. We have

$$\frac{ac}{bc} = \frac{a}{b} \cdot \frac{c}{c} = \frac{a}{b} \cdot 1 = \frac{a}{b}.$$

Note that c must be a factor of the numerator *and* the denominator. Thus, the basic rule of fractions simply says that we may divide out a *common* factor from the numerator and the denominator. This nonzero factor can be a number or an algebraic expression.

EXAMPLE 2 Simplify $\dfrac{2a^2 - ab - b^2}{a^2 - b^2}$.

$$\frac{(2a + b)(a - b)}{(a + b)(a - b)} = \frac{2a + b}{a + b} \cdot 1 = \frac{2a + b}{a + b}$$

As you become more familiar with this basic rule, you won't have to write out every step. We did so here to show the application of the rule. We cannot simplify this fraction any further.

Practice Problem 2 Simplify $\dfrac{x^2 - 36y^2}{x^2 - 3xy - 18y^2}$.

EXAMPLE 3 Simplify $\dfrac{2x - 3y}{2x^2 - 7xy + 6y^2}$.

$$\frac{(2x - 3y)1}{(2x - 3y)(x - 2y)} = \frac{1}{x - 2y}$$

Note: Do you see why it is necessary to have a 1 in the numerator of the answer.

Practice Problem 3 Simplify $\dfrac{9x^2y}{3xy^2 + 6x^2y}$.

EXAMPLE 4 Simplify $\dfrac{2x^2 + 2x - 12}{x^3 + 7x^2 + 12x}$.

$$\frac{2x^2 + 2x - 12}{x^3 + 7x^2 + 12x} = \frac{2(x^2 + x - 6)}{x(x^2 + 7x + 12)} = \frac{2(x + 3)(x - 2)}{x(x + 3)(x + 4)} = \frac{2(x - 2)}{x(x + 4)}$$

We usually leave the answer in factored form.

Practice Problem 4 Simplify $\dfrac{2x^2 - 8x - 10}{2x^2 - 20x + 50}$.

Be alert for situations in which one factor in the numerator is the opposite of another factor in the denominator. In such cases you should factor -1 from one of the factors.

EXAMPLE 5 Simplify $\dfrac{-2x + 14y}{x^2 - 5xy - 14y^2}$.

$$\frac{-2x + 14y}{x^2 - 5xy - 14y^2} = \frac{-2(x - 7y)}{(x + 2y)(x - 7y)}$$

Factor -2 from each term of the numerator and then factor the denominator.

$$= \frac{-2}{x + 2y}$$

Use the basic rule of fractions.

Practice Problem 5 Simplify $\dfrac{-3x + 6y}{x^2 - 7xy + 10y^2}$.

EXAMPLE 6 Simplify $\dfrac{25y^2 - 16x^2}{8x^2 - 14xy + 5y^2}$.

$$\frac{(5y + 4x)(5y - 4x)}{(4x - 5y)(2x - y)} = \frac{(5y + 4x)(5y - 4x)}{-1(-4x + 5y)(2x - y)} = \frac{5y + 4x}{-1(2x - y)} = \frac{5y + 4x}{y - 2x}$$

Observe that $4x - 5y = -1(-4x + 5y)$.

Practice Problem 6 Simplify $\dfrac{7a^2 - 23ab + 6b^2}{4b^2 - 49a^2}$.

2 *Simplifying the Product of Two or More Rational Expressions*

Multiplication of rational expressions follows the same rule as multiplication of integer fractions. However, it is particularly helpful to use the basic rule of fractions to simplify whenever possible.

Multiplying Rational Expressions

For any polynomials a, b, c, and d,

$$\frac{a}{b} \cdot \frac{c}{d} = \frac{ac}{bd}, \quad \text{where } b \text{ and } d \neq 0.$$

EXAMPLE 7 Multiply $\dfrac{2x^2 - 4x}{x^2 - 5x + 6} \cdot \dfrac{x^2 - 9}{2x^4 + 14x^3 + 24x^2}$.

We first use the basic rule of fractions; that is, we factor (if possible) the numerator and denominator and divide out common factors.

$$\frac{2x(x - 2)}{(x - 2)(x - 3)} \cdot \frac{(x + 3)(x - 3)}{2x^2(x^2 + 7x + 12)} = \frac{2x(x - 2)(x + 3)(x - 3)}{(2x)x(x - 2)(x - 3)(x + 3)(x + 4)}$$

$$= \frac{2x}{2x} \cdot \frac{1}{x} \cdot \frac{x - 2}{x - 2} \cdot \frac{x + 3}{x + 3} \cdot \frac{x - 3}{x - 3} \cdot \frac{1}{x + 4}$$

$$= 1 \cdot \frac{1}{x} \cdot 1 \cdot 1 \cdot 1 \cdot \frac{1}{x + 4}$$

$$= \frac{1}{x(x + 4)} \quad \text{or} \quad \frac{1}{x^2 + 4x}$$

Although either form of the answer is correct, we usually use the factored form.

Practice Problem 7 Multiply $\dfrac{2x^2 + 5xy + 2y^2}{4x^2 - y^2} \cdot \dfrac{2x^2 + xy - y^2}{x^2 + xy - 2y^2}$.

EXAMPLE 8 Multiply $\dfrac{7x + 7y}{4ax + 4ay} \cdot \dfrac{8a^2x^2 - 8b^2x^2}{35ax^3 - 35bx^3}$.

$$\frac{7(x + y)}{4a(x + y)} \cdot \frac{8x^2(a^2 - b^2)}{35x^3(a - b)} = \frac{7(x + y)}{4a(x + y)} \cdot \frac{8x^2(a + b)(a - b)}{35x^3(a - b)}$$

$$= \frac{\overset{1}{\cancel{7}}\cancel{(x + y)}}{\cancel{4}a\cancel{(x + y)}} \cdot \frac{\overset{2}{\cancel{8}}\cancel{x^2}(a + b)\cancel{(a - b)}}{\underset{5x}{\cancel{35}\cancel{x^3}}\cancel{(a - b)}}$$

$$= \frac{2(a + b)}{5ax} \quad \text{or} \quad \frac{2a + 2b}{5ax}$$

Note that we shortened our steps by not writing out every factor of 1 as we did in Example 7. Either way is correct.

Practice Problem 8 Multiply $\dfrac{2x^3 - 3x^2}{3x^2 + 3x} \cdot \dfrac{9x + 36}{10x^2 - 15x}$.

3 Simplifying the Quotient of Two or More Rational Expressions

When we divide fractions, we take the **reciprocal** of the second fraction and then multiply the fractions. (Remember that the reciprocal of a fraction $\dfrac{m}{n}$ is $\dfrac{n}{m}$. Thus, the reciprocal of $\dfrac{2}{3}$ is $\dfrac{3}{2}$, and the reciprocal of $\dfrac{3x}{11y^2}$ is $\dfrac{11y^2}{3x}$.) We divide rational expressions in the same way.

Dividing Rational Expressions

For any polynomials a, b, c, and d,

$$\frac{a}{b} \div \frac{c}{d} = \frac{a}{b} \cdot \frac{d}{c}, \quad \text{where } b, c, \text{ and } d \neq 0.$$

EXAMPLE 9 Divide $\dfrac{4x^2 - y^2}{x^2 + 4xy + 4y^2} \div \dfrac{4x - 2y}{3x + 6y}$.

We take the reciprocal of the second fraction and multiply the fractions.

$$\frac{4x^2 - y^2}{x^2 + 4xy + 4y^2} \cdot \frac{3x + 6y}{4x - 2y} = \frac{(2x + y)(2x - y)}{(x + 2y)(x + 2y)} \cdot \frac{3(x + 2y)}{2(2x - y)}$$

$$= \frac{3(2x + y)}{2(x + 2y)} \quad \text{or} \quad \frac{6x + 3y}{2x + 4y}$$

Practice Problem 9 Divide $\dfrac{8x^3 + 27}{64x^3 - 1} \div \dfrac{4x^2 - 9}{16x^2 + 4x + 1}$.

EXAMPLE 10 Divide $\dfrac{24 + 10x - 4x^2}{2x^2 + 13x + 15} \div (2x - 8)$.

We take the reciprocal of the second fraction and multiply the fractions. The reciprocal of $(2x - 8)$ is $\dfrac{1}{2x - 8}$.

$$\frac{-4x^2 + 10x + 24}{2x^2 + 13x + 15} \cdot \frac{1}{2x - 8} = \frac{-2(2x^2 - 5x - 12)}{(2x + 3)(x + 5)} \cdot \frac{1}{2(x - 4)}$$

$$= \frac{\overset{-1}{-2}(x - 4)(2x + 3)}{(2x + 3)(x + 5)} \cdot \frac{1}{\underset{1}{2}(x - 4)} = \frac{-1}{x + 5} \quad \text{or} \quad -\frac{1}{x + 5}$$

Practice Problem 10 Divide: $\dfrac{4x^2 - 9}{2x^2 + 11x + 12} \div (-6x + 9)$

6.1 Exercises

Find the domain of each of the following rational functions.

1. $f(x) = \dfrac{5x + 6}{2x - 6}$

2. $f(x) = \dfrac{3x - 8}{4x + 20}$

3. $g(x) = \dfrac{-7x + 2}{x^2 - 5x - 36}$

4. $g(x) = \dfrac{-8x + 9}{x^2 + 10x - 24}$

Simplify completely.

5. $\dfrac{-18x^4y}{12x^2y^6}$

6. $\dfrac{-7xy^2}{28x^5y}$

7. $\dfrac{3x^2 - 24x}{3x^2 + 12x}$

8. $\dfrac{10x^2 + 15x}{35x^2 - 5x}$

9. $\dfrac{9x^2}{12x^2 - 15x}$

10. $\dfrac{20x^2}{28x^2 - 12x}$

11. $\dfrac{2x^3y - 10x^2y}{2x^3y + 6x^2y}$

12. $\dfrac{a^2b + ab^2}{a^2b - ab^2}$

13. $\dfrac{2x + 10}{2x^2 - 50}$

14. $\dfrac{6x^2 - 15x}{3x}$

15. $\dfrac{2y^2 - 8}{2y + 4}$

16. $\dfrac{x + 2}{7x^2 - 28}$

17. $\dfrac{30x - x^2 - x^3}{x^3 - x^2 - 20x}$

18. $\dfrac{2x^2 - x^3 - x^4}{x^4 - x^3}$

19. $\dfrac{36 - b^2}{3b^2 - 16b - 12}$

20. $\dfrac{2y^2 + y - 10}{4 - y^2}$

Simplify.

21. $\dfrac{-8mn^5}{3m^4n^3} \cdot \dfrac{9m^3n^3}{6mn}$

22. $\dfrac{35x^2y^6}{10x^7y^2} \cdot \dfrac{-15y^3}{21xy}$

23. $\dfrac{3a^2}{a + 2} \cdot \dfrac{a^2 - 4}{3a}$

24. $\dfrac{8x^2}{x^2 - 9} \cdot \dfrac{x^2 + 6x + 9}{16x^3}$

25. $\dfrac{x^2 + 5x + 7}{x^2 - 5x + 6} \cdot \dfrac{3x - 6}{x^2 + 5x + 7}$

26. $\dfrac{x - 5}{10x - 2} \cdot \dfrac{25x^2 - 1}{x^2 - 10x + 25}$

27. $\dfrac{x^2 - 5xy - 24y^2}{x - y} \cdot \dfrac{x^2 + 6xy - 7y^2}{x + 3y}$

28. $\dfrac{x - 3y}{x^2 + 3xy - 18y^2} \cdot \dfrac{x^2 + xy - 30y^2}{x - 5y}$

29. $\dfrac{2y^2 - 5y - 12}{4y^2 + 8y + 3} \cdot \dfrac{2y^2 + 7y + 3}{y^2 - 16}$

30. $\dfrac{6y^2 + y - 1}{6y^2 + 5y + 1} \cdot \dfrac{3y^2 + 4y + 1}{3y^2 + 2y - 1}$

31. $\dfrac{x^3 - 125}{x^5 y} \cdot \dfrac{x^3 y^2}{x^2 + 5x + 25}$

32. $\dfrac{3a^3b^2}{8a^3 - b^3} \cdot \dfrac{4a^2 + 2ab + b^2}{12ab^4}$

Simplify.

33. $\dfrac{2mn - m}{15m^3} \div \dfrac{2n - 1}{3m^2}$

34. $\dfrac{3y + 12}{8y^3} \div \dfrac{9y + 36}{16y^3}$

35. $\dfrac{(b - 3)^2}{b^2 - b - 6} \div \dfrac{3b - 9}{3b + 4}$

36. $\dfrac{x^2 - x - 20}{3x^2 + 2x} \div \dfrac{(x - 5)^2}{3x}$

37. $\dfrac{x^2 - xy - 6y^2}{x^2 + 2} \div (x^2 + 2xy)$

38. $\dfrac{x^2 - 5x + 4}{2x - 8} \div (3x^2 - 3x)$

Mixed Practice

Perform the indicated operation. When no operation is indicated, simplify the rational expression completely.

39. $\dfrac{7x}{y^2} \div 21x^3$

40. $\dfrac{2y^4}{10x^2} \cdot \dfrac{5x^3}{4y^3}$

41. $\dfrac{3x^2 - 2x}{6x - 4}$

42. $\dfrac{-28x^5y}{35x^6y^2}$

43. $\dfrac{x^2y - 49y}{x^2y^3} \cdot \dfrac{3x^2y - 21xy}{x^2 - 14x + 49}$

44. $\dfrac{x^2 + 6x + 9}{2x^2y - 18y} \div \dfrac{6xy + 18y}{3x^2y - 27y}$

45. $\dfrac{-8 + 6x - x^2}{2x^3 - 8x}$

46. $\dfrac{x^2 - 7x + 10}{xy^6} \div \dfrac{x^2 - 11x + 30}{x^2y^5}$

47. $\dfrac{a^2 - a - 12}{2a^2 + 5a - 12}$

48. $\dfrac{5y^3 - 45y}{6 - y - y^2}$

Optional Graphing Calculator Problems

Try to find the domain of the following functions. Round any values that you exclude to the nearest tenth.

49. $f(x) = \dfrac{2x + 5}{3.6x^2 + 1.8x - 4.3}$

50. $f(x) = \dfrac{5x - 4}{1.6x^2 - 1.3x - 5.9}$

Applications

In business sometimes the demand for a product is reduced when more of the product becomes available. Suppose that the demand for a certain type of electronic toy is given by the demand function $D(x) = \frac{10{,}000}{x^2 + 3x}$*, where x is the number of units produced each day. Assume that x is an integer. When calculating the demand, round all answers to the nearest integer.*

51. What is the domain of the demand function from a purely mathematical point of view?

52. Realistically, what is the domain of the demand function from a business point of view?

53. What is the daily demand for this item if 10 units are produced each day?

54. What is the daily demand for this item if 20 units are produced each day?

55. What is the daily demand for this item if 30 units are produced each day?

56. Is the demand decreased at a greater rate if the production is increased from 20 to 30 units a day or from 10 to 20 units a day?

57. What is the daily demand for this item if 21 units are produced each day?

58. When you compare the answer to Exercise 54 with the answer to Exercise 57, what do you notice would be of significance to a business?

Cumulative Review Problems

Graph the straight line. Plot at least three points.

59. $y = -\frac{3}{2}x + 4$

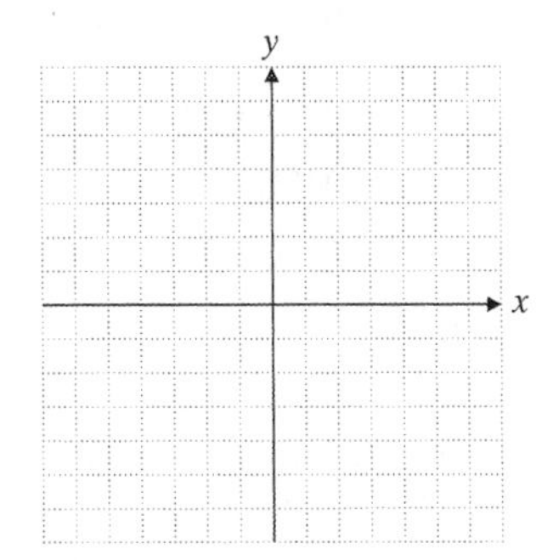

60. $6x - 3y = -12$

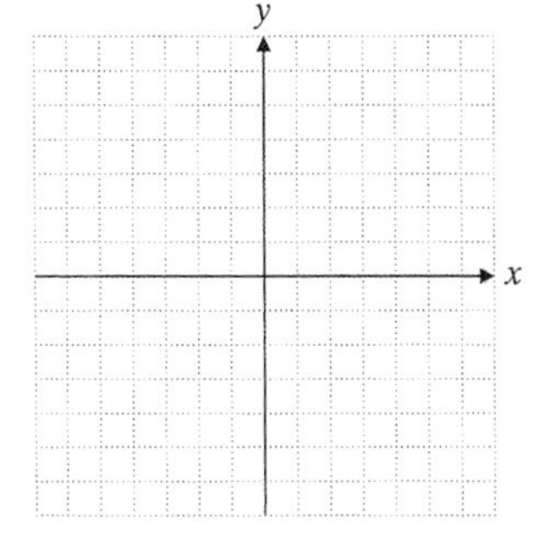

61. Find the standard form of the equation of the line that passes through $(0, 5)$ and $(-2, -3)$.

62. Find the standard form of the equation of the line that is perpendicular to $3x + 4y = 12$ and passes through $(-4, 4)$.

63. A directory assistance operator averages two inquiries per minute. If she works a 38-hour week and takes 1 hour each day for lunch (away from the phone), how many inquiries will she have answered in 1 week?

64. A hair stylist is able to service 21 customers in a 7-hour shift if he only *cuts* hair. The same hair stylist is able to service 14 customers in a 7-hour shift if he *cuts and colors* hair. He is able to service 18 customers in a 7-hour shift if he only *colors* hair. Can he feasibly service 12 cuts, 13 cuts and color, and 5 colors during one shift?

65. There is a great shortage of available donor organs in the United States. As of the spring of 2000, there were 69,399 patients waiting for organ transplants. Each organ donor helps an average of six people live longer, more productive lives. Every year 37% of the people waiting for a donor organ die. The number of patients waiting for an organ transplant has risen 7% per year since the spring of 1997. How many people have died waiting for a donor organ from the spring of 1997 to the spring of 2000? *Source:* National Center for Health Statistics.

6.2 Addition and Subtraction of Rational Expressions

Student Learning Objectives

After studying this section, you will be able to:

1. Find the LCD of two or more rational expressions.
2. Add or subtract two or more rational expressions.

SSM · PH TUTOR CENTER · CD & VIDEO · MATH PRO · WEB

1 *Finding the LCD of Two or More Rational Expressions*

Recall that if we wish to add or subtract fractions, the denominators must be the same. If the denominators are not the same, we use the basic rule of fractions to rewrite one or both fractions so that the denominations are the same. For example,

$$\frac{3}{7} + \frac{2}{7} = \frac{5}{7} \quad \text{and} \quad \frac{2}{3} + \frac{3}{4} = \frac{2}{3}\cdot\frac{4}{4} + \frac{3}{4}\cdot\frac{3}{3} = \frac{8}{12} + \frac{9}{12} = \frac{17}{12}.$$

How did we know that 12 was the least common denominator (LCD)? The least common denominator of two or more fractions is the product of the different prime factors in each denominator. If a factor is repeated, we use the highest power that appears on that factor in the denominators.

$$3 = 3$$
$$4 = 2 \cdot 2$$
$$\text{LCD} = 3 \cdot 2 \cdot 2 = 12$$

This same technique is used to add or subtract rational expressions.

How to Find the LCD

1. Factor each denominator completely into prime factors.
2. List all the different prime factors.
3. The LCD is the product of these factors, each of which is raised to the highest power that appears on that factor in the denominators.

Now we'll do some sample problems.

EXAMPLE 1 Find the LCD of the rational expressions $\frac{7}{x^2 - 4}$ and $\frac{2}{x - 2}$.

Step 1 We factor each denominator completely (into prime factors).

$$x^2 - 4 = (x + 2)(x - 2)$$
$$x - 2 \text{ cannot be factored.}$$

Step 2 We list all the *different* prime factors. The different factors are $x + 2$ and $x - 2$.

Step 3 Since no factor occurs more than once in the denominators, the LCD is the product $(x + 2)(x - 2)$.

Practice Problem 1 Find the LCD of the rational expressions $\frac{8}{x^2 - x - 12}$ and $\frac{3}{x - 4}$.

EXAMPLE 2 Find the LCD of the rational expressions $\frac{7}{12xy^2}$ and $\frac{4}{15x^3y}$.

Step 1 We factor each denominator.

$$12xy^2 = 2 \cdot 2 \cdot 3 \cdot x \cdot y \cdot y$$
$$15x^3y = 3 \cdot 5 \cdot x \cdot x \cdot x \cdot y$$

Step 2 Our LCD will require each of the different factors that appear in either denominator. They are 2, 3, 5, x, and y.

Step 3 The factor 2 and the factor y each occur twice in $12xy^2$.
The factor x occurs three times in $15x^3y$.
Thus, the LCD $= 2 \cdot 2 \cdot 3 \cdot 5 \cdot x \cdot x \cdot x \cdot y \cdot y$
$= 60x^3y^2$

Practice Problem 2 Find the LCD of the rational expressions $\frac{2}{15x^3y^2}$ and $\frac{13}{25xy^3}$.

2 Adding or Subtracting Two or More Rational Expressions

We can add and subtract rational expressions with the same denominator just as we do in arithmetic: We simply add or subtract the numerators.

Addition and Subtraction of Rational Expressions

For any polynomials a, b, and c we have the following:

$$\frac{a}{b} + \frac{c}{b} = \frac{a + c}{b}, \qquad b \neq 0$$

$$\frac{a}{b} - \frac{c}{b} = \frac{a - c}{b}, \qquad b \neq 0$$

EXAMPLE 3 Subtract: $\frac{5x + 2}{(x + 3)(x - 4)} - \frac{6x}{(x + 3)(x - 4)}$

$$\frac{5x + 2}{(x + 3)(x - 4)} - \frac{6x}{(x + 3)(x - 4)} = \frac{-x + 2}{(x + 3)(x - 4)}$$

Practice Problem 3 Subtract: $\frac{4x}{(x + 6)(2x - 1)} - \frac{3x + 1}{(x + 6)(2x - 1)}$

If the two rational expressions have different denominators, we first need to find the LCD. Then we must rewrite each fraction as an equivalent fraction that has the LCD as the denominator.

EXAMPLE 4 Add the rational expressions: $\frac{7}{(x + 2)(x - 2)} + \frac{2}{x - 2}$

The LCD $= (x + 2)(x - 2)$.

Before we can add the fractions, we must rewrite our fractions as fractions with the LCD. The first fraction needs no change, but the second fraction does.

$$\frac{7}{(x + 2)(x - 2)} + \frac{2}{x - 2} \cdot \frac{x + 2}{x + 2}$$

Since $\frac{x + 2}{x + 2} = 1$, we have not changed the *value* of the fraction. We are simply writing it in an equivalent form. Thus, we now have the following:

$$\frac{7}{(x + 2)(x - 2)} + \frac{2(x + 2)}{(x + 2)(x - 2)} = \frac{7 + 2(x + 2)}{(x + 2)(x - 2)}$$

$$= \frac{7 + 2x + 4}{(x + 2)(x - 2)}$$

$$= \frac{2x + 11}{(x + 2)(x - 2)}$$

Practice Problem 4 Add the rational expressions: $\frac{8}{(x - 4)(x + 3)} + \frac{3}{x - 4}$

Graphing Calculator

Exploration

You can verify the answer to Example 5 with a graphing calculator.

Graph $y_1 = \frac{4}{x+6} + \frac{5}{6x}$ and $y_2 = \frac{29x + 30}{6x(x+6)}$ on the same set of axes. Since y_1 is equivalent to y_2, you will obtain exactly the same curve.

Verify on your graphing calculator that y_1 *is* or *is not* equivalent to y_2 in each of the following:

1. $y_1 = \frac{x}{x+3} - \frac{3-x}{x^2-9}$ and $y_2 = \frac{x+1}{x+3}$

2. $y_1 = \frac{3x}{2x-3} + \frac{3x+6}{2x^2+x-6}$ and $y_2 = \frac{3x+3}{2x+3}$

EXAMPLE 5 Add: $\frac{4}{x+6} + \frac{5}{6x}$

The LCD $= 6x(x + 6)$. We need to multiply the fractions by 1 to obtain two equivalent fractions that have the LCD for the denominator. We multiply the first fraction by $1 = \frac{6x}{6x}$. We multiply the second fraction by $1 = \frac{x+6}{x+6}$.

$$\frac{4(6x)}{(x+6)(6x)} + \frac{5(x+6)}{6x(x+6)}$$

$$\frac{24x}{6x(x+6)} + \frac{5x+30}{6x(x+6)} = \frac{29x+30}{6x(x+6)}$$

Practice Problem 5 Add: $\frac{5}{x+4} + \frac{3}{4x}$

EXAMPLE 6 Add: $\frac{7}{2x^2y} + \frac{3}{xy^2}$

You should be able to see that the LCD of these fractions is $2x^2y^2$.

$$\frac{7}{2x^2y} \cdot \frac{y}{y} + \frac{3}{xy^2} \cdot \frac{2x}{2x} = \frac{7y}{2x^2y^2} + \frac{6x}{2x^2y^2} = \frac{6x+7y}{2x^2y^2}$$

Practice Problem 6 Add: $\frac{7}{4ab^3} + \frac{1}{3a^3b^2}$

When two rational expressions are subtracted, we must be very careful with the signs in the numerator of the second fraction.

EXAMPLE 7 Subtract: $\frac{2}{x^2+3x+2} - \frac{4}{x^2+4x+3}$

$$x^2 + 3x + 2 = (x+1)(x+2)$$

$$x^2 + 4x + 3 = (x+1)(x+3)$$

Therefore, the LCD is $(x + 1)(x + 2)(x + 3)$. We now have the following:

$$\frac{2}{(x+1)(x+2)} \cdot \frac{x+3}{x+3} - \frac{4}{(x+1)(x+3)} \cdot \frac{x+2}{x+2}$$

$$= \frac{2x+6}{(x+1)(x+2)(x+3)} - \frac{4x+8}{(x+1)(x+2)(x+3)} = \frac{2x+6-4x-8}{(x+1)(x+2)(x+3)}$$

$$= \frac{-2x-2}{(x+1)(x+2)(x+3)} = \frac{-2\cancel{(x+1)}}{\cancel{(x+1)}(x+2)(x+3)}$$

$$= \frac{-2}{(x+2)(x+3)}$$

Study this problem carefully. Be sure you understand the reason for each step. You'll see this type of problem often.

Practice Problem 7 Subtract: $\frac{4x+2}{x^2+x-12} - \frac{3x+8}{x^2+6x+8}$

The following example involves repeated factors in the denominator. Read it through carefully to be sure you understand each step.

EXAMPLE 8 Subtract: $\dfrac{2x + 1}{25x^2 + 10x + 1} - \dfrac{6x}{25x + 5}$

Step 1 Factor each denominator into prime factors.

$$25x^2 + 10x + 1 = (5x + 1)^2$$
$$25x + 5 = 5(5x + 1)$$

Step 2 The different factors are 5 and $5x + 1$. However, $5x + 1$ appears to the first power *and* to the second power. So we need step 3.

Step 3 We must use the *highest* power of each factor. In this example the highest power of the factor 5 is 1, and the highest power of the factor $5x + 1$ is 2. So we use $(5x + 1)^2$. Thus, the LCD is $5(5x + 1)^2$.

So first we write our problem in factored form.

$$\frac{2x + 1}{(5x + 1)^2} - \frac{6x}{5(5x + 1)}$$

Next, we must multiply our fractions by the appropriate factor to change them to equivalent fractions with the LCD.

$$\frac{2x + 1}{(5x + 1)^2} \cdot \frac{5}{5} - \frac{6x}{5(5x + 1)} \cdot \frac{5x + 1}{5x + 1} = \frac{5(2x + 1) - 6x(5x + 1)}{5(5x + 1)^2}$$
$$= \frac{10x + 5 - 30x^2 - 6x}{5(5x + 1)^2}$$
$$= \frac{-30x^2 + 4x + 5}{5(5x + 1)^2}$$

Practice Problem 8 Subtract: $\dfrac{7x - 3}{4x^2 + 20x + 25} - \dfrac{3x}{4x + 10}$

CAUTION Adding and subtracting rational expressions is somewhat difficult. You should take great care in selecting the LCD. Students sometimes make careless errors when picking the LCD.

Likewise, great care should be taken to copy correctly all + and − signs. It is very easy to make a sign error when combining the equivalent fractions. Try to work very neatly and very carefully. A little extra diligence will result in greater accuracy.

6.2 Exercises

Verbal and Writing Skills

1. Explain how to find the LCD of the fractions $\frac{3}{5xy}$ and $\frac{11}{y^3}$.

2. Explain how to find the LCD of the fractions $\frac{8}{7xy}$ and $\frac{3}{x^2}$.

Find the LCD.

3. $\frac{1}{x^2 + 7xy + 12y^2}, \frac{3}{x + 4y}$

4. $\frac{2}{4x^2 - 8x + 3}, \frac{1}{2x - 1}$

5. $\frac{5x}{(3x + 4)^3}, \frac{2x - 1}{(x + 2)(3x + 4)^2}$

6. $\frac{9x}{(x - 5)(x + 2)^2}, \frac{11xy}{(x + 2)^3}$

7. $\frac{15xy}{3x^2 + 2x}, \frac{17y}{18x^2 + 9x - 2}$

8. $\frac{8x}{3x^2 - 4x}, \frac{10xy}{3x^2 + 5x - 12}$

9. $\frac{5y}{9y^2 - 49}, \frac{2y + 1}{9y^2 - 42y + 49}$

10. $\frac{2y + 1}{16y^2 - 25}, \frac{3y - 1}{16y^2 + 40y + 25}$

Add or subtract and simplify your answers.

11. $\frac{2}{x + 2} - \frac{3}{2x}$

12. $\frac{5}{3x + y} + \frac{2}{3xy}$

13. $\frac{12}{5x^2} + \frac{2}{5xy}$

14. $\frac{7}{4ab} + \frac{3}{4b^2}$

15. $\frac{3}{x^2 - 7x + 12} + \frac{5}{x^2 - 4x}$

16. $\frac{7}{x^2 - 1} + \frac{5}{3x^2 + 3x}$

17. $\frac{6x}{2x - 5} + 4$

18. $\frac{15}{7a + 3} + 5$

19. $\frac{-5y}{y^2 - 1} + \frac{6}{y^2 - 2y + 1}$

20. $\frac{7y}{y^2 + 6y + 9} + \frac{5}{y^2 - 9}$

21. $\frac{a+5}{a^2-4}+\frac{a-3}{2a-4}$

22. $\frac{4b}{b^2-b-6}+\frac{b-1}{3b-9}$

23. $\frac{2x-1}{x-6}-1$

24. $\frac{8x+3}{2x-1}-3$

25. $\frac{3x}{x^2+3x-10}-\frac{2x}{x^2+x-6}$

26. $\frac{1}{x^2-x-2}-\frac{3}{x^2+2x+1}$

27. $\frac{3y^2}{y^2-1}-\frac{y+2}{y+1}$

28. $\frac{4y}{y^2+3y+2}-\frac{y-3}{y+2}$

29. $a+3+\frac{2}{3a-5}$

30. $a-2+\frac{3}{2a+1}$

Applications

31. If an artificial lung company manufactures more than five machines per day, the revenue function in thousands of dollars to manufacture and sell x machines is given by

$$R(x)=\frac{80-24x}{2-x}.$$

The cost function in thousands of dollars to manufacture x machines is given by

$$C(x)=\frac{60-12x}{3-x}.$$

Determine the profit function in thousands of dollars for this company when more than five machines per day are manufactured by obtaining $P(x)=R(x)-C(x)$.

32. If an artificial heart company manufactures more than five machines per day, the revenue function in thousands of dollars to manufacture and sell x machines is given by

$$R(x)=\frac{150-38x}{3-x}.$$

The cost function in thousands of dollars to manufacture x machines is given by

$$C(x)=\frac{120-25x}{2-x}.$$

Determine the profit function in thousands of dollars for this company when more than five machines per day are manufactured by obtaining $P(x)=R(x)-C(x)$.

33. Determine the daily profit of the artificial lung company in Exercise 31 if ten machines per day are manufactured. Round your answer to the nearest dollar.

34. Determine the daily profit of the artificial heart company in Exercise 32 if twenty machines per day are manufactured. Round your answer to the nearest dollar.

To Think About

Perform the operations indicated.

35. $3x - 2 + \dfrac{5x}{3x - 2} + \dfrac{2x^2}{(3x - 2)^2}$

36. $\left[x + 1 + \dfrac{1}{x - 1}\right] \div \left[\dfrac{1}{x} + \dfrac{1}{x - 1}\right]$

Cumulative Review Problems

37. Charlie Chaplin was one of the most celebrated men of the 1920s and 1930s. During a visit to London, England, he received 73,000 letters in just 2 days. If he had had five people reading his letters, and each person was able to read ten letters per hour, how long would it have taken his assistants to read these letters?

38. There were 985 new prescription drugs introduced into the United States between 1940 and 1976. Of these, the United States originated 630.

(a) What percentage of these prescription drugs were formulated in the United States?

(b) If 7% of the new prescription drugs came from Switzerland, how many actual medications would have been formulated there? *Source:* National Center for Health Statistics.

39. Alreda, Tony, and Melissa each purchased a car. The total cost of the cars was $26,500. Alreda purchased a used car that cost $1500 more than the one Tony purchased. Melissa purchased a car that cost $1000 more than double the cost of Tony's car. How much did each car cost?

40. A chemist at Argonne Laboratories must combine a mixture that is 15% acid with a mixture that is 30% acid to obtain 60 liters of a mixture that is 20% acid. How much of each kind should he use?

41. A Four Winns speedboat traveled up the Hudson River against the current a distance of 75 kilometers in 5 hours. The return trip with the current took only 3 hours. Find the speed of the current and the speed of the speedboat in still water.

42. The Health Department of Springfield recently inspected fifteen thousand restaurants. A total of 22% of the restaurants passed inspection. The remainder had one or more health violations. Of the restaurants that did not pass inspection, 3200 had only a cleanliness violation (e.g., vents, stores, floors, or walls). Of the restaurants that did not pass, 3500 had only a vermin violation (e.g., flies, rodents, or other insects). How many restaurants had both a cleanliness violation and a vermin violation?

6.3 Complex Rational Expressions

1 Simplifying Complex Rational Expressions

Student Learning Objective

After studying this section, you will be able to:

1 Simplify complex rational expressions.

A **complex rational expression** is a large fraction that has at least one rational expression in the numerator, in the denominator, or in both the numerator and the denominator. The following are three examples of complex rational expressions.

$$\frac{7+\frac{1}{x}}{x+2}, \quad \frac{2}{\frac{x}{y}+3}, \quad \frac{\frac{a+b}{7}}{\frac{1}{x}+\frac{1}{x+a}}$$

There are two ways to simplify complex rational expressions. You can use whichever method you like.

EXAMPLE 1 Simplify $\dfrac{x+\frac{1}{x}}{\frac{1}{x}+\frac{3}{x^2}}$.

Method 1

1. Simplify numerator and denominator.

$$x+\frac{1}{x}=\frac{x^2+1}{x}$$

$$\frac{1}{x}+\frac{3}{x^2}=\frac{x+3}{x^2}$$

2. Divide the numerator by the denominator.

$$\frac{\frac{x^2+1}{x}}{\frac{x+3}{x^2}}=\frac{x^2+1}{x}\div\frac{x+3}{x^2}$$

$$=\frac{x^2+1}{x}\cdot\frac{x^2}{x+3}$$

$$=\frac{x^2+1}{\cancel{x}}\cdot\frac{\overset{x}{\cancel{x^2}}}{x+3}$$

$$=\frac{x(x^2+1)}{x+3}$$

3. The result is already simplified.

Method 2

1. Find the LCD of all the fractions in the numerator and denominator. The LCD is x^2.

2. Multiply the numerator and denominator by the LCD. Use the distributive property.

$$\frac{x+\frac{1}{x}}{\frac{1}{x}+\frac{3}{x^2}}\cdot\frac{x^2}{x^2}=\frac{x^3+x}{x+3}$$

3. The result is already simplified, but we will write it in factored form.

$$\frac{x^3+x}{x+3}=\frac{x(x^2+1)}{x+3}$$

Practice Problem 1 Simplify $\dfrac{y+\frac{3}{y}}{\frac{2}{y^2}+\frac{5}{y}}$.

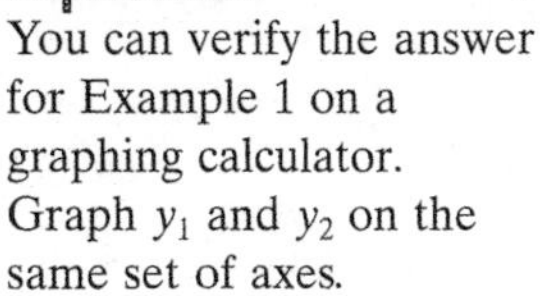

Exploration

You can verify the answer for Example 1 on a graphing calculator. Graph y_1 and y_2 on the same set of axes.

$$y_1=\frac{x+\frac{1}{x}}{\frac{1}{x}+\frac{3}{x^2}}$$

$$y_2=\frac{x(x^2+1)}{x+3}$$

The domain of y_1 is more restrictive than that of y_2. If we use the domain of y_1, then the graphs of y_1 and y_2 should be identical.

Show on your graphing calculator whether y_1 is or is not equivalent to y_2 in each of the following:

1. $y_1=\dfrac{1+\frac{3}{x+2}}{1+\frac{6}{x-1}}$

   $y_2=\dfrac{x-1}{x+2}$

2. $y_1=\dfrac{\frac{1}{x+1}-\frac{1}{x}}{\frac{1}{x}}$

   $y_2=\dfrac{1}{x+1}$

Method 1: Combining Fractions in Both Numerator and Denominator

1. Simplify the numerator and denominator, if possible, by combining quantities to obtain one fraction in the numerator and one fraction in the denominator.
2. Divide the numerator by the denominator (that is, multiply the numerator by the reciprocal of the denominator).
3. Simplify the expression.

EXAMPLE 2 Simplify $\dfrac{\dfrac{1}{2x+6}+\dfrac{3}{2}}{\dfrac{3}{x^2-9}+\dfrac{x}{x-3}}$.

Method 1

1. Simplify the numerator.

$$\frac{1}{2x+6}+\frac{3}{2}=\frac{1}{2(x+3)}+\frac{3}{2}$$
$$=\frac{1}{2(x+3)}+\frac{3(x+3)}{2(x+3)}$$
$$=\frac{1+3x+9}{2(x+3)}$$
$$=\frac{3x+10}{2(x+3)}$$

Simplify the denominator.

$$\frac{3}{x^2-9}+\frac{x}{x-3}=\frac{3}{(x+3)(x-3)}+\frac{x}{x-3}$$
$$=\frac{3}{(x+3)(x-3)}+\frac{x(x+3)}{(x+3)(x-3)}$$
$$=\frac{x^2+3x+3}{(x+3)(x-3)}$$

2. Divide the numerator by the denominator.

$$\frac{3x+10}{2(x+3)}\div\frac{x^2+3x+3}{(x+3)(x-3)}=\frac{3x+10}{2\cancel{(x+3)}}\cdot\frac{\cancel{(x+3)}(x-3)}{x^2+3x+3}$$
$$=\frac{(3x+10)(x-3)}{2(x^2+3x+3)}$$

3. Simplify. The answer is already simplified.

Before we continue the example, we state Method 2 in the following box.

Method 2: Multiplying Each Term of the Numerator and Denominator by the LCD of All Individual Fractions

1. Find the LCD of all the rational expressions in the numerator and denominator.
2. Multiply the numerator and denominator of the complex fraction by the LCD.
3. Simplify the result.

We will now proceed to do Example 2 by Method 2.

Method 2

1. To find the LCD, we factor.

$$\frac{\dfrac{1}{2x+6}+\dfrac{3}{2}}{\dfrac{3}{x^2-9}+\dfrac{x}{x-3}}=\frac{\dfrac{1}{2(x+3)}+\dfrac{3}{2}}{\dfrac{3}{(x+3)(x-3)}+\dfrac{x}{x-3}}$$

The LCD of the two fractions in the numerator and the two fractions in the denominator is

$$2(x+3)(x-3).$$

2. Multiply the numerator and the denominator by the LCD.

$$\frac{\dfrac{1}{2(x+3)}+\dfrac{3}{2}}{\dfrac{3}{(x+3)(x-3)}+\dfrac{x}{x-3}}\cdot\frac{2(x+3)(x-3)}{2(x+3)(x-3)}$$

$$=\frac{\dfrac{1}{\cancel{2}\cancel{(x+3)}}\cdot\cancel{2}\cancel{(x+3)}(x-3)+\dfrac{3}{\cancel{2}}\cdot\cancel{2}(x+3)(x-3)}{\dfrac{3}{\cancel{(x+3)}\cancel{(x-3)}}\cdot 2\cancel{(x+3)}\cancel{(x-3)}+\dfrac{x}{\cancel{x-3}}\cdot 2(x+3)\cancel{(x-3)}}$$

$$=\frac{x-3+3(x+3)(x-3)}{6+2x(x+3)}$$

$$=\frac{3x^2+x-30}{2x^2+6x+6}=\frac{(3x+10)(x-3)}{2(x^2+3x+3)}$$

3. Simplify. The answer is already simplified.
   Whether we use Method 1 or Method 2, we can leave the answer in factored form, or we can multiply it out to obtain

$$\frac{3x^2+x-30}{2x^2+6x+6}.$$

Practice Problem 2 Simplify $\dfrac{\dfrac{4}{16x^2-1}+\dfrac{3}{4x+1}}{\dfrac{x}{4x-1}+\dfrac{5}{4x+1}}$.

EXAMPLE 3 Simplify by Method 1: $\dfrac{x+3}{\dfrac{9}{x}-x}$

$$\frac{x+3}{\frac{9}{x}-\frac{x}{1}\cdot\frac{x}{x}}=\frac{x+3}{\frac{9}{x}-\frac{x^2}{x}}=\frac{\frac{x+3}{1}}{\frac{9-x^2}{x}}=\frac{x+3}{1}\div\frac{9-x^2}{x}=\frac{x+3}{1}\cdot\frac{x}{9-x^2}$$

$$=\frac{\cancel{(x+3)}}{1}\cdot\frac{x}{\cancel{(3+x)}(3-x)}=\frac{x}{3-x}$$

Practice Problem 3 Simplify by Method 1: $\dfrac{4+\dfrac{1}{x+3}}{\dfrac{2}{x^2+4x+3}}$

EXAMPLE 4 Simplify by Method 2: $\dfrac{\dfrac{3}{x+2}+\dfrac{1}{x}}{\dfrac{3}{y}-\dfrac{2}{x}}$

The LCD of the numerator is $x(x+2)$. The LCD of the denominator is xy. Thus, the LCD of the complex fraction is $xy(x+2)$.

$$\frac{\frac{3}{x+2}+\frac{1}{x}}{\frac{3}{y}-\frac{2}{x}}\cdot\frac{xy(x+2)}{xy(x+2)}=\frac{3xy+xy+2y}{3x(x+2)-2y(x+2)}$$

$$=\frac{4xy+2y}{(x+2)(3x-2y)}$$

$$=\frac{2y(2x+1)}{(x+2)(3x-2y)}$$

Practice Problem 4 Simplify by Method 2: $\dfrac{\dfrac{7}{y+3}-\dfrac{3}{y}}{\dfrac{2}{y}+\dfrac{5}{y+3}}$

6.3 Exercises

Simplify the complex fractions by any method.

1. $\dfrac{1 - \dfrac{6}{5y}}{\dfrac{3}{y} + 1}$

2. $\dfrac{2 - \dfrac{3}{4y}}{\dfrac{1}{2y} + 1}$

3. $\dfrac{\dfrac{y}{6} - \dfrac{1}{2y}}{\dfrac{3}{2y} - \dfrac{1}{y}}$

4. $\dfrac{\dfrac{1}{3y} + \dfrac{1}{6y}}{\dfrac{1}{2y} + \dfrac{3}{4y}}$

5. $\dfrac{\dfrac{2}{y^2 - 9}}{\dfrac{3}{y + 3} + 1}$

6. $\dfrac{\dfrac{2}{y + 4}}{\dfrac{3}{y - 4} - \dfrac{1}{y^2 - 16}}$

7. $\dfrac{3 - \dfrac{5}{x}}{\dfrac{x + 2}{4}}$

8. $\dfrac{\dfrac{1}{x} + 2}{\dfrac{x - 5}{3}}$

9. $\dfrac{6}{2x - \dfrac{10}{x - 4}}$

10. $\dfrac{-8}{\dfrac{6x}{x - 1} - 4}$

11. $\dfrac{\dfrac{1}{2x + 3} + \dfrac{2}{4x^2 + 12x + 9}}{\dfrac{5}{2x^2 + 3x}}$

12. $\dfrac{\dfrac{3}{5x - 2} - \dfrac{2}{25x^2 - 4}}{\dfrac{7x}{5x^2 - 2x}}$

13. $\dfrac{\dfrac{2}{a} + \dfrac{3}{b}}{\dfrac{4}{a + b} - \dfrac{1}{a}}$

14. $\dfrac{\dfrac{5}{a - b} + \dfrac{1}{b}}{2 - \dfrac{a}{a - b}}$

15. $\dfrac{\dfrac{1}{x - a} - \dfrac{1}{x}}{a}$

16. $\dfrac{\dfrac{1}{x + a} - \dfrac{1}{x}}{a}$

To Think About

Simplify the complex fractions.

17. $1 - \dfrac{1}{1 - \dfrac{1}{y - 2}}$

18. $\dfrac{x}{1 + \dfrac{1}{x}} + \dfrac{2x}{2 + \dfrac{2}{x}}$

Applications

19. The amount of electrical current in amps in a certain alternating current circuit can be described by the expression

$$\frac{\dfrac{x^2 - 1}{6x^2 + 3x}}{\dfrac{x - 1}{2x^2}},$$

where x is the number of milliseconds since the power has started to flow through the circuit. Simplify this expression.

20. If an object is traveling toward you at x miles per hour and is emitting a sound (like a train whistle or an ambulance siren) of pitch y, then the actual pitch that you hear is given by the expression

$$\frac{y}{1 - \dfrac{x}{770}}.$$

Simplify this expression.

Cumulative Review Problems

Solve for x.

21. $|2 - 3x| = 4$

22. $\left|\dfrac{1}{2}(5 - x)\right| = 5$

23. $|7x - 3 - 2x| < 6$

24. $|0.6x + 0.3| \geq 1.2$

25. The price of building an interstate highway project in the late 1970s near New York City was $4000 per inch.

(a) How much money was spent per mile?

(b) Now a new interstate highway connector will be built in the same area beginning in 2002 for $660 million per mile. If the land acquisition cost was $570 million, how many miles can be built if the total budget limit is $4,860,000,000?

26. Jan Robbins and her family are being relocated by her corporation from Dallas to Stockholm, Sweden. The moving company charges $2.50 per kilogram for airfreight and $1.30 per kilogram for belongings shipped by ocean freighter. Jan needs to ship 5600 kilograms of her belongings to Stockholm. Her corporation will pay only $9380 for the shipments. How many kilograms should she ship by airfreight and how many kilograms should she ship by ocean freighter?

6.4 Rational Equations

1 Solving a Rational Equation

A **rational equation** is an equation that has one or more rational expressions as terms. To solve a rational equation, we find the LCD of all fractions in the equation and multiply each side of the equation by the LCD. We then solve the resulting linear equation.

EXAMPLE 1 Solve $\frac{9}{4} - \frac{1}{2x} = \frac{4}{x}$. Check your solution.

First we multiply each side of the equation by the LCD, which is $4x$.

$$4x\left(\frac{9}{4} - \frac{1}{2x}\right) = 4x\left(\frac{4}{x}\right)$$

$$4x\left(\frac{9}{4}\right) - 4x\left(\frac{1}{2x}\right) = 4x\left(\frac{4}{x}\right) \quad \text{Use the distributive property.}$$

$$9x - 2 = 16 \quad \text{Simplify.}$$

$$9x = 18 \quad \text{Collect like terms.}$$

$$x = 2 \quad \text{Divide each side by the coefficient of } x.$$

Check: $\frac{9}{4} - \frac{1}{2(2)} \stackrel{?}{=} \frac{4}{2}$

$$\frac{9}{4} - \frac{1}{4} \stackrel{?}{=} 2$$

$$\frac{8}{4} \stackrel{?}{=} 2$$

$$2 = 2 \checkmark$$

Practice Problem 1 Solve and check $\frac{4}{3x} + \frac{x+1}{x} = \frac{1}{2}$.

Usually, we combine the first two steps of the exercise and show only the step of multiplying each term of the equation by the LCD. We will follow this approach in the remaining examples in this section.

This is another illustration of the need to understand a mathematical principle rather than merely copying down a step without understanding it. Because we understand the distributive property, we can move directly to simplifying a rational equation by multiplying each term of the equation by the LCD.

EXAMPLE 2 Solve $\frac{2}{3x+6} = \frac{1}{6} - \frac{1}{2x+4}$.

$$\frac{2}{3(x+2)} = \frac{1}{6} - \frac{1}{2(x+2)} \quad \text{Factor each denominator.}$$

$$6(x+2)\left[\frac{2}{3(x+2)}\right] = 6(x+2)\left[\frac{1}{6}\right] - 6(x+2)\left[\frac{1}{2(x+2)}\right] \quad \text{Multiply each term by the LCD } 6(x+2).$$

$$4 = x + 2 - 3 \quad \text{Simplify.}$$

$$4 = x - 1 \quad \text{Collect like terms.}$$

$$5 = x \quad \text{Solve for } x.$$

Check: Verify that 5 is the solution.

Practice Problem 2 Solve and check $\frac{1}{3x-9} = \frac{1}{2x-6} - \frac{5}{6}$.

Student Learning Objectives

After studying this section, you will be able to:

1. Solve a rational equation that has a solution and be able to check the solution.

2. Identify those rational equations that have no solution.

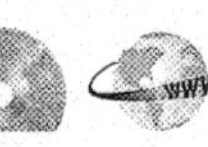

PH TUTOR CENTER CD & VIDEO MATH PRO WEB

Graphing Calculator

Solving Rational Equations

To solve Example 2 on your graphing calculator, find the point of intersection of

$$y_1 = \frac{2}{3x+6}$$

and $y_2 = \frac{1}{6} - \frac{1}{2x+4}$.

Use the Zoom and Trace features or the intersection command to find that the solution is 5.00 (to the nearest hundredth). What two difficulties do you observe in the graph that make this exploration more challenging? How can these be overcome?

Use this method to find the solutions to the following equations on your graphing calculator. (Round your answers to the nearest hundredth.)

1. $\frac{3}{x+3} + \frac{5}{x+4} = \frac{12x+19}{x^2+7x+12}$

2. $\frac{x-2.84}{x+1.12} = \frac{x-5.93}{x+5.06}$

EXAMPLE 3 Solve $\frac{y^2 - 10}{y^2 - y - 20} = 1 + \frac{7}{y - 5}$.

$\frac{y^2 - 10}{(y - 5)(y + 4)} = 1 + \frac{7}{y - 5}$ Factor each denominator. Multiply each term by the LCD $(y - 5)(y + 4)$.

$$\cancel{(y-5)}\cancel{(y+4)}\left[\frac{y^2 - 10}{\cancel{(y-5)}\cancel{(y+4)}}\right] = (y - 5)(y + 4)(1) + \cancel{(y-5)}(y + 4)\left[\frac{7}{\cancel{(y-5)}}\right]$$

$y^2 - 10 = (y - 5)(y + 4)(1) + 7(y + 4)$ Divide out common factors.

$y^2 - 10 = y^2 - y - 20 + 7y + 28$ Simplify.

$y^2 - 10 = y^2 + 6y + 8$ Collect like terms.

$-10 = 6y + 8$ Subtract y^2 from each side.

$-18 = 6y$ Add -8 to each side.

$-3 = y$ Divide each side by the coefficient of y.

Check: $\frac{(-3)^2 - 10}{(-3)^2 - (-3) - 20} \stackrel{?}{=} 1 + \frac{7}{-3 - 5}$

$$\frac{9 - 10}{9 + 3 - 20} \stackrel{?}{=} 1 + \frac{7}{-8}$$

$$\frac{-1}{-8} \stackrel{?}{=} 1 - \frac{7}{8}$$

$$\frac{1}{8} = \frac{1}{8} \checkmark$$

Practice Problem 3 Solve $\frac{y^2 + 4y - 2}{y^2 - 2y - 8} = 1 + \frac{4}{y - 4}$.

2 Identifying Equations with No Solution

Some rational equations have no solution. This can happen in two distinct ways. In the first case, when you attempt to solve the equation, you obtain a contradiction, such as $0 = 1$. This occurs because the variable "drops out" of the equation. No solution can be obtained. In the second case, we may solve an equation to get an *apparent* solution, but it may not satisfy the original equation. We call the apparent solution an **extraneous solution**. An equation that yields an extraneous solution has no solution.

Case 1: The Variable Drops Out

In this case, when you attempt to solve the equation, the coefficient of the variable term becomes zero. Thus, you are left with a statement such as $0 = 1$, which is false. In such a case you know that there is no value for the variable that could make $0 = 1$; hence, there cannot be any solution.

EXAMPLE 4 Solve $\frac{z + 1}{z^2 - 3z + 2} + \frac{3}{z - 1} = \frac{4}{z - 2}$.

$\frac{z + 1}{(z - 2)(z - 1)} + \frac{3}{z - 1} = \frac{4}{z - 2}$ Factor to find the LCD $(z - 2)(z - 1)$. Then multiply each term by the LCD.

$$\cancel{(z-2)}\cancel{(z-1)}\left[\frac{z + 1}{\cancel{(z-2)}\cancel{(z-1)}}\right] + (z - 2)\cancel{(z-1)}\left[\frac{3}{\cancel{z-1}}\right] = \cancel{(z-2)}(z - 1)\left[\frac{4}{\cancel{(z-2)}}\right]$$

$$z + 1 + 3(z - 2) = 4(z - 1) \quad \text{Divide out common factors.}$$
$$z + 1 + 3z - 6 = 4z - 4 \quad \text{Simplify.}$$
$$4z - 5 = 4z - 4 \quad \text{Collect like terms.}$$
$$4z - 4z = -4 + 5 \quad \text{Obtain variable terms on one side}$$
$$0 = 1 \quad \text{and constant values on the other.}$$

Of course, $0 \neq 1$. Therefore, no value of z makes the original equation true. Hence, the equation has **no solution**.

Practice Problem 4 Solve $\dfrac{2x - 1}{x^2 - 7x + 10} + \dfrac{3}{x - 5} = \dfrac{5}{x - 2}$.

Case 2: The Obtained Value of the Variable Leads to a Denominator of Zero

EXAMPLE 5 Solve $\dfrac{4y}{y + 3} - \dfrac{12}{y - 3} = \dfrac{4y^2 + 36}{y^2 - 9}$.

$$\frac{4y}{y + 3} - \frac{12}{y - 3} = \frac{4y^2 + 36}{(y + 3)(y - 3)}$$

Factor each denominator to find the LCD $(y + 3)(y - 3)$. Multiply each term by the LCD.

$$\cancel{(y + 3)}(y - 3)\left[\frac{4y}{\cancel{y + 3}}\right] - (y + 3)\cancel{(y - 3)}\left[\frac{12}{\cancel{y - 3}}\right] = \cancel{(y + 3)}\cancel{(y - 3)}\left[\frac{4y^2 + 36}{\cancel{(y + 3)}\cancel{(y - 3)}}\right]$$

$$4y(y - 3) - 12(y + 3) = 4y^2 + 36 \quad \text{Divide out common factors.}$$
$$4y^2 - 12y - 12y - 36 = 4y^2 + 36 \quad \text{Remove parentheses.}$$
$$4y^2 - 24y - 36 = 4y^2 + 36 \quad \text{Collect like terms.}$$
$$-24y - 36 = 36 \quad \text{Subtract } 4y^2 \text{ from each side.}$$
$$-24y = 72 \quad \text{Add 36 to each side.}$$
$$y = \frac{72}{-24} \quad \text{Divide each side by } -24.$$
$$y = -3$$

Check:
$$\frac{4(-3)}{-3 + 3} - \frac{12}{-3 - 3} \stackrel{?}{=} \frac{4(-3)^2 + 36}{(-3)^2 - 9}$$
$$\frac{-12}{0} - \frac{12}{-6} \stackrel{?}{=} \frac{36 + 36}{0}$$

You cannot divide by zero. Division by zero is not defined. A value of a variable that makes a denominator in the original equation zero is not a solution to the equation. Thus, this equation has **no solution**.

Sometimes you may find that you do not have sufficient time for a complete check, but you still wish to make sure that you do not have a "no solution" situation. In those instances you can do a quick analysis to be sure that your obtained value for the variable does not make a denominator zero. If you were solving the equation $\dfrac{4x - 1}{x^2 + 5x - 14} = \dfrac{1}{x - 2} - \dfrac{2}{x + 7}$, you would know immediately that you could not have 2 or -7 as a solution. Do you see why?

Practice Problem 5 Solve and check $\dfrac{y}{y - 2} - 3 = 1 + \dfrac{2}{y - 2}$.

6.4 Exercises

Solve the equations and check your solutions. If there is no solution, say so.

1. $\frac{2}{x} + \frac{3}{2x} = \frac{7}{6}$

2. $\frac{1}{x} + \frac{2}{3x} = \frac{1}{3}$

3. $3 - \frac{2}{x} = \frac{1}{4x}$

4. $\frac{5}{3x} + 2 = \frac{1}{x}$

5. $\frac{7}{2x} - 1 = \frac{3}{x}$

6. $4 - \frac{2}{5y} = \frac{2}{y}$

7. $\frac{2}{y} = \frac{5}{y - 3}$

8. $\frac{10}{3x - 8} = \frac{2}{x}$

9. $\frac{y + 6}{y + 3} - 2 = \frac{3}{y + 3}$

10. $4 - \frac{8x}{x + 1} = \frac{8}{x + 1}$

11. $\frac{3}{x} + \frac{4}{2x} = \frac{4}{x - 1}$

12. $\frac{1}{2x} + \frac{5}{x} = \frac{3}{x - 1}$

13. $\frac{2x + 3}{x + 3} = \frac{2x}{x + 1}$

14. $\frac{3x}{x - 2} = \frac{3x + 5}{x - 1}$

15. $\frac{3y}{y + 1} + \frac{4}{y - 2} = 3$

16. $\frac{4y}{y + 2} + \frac{2}{y - 1} = 4$

17. $\frac{3}{2x - 1} + \frac{3}{2x + 1} = \frac{8x}{4x^2 - 1}$

18. $\frac{6}{x} - \frac{3}{x^2 - x} = \frac{7}{x - 1}$

19. $\frac{5}{y - 3} + 2 = \frac{3}{3y - 9}$

20. $\frac{2}{3} + \frac{5}{y - 4} = \frac{y + 6}{3y - 12}$

21. $1 - \frac{10}{z - 3} = \frac{-5}{3z - 9}$

22. $\frac{3}{2} + \frac{2}{2z - 8} = \frac{1}{z - 4}$

23. $\frac{4}{y+5} - \frac{32}{y^2-25} = \frac{-2}{y-5}$

24. $\frac{-12}{y^2-9} - \frac{1}{y+3} = \frac{1}{y-3}$

25. $\frac{4}{z^2-9} = \frac{2}{z^2-3z}$

26. $\frac{z^2+16}{z^2-16} = \frac{z}{z+4} - \frac{4}{z-4}$

27. $\frac{2x+3}{2} + \frac{1}{x+1} = x$

28. $\frac{3x-4}{3} - x = -\frac{4}{x+3}$

Verbal and Writing Skills

29. In what situations will a rational equation have no solution?

30. What does "extraneous solution" mean? What must we do to determine whether a solution is an extraneous solution?

Optional Graphing Calculator Problems

Solve each equation. Round your answers to the nearest tenth.

31. $\frac{5}{x+3.6} - \frac{4.2}{x-7.6} = \frac{3.3}{x^2-4x-27.36}$

32. $\frac{153.8}{x^2+4.9x-39.56} = \frac{75.3}{x+9.2} + \frac{84.2}{x-4.3}$

Cumulative Review Problems

Factor completely.

33. $7x^2 - 63$

34. $2x^2 + 20x + 50$

35. $64x^3 - 27y^3$

36. $3x^2 - 13x + 14$

A recent study from Rutgers University showed that the number of couples who intend to divorce decreases rapidly if those couples undergo marital counseling. Those who stay in counseling less than 1 year have a 10% chance of not getting divorced. Couples who remain in counseling at least 1 year but less than 2 years have a 25% chance of not getting divorced. Couples who remain in counseling 2 years or more have a 78% chance of not getting divorced. Suppose 160,000 couples in the Midwest have marriage problems and intend to divorce. Of these couples, 15% refuse to attend counseling, 10% decide to attend counseling for less than 1 year, 50% decide to attend counseling for at least a year but less than 2 years, and 25% decide to attend counseling for 2 years or more.

37. How many couples will attend counseling for at least 1 year but less than 2 years? How many of these couples will likely remain married?

38. How many of the original 160,000 couples will likely remain married? (Assume that all couples refusing to attend counseling do in fact get divorced.)

6.5 Applications: Formulas and Advanced Ratio Exercises

Student Learning Objectives

After studying this section, you will be able to:

 Solve a formula for a particular variable.

 Solve advanced exercises involving ratio and rate.

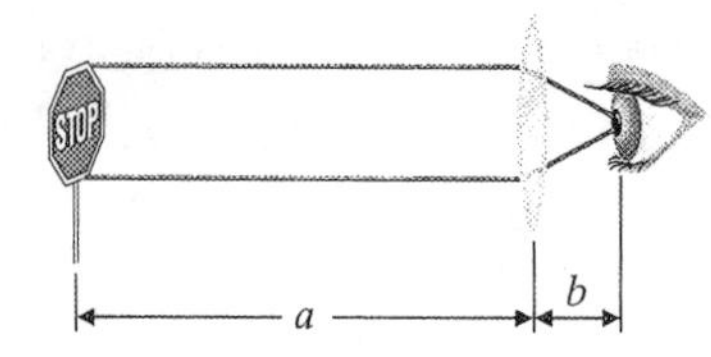

 Solving a Formula for a Particular Variable

In science, economics, business, and mathematics, we use formulas that contain rational expressions. We often have to solve these formulas for a specific variable in terms of the other variables.

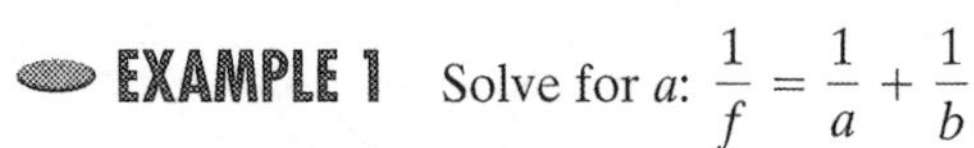

EXAMPLE 1 Solve for a: $\frac{1}{f} = \frac{1}{a} + \frac{1}{b}$

This formula is used in optics in the study of light passing through a lens. It relates the focal length f of the lens to the distance a of an object from the lens and the distance b of the image from the lens.

$$ab\cancel{f}\left[\frac{1}{\cancel{f}}\right] = \cancel{a}bf\left[\frac{1}{\cancel{a}}\right] + a\cancel{b}f\left[\frac{1}{\cancel{b}}\right] \quad \text{Multiply each term by the LCD } abf.$$

$$ab = bf + af \quad \text{Simplify.}$$

$$ab - af = bf \quad \text{Obtain all the terms containing the variable } a \text{ on one side of the equation.}$$

$$a(b - f) = bf \quad \text{Factor.}$$

$$a = \frac{bf}{b - f} \quad \text{Divide each side by } b - f.$$

Practice Problem 1 Solve for t: $\frac{1}{t} = \frac{1}{c} + \frac{1}{d}$

This formula relates the total amount of time t in hours that is required for two workers to complete a job working together if one worker can complete it alone in c hours and the other worker in d hours.

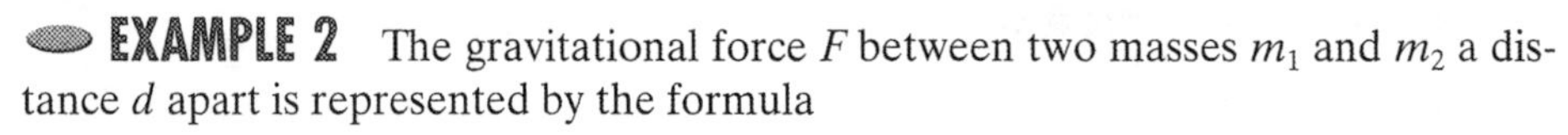

EXAMPLE 2 The gravitational force F between two masses m_1 and m_2 a distance d apart is represented by the formula

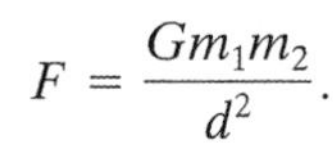

$$F = \frac{Gm_1m_2}{d^2}.$$

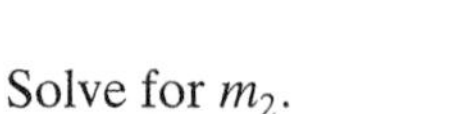

Solve for m_2.

The subscripts on the variable m mean that m_1 and m_2 are *different*. (The m stands for "mass.")

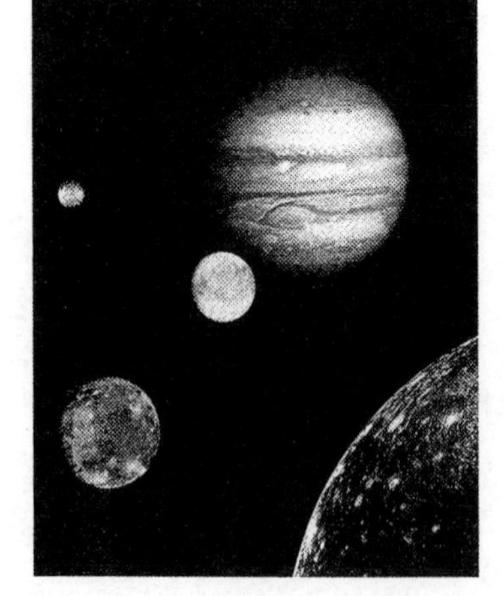

$$F = \frac{Gm_1m_2}{d^2}$$

$$d^2[F] = \cancel{d^2}\left[\frac{Gm_1m_2}{\cancel{d^2}}\right] \quad \text{Multiply each side by the LCD } d^2.$$

$$d^2F = Gm_1m_2 \quad \text{Simplify.}$$

$$\frac{d^2F}{Gm_1} = \frac{Gm_1m_2}{Gm_1} \quad \text{Divide each side by the coefficient of } m_2, \text{ which is } Gm_1.$$

$$\frac{d^2F}{Gm_1} = m_2$$

Practice Problem 2 The number of telephone calls C between two cities of populations p_1 and p_2 that are a distance d apart may be represented by the formula

$$C = \frac{Bp_1p_2}{d^2}.$$

Solve this equation for p_1.

2 Solving Advanced Exercises Involving Ratio and Rate

You have already encountered the simple idea of proportions in a previous course. In that course you learned that a **proportion** is an equation that says that two ratios are equal.

For example, if Wendy's car traveled 180 miles on 7 gallons of gas, how many miles can the car travel on 11 gallons of gas? You probably remember that you can solve this type of exercise quickly if you let x be the number of miles the car can travel. Then to find x you solve the proportion $\frac{7}{180} = \frac{11}{x}$. Rounded to the nearest mile, the answer is 283 miles. Can you obtain that answer? So far in Chapters 1–5 in this book in the Cumulative Review Exercises, there have been several ratio and proportion exercises for you to solve at this elementary level.

Now we proceed with more advanced exercises in which the ratio of two quantities is more difficult to establish. Study carefully the next two examples. See whether you can follow the reasoning in each case.

EXAMPLE 3 A company plans to employ 910 people with a ratio of two managers for every eleven workers. How many managers should be hired? How many workers?

If we let $x =$ the number of managers, then $910 - x =$ the number of workers. We are given the ratio of managers to workers, so let's set up our proportion in that way.

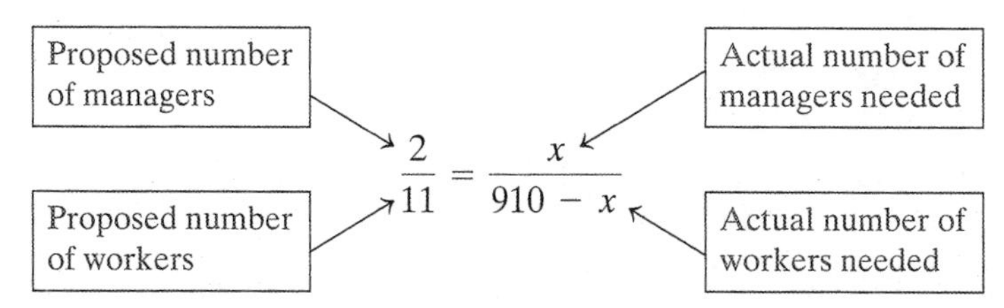

The LCD is $11(910 - x)$. Multiplying by the LCD, we get the following:

$$11(910 - x)\left[\frac{2}{11}\right] = 11(910 - x)\left[\frac{x}{910 - x}\right]$$

$$2(910 - x) = 11x$$

$$1820 - 2x = 11x$$

$$1820 = 13x$$

$$140 = x$$

$$910 - x = 910 - 140 = 770$$

The number of managers needed is 140. The number of workers needed is 770.

Practice Problem 3 Western University has 168 faculty. The university always maintains a student-to-faculty ratio of 21:2. How many students should they enroll to maintain that ratio?

The next example concerns **similar triangles**. These triangles have corresponding angles that are equal and corresponding sides that are *proportional* (not equal). Similar triangles are frequently used to determine distances that cannot be conveniently measured. For example, in the following sketch, x and X are corresponding angles, y and Y are corresponding angles, and s and S are corresponding sides.

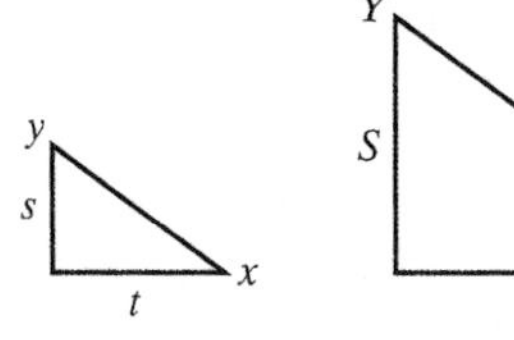

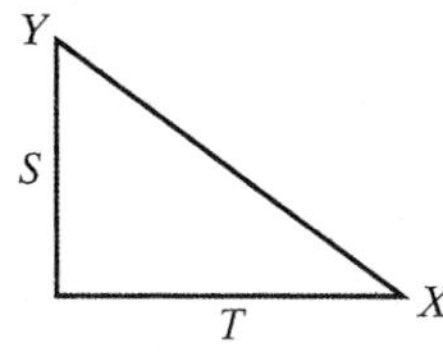

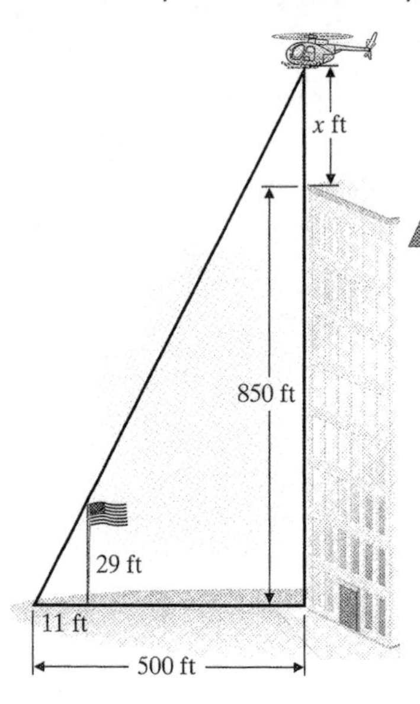

Hence, angle x = angle X, angle y = angle Y, and side s is proportional to side S. (Again, note that we did not say that side s is equal to side S.) Also, side t is proportional to side T. So, really, one triangle is just a magnification of the other triangle. If the sides are proportional, they are in the same ratio.

EXAMPLE 4 A helicopter is hovering an unknown distance above an 850-foot building. A man watching the helicopter is 500 feet from the base of the building and 11 feet from a flagpole that is 29 feet tall. The man's line of sight to the helicopter is directly above the flagpole, as you can see in the sketch. How far above the building is the helicopter? Round your answer to the nearest foot.

1. ***Understand the problem.***
   Can you see the two triangles in the diagram in the margin? For convenience, we separate them out in the sketch on the right. We want to find the distance x. Are the triangles similar? The angles at the bases of the triangles are equal. (Why?) It follows, then, that the top angles must also be equal. (Remember that the angles of any triangle add up to 180°.) Since the angles are equal, the triangles are similar and the sides are proportional.

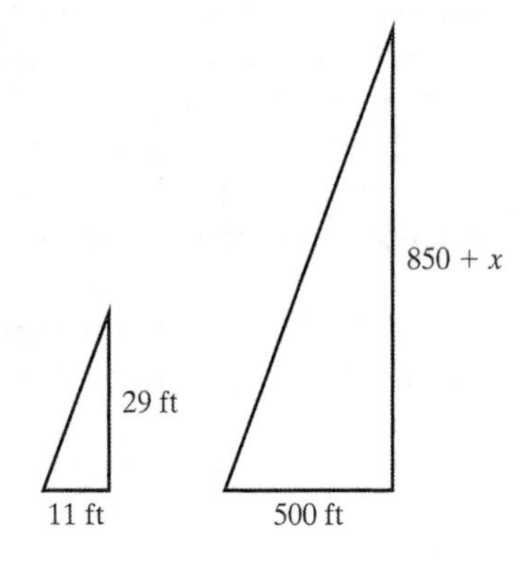

2. ***Write an equation.***
   We can set up our proportion like this:

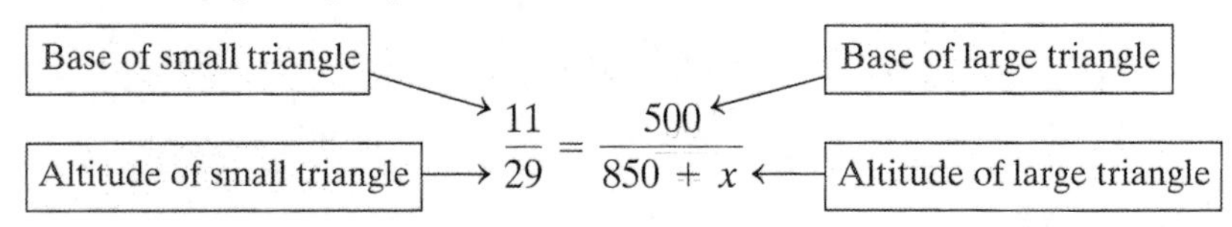

$$\frac{11}{29} = \frac{500}{850 + x}$$

3. ***Solve the equation and state the answer.***
   The LCD is $29(850 + x)$.

$$\cancel{29}(850 + x)\left[\frac{11}{\cancel{29}}\right] = 29\cancel{(850 + x)}\left[\frac{500}{\cancel{850 + x}}\right]$$

$$11(850 + x) = 29(500)$$

$$9350 + 11x = 14{,}500$$

$$11x = 5150$$

$$x = \frac{5150}{11} = 468.\overline{18}$$

So the helicopter is about 468 feet above the building.

Practice Problem 4 Solve the exercise in Example 4 for a man watching 450 feet from the base of a 900-foot building as shown in the figure in the margin. The flagpole is 35 feet tall, and the man is 10 feet from the flagpole.

We will see some challenging exercises involving similar triangles in Exercises 55 and 56.

We will sometimes encounter exercises in which two or more people or machines are working together to complete a certain task. These types of exercises are sometimes called *work problems*. In general, these types of exercises can be analyzed by using the following concept.

Part of task done by first person	+	part of task done by second person	=	1 (one complete task finished)

We will also use a general idea about the rate at which something is done. If Robert can do a task in 3 hours, then he can do $\frac{1}{3}$ of the task in 1 hour. If Susan can do the same task in 2 hours, then she can do $\frac{1}{2}$ of the task in 1 hour. In general, if a person can do a task in t hours, then that person can do $\frac{1}{t}$ of the task in 1 hour.

EXAMPLE 5 Robert can paint the kitchen in 3 hours. Susan can paint the kitchen in 2 hours. How long will it take Robert and Susan to paint the kitchen if they work together?

1. *Understand the problem.*
Robert can paint $\frac{1}{3}$ of the kitchen in 1 hour.
Susan can paint $\frac{1}{2}$ of the kitchen in 1 hour.
We do not know how long it will take them working together, so we let x = the number of hours it takes them to paint the kitchen working together. To assist us, we will construct a table that relates the data. We will use the concept that (rate)(time) = fraction of task done.

	Rate of Work per Hour	Time Worked in Hours	Fraction of Task Done
Robert	$\frac{1}{3}$	x	$\frac{x}{3}$
Susan	$\frac{1}{2}$	x	$\frac{x}{2}$

2. *Write an equation.*

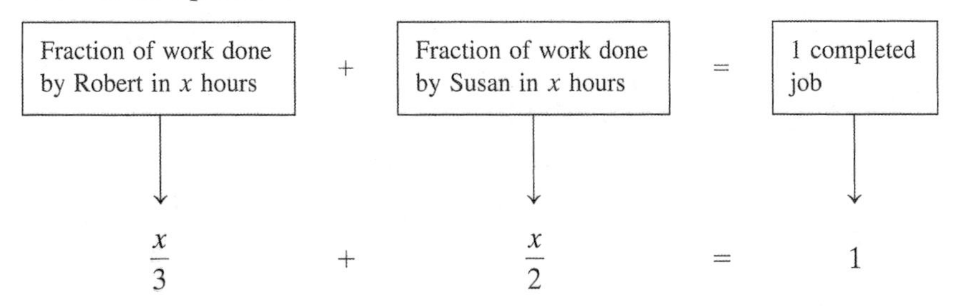

3. *Solve the equation and state the answer.*
Multiply each side of the equation by the LCD and use the distributive property.

$$6\left(\frac{x}{3}\right) + 6\left(\frac{x}{2}\right) = 6(1)$$
$$2x + 3x = 6$$
$$5x = 6$$
$$x = \frac{6}{5} = 1\frac{1}{5} = 1.2 \text{ hours}$$

Working together, Robert and Susan can paint the kitchen in 1.2 hours.

Practice Problem 5 Alfred can mow the huge lawn at his Vermont farm with his new lawn mower in 4 hours. His young son can mow the lawn with the old lawn mower in 5 hours. If they work together, how long will it take them to mow the lawn?

6.5 Exercises

Solve for the variable indicated.

1. $x = \dfrac{y - b}{m}$; for m

2. $m = \dfrac{y - b}{x}$; for x

3. $\dfrac{1}{f} = \dfrac{1}{a} + \dfrac{1}{b}$; for b

4. $\dfrac{1}{f} = \dfrac{1}{a} + \dfrac{1}{b}$; for f

5. $R = \dfrac{ab}{3x}$; for x

6. $A^2 = \dfrac{Q}{5M}$; for M

7. $F = \dfrac{xy + xz}{2}$; for x

8. $A = \dfrac{ha + hb}{2}$; for h

9. $\dfrac{3V}{4\pi} = r^3$; for V

10. $\dfrac{V}{\pi r^2} = h$; for r^2

11. $\dfrac{E}{e} = \dfrac{R + r}{r}$; for e

12. $\dfrac{E}{e} = \dfrac{Rer}{r}$; for R

13. $\dfrac{P_1V_1}{T_1} = \dfrac{P_2V_2}{T_2}$; for T_1

14. $\dfrac{P_1V_1}{T_1} = \dfrac{P_2V_2}{T_2}$; for T_2

15. $F = \dfrac{Gm_1m_2}{d^2}$; for d^2

16. $F = \dfrac{Gm_1m_2}{d^2}$; for G

17. $E = T_1 - \dfrac{T_1}{T_2}$; for T_1

18. $E = T_1 - \dfrac{T_1}{T_2}$; for T_2

19. $m = \dfrac{y_2 - y_1}{x_2 - x_1}$; for x_1

20. $m = \dfrac{y_2 - y_1}{x_2 - x_1}$; for x_2

21. $\dfrac{2D - at^2}{2t} = V$; for D

22. $\dfrac{2D - at^2}{2t} = V$; for a

23. $Q = \dfrac{kA(t_1 - t_2)}{L}$; for t_2

24. $Q = \dfrac{kA(t_1 - t_2)}{L}$; for A

25. $\dfrac{T_2W}{T_2 - T_1} = q$; for T_2

26. $d = \dfrac{LR_2}{R_2 + R_1}$; for R_1

27. $\dfrac{s - s_0}{v_0 + gt} = t$; for v_0

28. $\dfrac{A - P}{Pr} = t$; for P

Round your answers to four decimal places.

29. Solve for T: $\dfrac{1.98V}{1.96V_0} = 0.983 + 5.936(T - T_0)$

30. Solve for r_1: $\dfrac{1}{R} = \dfrac{1}{r_1} + \dfrac{1}{0.368} + \dfrac{1}{0.736}$

Applications

31. On a map of Nigeria, the cities of Benin City and Onitsha are 6.5 centimeters apart. The map scale shows that 3 centimeters = 55 kilometers on the map. How far apart are the two cities?

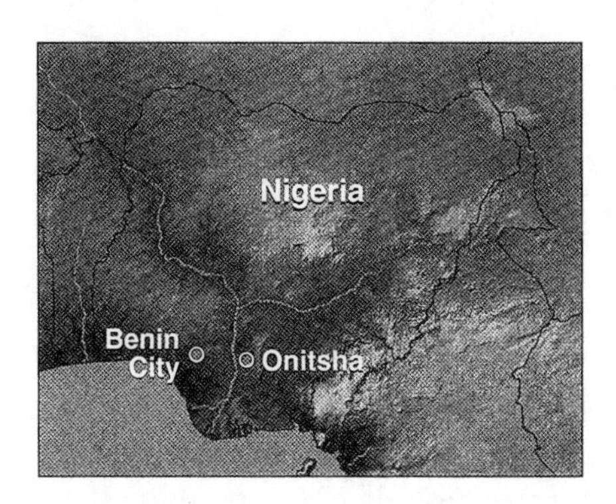

32. The lobby of the new athletic center at Mansfield Community College is shown on a blueprint made by the architect. The scale drawing is 6 inches wide and 12 inches long. The blueprint has a scale of 3:100. Find the length and width of the lobby measured in inches. Find the length and width of the lobby measured in feet.

33. A speed of 60 miles per hour (mph) is equivalent to 88 kilometers per hour (km/h). On a trip through Nova Scotia, Lora passes a sign stating that the speed limit is 80 km/h. What is the speed limit in miles per hour?

34. Jane Wells is the team captain of the Pioneers, a traveling women's softball team. Jane hit five home runs in the first six games. If the season has forty-four games and she continues to hit home runs at this rate, how many more home runs is she likely to hit during the season? Round your answer to the nearest whole number. Does it seem reasonable that if she hits home runs at this rate, she will break the record of forty-one home runs in one season?

In Exercises 35–54, round your answers to the nearest hundredth, unless otherwise directed.

35. Thirty-five grizzly bears were captured and tagged by wildlife personnel in the Yukon and then released back into the wild. Later that same year, fifty were captured, and twenty-two had tags. Estimate the number of grizzly bears in that part of the Yukon. (Round this answer to the nearest whole number.)

36. Thirty alligators were captured in the Louisiana bayou (swamp) and tagged by National Park officials and then put back into the bayou. One month later, fifty alligators were captured from the same part of the bayou, eighteen of which had been tagged. Estimate to the nearest whole number how many alligators are in that part of Louisiana.

37. A ship in the Russian navy has a ratio of two officers for every seven seamen. The crew of the ship totals 117 people. How many officers and how many seamen are on this ship?

38. A Maine logging company has a total of 210 people at the north camp. The ratio of workers is three new employees for every eleven experienced employees. How many new employees are there at the north camp? How many experienced employees are there at the north camp?

39. Southwestern Cell Phones has a total of 187 employees in the marketing and sales offices in Dallas. For every four people employed in marketing, there are thirteen people employed in sales. How many people in the Dallas office work in marketing? How many people in the Dallas office work in sales?

40. At Elmwood University there are nine men for every five women on the faculty. If Elmwood University employees 182 faculty members, how many are men and how many are women?

▲ 41. Becky DeWitt is a photographer at Photographics. She wants to enlarge a photograph that measures 3 inches wide and 5 inches long to an oversize photograph with the same width-to-length ratio. The perimeter of the new photograph is 115.2 inches. What are the length and the width of the new oversize photograph?

▲ 42. Ron Morrell is helping his parents expand the pasture for the horses at their Montana ranch. The old rectangular pasture measured 500 yards wide by 800 yards long. The perimeter of the new pasture is 6240 yards. The new pasture has the same width-to-length ratio as the old one. What are the length and the width of the new pasture?

43. A college recently installed new e-mail software on all of its computers. A poll was taken to find out how many of the faculty and staff preferred the new software. The ratio of those preferring the new software to the old software was 3:11. If there are 280 faculty and staff at the college, how many prefer the new software?

44. The ratio of detectives to patrol officers at Center City is 2:9. The police force has 187 detectives and patrol officers. How many are detectives? How many are patrol officers?

45. When Jino D'Alessandro retired, his doctor told him to run 2 miles for every 7 miles he walks. If he plans to cover 63 miles in total each week, how many miles should he walk? How many miles should he run?

46. The harbormaster said that last year the ratio of powerboats to sailboats moored in the harbor was 4:9. If a total of seventy-eight boats was moored in the harbor, how many boats were powerboats? How many boats were sailboats?

▲ 47. A 12-foot marble statue in Italy casts a shadow that is 15 feet long. At the same time of day, a wall casts a shadow that is 8 feet long. How high is the wall?

▲ 48. A 3-foot-tall child casts a shadow that is 4.8 feet long. At the same time of day, a building casts a shadow that extends 177 feet. How tall is the building?

49. A nutritionist told Maggie that for health reasons, she should eat fish seven times for every four times she eats red meat. If over the next 5 months she eats red meat 112 times, how many times should she eat fish?

50. The manager of a mattress store knows that he should stock five queen-size mattresses for every eleven double-size mattresses. Next week he will have 448 mattresses in stock that are either queen-size or doubles. How many of each type should he have?

51. Matt can plow out all the driveways on his street in Duluth, Minnesota, with his new four-wheel-drive truck in 6 hours. Using a snow blade on a lawn tractor, his neighbor can plow out the same number of driveways in 9 hours. How long would it take them to do the work together?

52. The new mechanic at Speedy Lube can perform thirty oil changes in 4 hours. His assistant can perform the same number of oil changes in 6 hours. How long would it take them to do the work together?

53. A lumberjack and his cousin Fred can split a cord of seasoned oak firewood in 3 hours. The lumberjack can split the wood alone without any help from Fred in 4 hours. How long would it take Fred if he worked without the lumberjack?

54. Houghton College has just built a new Olympic-size swimming pool. One large pipe with cold water and one small pipe with hot water are used to fill the pool. When both pipes are used, the pool can be filled in 2 hours. If only the cold water pipe is used, the pool can be filled in 3 hours. How long would it take to fill the pool with just the hot water pipe?

To Think About

To find the width of a river, a hiking club laid out a triangular pattern of measurements. See the figure. Use your knowledge of similar triangles to solve Exercises 55 and 56.

▲ **55.** If any observer stands at the point shown in the figure, then $a = 2$ feet, $b = 5$ feet, and $c = 116$ feet. What is the width of the river?

▲ **56.** What is the width of the river if $a = 3$ feet, $b = 8$ feet, and $c = 297$ feet?

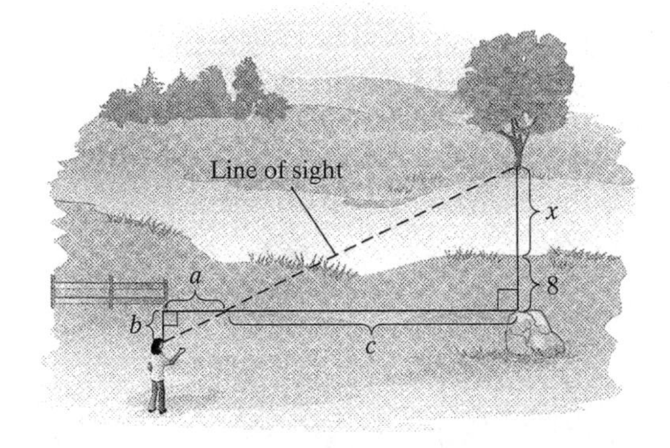

Cumulative Review Problems

Factor completely.

57. $8x^2 - 6x - 5$

58. $x^2 - 2x - 120$

59. $25x^2 - 90xy + 81y^2$

60. $5yx^2 - 20y$

61. A philanthropic organization cofounded by Theodore J. Forstmann, the billionaire financier, and John T. Walton, the son of Wal-Mart founder Sam Walton, offered $50 million in partial and full scholarships for a certain fall term to 7500 underpriviledged students. Full scholarships were twice as large as partial scholarships, and there were an equal number of full scholarships and partial scholarships. What was the average partial scholarship award per student and the average full scholarship award per student? Round your answers to the nearest cent.

Developing Your Study Skills

Why Is Review Necessary?

You master a course in mathematics by learning the concepts one at a time. There are basic concepts like addition, subtraction, multiplication, and division of whole numbers, which are considered the foundation upon which all of mathematics is built. These must be mastered first. The study of mathematics is built upon this foundation, each concept supporting the next. The process is a carefully designed procedure, and no steps can be skipped. A student of mathematics needs to realize the importance of this building process to succeed.

Because new concepts depend on those previously learned, students often need to take time to review. Reviewing at the right time on the right concepts can strengthen previously learned skills and make progress possible.

Timely, periodic review of previously learned mathematical concepts is absolutely necessary in order to master new concepts. You may have forgotten a concept or grown a bit rusty in applying it. Reviewing is the answer. Make use of any review sections in your textbook, whether they are assigned or not. Look back to previous chapters whenever you have forgotten how to do something. Study the examples and practice some exercises to refresh your understanding.

Be sure that you understand and can perform the computations of each new concept. This will enable you to move successfully on to the next ones.

Remember that mathematics is a step-by-step building process. Learn one concept at a time, skipping none, and reinforce and strengthen skills with review whenever necessary.

Putting Your Skills to Work

Analysis of Foreign Exchange Rates When Traveling

Sylvia and Curt Stahl went to France, Italy, and Spain in 2000 for their forty-fifth wedding anniversary. They had traveled to these same countries in 1985 and 1992. The following are the exchange rates that were in effect during their three trips.

Equivalent Currency for One U.S. Dollar

Year	French Francs	Italian Lire	Spanish Pesetas
1985	10.56	2159	191.57
1992	4.74	1064	90.35
2000	7.31	2158	185.45

The Stahl's spending budget, not including hotel and airfare, grew by 8.5% per trip. Their budget for the 1992 trip was $10,000. In 1985, the Stahls spent 43% of their budget in Italy and 20% of their budget in Spain. The Stahls spent 18% more money in Italy in 1992 than they did in 1985. They spent 12% more money in Spain in 2000 than they did in 1992. They spent 21% more money in France in 1992 than they did in 1985. In 2000 the Stahls spent $1000 more in Italy than they did in Spain.

Problems for Individual Investigation

1. What was the spending budget for the Stahls in 1985? Round to the nearest cent.
2. What was the spending budget for the Stahls in 2000? Round to the nearest cent.

Problems for Group Investigation and Cooperative Learning

3. How much did the Stahls spend in Italy in 1985? In 1992? In 2000? Give your answers in American dollars and in Italian lire. Round to the nearest hundredth.
4. How much did the Stahls spend in Spain in 1985? In 1992? In 2000? Give your answers in American dollars and in Spanish pesetas. Round to the nearest hundredth.

Internet Connections

Netsite:  http://www.prenhall.com/tobey_intermediate 

Site: Currency Exchange Past and Present

5. On which day during the last year did a traveler to France get the most French francs for one U.S. dollar? On that day how many French francs could be obtained for 3000 U.S. dollars? On that day how many U.S. dollars were needed to obtain 50,000 French francs?
6. On which day during the last year did a traveler to Spain get the most Spanish pesetas for one U.S. dollar? On that day how many Spanish pesetas could be obtained for 4000 U.S. dollars? On that day how many U.S. dollars were needed to obtain 200,000 Spanish pesetas?

Math in the Media

Math Behind the Scenes

At close to 200 million dollars, *Titanic* is one of the most expensive movies ever made. For the movie, a replica of the original ship was constructed. *Entertainment Weekly Online* reported the replica to be 770 feet long—close to 90% to scale of the real ship.

Details of the original ship were followed closely to create the replica. A special studio was built for filming. The ship "sailed" in an enormous tank that held 17 million gallons of water.

Although movies frequently use models when filming, replicas tend to be on a much smaller scale than that used for the *Titanic*. In the questions that follow, you can use your own calculations to compare model and actual scales.

EXERCISES

1. The original Titanic was 880 feet long and 92 feet high. Use the exact length of the original Titanic and the exact length of the model to determine the percentage to scale of the real ship. Using this information, determine the height of the replica.

2. Does your calculation in Exercise 1 verify that the replica is 90% to scale of the actual ship? How much does your answer differ from the original estimate of 90%?

3. In the movie *The Hunt for Red October*, the story centers on the search for a Russian ballistic missile submarine that is reported to be 610 feet long and has a beam (width) of 46 feet. In filming some of the underwater sequences, a model of the hull of a submarine was used that was reported to be 14 feet wide. If that report is true what percent to scale is the model to the actual submarine in the story? If the entire model was built to that scale, what would be the expected length of the model submarine used in the filming?

Chapter 6 Organizer

Topic	Procedure	Examples
Simplifying rational expressions, p. 315.	**1.** Factor the numerator and denominator, if possible. **2.** Any factor that is common to both numerator and denominator can be divided out. This is an application of the basic rule of fractions. *Basic rule of fractions:* For any polynomials a, b, and c (where $b \neq 0$ and $c \neq 0$), $\frac{ac}{bc} = \frac{a}{b}$.	Simplify $\frac{6x^2 - 14x + 4}{6x^2 - 20x + 6}$. $\frac{2(3x^2 - 7x + 2)}{2(3x^2 - 10x + 3)} = \frac{\cancel{2}\cancel{(3x-1)}(x-2)}{\cancel{2}\cancel{(3x-1)}(x-3)}$ $= \frac{x-2}{x-3}$
Multiplying rational expressions, p. 317.	**1.** Factor all numerators and denominators, if possible. **2.** Any factor that is common to a numerator of one fraction and the denominator of the same fraction or any fraction that is multiplied by it can be divided out. **3.** Write the product of the remaining factors in the numerator. Write the product of the remaining factors in the denominator. $\frac{a}{b} \cdot \frac{c}{d} = \frac{ac}{bd}$	Multiply: $\frac{x^2 - 4x}{6x - 12} \cdot \frac{3x^2 - 6x}{x^3 + 3x^2}$ $\frac{\cancel{x}(x-4)}{\underset{2}{\cancel{6}}\cancel{(x-2)}} \cdot \frac{\overset{1}{\cancel{3}}\cancel{x}\cancel{(x-2)}}{\cancel{x^2}(x+3)} = \frac{x-4}{2(x+3)}$ or $\frac{x-4}{2x+6}$
Dividing rational expressions, p. 318.	**1.** Invert the second fraction and multiply it by the first fraction. $\frac{a}{b} \div \frac{c}{d} = \frac{a}{b} \cdot \frac{d}{c}$ **2.** Apply the steps for multiplying rational expressions.	Divide: $\frac{6x^2 - 5x - 6}{24x^2 + 13x - 2} \div \frac{4x^2 + x - 3}{8x^2 + 7x - 1}$ $\frac{6x^2 - 5x - 6}{24x^2 + 13x - 2} \cdot \frac{8x^2 + 7x - 1}{4x^2 + x - 3}$ $= \frac{\cancel{(3x+2)}(2x-3)}{\cancel{(3x+2)}\cancel{(8x-1)}} \cdot \frac{\cancel{(8x-1)}\cancel{(x+1)}}{\cancel{(x+1)}(4x-3)} = \frac{2x-3}{4x-3}$
Adding rational expressions, p. 323.	**1.** If all fractions have a common denominator, add the numerators and place the result over the common denominator. $\frac{a}{c} + \frac{b}{c} = \frac{a+b}{c}$ **2.** If the fractions do not have a common denominator, factor the denominators (if necessary) and determine the least common denominator (LCD). **3.** Rewrite each fraction as an equivalent fraction with the LCD as the denominator. **4.** Add the numerators and place the result over the common denominator. **5.** Simplify, if possible.	Add: $\frac{7x}{x^2 - 9} + \frac{x+2}{x+3}$ $\frac{7x}{(x+3)(x-3)} + \frac{x+2}{x+3}$ The LCD $= (x+3)(x-3)$. $\frac{7x}{(x+3)(x-3)} + \frac{x+2}{x+3} \cdot \frac{x-3}{x-3}$ $= \frac{7x}{(x+3)(x-3)} + \frac{x^2 - x - 6}{(x+3)(x-3)}$ $= \frac{x^2 + 6x - 6}{(x+3)(x-3)}$
Subtracting rational expressions, p. 324.	Follow the procedure for adding rational expressions through step 3. Then subtract the second numerator from the first and place the result over the common denominator. $\frac{a}{c} - \frac{b}{c} = \frac{a-b}{c}$ Simplify, if possible.	Subtract: $\frac{4x}{3x-2} - \frac{5x}{x+4}$ The LCD $= (3x-2)(x+4)$. $\frac{4x}{3x-2} \cdot \frac{x+4}{x+4} - \frac{5x}{x+4} \cdot \frac{3x-2}{3x-2}$ $= \frac{4x^2 + 16x}{(3x-2)(x+4)} - \frac{15x^2 - 10x}{(x+4)(3x-2)}$ $= \frac{-11x^2 + 26x}{(3x-2)(x+4)}$

Topic	Procedure	Examples
Simplifying a complex rational expression by Method 1, p. 330.	**1.** Simplify the numerator and denominator, if possible, by combining quantities to obtain one fraction in the numerator and one fraction in the denominator. **2.** Divide the numerator by the denominator. (That is, multiply the numerator by the reciprocal of the denominator.) **3.** Simplify the result.	Simplify by Method 1: $\dfrac{4-\frac{1}{x^2}}{\frac{2}{x}+\frac{1}{x^2}}$ **Step 1:** $\dfrac{\frac{4x^2}{x^2}-\frac{1}{x^2}}{\frac{2x}{x^2}+\frac{1}{x^2}} = \dfrac{\frac{4x^2-1}{x^2}}{\frac{2x+1}{x^2}}$ **Step 2:** $\dfrac{4x^2-1}{x^2}\cdot\dfrac{x^2}{2x+1}$ **Step 3:** $\dfrac{\cancel{(2x+1)}(2x-1)}{\cancel{x^2}}\cdot\dfrac{\cancel{x^2}}{\cancel{2x+1}} = 2x-1$
Simplifying a complex rational expression by Method 2, p. 331.	**1.** Find the LCD of the rational expressions in the numerator and the denominator. **2.** Multiply the numerator and the denominator of the complex fraction by the LCD. **3.** Simplify the results.	Simplify by Method 2: $\dfrac{4-\frac{1}{x^2}}{\frac{2}{x}-\frac{1}{x^2}}$ **Step 1:** The LCD of the rational expressions is x^2. **Step 2:** $\dfrac{\left[4-\frac{1}{x^2}\right]x^2}{\left[\frac{2}{x}-\frac{1}{x^2}\right]x^2} = \dfrac{4(x^2)-\left(\frac{1}{x^2}\right)(x^2)}{\left(\frac{2}{x}\right)(x^2)-\left(\frac{1}{x^2}\right)(x^2)}$ $= \dfrac{4x^2-1}{2x-1}$ **Step 3:** $\dfrac{(2x+1)\cancel{(2x-1)}}{\cancel{(2x-1)}} = 2x+1$
Solving rational equations, p. 335.	**1.** Determine the LCD of all denominators in the equation. **2.** Multiply each term in the equation by the LCD. **3.** Simplify and remove parentheses. **4.** Collect any like terms. **5.** Solve for the variable. If the variable term drops out, there is no solution. **6.** Check your answer. Be sure that the value you obtained does not make any denominator in the original equation 0. If so, there is no solution.	Solve $\dfrac{4}{y-1}+\dfrac{-y+5}{3y^2-4y+1}=\dfrac{9}{3y-1}$. The LCD $=(y-1)(3y-1)$. $\cancel{(y-1)}(3y-1)\left[\dfrac{4}{\cancel{y-1}}\right]$ $+\cancel{(y-1)}\cancel{(3y-1)}\left[\dfrac{-y+5}{\cancel{(y-1)}\cancel{(3y-1)}}\right]$ $=(y-1)\cancel{(3y-1)}\left[\dfrac{9}{\cancel{3y-1}}\right]$ $4(3y-1)+(-y)+5=9(y-1)$ $12y-4-y+5=9y-9$ $11y+1=9y-9$ $11y-9y=-9-1$ $2y=-10$ $y=-5$ *Check:* $\dfrac{4}{-5-1}+\dfrac{-(-5)+5}{3(-5)^2-4(-5)+1}\stackrel{?}{=}\dfrac{9}{3(-5)-1}$ $\dfrac{4}{-6}+\dfrac{10}{96}\stackrel{?}{=}\dfrac{9}{-16}$ $-\dfrac{9}{16}=-\dfrac{9}{16}$ ✓

Topic	Procedure	Examples
Solving formulas containing rational expressions for a specified variable, p. 340.	**1.** Remove any parentheses. **2.** Multiply each term of the equation by the LCD. **3.** Add a quantity to or subtract a quantity from each side of the equation so that only terms containing the desired variable are on one side of the equation while all other terms are on the other side. **4.** If there are two or more unlike terms containing the desired variable, remove that variable as a common factor. **5.** Divide each side of the equation by the coefficient of the desired variable. **6.** Simplify, if possible.	Solve for n: $v = c\left(1 - \frac{t}{n}\right)$ $v = c - \frac{ct}{n}$ $n(v) = n(c) - n\left(\frac{ct}{n}\right)$ $nv = nc - ct$ $nv - nc = -ct$ $n(v - c) = -ct$ $n = \frac{-ct}{v - c}$ or $\frac{ct}{c - v}$
Using advanced ratios to solve applied problems, p. 341.	**1.** Determine a given ratio in the problem for which both values are known. **2.** Use variables to describe each of the quantities in the other ratio. **3.** Set the two ratios equal to each other to form an equation. **4.** Solve the resulting equation. Determine both quantities in the second ratio.	A new navy cruiser has a crew of 304 people. For every thirteen seamen there are three officers. How many officers and how many seamen are in the crew? The ratio of seamen to officers is: $\frac{13}{3}$ Let x be the number of officers. Because the crew totals 304, it follows that $304 - x$ represents the number of seamen. seamen → $\frac{13}{3} = \frac{304 - x}{x}$ ← seamen officers → ← officers $13x = 3(304 - x)$ $13x = 912 - 3x$ $16x = 912$ $x = 57$ $304 - x = 247$ There are 57 officers and 247 seamen.

Chapter 6 Review Problems

Simplify.

1. $\dfrac{6x^3 - 9x^2}{12x^2 - 18x}$

2. $\dfrac{15x^4}{5x^2 - 20x}$

3. $\dfrac{26x^3y^2}{39xy^4}$

4. $\dfrac{x^2 - 2x - 35}{x^2 - x - 42}$

5. $\dfrac{2x^2 - 5x + 3}{3x^2 + 2x - 5}$

6. $\dfrac{ax + 2a - bx - 2b}{3x^2 - 12}$

7. $\dfrac{4x^2 - 1}{x^2 - 4} \cdot \dfrac{2x^2 + 4x}{4x + 2}$

8. $\dfrac{3y}{4xy - 6y^2} \cdot \dfrac{2x - 3y}{12xy}$

9. $\dfrac{y^2 + 8y - 20}{y^2 + 6y - 16} \cdot \dfrac{y^2 + 3y - 40}{y^2 + 6y - 40}$

10. $\dfrac{3x^3y}{x^2 + 7x + 12} \cdot \dfrac{x^2 + 8x + 15}{6xy^2}$

11. $\dfrac{2x + 12}{3x - 15} \div \dfrac{2x^2 - 6x - 20}{x^2 - 10x + 25}$

12. $\dfrac{6x^2 - 6a^2}{3x^2 + 3} \div \dfrac{x^4 - a^4}{a^2x^2 + a^2}$

13. $\dfrac{9y^2 - 3y - 2}{6y^2 - 13y - 5} \div \dfrac{3y^2 + 10y - 8}{2y^2 + 13y + 20}$

14. $\dfrac{4a^2 + 12a + 5}{2a^2 - 7a - 13} \div (4a^2 + 2a)$

Add or subtract the rational expressions and simplify your answers.

15. $\dfrac{x - 5}{2x + 1} - \dfrac{x + 1}{x - 2}$

16. $\dfrac{5}{4x} + \dfrac{-3}{x + 4}$

17. $\dfrac{2y - 1}{12y} - \dfrac{3y + 2}{9y}$

18. $\dfrac{4}{y + 5} + \dfrac{3y + 2}{y^2 - 25}$

19. $\dfrac{4y}{y^2 + 2y + 1} + \dfrac{3}{y^2 - 1}$

20. $\dfrac{y^2 - 4y - 19}{y^2 + 8y + 15} - \dfrac{2y - 3}{y + 5}$

21. $\dfrac{a}{5 - a} - \dfrac{2}{a + 3} + \dfrac{2a^2 - 2a}{a^2 - 2a - 15}$

22. $\dfrac{5}{a^2 + 3a + 2} + \dfrac{6}{a^2 + 4a + 3} - \dfrac{7}{a^2 + 5a + 6}$

23. $4a + 3 - \dfrac{2a + 1}{a + 4}$

24. $\dfrac{1}{x} + \dfrac{3}{2x} + 3 + 2x$

Simplify the complex rational expressions.

25. $\dfrac{\dfrac{5}{x} + 1}{1 - \dfrac{25}{x^2}}$

26. $\dfrac{\dfrac{4}{x + 3}}{\dfrac{2}{x - 2} - \dfrac{1}{x^2 + x - 6}}$

27. $\dfrac{\dfrac{y}{y + 1} + \dfrac{1}{y}}{\dfrac{y}{y + 1} - \dfrac{1}{y}}$

28. $\dfrac{\dfrac{10}{a + 2} - 5}{\dfrac{4}{a + 2} - 2}$

29. $\dfrac{\dfrac{2}{x + 4} - \dfrac{1}{x^2 + 4x}}{\dfrac{3}{2x + 8}}$

30. $\dfrac{\dfrac{y^2}{y^2 - x^2} - 1}{x + \dfrac{xy}{x - y}}$

31. $\dfrac{\dfrac{2x + 1}{x - 1}}{1 + \dfrac{x}{x + 1}}$

32. $\dfrac{\dfrac{3}{x} - \dfrac{2}{x + 1}}{\dfrac{5}{x^2 + 5x + 4} - \dfrac{1}{x + 4}}$

Solve for the variable and check your solutions. If there is no solution, say so.

33. $\frac{3}{2} = 1 - \frac{1}{x - 1}$

34. $\frac{3}{7} + \frac{4}{x + 1} = 1$

35. $\frac{3}{x - 2} + \frac{8}{x + 3} = \frac{6}{x - 2}$

36. $\frac{1}{x + 2} - \frac{1}{x} = \frac{-2}{x}$

37. $\frac{5}{2a} = \frac{2}{a} - \frac{1}{12}$

38. $\frac{1}{2a} = \frac{2}{a} - \frac{3}{10}$

39. $\frac{1}{y} + \frac{1}{2y} = 2$

40. $\frac{5}{y^2} + \frac{7}{y} = \frac{6}{y^2}$

41. $\frac{a + 2}{2a + 6} = \frac{3}{2} - \frac{3}{a + 3}$

42. $\frac{5}{a + 5} + \frac{a + 4}{2a + 10} = \frac{3}{2}$

43. $\frac{1}{x + 2} - \frac{5}{x - 2} = \frac{-15}{x^2 - 4}$

44. $\frac{y + 1}{y^2 + 2y - 3} - \frac{1}{y + 3} = \frac{1}{y - 1}$

Solve for the variable indicated.

45. $\frac{N}{V} = \frac{m}{M + N}$; for M

46. $m = \frac{y - y_0}{x - x_0}$; for x

47. $\frac{1}{f} = \frac{1}{a} + \frac{1}{b}$; for a

48. $S = \frac{V_1 t + V_2 t}{2}$; for t

49. $d = \frac{LR_2}{R_2 + R_1}$; for R_2

50. $\frac{S - P}{Pr} = t$; for r

Solve the following exercises. If necessary, round your answers to the nearest hundredth.

51. The campus bookstore at Boston University ordered 253 scientific and graphing calculators for the spring semester. For every seven scientific calculators they ordered they also ordered four graphing calculators. How many scientific calculators did they order? How many graphing calculators did they order?

52. Walter Johnson built a new development of 112 homes in Naperville, Illinois. For every three one-story homes, he built thirteen two-story homes. How many one-story homes did he build? How many two-story homes did he build?

▲ **53.** Jill VanderWoude decided to enlarge a photograph that measures 5 inches wide and 7 inches long into a poster-size photograph with a perimeter of 168 inches. The new photograph will maintain the same width-to-length ratio. How wide will the enlarged photograph be? How long will the enlarged photograph be?

54. How long will it take a pump to empty a 4900-gallon pool if the same pump can empty a 3500-gallon pool in 4 hours?

55. In a sanctuary a sample of one hundred wild rabbits is tagged and released by the wildlife management team. In a few weeks, after they have mixed with the general rabbit population, a sample of forty rabbits is caught, and eight have a tag. Estimate the population of rabbits in the sanctuary.

56. The ratio of officers to state troopers is 2:9 If there are 154 men and women on the force, how many are officers?

57. The scale on a maritime sailing chart shows that 2 centimeters is equivalent to 7 nautical miles. A boat captain lays out a course on the chart that is 3.5 cm long. How many nautical miles will this be?

▲ **58.** A 7-foot-tall tree casts a shadow that is 6 feet long. At the same time of day, a building casts a shadow that is 156 feet long. How tall is the building?

59. If the hot water faucet at Mike's house is left on, it takes 15 minutes to fill the jacuzzi. If the cold water faucet is left on, it takes 10 minutes to fill the jacuzzi. How many minutes would it take if both faucets are left on?

60. In the summer it takes Dominic 12 hours to paint the barn. It takes his young son 18 hours to paint the barn. How many hours would it take if they both worked together?

The growth in instant messenger e-mail has been more rapid in the last few years than the growth of regular e-mail.

The bar graph below shows the growth in usage of instant messenger e-mail. Use this bar graph to answer Exercises 61–64. Round all answers to the nearest million.

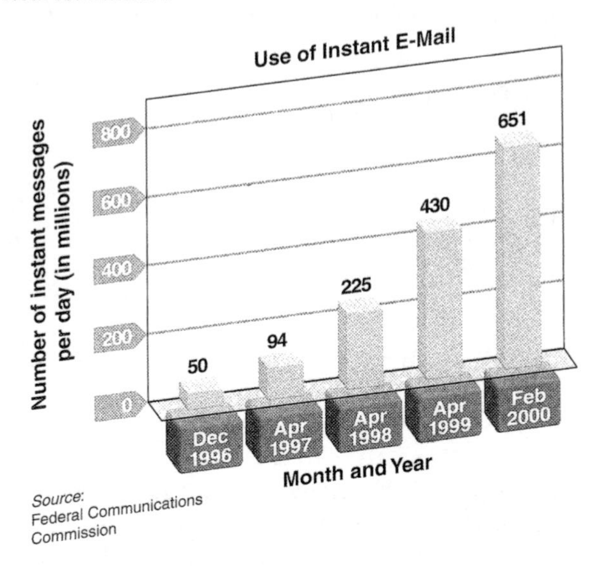

61. If the increase in usage per month that occurred over the period from April 1999 to February 2000 continues at the same increase per month, what would be the expected number of daily instant messages in July 2001?

62. If the increase in usage per month that occurred from April 1999 to February 2000 is proportional to the increase in usage from February 2000 to December 2000, what would be the expected number of daily instant messages in December 2000?

63. If the increase in usage per month that occurred from April 1999 to February 2000 is one half as great as the increase in usage from February 2000 to December 2000, what would be the expected number of daily instant messages in December 2000?

64. If the increase in usage per month that occurred from April 1997 to April 1999 is double the increase in usage from April 1999 to April 2001, what would be the expected number of daily instant messages in April 2001?

Chapter 6 Test

1. ______

2. ______

3. ______

4. ______

5. ______

6. ______

7. ______

8. ______

9. ______

10. ______

11. ______

12. ______

13. ______

14. ______

15. ______

16. ______

Simplify.

1. $\dfrac{x^3 + 3x^2 + 2x}{x^3 - 2x^2 - 3x}$

2. $\dfrac{y^3 + 8}{y^2 - 4}$

3. $\dfrac{2y^2 + 7y - 4}{y^2 + 2y - 8} \cdot \dfrac{2y^2 - 8}{3y^2 + 11y + 10}$

4. $\dfrac{4 - 2x}{3x^2 - 2x - 8} \div \dfrac{2x^2 + x - 1}{9x + 12}$

5. $\dfrac{3x + 8}{x^2 - 25} - \dfrac{5}{x - 5}$

6. $\dfrac{2}{x^2 + 5x + 6} + \dfrac{3x}{x^2 + 6x + 9}$

7. $\dfrac{\dfrac{4}{y + 2} - 2}{5 - \dfrac{10}{y + 2}}$

8. $\dfrac{\dfrac{1}{x} - \dfrac{3}{x + 2}}{\dfrac{2}{x^2 + 2x}}$

Solve for the variable and check your answers. If no solution exists, say so.

9. $\dfrac{7}{4} = \dfrac{x + 4}{x}$

10. $2 + \dfrac{x}{x + 4} = \dfrac{3x}{x - 4}$

11. $\dfrac{1}{2y + 4} - \dfrac{1}{6} = \dfrac{-2}{3y + 6}$

12. $\dfrac{3}{2x + 3} - \dfrac{1}{2x - 3} = \dfrac{2}{4x^2 - 9}$

13. Solve for W: $h = \dfrac{S - 2WL}{2W + 2L}$

14. Solve for b: $\dfrac{4}{a} = \dfrac{3}{b} + \dfrac{2}{c}$

15. A total of 286 employees at Kaiser Telecommunication Systems were eligible this year for a high-performance bonus. The company president announced that for every three employees who got the bonus, nineteen employees did not. If the president was correct, how many employees got the high-performance bonus? How many did not get the high-performance bonus?

▲ **16.** The Newbury Elementary School had a rectangular playground that measured 500 feet wide and 850 feet long. When the school had a major addition to its property, it was decided to increase the playground to a large rectangular shape with the same proportional ratio that had a perimeter of 8100 feet. What is the width and the length of the new playground?

Cumulative Test for Chapters 1–6

Approximately one half of this test covers the content of Chapters 1–5. The remainder covers the content of Chapter 6.

1. ______
2. ______
3. ______
4. ______
5. ______
6. ______
7. ______
8. ______
9. ______
10. ______
11. ______
12. ______

1. Simplify $\left(\frac{3x^{-2}y^{3}}{z^{4}}\right)^{-2}$.

2. Solve for x: $\frac{2}{3}(3x - 1) = \frac{2}{5}x + 3$

3. Graph the straight line $-6x + 2y = -12$.

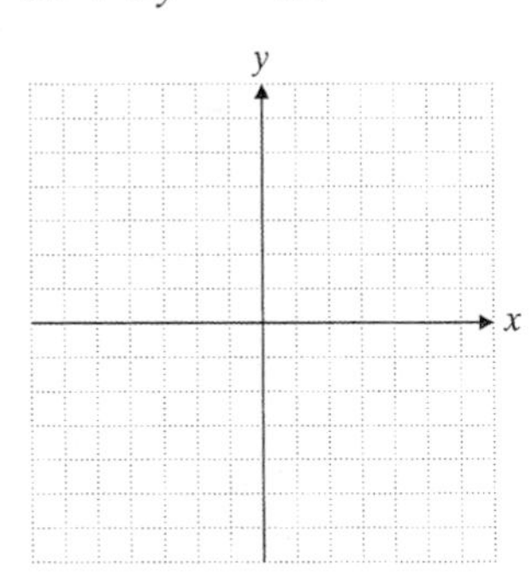

4. Find the standard form of the equation of the line parallel to $5x - 6y = 8$ that passes through $(-1, -3)$.

5. Brenda invested \$7000 in two accounts at the bank. One account earns 5% simple interest. The other earns 8% simple interest. She earned \$539 interest in 1 year. How much was invested at each rate?

6. Solve for x and graph. $3(2 - 6x) > 4(x + 1) + 24$

−3 −2 −1 0 1 2 3

7. Evaluate $2x^2 - 3x - 4y^2$ when $x = -2$ and $y = 3$.

8. Solve for x: $|3x - 4| \leq 10$

Factor.

9. $8x^3 - 125y^3$

10. $81x^3 - 90x^2y + 25xy^2$

Solve for x.

11. $x^2 + 20x + 36 = 0$

12. $3x^2 - 11x - 4 = 0$

Simplify.

13. ______

13. $\dfrac{7x^2 - 28}{x^2 + 6x + 8}$

14. ______

14. $\dfrac{2x^2 + x - 1}{2x^2 - 9x + 4} \cdot \dfrac{3x^2 - 12x}{6x + 15}$

15. $\dfrac{x^3 + 27}{x^2 + 7x + 12} \div \dfrac{x^2 - 6x + 9}{2x^2 + 13x + 20}$

15. ______

16. $\dfrac{5}{2x - 8} - \dfrac{3x}{x^2 - 9x + 20}$

16. ______

17. $\dfrac{\dfrac{1}{2x + 1} + 1}{4 - \dfrac{3}{4x^2 - 1}}$

17. ______

18. $\dfrac{3}{x - 6} + \dfrac{4}{x + 4}$

18. ______

Solve for the variable and check your answers.

19. ______

19. $\dfrac{1}{2x + 3} - \dfrac{4}{4x^2 - 9} = \dfrac{3}{2x - 3}$

20. ______

20. $\dfrac{1}{4x} - \dfrac{3}{2x} = \dfrac{5}{8}$

21. Solve for b: $H = \dfrac{3b + 2x}{5 - 4b}$

21. ______

22. The mayor of Chicago decided that in the coming year the city police force should be deployed in a particular ratio. He decided that for every three police officers who patrol on foot, there should be eleven police officers patrolling in squad cars. If 3234 police officers are normally on duty during the day, how many are patrolling on foot, and how many are patrolling in squad cars?

22. ______

Chapter 7

Rational Exponents and Radicals

You have probably seen a picture of a sailor standing in the crow's nest of a tall sailing ship and looking out over the horizon. Do you have any idea how far that sailor is able to see? Do you know that the distance can be estimated with a mathematical equation that sailors have used for over 200 years? Turn to the Putting Your Skills to Work exercises on page 415 to find out how this is done.

Pretest Chapter 7

1. ____________________

2. ____________________

3. ____________________

4. ____________________

5. ____________________

6. ____________________

7. ____________________

8. ____________________

9. ____________________

10. ____________________

11. ____________________

12. ____________________

13. ____________________

14. ____________________

15. ____________________

16. ____________________

17. ____________________

18. ____________________

19. ____________________

20. ____________________

If you are familiar with the topics in this chapter, take this test now. Check your answers with those in the back of the book. If an answer is wrong or you can't do an exercise, study the appropriate section of the chapter.

If you are not familiar with the topics in this chapter, don't take this test now. Instead, study the examples, work the practice exercises, and then take the test.

This test will help you identify those concepts that you have mastered and those that need more study.

Section 7.1

1. Multiply and simplify your answer. $(-3x^{1/4}y^{1/2})(-2x^{-1/2}y^{1/3})$

Simplify.

2. $(-4x^{-1/4}y^{1/3})^3$

3. $\dfrac{-18x^{-2}y^2}{-3x^{-5}y^{1/3}}$

4. $\left(\dfrac{27x^2y^{-5}}{x^{-4}y^4}\right)^{2/3}$

Section 7.2

Evaluate.

5. $27^{-4/3}$

6. $\sqrt{169} + \sqrt[3]{-64}$

7. $\sqrt[3]{27a^{12}b^6c^{15}}$

Section 7.3

8. Simplify $\sqrt[4]{32x^8y^{15}}$.

9. Combine like terms where possible. $3\sqrt{48y^3} - 2\sqrt[3]{16} + 3\sqrt[3]{54} - 5y\sqrt{12y}$

Section 7.4

10. Multiply and simplify $(3\sqrt{3} - 5\sqrt{6})(\sqrt{12} - 3\sqrt{6})$.

11. Rationalize the denominator and simplify your answer. $\dfrac{6}{\sqrt[3]{9x}}$

12. Rationalize the denominator and simplify your answer. $\dfrac{\sqrt{2} + \sqrt{3}}{\sqrt{2} - \sqrt{3}}$

Section 7.5

Solve and check your solution(s).

13. $\sqrt{3x + 4} + 2 = x$

14. $\sqrt{2x + 3} - \sqrt{x - 2} = 2$

Section 7.6

Perform the operations indicated.

15. $(3 - 2i) - (-1 + 3i)$

16. $i^{15} + \sqrt{-25}$

17. $(3 + 5i)^2$

18. $\dfrac{3 + 2i}{2 + 3i}$

Section 7.7

19. If y varies directly with x^2, and $y = 18$ when $x = 3$, find the value of y when $x = 5$.

20. If y varies inversely with x, and $y = 12$ when $x = 6$, find the value of y when $x = 10$.

7.1 Rational Exponents

 Simplifying Expressions with Rational Exponents

Student Learning Objectives

After studying this section, you will be able to apply the laws of exponents to:

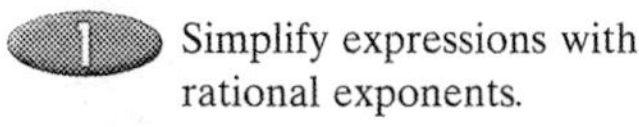

1. Simplify expressions with rational exponents.
2. Add expressions with rational exponents.
3. Factor expressions with rational exponents.

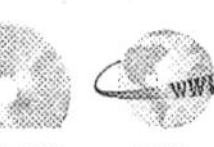

SSM PH TUTOR CENTER CD & VIDEO MATH PRO WEB

Before studying this section, you may need to review Section 1.4. For convenience, we list the rules of exponents that we learned there.

$$x^m x^n = x^{m+n} \qquad x^0 = 1$$

$$\frac{x^m}{x^n} = x^{m-n} \qquad (x^m)^n = x^{mn}$$

$$x^{-n} = \frac{1}{x^n} \qquad (xy)^n = x^n y^n$$

$$\frac{x^{-n}}{y^{-m}} = \frac{y^m}{x^n} \qquad \left(\frac{x}{y}\right)^n = \frac{x^n}{y^n}$$

To ensure that you understand these rules, study Example 1 carefully and work Practice Problem 1.

EXAMPLE 1 Simplify $\left(\frac{5xy^{-3}}{2x^{-4}y}\right)^{-2}$.

$$\begin{aligned}
\left(\frac{5xy^{-3}}{2x^{-4}y}\right)^{-2} &= \frac{(5xy^{-3})^{-2}}{(2x^{-4}y)^{-2}} && \left(\frac{x}{y}\right)^n = \frac{x^n}{y^n}. \\
&= \frac{5^{-2}x^{-2}(y^{-3})^{-2}}{2^{-2}(x^{-4})^{-2}y^{-2}} && (xy)^n = x^n y^n. \\
&= \frac{5^{-2}x^{-2}y^6}{2^{-2}x^8y^{-2}} && (x^m)^n = x^{mn}. \\
&= \frac{5^{-2}}{2^{-2}} \cdot \frac{x^{-2}}{x^8} \cdot \frac{y^6}{y^{-2}} \\
&= \frac{2^2}{5^2} \cdot x^{-2-8} \cdot y^{6+2} && \frac{x^{-n}}{y^{-m}} = \frac{y^m}{x^n}; \frac{x^m}{x^n} = x^{m-n}. \\
&= \frac{4}{25}x^{-10}y^8
\end{aligned}$$

The answer can also be written as $\frac{4y^8}{25x^{10}}$. Explain why.

Practice Problem 1 Simplify $\left(\frac{3x^{-2}y^4}{2x^{-5}y^2}\right)^{-3}$.

Sidelight Deciding when to use the rule $\frac{x^{-n}}{y^{-m}} = \frac{y^m}{x^n}$ is entirely up to you. In Example 1, we could have begun by writing

$$\left(\frac{5xy^{-3}}{2x^{-4}y}\right)^{-2} = \left(\frac{5x \cdot x^4}{2y \cdot y^3}\right)^{-2} = \left(\frac{5x^5}{2y^4}\right)^{-2}.$$

Complete the steps to simplify this expression.

Likewise, in the fourth step in Example 1, we could have written

$$\frac{5^{-2}x^{-2}y^6}{2^{-2}x^8y^{-2}} = \frac{2^2y^6y^2}{5^2x^8x^2}.$$

Complete the steps to simplify this expression. Are the two answers the same as the answer in Example 1? Why or why not?

We generally begin to simplify a rational expression with exponents by raising a power to a power because sometimes negative powers become positive. The order in which you use the rules of exponents is up to you. Work carefully. Keep track of your exponents and where you are as you simplify the rational expression.

These rules for exponents can also be extended to include rational exponents—that is, exponents that are fractions. As you recall, rational numbers are of the form $\frac{a}{b}$, where a and b are integers and b does not equal zero. We will write fractional exponents using diagonal lines. Thus, we will write $\frac{5}{6}$ as $5/6$ and $\frac{a}{b}$ as a/b throughout this chapter when writing fractional exponents. For now we restrict the base to *positive* real numbers. Later we will talk about negative bases.

EXAMPLE 2 Simplify.

(a) $(x^{2/3})^4$ **(b)** $\dfrac{x^{5/6}}{x^{1/6}}$ **(c)** $x^{2/3} \cdot x^{-1/3}$ **(d)** $5^{3/7} \cdot 5^{2/7}$

We will not write out every step or every rule of exponents that we use. You should be able to follow the solutions.

(a) $(x^{2/3})^4 = x^{(2/3)(4/1)} = x^{8/3}$ **(b)** $\dfrac{x^{5/6}}{x^{1/6}} = x^{5/6-1/6} = x^{4/6} = x^{2/3}$

(c) $x^{2/3} \cdot x^{-1/3} = x^{2/3-1/3} = x^{1/3}$ **(d)** $5^{3/7} \cdot 5^{2/7} = 5^{3/7+2/7} = 5^{5/7}$

Practice Problem 2 Simplify.

(a) $(x^4)^{3/8}$ **(b)** $\dfrac{x^{3/7}}{x^{2/7}}$ **(c)** $x^{-7/5} \cdot x^{4/5}$

Sometimes fractional exponents will not have the same denominator. Remember that you need to change the fractions to equivalent fractions with the same denominator when the rule of exponents requires you to add or to subtract them.

EXAMPLE 3 Simplify. Express your answers with positive exponents only.

(a) $(2x^{1/2})(3x^{1/3})$ **(b)** $\dfrac{18x^{1/4}y^{-1/3}}{-6x^{-1/2}y^{1/6}}$

(a) $(2x^{1/2})(3x^{1/3}) = 6x^{1/2+1/3} = 6x^{3/6+2/6} = 6x^{5/6}$

(b)
$$\begin{aligned}\frac{18x^{1/4}y^{-1/3}}{-6x^{-1/2}y^{1/6}} &= -3x^{1/4-(-1/2)}y^{-1/3-1/6}\\ &= -3x^{1/4+2/4}y^{-2/6-1/6}\\ &= -3x^{3/4}y^{-3/6}\\ &= -3x^{3/4}y^{-1/2}\\ &= \frac{-3x^{3/4}}{y^{1/2}}\end{aligned}$$

Practice Problem 3 Simplify. Express your answers with positive exponents only.

(a) $(-3x^{1/4})(2x^{1/2})$ **(b)** $\dfrac{13x^{1/12}y^{-1/4}}{26x^{-1/3}y^{1/2}}$

EXAMPLE 4 Multiply and simplify $-2x^{5/6}(3x^{1/2} - 4x^{-1/3})$.

We will need to be very careful when we add the exponents for x as we use the distributive property. Study each step of the following example. Be sure you understand each operation.

$$\begin{aligned} -2x^{5/6}(3x^{1/2} - 4x^{-1/3}) &= -6x^{5/6+1/2} + 8x^{5/6-1/3} \\ &= -6x^{5/6+3/6} + 8x^{5/6-2/6} \\ &= -6x^{8/6} + 8x^{3/6} \\ &= -6x^{4/3} + 8x^{1/2} \end{aligned}$$

Practice Problem 4 Multiply and simplify $-3x^{1/2}(2x^{1/4} + 3x^{-1/2})$.

Sometimes we can use the rules of exponents to simplify numerical values raised to rational powers.

EXAMPLE 5 Evaluate: **(a)** $(25)^{3/2}$ **(b)** $(27)^{2/3}$

(a) $(25)^{3/2} = (5^2)^{3/2} = 5^{2/1 \cdot 3/2} = 5^3 = 125$

(b) $(27)^{2/3} = (3^3)^{2/3} = 3^{3/1 \cdot 2/3} = 3^2 = 9$

Practice Problem 5 Evaluate: **(a)** $(4)^{5/2}$ **(b)** $(27)^{4/3}$

2 Adding Expressions with Rational Exponents

Adding expressions with rational exponents may require several steps. Sometimes this involves removing negative exponents. For example, to add $2x^{-1/2} + x^{1/2}$, we begin by writing $2x^{-1/2}$ as $\frac{2}{x^{1/2}}$. This is a rational expression. Recall that to add rational expressions we need to have a common denominator. Take time to look at the steps needed to write $2x^{-1/2} + x^{1/2}$ as one term.

EXAMPLE 6 Write as one fraction with positive exponents. $2x^{-1/2} + x^{1/2}$

$$2x^{-1/2} + x^{1/2} = \frac{2}{x^{1/2}} + \frac{x^{1/2} \cdot x^{1/2}}{x^{1/2}} = \frac{2}{x^{1/2}} + \frac{x^1}{x^{1/2}} = \frac{2 + x}{x^{1/2}}$$

Practice Problem 6 Write as one fraction with only positive exponents. $3x^{1/3} + x^{-1/3}$

3 Factoring Expressions with Rational Exponents

To factor expressions, we need to be able to recognize common factors. If the terms of the expression contain exponents, we look for the same exponential factor in each term. For example, in the expression $6x^5 + 4x^3 - 8x^2$, the common factor of each term is $2x^2$. Thus, we can factor out the common factor $2x^2$ from each term. The expression then becomes $2x^2(3x^3 + 2x - 4)$.

We do exactly the same thing when we factor expressions with rational exponents. The key is to identify the exponent of the common factor. In the expression $6x^{3/4} + 4x^{1/2} - 8x^{1/4}$, the common factor is $2x^{1/4}$. Thus, we factor the expression $6x^{3/4} + 4x^{1/2} - 8x^{1/4}$ as $2x^{1/4}(3x^{1/2} + 2x^{1/4} - 4)$. We do not always need to factor out the greatest common factor. In the following examples we simply factor out a common factor.

EXAMPLE 7 Factor out the common factor of $2x$ from $2x^{3/2} + 4x^{5/2}$.

We rewrite the exponent of each term so that we can see that each term contains the factor $2x$ or $2x^{2/2}$.

$$\begin{aligned} 2x^{3/2} + 4x^{5/2} &= 2x^{2/2+1/2} + 4x^{2/2+3/2} \\ &= 2(x^{2/2})(x^{1/2}) + 4(x^{2/2})(x^{3/2}) \\ &= 2x(x^{1/2} + 2x^{3/2}) \end{aligned}$$

Practice Problem 7 Factor out the common factor of $4y$ from $4y^{3/2} - 8y^{5/2}$.

For convenience we list here the properties of exponents that we have discussed in this section, as well as the property $x^0 = 1$.

When x and y are **positive real numbers** and a and b are **rational numbers**:

$$x^a x^b = x^{a+b} \qquad \frac{x^a}{x^b} = x^{a-b} \qquad x^0 = 1$$

$$x^{-a} = \frac{1}{x^a} \qquad \frac{x^{-a}}{y^{-b}} = \frac{y^b}{x^a}$$

$$(x^a)^b = x^{ab} \qquad (xy)^a = x^a y^a \qquad \left(\frac{x}{y}\right)^a = \frac{x^a}{y^a}$$

7.1 Exercises

Simplify.

1. $\left(\frac{4x^2y^{-3}}{x}\right)^2$ **2.** $\left(\frac{3xy^{-2}}{x^3}\right)^2$ **3.** $\left(\frac{2a^{-1}b^3}{-3b^2}\right)^3$ **4.** $\left(\frac{-a^{-2}b}{5b^2}\right)^2$

5. $(x^{3/4})^2$ **6.** $(x^{4/3})^6$ **7.** $(y^{12})^{2/3}$ **8.** $(y^2)^{5/2}$

9. $\frac{x^{7/12}}{x^{1/12}}$ **10.** $\frac{x^{7/8}}{x^{3/8}}$ **11.** $\frac{x^3}{x^{1/2}}$ **12.** $\frac{x^2}{x^{1/3}}$

13. $x^{1/7} \cdot x^{3/7}$ **14.** $x^{3/5} \cdot x^{1/5}$ **15.** $y^{3/5} \cdot y^{-1/10}$ **16.** $y^{7/10} \cdot y^{-1/5}$

Write each expression with positive exponents.

17. $x^{-3/4}$ **18.** $x^{-5/6}$ **19.** $a^{-5/6}b^{1/3}$ **20.** $2a^{-1/6}b^{3/4}$

21. $6^{-1/2}$ **22.** $4^{-1/3}$ **23.** $2a^{-1/4}$ **24.** $3^{-2/5} \cdot 2^{1/3}$

Mixed Practice

Simplify and express your answers with positive exponents. Evaluate or simplify the numerical expressions.

25. $(x^{1/2}y^{1/3})(x^{1/3}y^{2/3})$ **26.** $(x^{-1/3}y^{2/3})(x^{1/3}y^{1/4})$ **27.** $(7x^{1/3}y^{1/4})(-2x^{1/4}y^{-1/6})$

28. $(8x^{-1/5}y^{1/3})(-3x^{-1/4}y^{1/6})$ **29.** $6^2 \cdot 6^{-2/3}$ **30.** $11^{1/2} \cdot 11^3$

31. $\frac{2x^{1/5}}{x^{-1/2}}$ **32.** $\frac{3y^{2/3}}{y^{-1/4}}$ **33.** $\frac{-20x^2y^{-1/5}}{5x^{-1/2}y}$

34. $\frac{12x^{-2/3}y}{-6xy^{-3/4}}$ **35.** $\left(\frac{8a^2b^6}{a^{-1}b^3}\right)^{1/3}$ **36.** $\left(\frac{16a^5b^{-2}}{a^{-1}b^{-6}}\right)^{1/2}$

37. $(-3x^{2/5}y^{3/2}z^{1/3})^2$

38. $(5x^{-1/2}y^{1/3}z^{4/5})^3$

39. $x^{2/3}(x^{4/3} - x^{1/5})$

40. $y^{-2/3}(y^{2/3} + y^{3/2})$

41. $m^{7/8}(m^{-1/2} + 2m)$

42. $\dfrac{(x^{-1/6}x)^{3/2}}{x^2}$

43. $\dfrac{(x^2 \cdot x^{-3/2})^{1/2}}{x^{1/2}}$

44. $(25)^{1/2}$

45. $(27)^{2/3}$

46. $(16)^{3/4}$

47. $(4)^{3/2}$

48. $9^{3/2} + 4^{1/2}$

49. $(81)^{3/4} + (25)^{1/2}$

Write each expression as one fraction with positive exponents.

50. $3y^{1/2} + y^{-1/2}$

51. $2y^{1/3} + y^{-2/3}$

52. $x^{-1/3} + 6^{4/3}$

53. $5^{-1/4} + x^{-1/2}$

Factor out the common factor of 2a.

54. $10a^{5/4} - 4a^{8/5}$

55. $6a^{4/3} - 8a^{3/2}$

To Think About

56. What is the value of a if $x^a \cdot x^{1/4} = x^{-1/8}$?

57. What is the value of b if $x^b \div x^{1/3} = x^{-1/12}$?

Applications

The radius needed to create a sphere with a given volume V can be approximated by the equation $r = 0.62(V)^{1/3}$ *Find the radius of the spheres with the following volumes.*

▲ **58.** 27 cubic meters

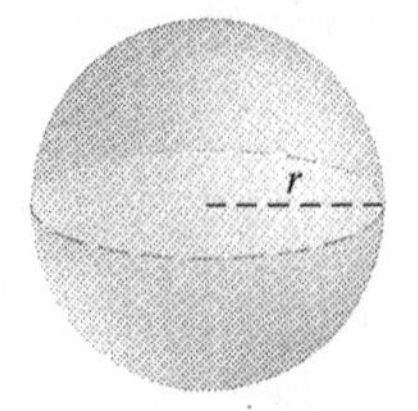

▲ **59.** 64 cubic meters

The radius required for a cone to have a volume V and a height h is given by the equation

$$r = \left(\frac{3V}{\pi h}\right)^{1/2}$$

Find the necessary radius to have a cone with the properties below. Use $\pi \approx 3.14$.

▲ **60.** $V = 314$ cubic feet and $h = 12$ feet.

▲ **61.** $V = 3140$ cubic feet and $h = 30$ feet.

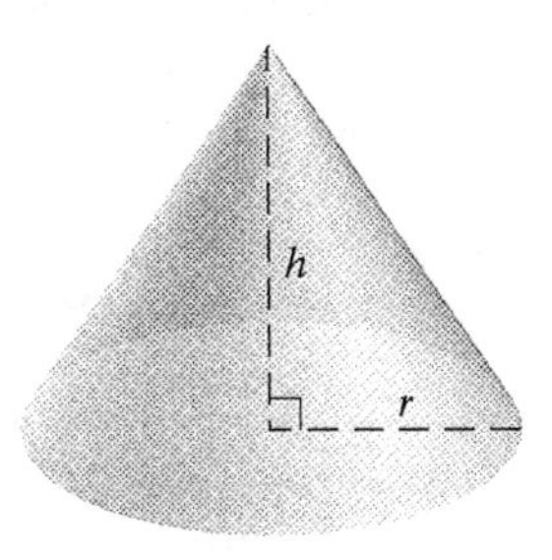

Cumulative Review Problems

Solve for x.

62. $-4(x + 1) = \frac{1}{3}(3 - 2x)$

Solve for b.

63. $A = \frac{h}{2}(a + b)$

Giving a young patient the wrong amount of medication can have serious and even fatal consequences. A formula used by doctors, nurses, and pharmacists to verify the correct dosage of a prescription drug for a child is

$$y = \frac{ax}{a + 12},$$

where y = the child dosage, x = the adult dosage, and a = the age of the child in years.

64. If the adult dosage of a medication is 400 milligrams, how much should a 7-year-old child receive? Round your answer to the nearest milligram.

65. The adult dosage of a medication is 250 milligrams, and a certain child was assigned the correct dosage level of 75 milligrams. How old was the child? Round your answer to the nearest year.

7.2 Radical Expressions and Functions

Student Learning Objectives

After studying this section, you will be able to:

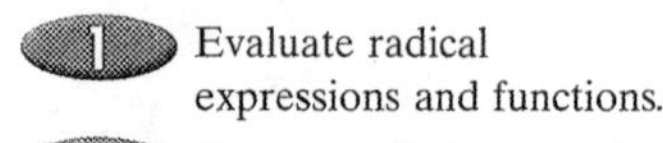

1. Evaluate radical expressions and functions.

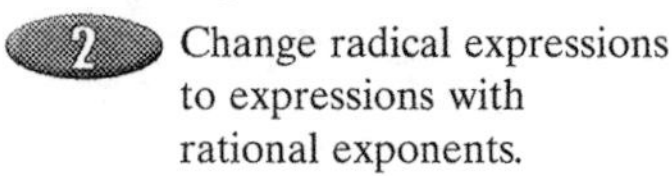

2. Change radical expressions to expressions with rational exponents.

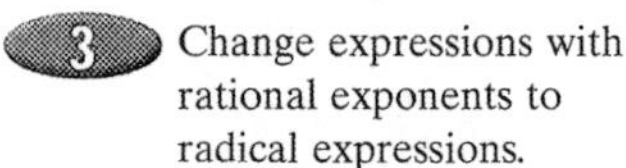

3. Change expressions with rational exponents to radical expressions.
4. Evaluate higher-order radicals containing a variable radicand that represents any real number (including a negative real number).

SSM PH TUTOR CENTER CD & VIDEO MATH PRO WEB

1 Evaluating Radical Expressions and Functions

In Section 1.3 we studied simple radical expressions called square roots. The **square root** of a number is a value that when multiplied by itself is equal to the original number. That is, since $3 \cdot 3 = 9$, 3 is a square root of 9. But $(-3) \cdot (-3) = 9$, so -3 is also a square root. We call the positive square root the **principal square root**.

The symbol $\sqrt{\ }$ is called a **radical sign**. We use it to denote positive square roots (and positive higher-order roots also). A negative square root is written $-\sqrt{\ }$. Thus, we have the following:

$$\sqrt{9} = 3 \qquad \sqrt{9} = 3 \qquad -\sqrt{9} = -3$$
$$\sqrt{64} = 8 \qquad \sqrt{64} = 8 \qquad \text{(because } 8 \cdot 8 = 64)$$
$$\sqrt{121} = 11 \qquad \sqrt{121} = 11 \qquad \text{(because } 11 \cdot 11 = 121)$$

Because $\sqrt{9} = \sqrt{3 \cdot 3} = \sqrt{3^2} = 3$, we can say the following:

Definition of Square Root

If x is a nonnegative real number, then $\sqrt{x}$ is the *nonnegative* (or principal) *square root* of x; in other words, $(\sqrt{x})^2 = x$.

Note that x must be *nonnegative*. Why? Suppose we want to find $\sqrt{-36}$. We must find a number that when multiplied by itself gives -36. Is there one? No, because

$$6 \cdot 6 = 36 \quad \text{and}$$
$$(-6)(-6) = 36.$$

So there is no real number that we can square to get -36.

We call $\sqrt[n]{x}$ a **radical expression**. The $\sqrt{\ }$ symbol is the radical sign, the x is the **radicand**, and the n is the **index** of the radical. When no number for n appears in the radical expression, it is understood that 2 is the index, which means that we are looking for the square root. For example, in the radical expression $\sqrt{25}$, with no number given for the index n we take the index to be 2. Thus, $\sqrt{25}$ is the principal square root of 25.

We can extend the notion of square root to **higher-order roots**, such as cube roots, fourth roots, and so on. A **cube root** of a number is a value that when cubed is equal to the original number. The index n of the radical is 3, and the radical used is $\sqrt[3]{\ }$. Similarly, a **fourth root** of a number is a value that when raised to the fourth power is equal to the original number. The index n of the radical is 4, and the radical used is $\sqrt[4]{\ }$. Thus, we have the following:

$$\sqrt[3]{27} = 3 \qquad \text{because } 3 \cdot 3 \cdot 3 = 3^3 = 27.$$
$$\sqrt[3]{8} = 2 \qquad \text{because } 2 \cdot 2 \cdot 2 = 2^3 = 8.$$
$$\sqrt[4]{81} = 3 \qquad \text{because } 3 \cdot 3 \cdot 3 \cdot 3 = 3^4 = 81.$$
$$\sqrt[5]{32} = 2 \qquad \text{because } 2 \cdot 2 \cdot 2 \cdot 2 \cdot 2 = 2^5 = 32.$$
$$\sqrt[3]{-64} = -4 \qquad \text{because } (-4)(-4)(-4) = (-4)^3 = -64.$$

You should be able to see a pattern here.

$$\sqrt[3]{27} = \sqrt[3]{3^3} = 3$$
$$\sqrt[4]{81} = \sqrt[4]{3^4} = 3$$
$$\sqrt[5]{32} = \sqrt[5]{2^5} = 2$$
$$\sqrt[6]{729} = \sqrt[6]{3^6} = 3$$
$$\sqrt[3]{-64} = \sqrt[3]{(-4)^3} = -4$$

In these cases, we see that $\sqrt[n]{x^n} = x$. We now give the following definition.

Definition of Higher-Order Roots

1. If x is a *nonnegative* real number, then $\sqrt[n]{x}$ is a nonnegative nth root and has the property that

$$(\sqrt[n]{x})^n = x.$$

2. If x is a *negative* real number, then
   (a) $(\sqrt[n]{x})^n = x$ when n is an *odd integer.*
   (b) $(\sqrt[n]{x})^n$ is *not* a real number when n is an *even integer.*

EXAMPLE 1 If possible, find the root of each negative number. If there is no real number root, say so.

(a) $\sqrt[3]{-216}$ **(b)** $\sqrt[5]{-32}$ **(c)** $\sqrt[4]{-16}$ **(d)** $\sqrt[6]{-64}$

(a) $\sqrt[3]{-216} = \sqrt[3]{(-6)^3} = -6$ **(b)** $\sqrt[5]{-32} = \sqrt[5]{(-2)^5} = -2$

(c) $\sqrt[4]{-16}$ is not a real number because n is even and x is negative.

(d) $\sqrt[6]{-64}$ is not a real number because n is even and x is negative.

Practice Problem 1 If possible, find the roots. If there is no real number root, say so.

(a) $\sqrt[3]{216}$ **(b)** $\sqrt[5]{32}$ **(c)** $\sqrt[3]{-8}$ **(d)** $\sqrt[4]{-81}$

Because the symbol $\sqrt{x}$ represents exactly one real number for all real numbers x that are nonnegative, we can use it to define the **square root function** $f(x) = \sqrt{x}$.

This function has a domain of all real numbers x that are greater than or equal to zero.

EXAMPLE 2 Find the indicated function values of the function $f(x) = \sqrt{2x + 4}$.

Round your answers to the nearest tenth when necessary.

(a) $f(-2)$ **(b)** $f(6)$ **(c)** $f(3)$

(a) $f(-2) = \sqrt{2(-2) + 4} = \sqrt{-4 + 4} = \sqrt{0} = 0$ The square root of zero is zero.

(b) $f(6) = \sqrt{2(6) + 4} = \sqrt{12 + 4} = \sqrt{16} = 4$

(c) $f(3) = \sqrt{2(3) + 4} = \sqrt{6 + 4} = \sqrt{10} \approx 3.2$ We use a calculator or a square root table to approximate $\sqrt{10}$.

Practice Problem 2 Find the indicated values of the function $f(x) = \sqrt{4x - 3}$. Round your answers to the nearest tenth when necessary.

(a) $f(3)$ **(b)** $f(4)$ **(c)** $f(7)$

EXAMPLE 3 Find the domain of the function $f(x) = \sqrt{3x - 6}$.

We know that the expression $3x - 6$ must be nonnegative. That is, $3x - 6 \geq 0$.

$$3x - 6 \geq 0$$
$$3x \geq 6$$
$$x \geq 2$$

Thus, the domain is all real numbers x where $x \geq 2$.

Practice Problem 3 Find the domain of the function $f(x) = \sqrt{0.5x + 2}$.

EXAMPLE 4 Graph the function $f(x) = \sqrt{x + 2}$. Use the values $f(-2), f(-1)$, $f(0), f(1), f(2)$, and $f(7)$. Round your answers to the nearest tenth when necessary.

We show the table of values here.

x	$f(x)$
−2	0
−1	1
0	1.4
1	1.7
2	2
7	3

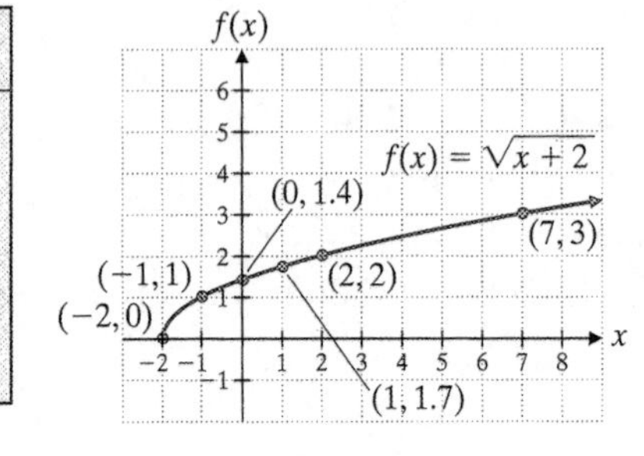

Practice Problem 4 Graph the function $f(x) = \sqrt{3x - 9}$. Use the values $f(3), f(4)$, $f(5), f(6)$, and $f(15)$.

2 Changing Radical Expressions to Expressions with Rational Exponents

Now we want to extend our definition of roots to rational exponents. By the laws of exponents we know that

$$x^{1/2} \cdot x^{1/2} = x^{1/2+1/2} = x^1 = x.$$

Since $x^{1/2}x^{1/2} = x$, $x^{1/2}$ must be a square root of x. That is, $x^{1/2} = \sqrt{x}$. Is this true? By the definition of square root, $(\sqrt{x})^2 = x$. Does $(x^{1/2})^2 = x$? Using the law of exponents we have

$$(x^{1/2})^2 = x^{(1/2)(2)} = x^1 = x.$$

We conclude that

$$x^{1/2} = \sqrt{x}.$$

In the same way we can write the following:

$$x^{1/3} \cdot x^{1/3} \cdot x^{1/3} = x \qquad x^{1/3} = \sqrt[3]{x}$$
$$x^{1/4} \cdot x^{1/4} \cdot x^{1/4} \cdot x^{1/4} = x \qquad x^{1/4} = \sqrt[4]{x}$$
$$\vdots \qquad\qquad \vdots$$
$$\underbrace{x^{1/n} \cdot x^{1/n} \cdot \cdots \cdot x^{1/n}}_{n \text{ factors}} = x \qquad x^{1/n} = \sqrt[n]{x}$$

Therefore, we are ready to define fractional exponents in general.

Definition

If n is a positive integer and x is a nonnegative real number, then

$$x^{1/n} = \sqrt[n]{x}.$$

EXAMPLE 5 Change to rational exponents and simplify. Assume that all variables are nonnegative real numbers.

(a) $\sqrt[4]{x^4}$ **(b)** $\sqrt[5]{(32)^5}$

(a) $\sqrt[4]{x^4} = (x^4)^{1/4} = x^{4/4} = x^1 = x$ **(b)** $\sqrt[5]{(32)^5} = (32^5)^{1/5} = 32^{5/5} = 32^1 = 32$

Practice Problem 5 Change to rational exponents and simplify. Assume that all variables are nonnegative real numbers.

(a) $\sqrt[3]{x^3}$ **(b)** $\sqrt[4]{y^4}$

EXAMPLE 6 Replace all radicals with rational exponents.

(a) $\sqrt[3]{x^2}$ **(b)** $(\sqrt[5]{w})^7$

(a) $\sqrt[3]{x^2} = (x^2)^{1/3} = x^{2/3}$ **(b)** $(\sqrt[5]{w})^7 = (w^{1/5})^7 = w^{7/5}$

Practice Problem 6 Replace all radicals with rational exponents.

(a) $\sqrt[4]{x^3}$ **(b)** $\sqrt[5]{(xy)^7}$

EXAMPLE 7 Evaluate or simplify. Assume that all variables are positive.

(a) $\sqrt[5]{32x^{10}}$ **(b)** $\sqrt[3]{125x^9}$ **(c)** $(16x^4)^{3/4}$

(a) $\sqrt[5]{32x^{10}} = (2^5x^{10})^{1/5} = 2x^2$ **(b)** $\sqrt[3]{125x^9} = [(5)^3x^9]^{1/3} = 5x^3$

(c) $(16x^4)^{3/4} = (2^4x^4)^{3/4} = 2^3x^3 = 8x^3$

Practice Problem 7 Evaluate or simplify. Assume that all variables are nonnegative.

(a) $\sqrt[4]{81x^{12}}$ **(b)** $\sqrt[3]{27x^6}$ **(c)** $(32x^5)^{3/5}$

3 Changing Expressions with Rational Exponents to Radical Expressions

Sometimes we need to change an expression with rational exponents to a radical expression. This is especially helpful because the value of the radical form of an expression is sometimes more recognizable. For example, because of our experience with radicals, we know that $\sqrt{25} = 5$. It is not as easy to see that $25^{1/2} = 5$. Therefore, we simplify expressions with rational exponents by first rewriting them as radical expressions. Recall that

$$x^{1/n} = \sqrt[n]{x}.$$

Again, using the laws of exponents, we know that

$$x^{m/n} = (x^m)^{1/n} = (x^{1/n})^m,$$

when x is nonnegative. We can make the following general definition.

Definition

For positive integers m and n and any real number x for which $x^{1/n}$ is defined,

$$x^{m/n} = (\sqrt[n]{x})^m = \sqrt[n]{x^m}.$$

If it is also true that $x \neq 0$, then

$$x^{-m/n} = \frac{1}{x^{m/n}} = \frac{1}{(\sqrt[n]{x})^m} = \frac{1}{\sqrt[n]{x^m}}.$$

EXAMPLE 8 Change to radical form.

(a) $(xy)^{5/7}$ **(b)** $w^{-2/3}$ **(c)** $3x^{3/4}$ **(d)** $(3x)^{3/4}$

(a) $(xy)^{5/7} = \sqrt[7]{(xy)^5} = \sqrt[7]{x^5y^5}$

or $(xy)^{5/7} = (\sqrt[7]{xy})^5$

(b) $w^{-2/3} = \dfrac{1}{w^{2/3}} = \dfrac{1}{\sqrt[3]{w^2}}$

or $w^{-2/3} = \dfrac{1}{w^{2/3}} = \dfrac{1}{(\sqrt[3]{w})^2}$

(c) $3x^{3/4} = 3\sqrt[4]{x^3}$

or $3x^{3/4} = 3(\sqrt[4]{x})^3$

(d) $(3x)^{3/4} = \sqrt[4]{(3x)^3} = \sqrt[4]{27x^3}$

or $(3x)^{3/4} = (\sqrt[4]{3x})^3$

Practice Problem 8 Change to radical form.

(a) $x^{3/4}$ **(b)** $y^{-1/3}$ **(c)** $(2x)^{4/5}$ **(d)** $2x^{4/5}$

Graphing Calculator

Rational Exponents

To evaluate Exampla 9(a) on a graphing calculator we use

125 [∧] [(] 2 [÷] 3 [)] [enter].

Note the need to include the parentheses around the quantity 2/3. Try each part of Example 9 on your graphing calculator.

EXAMPLE 9 Change to radical form and evaluate.

(a) $125^{2/3}$ **(b)** $(-16)^{5/2}$ **(c)** $144^{-1/2}$

(a) $125^{2/3} = (\sqrt[3]{125})^2 = (5)^2 = 25$

(b) $(-16)^{5/2} = (\sqrt{-16})^5$; however, $\sqrt{-16}$ is not a real number. Thus, $(-16)^{5/2}$ is not a real number.

(c) $144^{-1/2} = \dfrac{1}{144^{1/2}} = \dfrac{1}{\sqrt{144}} = \dfrac{1}{12}$

Practice Problem 9 Change to radical form and evaluate.

(a) $8^{2/3}$ **(b)** $(-8)^{4/3}$ **(c)** $100^{-3/2}$

4 Evaluating Higher-Order Radicals Containing a Variable Radicand That Represents Any Real Number (Including a Negative Real Number)

We now give a definition of higher-order radicals that works for all radicals, no matter what their signs are.

Definition

For all real numbers x (including negative real numbers),

$\sqrt[n]{x^n} = |x|$ when n is an *even* positive integer, and

$\sqrt[n]{x^n} = x$ when n is an *odd* positive integer.

EXAMPLE 10 Evaluate; x may be any real number.

(a) $\sqrt[3]{(-2)^3}$ **(b)** $\sqrt[4]{(-2)^4}$ **(c)** $\sqrt[5]{x^5}$ **(d)** $\sqrt[6]{x^6}$

(a) $\sqrt[3]{(-2)^3} = -2$ because the index is odd.

(b) $\sqrt[4]{(-2)^4} = |-2| = 2$ because the index is even.

(c) $\sqrt[5]{x^5} = x$ because the index is odd.

(d) $\sqrt[6]{x^6} = |x|$ because the index is even.

Practice Problem 10 Evaluate; y and w may be any real numbers.

(a) $\sqrt[5]{(-3)^5}$ **(b)** $\sqrt[4]{(-5)^4}$ **(c)** $\sqrt[4]{w^4}$ **(d)** $\sqrt[7]{y^7}$

EXAMPLE 11 Simplify. Assume that x and y may be any real numbers.

(a) $\sqrt{49x^2}$ **(b)** $\sqrt[4]{81y^{16}}$ **(c)** $\sqrt[3]{27x^6y^9}$

(a) We observe that the index is an even positive number. We will need the absolute value. $\sqrt{49x^2} = 7|x|$

(b) Again, we need the absolute value. $\sqrt[4]{81y^{16}} = 3|y^4|$
Since we know that $3y^4$ is positive (anything to the fourth power will be positive), we can write $3|y^4|$ without the absolute value symbol. Thus, $\sqrt[4]{81y^{16}} = 3y^4$.

(c) The index is an odd integer. The absolute value is never needed in such a case.
$\sqrt[3]{27x^6y^9} = \sqrt[3]{(3)^3(x^2)^3(y^3)^3} = 3x^2y^3$

Practice Problem 11 Simplify. Assume that x and y may be any real numbers.

(a) $\sqrt{36x^2}$ **(b)** $\sqrt[3]{125x^3y^6}$ **(c)** $\sqrt[4]{16y^8}$

7.2 Exercises

Verbal and Writing Skills

1. In a simple sentence, explain what a square root is.

2. In a simple sentence, explain what a cube root is.

3. Give an example to show why the cube root of a negative number is a negative number.

4. Give an example to show why it is not possible to find a real number that is the square root of a negative number.

Evaluate if possible.

5. $\sqrt{64}$

6. $\sqrt{100}$

7. $\sqrt{25} + \sqrt{49}$

8. $\sqrt{16} + \sqrt{81}$

9. $-\sqrt{\frac{1}{9}}$

10. $-\sqrt{\frac{4}{25}}$

11. $\sqrt{36} - \sqrt{25}$

12. $\sqrt{49} + \sqrt{100}$

13. $\sqrt{0.04}$

14. $\sqrt{0.16}$

For the given function, find the indicated function values. Find the domain of each function. Round your answers to the nearest tenth when necessary.

15. $f(x) = \sqrt{10x + 5}$; $f(0), f(1), f(2), f(3)$

16. $f(x) = \sqrt{3x + 21}$; $f(0), f(1), f(5), f(-4)$

17. $f(x) = \sqrt{0.5x - 3}$; $f(6), f(8), f(14), f(16)$

18. $f(x) = \sqrt{1.5x - 4}$; $f(4), f(6), f(8), f(14)$

Graph each of the following functions. Plot at least four points for each function.

19. $f(x) = \sqrt{x - 3}$

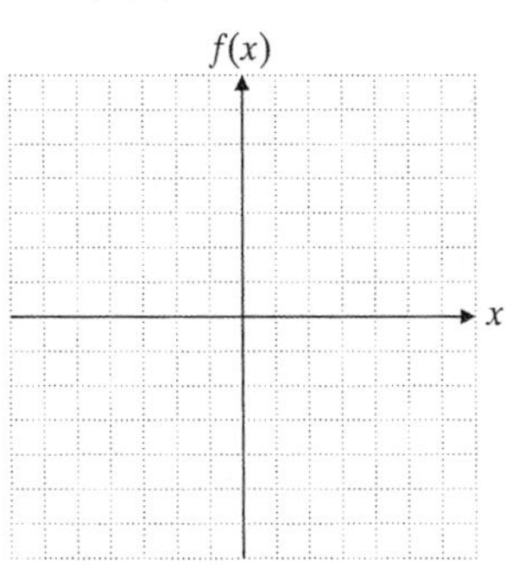

20. $f(x) = \sqrt{x - 1}$

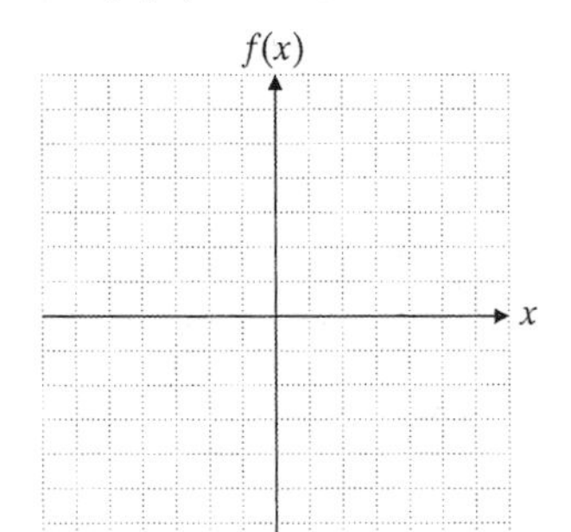

21. $f(x) = \sqrt{2x + 4}$

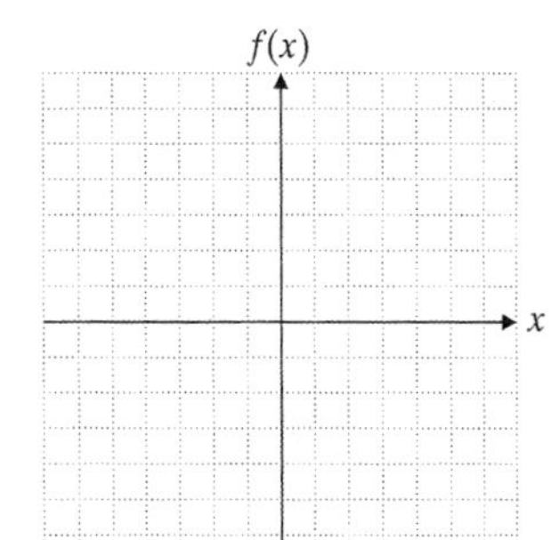

22. $f(x) = \sqrt{3x + 9}$

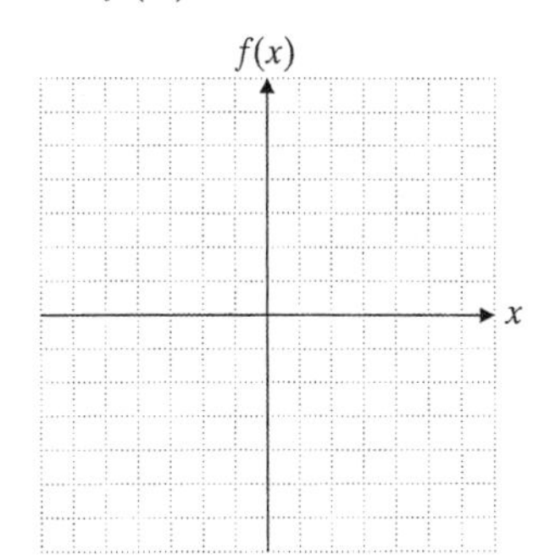

Evaluate if possible.

23. $\sqrt[3]{216}$ **24.** $\sqrt[3]{27}$ **25.** $\sqrt[3]{64}$ **26.** $\sqrt[3]{-125}$ **27.** $\sqrt[3]{-8}$

28. $\sqrt[4]{625}$ **29.** $\sqrt[4]{81}$ **30.** $-\sqrt[6]{64}$ **31.** $\sqrt[5]{(8)^5}$ **32.** $\sqrt[6]{(9)^6}$

33. $\sqrt[8]{(5)^8}$ **34.** $\sqrt[7]{(11)^7}$ **35.** $\sqrt[3]{-\frac{1}{64}}$ **36.** $\sqrt[3]{-\frac{8}{27}}$ **37.** $\sqrt[3]{\frac{27}{125}}$

For Exercises 38–83, assume that variables represent positive real numbers. Replace all radicals with rational exponents.

38. $\sqrt[3]{y}$ **39.** $\sqrt{a}$ **40.** $\sqrt[5]{2x}$ **41.** $\sqrt[4]{3y}$ **42.** $\sqrt[7]{(a+b)^3}$

43. $\sqrt[9]{(a-b)^5}$ **44.** $\sqrt{\sqrt[3]{x}}$ **45.** $\sqrt[5]{\sqrt{y}}$ **46.** $(\sqrt[6]{3x})^5$ **47.** $(\sqrt[5]{2x})^3$

Simplify.

48. $\sqrt[6]{(12)^6}$ **49.** $\sqrt[5]{(-11)^5}$ **50.** $\sqrt[3]{x^3y^6}$ **51.** $\sqrt[4]{a^8b^4}$ **52.** $\sqrt{36x^8y^4}$

53. $\sqrt{49x^2y^8}$ **54.** $\sqrt[4]{16a^8b^4}$ **55.** $\sqrt[4]{81a^{12}b^{20}}$ **56.** $\sqrt[3]{-125x^{30}}$ **57.** $\sqrt[3]{8x^3y^9}$

Change to radical form.

58. $y^{4/7}$ **59.** $x^{5/6}$ **60.** $7^{-2/3}$ **61.** $5^{-3/5}$ **62.** $(2a+b)^{5/7}$

63. $(x+3y)^{4/7}$ **64.** $(-x)^{3/5}$ **65.** $(-y)^{5/7}$ **66.** $(2xy)^{3/5}$ **67.** $(3ab)^{2/7}$

Mixed Practice

Evaluate or simplify.

68. $4^{3/2}$ **69.** $27^{2/3}$ **70.** $(-64)^{1/3}$ **71.** $\left(\frac{4}{25}\right)^{1/2}$

72. $\left(\frac{16}{81}\right)^{3/4}$ **73.** $(-125)^{2/3}$ **74.** $(25x^4)^{-1/2}$ **75.** $(36y^8)^{-1/2}$

76. $\sqrt{121x^4}$ **77.** $\sqrt{49x^8}$ **78.** $\sqrt{144a^6b^{24}}$ **79.** $\sqrt{25a^{14}b^{18}}$

80. $\sqrt{36x^6y^8z^{10}}$ **81.** $\sqrt{100x^{10}y^{12}z^2}$ **82.** $\sqrt[3]{216a^3b^9c^{12}}$ **83.** $\sqrt[3]{-125a^6b^{15}c^{21}}$

To Think About

Simplify. Assume that the variables represent any positive or negative real number.

84. $\sqrt{25x^2}$ **85.** $\sqrt{100x^2}$ **86.** $\sqrt[3]{-8x^6}$ **87.** $\sqrt[3]{-27x^9}$ **88.** $\sqrt[4]{x^8y^{16}}$

89. $\sqrt[4]{x^{16}y^{40}}$ **90.** $\sqrt[4]{a^{12}b^4}$ **91.** $\sqrt[4]{a^4b^{20}}$ **92.** $\sqrt{4x^8y^4}$ **93.** $\sqrt{49a^{12}b^4}$

Applications

A company finds that the daily cost of producing appliances at one of its factories is represented by the equation $C = 120\sqrt[3]{n} + 375$, *where n is the number of parts produced in a day and C is the cost in dollars.*

94. Find the cost if 343 parts are produced per day.

95. Find the cost if 216 parts are produced per day.

Cumulative Review Problems

96. In the year 2000 the world produced 4.027×10^{17} Btu of energy. Use the pie graph to determine how much energy was produced that year in the Middle East.

97. The total world production of energy is predicted to increase by 52% of its year 2000 level by the year 2020. If North America increases its production of energy by only 24%, what percent of the world's energy in 2020 will be produced in North America?

World Energy Production in 2000

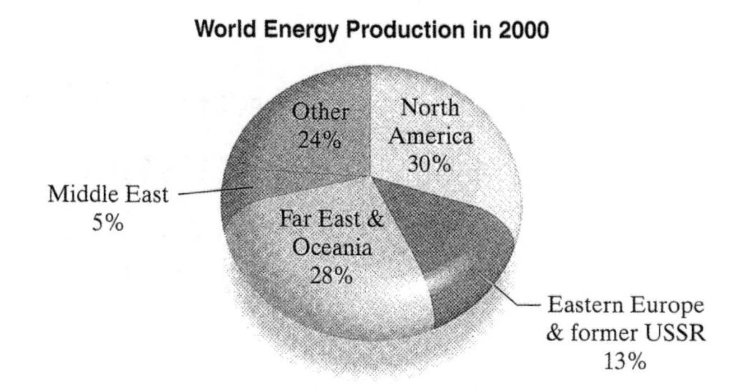

Source: U.S. Energy Information Administration

7.3 Simplifying, Adding, and Subtracting Radicals

Student Learning Objectives

After studying this section, you will be able to:

Simplify a radical by using the product rule.

Add and subtract like radical terms.

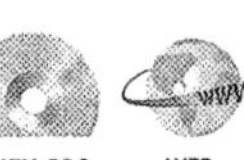

1 Simplifying a Radical by Using the Product Rule

When we simplify a radical, we want to get an equivalent expression with the smallest possible quantity in the radicand. We can use the product rule for radicals to simplify radicals.

Product Rule for Radicals

For all nonnegative real numbers a and b and positive integers n,

$$\sqrt[n]{a}\sqrt[n]{b} = \sqrt[n]{ab}.$$

You should be able to derive the product rule from your knowledge of the laws of exponents. We have

$$\sqrt[n]{a}\sqrt[n]{b} = a^{1/n}b^{1/n} = (ab)^{1/n} = \sqrt[n]{ab}.$$

Throughout the remainder of this chapter, assume that all variables in any radicand represent nonnegative numbers, unless a specific statement is made to the contrary.

EXAMPLE 1 Simplify $\sqrt{32}$.

Solution 1: $\sqrt{32} = \sqrt{16 \cdot 2} = \sqrt{16}\sqrt{2} = 4\sqrt{2}$

Solution 2: $\sqrt{32} = \sqrt{4 \cdot 8} = \sqrt{4}\sqrt{8} = 2\sqrt{8} = 2\sqrt{4 \cdot 2} = 2\sqrt{4}\sqrt{2} = 4\sqrt{2}$

Although we obtained the same answer both times, the first solution is much shorter. You should try to use the largest factor that is a perfect square when you use the product rule.

Practice Problem 1 Simplify $\sqrt{20}$.

EXAMPLE 2 Simplify $\sqrt{48}$.

$$\sqrt{48} = \sqrt{16}\sqrt{3} = 4\sqrt{3}$$

Practice Problem 2 Simplify $\sqrt{27}$.

EXAMPLE 3 Simplify. **(a)** $\sqrt[3]{16}$ **(b)** $\sqrt[3]{-81}$

(a) $\sqrt[3]{16} = \sqrt[3]{8}\sqrt[3]{2} = 2\sqrt[3]{2}$ **(b)** $\sqrt[3]{-81} = \sqrt[3]{-27}\sqrt[3]{3} = -3\sqrt[3]{3}$

Practice Problem 3 Simplify. **(a)** $\sqrt[3]{24}$ **(b)** $\sqrt[3]{-108}$

EXAMPLE 4 Simplify $\sqrt[4]{48}$.

$$\sqrt[4]{48} = \sqrt[4]{16}\sqrt[4]{3} = 2\sqrt[4]{3}$$

Practice Problem 4 Simplify $\sqrt[4]{64}$.

EXAMPLE 5 Simplify.

(a) $\sqrt{27x^3y^4}$ **(b)** $\sqrt[3]{16x^4y^3z^6}$

(a) $\sqrt{27x^3y^4} = \sqrt{9 \cdot 3 \cdot x^2 \cdot x \cdot y^4} = \sqrt{9x^2y^4}\sqrt{3x}$ Factor out the perfect squares.

$$= 3xy^2\sqrt{3x}$$

(b) $\sqrt[3]{16x^4y^3z^6} =$

$\sqrt[3]{8 \cdot 2 \cdot x^3 \cdot x \cdot y^3 \cdot z^6} = \sqrt[3]{8x^3y^3z^6}\sqrt[3]{2x}$ Factor out the perfect cubes.

$$= 2xyz^2\sqrt[3]{2x}$$

Why is z^6 a perfect cube?

Practice Problem 5 Simplify.

(a) $\sqrt{45x^6y^7}$ **(b)** $\sqrt{27a^7b^8c^9}$

2 Adding and Subtracting Like Radical Terms

Only like radicals can be added or subtracted. Two radicals are **like radicals** if they have the same radicand and the same index. $2\sqrt{5}$ and $3\sqrt{5}$ are like radicals. $2\sqrt{5}$ and $2\sqrt{3}$ are not like radicals; $2\sqrt{5}$ and $2\sqrt[3]{5}$ are not like radicals. When we combine radicals, we combine like terms by using the distributive property.

EXAMPLE 6 Combine $2\sqrt{5} + 3\sqrt{5} - 4\sqrt{5}$.

$$2\sqrt{5} + 3\sqrt{5} - 4\sqrt{5} = (2 + 3 - 4)\sqrt{5} = 1\sqrt{5} = \sqrt{5}$$

Practice Problem 6 Combine $19\sqrt{xy} + 5\sqrt{xy} - 10\sqrt{xy}$.

Sometimes when you simplify radicands, you may find you have like radicals.

EXAMPLE 7 Combine $5\sqrt{3} - \sqrt{27} + 2\sqrt{48}$.

$$\begin{aligned} 5\sqrt{3} - \sqrt{27} + 2\sqrt{48} &= 5\sqrt{3} - \sqrt{9}\sqrt{3} + 2\sqrt{16}\sqrt{3} \\ &= 5\sqrt{3} - 3\sqrt{3} + 2(4)\sqrt{3} \\ &= 5\sqrt{3} - 3\sqrt{3} + 8\sqrt{3} \\ &= 10\sqrt{3} \end{aligned}$$

Practice Problem 7 Combine $4\sqrt{2} - 5\sqrt{50} - 3\sqrt{98}$.

EXAMPLE 8 Combine $6\sqrt{x} + 4\sqrt{12x} - \sqrt{75x} + 3\sqrt{x}$.

$$\begin{aligned} 6\sqrt{x} + 4\sqrt{12x} - \sqrt{75x} + 3\sqrt{x} &= 6\sqrt{x} + 4\sqrt{4}\sqrt{3x} - \sqrt{25}\sqrt{3x} + 3\sqrt{x} \\ &= 6\sqrt{x} + 8\sqrt{3x} - 5\sqrt{3x} + 3\sqrt{x} \\ &= 6\sqrt{x} + 3\sqrt{x} + 8\sqrt{3x} - 5\sqrt{3x} \\ &= 9\sqrt{x} + 3\sqrt{3x} \end{aligned}$$

Practice Problem 8 Combine $4\sqrt{2x} + \sqrt{18x} - 2\sqrt{125x} - 6\sqrt{20x}$.

EXAMPLE 9 Combine $2\sqrt[3]{81x^3y^4} + 3xy\sqrt[3]{24y}$.

$$\begin{aligned} 2\sqrt[3]{81x^3y^4} + 3xy\sqrt[3]{24y} &= 2\sqrt[3]{27x^3y^3}\sqrt[3]{3y} + 3xy\sqrt[3]{8}\sqrt[3]{3y} \\ &= 2(3xy)\sqrt[3]{3y} + 3xy(2)\sqrt[3]{3y} \\ &= 6xy\sqrt[3]{3y} + 6xy\sqrt[3]{3y} \\ &= 12xy\sqrt[3]{3y} \end{aligned}$$

Practice Problem 9 Combine $3x\sqrt[3]{54x^4} - 3\sqrt[3]{16x^7}$.

7.3 Exercises

Simplify. Assume that all variables are nonnegative real numbers.

1. $\sqrt{8}$ **2.** $\sqrt{12}$ **3.** $\sqrt{18}$ **4.** $\sqrt{75}$

5. $\sqrt{120}$ **6.** $\sqrt{80}$ **7.** $\sqrt{44}$ **8.** $\sqrt{90}$

9. $\sqrt{9x^3}$ **10.** $\sqrt{16x^5}$ **11.** $\sqrt{60a^4b^5}$

12. $\sqrt{45a^3b^8}$ **13.** $\sqrt{98x^5y^6z}$ **14.** $\sqrt{24xy^8z^3}$

15. $\sqrt[3]{8}$ **16.** $\sqrt[3]{27}$ **17.** $\sqrt[3]{108}$

18. $\sqrt[3]{128}$ **19.** $\sqrt[3]{56y}$ **20.** $\sqrt[3]{54x}$

21. $\sqrt[3]{8a^3b^8}$ **22.** $\sqrt[3]{125a^6b^2}$ **23.** $\sqrt[3]{24x^6y^{11}}$

24. $\sqrt[3]{40x^7y^{26}}$ **25.** $\sqrt[4]{81kp^{23}}$ **26.** $\sqrt[4]{16k^{12}p^{18}}$

27. $\sqrt[5]{-32x^5y^6}$ **28.** $\sqrt[5]{-243x^4y^{10}}$

To Think About

29. $\sqrt[4]{1792} = a\sqrt[4]{7}$. What is the value of a?

30. $\sqrt[3]{3072} = b\sqrt[3]{6}$. What is the value of b?

Combine. Assume that all variables represent nonnegative real numbers.

31. $\sqrt{49} + \sqrt{100}$ **32.** $\sqrt{25} + \sqrt{81}$ **33.** $\sqrt{3} + 7\sqrt{3} - 2\sqrt{3}$

34. $\sqrt{11} - 5\sqrt{11} + 3\sqrt{11}$ **35.** $3\sqrt{18} - \sqrt{2}$ **36.** $\sqrt{40} - \sqrt{10}$

37. $-2\sqrt{50} + \sqrt{32} - 3\sqrt{8}$

38. $-\sqrt{12} + 2\sqrt{48} - \sqrt{75}$

39. $-5\sqrt{45} + 6\sqrt{20} + 3\sqrt{5}$

40. $-7\sqrt{10} + 4\sqrt{40} - 8\sqrt{90}$

41. $\sqrt{44} - 3\sqrt{63x} + 4\sqrt{28x}$

42. $\sqrt{75x} + 2\sqrt{108x} - 6\sqrt{3x}$

43. $\sqrt{200x^3} - x\sqrt{32x}$

44. $\sqrt{75a^3} + a\sqrt{12a}$

45. $\sqrt[3]{16} + 3\sqrt[3]{54}$

46. $\sqrt[3]{128} - 4\sqrt[3]{16}$

47. $-2\sqrt[3]{125x^3y^4} + 3y^2\sqrt[3]{8x^3}$

48. $2x\sqrt[3]{40xy} - 3\sqrt[3]{5x^4y}$

To Think About

49. Use a calculator to show that $\sqrt{48} + \sqrt{27} + \sqrt{75} = 12\sqrt{3}$.

50. Use a calculator to show that $\sqrt{98} + \sqrt{50} + \sqrt{128} = 20\sqrt{2}$.

Applications

We can approximate the amount of current in amps I (amperes) drawn by an appliance in the home using the formula

$$I = \sqrt{\frac{P}{R}},$$

where P is the power measured in watts and R is the resistance measured in ohms. In Exercises 51 and 52 round your answers to three decimal places.

51. What is the current I if $P = 500$ watts and $R = 10$ ohms?

52. What is the current I if $P = 480$ watts and $R = 8$ ohms?

*The **period** of a pendulum is the amount of time it takes the pendulum to make one complete swing back and forth. If the length of the pendulum L is measured in feet, then its period T measured in seconds is given by the formula*

$$T = 2\pi\sqrt{\frac{L}{32}}.$$

Use $\pi \approx 3.14$ *for exercises 53–54.*

53. Find the period of a pendulum if its length is 8 feet.

54. A person suspended on a rope swinging back and forth acts like a human pendulum. What is the period of a person swinging on a rope that is 128 feet long?

Cumulative Review Problems

Factor completely.

55. $81x^2y - 25y$

56. $16x^3 - 56x^2y + 49xy^2$

The FDA recommends that an adult's minimum daily intake of the mineral phosphorus be 1 gram. A small serving of scallops (six average-size scallops) has 0.2 gram of phosphorus, while one small serving of skim milk (1 cup) has 0.25 gram of phosphorus.

57. If you eat only scallops, how many servings would you need to obtain the minimum daily requirement of phosphorus? If you drink only skim milk, how many servings would you need to obtain the daily requirement for phosphorus?

58. If the number of servings of scallops and the number of servings of skim milk totals 4.5 servings, how many of each would you need to meet the minimum daily requirement of phosphorus?

According to the United Nations, since the collapse of communism in 1989, there has been a marked drop in the fertility rate throughout Eastern and Central Europe. The population of the former Soviet Union, which was 307 million in the year 2000, could fall to about 250 million by the year 2050. Source: United Nations Statistics Division.

59. What is the projected percent of decrease in the population during the 50 years from 2000 to 2050?

60. What is the projected percent of decrease in the population per year during these 50 years?

61. If this trend is slowed so that there are 280 million people in the former Soviet Union in 2050, what will be the projected percent of decrease in the population from 2000 to 2050?

7.4 Multiplication and Division of Radicals

1 Multiplying Radical Expressions

Student Learning Objectives

After studying this section, you will be able to:

1. Multiply radical expressions.
2. Divide radical expressions.
3. Simplify radical expressions by rationalizing the denominator.

We use the product rule for radicals to multiply radical expressions. Recall that $\sqrt[n]{a}\sqrt[n]{b} = \sqrt[n]{ab}$.

EXAMPLE 1 Multiply $(3\sqrt{2})(5\sqrt{11x})$.

$$(3\sqrt{2})(5\sqrt{11x}) = (3)(5)\sqrt{2 \cdot 11x} = 15\sqrt{22x}$$

Practice Problem 1 Multiply $(-4\sqrt{2})(-3\sqrt{13x})$.

EXAMPLE 2 Multiply $\sqrt{6x}(\sqrt{3} + \sqrt{2x} + \sqrt{5})$.

$$\begin{aligned}\sqrt{6x}(\sqrt{3} + \sqrt{2x} + \sqrt{5}) &= (\sqrt{6x})(\sqrt{3}) + (\sqrt{6x})(\sqrt{2x}) + (\sqrt{6x})(\sqrt{5})\\ &= \sqrt{18x} + \sqrt{12x^2} + \sqrt{30x}\\ &= \sqrt{9}\sqrt{2x} + \sqrt{4x^2}\sqrt{3} + \sqrt{30x}\\ &= 3\sqrt{2x} + 2x\sqrt{3} + \sqrt{30x}\end{aligned}$$

Practice Problem 2 Multiply $\sqrt{2x}(\sqrt{5} + 2\sqrt{3x} + \sqrt{8})$.

To multiply two binomials containing radicals, we can use the distributive property. Most students find that the FOIL method is helpful in remembering how to find the four products.

EXAMPLE 3 Multiply $(\sqrt{2} + 3\sqrt{5})(2\sqrt{2} - \sqrt{5})$.

By FOIL:

$$\begin{aligned}(\sqrt{2} + 3\sqrt{5})(2\sqrt{2} - \sqrt{5}) &= 2\sqrt{4} - \sqrt{10} + 6\sqrt{10} - 3\sqrt{25}\\ &= 4 + 5\sqrt{10} - 15\\ &= -11 + 5\sqrt{10}\end{aligned}$$

By the distributive property:

$$\begin{aligned}(\sqrt{2} + 3\sqrt{5})(2\sqrt{2} - \sqrt{5}) &= (\sqrt{2} + 3\sqrt{5})(2\sqrt{2}) - (\sqrt{2} + 3\sqrt{5})\sqrt{5}\\ &= (\sqrt{2})(2\sqrt{2}) + (3\sqrt{5})(2\sqrt{2}) - (\sqrt{2})(\sqrt{5}) - (3\sqrt{5})(\sqrt{5})\\ &= 2\sqrt{4} + 6\sqrt{10} - \sqrt{10} - 3\sqrt{25}\\ &= 4 + 5\sqrt{10} - 15\\ &= -11 + 5\sqrt{10}\end{aligned}$$

Practice Problem 3 Multiply $(\sqrt{7} + 4\sqrt{2})(2\sqrt{7} - 3\sqrt{2})$.

EXAMPLE 4 Multiply $(7 - 3\sqrt{2})(4 - \sqrt{3})$.

$$(7 - 3\sqrt{2})(4 - \sqrt{3}) = 28 - 7\sqrt{3} - 12\sqrt{2} + 3\sqrt{6}$$

Practice Problem 4 Multiply $(2 - 5\sqrt{5})(3 - 2\sqrt{2})$.

EXAMPLE 5 Multiply $(\sqrt{7} + \sqrt{3x})^2$.

Method 1: We can use the FOIL method or the distributive property.

$$\begin{aligned}(\sqrt{7} + \sqrt{3x})(\sqrt{7} + \sqrt{3x}) &= \sqrt{49} + \sqrt{21x} + \sqrt{21x} + \sqrt{9x^2}\\ &= 7 + \sqrt{21x} + \sqrt{21x} + 3x\\ &= 7 + 2\sqrt{21x} + 3x\end{aligned}$$

Method 2: We could also use the Chapter 4 formula.

$$(a + b)^2 = a^2 + 2ab + b^2,$$

where $a = \sqrt{7}$ and $b = \sqrt{3x}$. Then

$$(\sqrt{7} + \sqrt{3x})^2 = (\sqrt{7})^2 + 2\sqrt{7}\sqrt{3x} + (\sqrt{3x})^2$$
$$= 7 + 2\sqrt{21x} + 3x$$

Practice Problem 5 Multiply $(\sqrt{5x} + \sqrt{10})^2$. Use the approach that seems easiest to you.

EXAMPLE 6 Multiply.

(a) $\sqrt[3]{3x}(\sqrt[3]{x^2} + 3\sqrt[3]{4y})$ **(b)** $(\sqrt[3]{2y} + \sqrt[3]{4})(2\sqrt[3]{4y^2} - 3\sqrt[3]{2})$

(a) $\sqrt[3]{3x}(\sqrt[3]{x^2} + 3\sqrt[3]{4y}) = (\sqrt[3]{3x})(\sqrt[3]{x^2}) + 3(\sqrt[3]{3x})(\sqrt[3]{4y})$
$$= \sqrt[3]{3x^3} + 3\sqrt[3]{12xy}$$
$$= x\sqrt[3]{3} + 3\sqrt[3]{12xy}$$

(b) $(\sqrt[3]{2y} + \sqrt[3]{4})(2\sqrt[3]{4y^2} - 3\sqrt[3]{2}) = 2\sqrt[3]{8y^3} - 3\sqrt[3]{4y} + 2\sqrt[3]{16y^2} - 3\sqrt[3]{8}$
$$= 2(2y) - 3\sqrt[3]{4y} + 2\sqrt[3]{8}\sqrt[3]{2y^2} - 3(2)$$
$$= 4y - 3\sqrt[3]{4y} + 4\sqrt[3]{2y^2} - 6$$

Practice Problem 6 Multiply.

(a) $\sqrt[3]{2x}(\sqrt[3]{4x^2} + 3\sqrt[3]{y})$ **(b)** $(\sqrt[3]{7} + \sqrt[3]{x^2})(2\sqrt[3]{49} - \sqrt[3]{x})$

2 Dividing Radical Expressions

We can use the laws of exponents to develop a rule for dividing two radicals.

$$\sqrt[n]{\frac{a}{b}} = \left(\frac{a}{b}\right)^{1/n} = \frac{a^{1/n}}{b^{1/n}} = \frac{\sqrt[n]{a}}{\sqrt[n]{b}}$$

This quotient rule is very useful. We now state it more formally.

Quotient Rule for Radicals

For all nonnegative real numbers a, all positive real numbers b, and positive integers n,

$$\frac{\sqrt[n]{a}}{\sqrt[n]{b}} = \sqrt[n]{\frac{a}{b}}.$$

Sometimes it will be best to change $\sqrt[n]{\frac{a}{b}}$ to $\frac{\sqrt[n]{a}}{\sqrt[n]{b}}$, whereas at other times it will be best to change $\frac{\sqrt[n]{a}}{\sqrt[n]{b}}$ to $\sqrt[n]{\frac{a}{b}}$. To use the quotient rule for radicals, you need to have good number sense. You should know your squares up to 15^2 and your cubes up to 5^3.

EXAMPLE 7 Divide.

(a) $\frac{\sqrt{48}}{\sqrt{3}}$ **(b)** $\sqrt[3]{\frac{125}{8}}$ **(c)** $\frac{\sqrt{28x^5y^3}}{\sqrt{7x}}$

(a) $\frac{\sqrt{48}}{\sqrt{3}} = \sqrt{\frac{48}{3}} = \sqrt{16} = 4$

(b) $\sqrt[3]{\dfrac{125}{8}} = \dfrac{\sqrt[3]{125}}{\sqrt[3]{8}} = \dfrac{5}{2}$

(c) $\dfrac{\sqrt{28x^5y^3}}{\sqrt{7x}} = \sqrt{\dfrac{28x^5y^3}{7x}} = \sqrt{4x^4y^3} = 2x^2y\sqrt{y}$

Practice Problem 7 Divide.

(a) $\dfrac{\sqrt{75}}{\sqrt{3}}$ **(b)** $\sqrt[3]{\dfrac{27}{64}}$ **(c)** $\dfrac{\sqrt{54a^3b^7}}{\sqrt{6b^5}}$

3 Simplifying Radical Expressions by Rationalizing the Denominator

Recall that to simplify a radical we want to get the smallest possible quantity in the radicand. Whenever possible, we find the square root of a perfect square. Thus, to simplify $\sqrt{\frac{7}{16}}$ we have

$$\sqrt{\frac{7}{16}} = \frac{\sqrt{7}}{\sqrt{16}} = \frac{\sqrt{7}}{4}.$$

Notice that the denominator does not contain a square root. The expression $\dfrac{\sqrt{7}}{4}$ is in simplest form.

Let's look at $\sqrt{\frac{16}{7}}$. We have

$$\sqrt{\frac{16}{7}} = \frac{\sqrt{16}}{\sqrt{7}} = \frac{4}{\sqrt{7}}.$$

Notice that the denominator contains a square root. If an expression contains a square root in the denominator, it is not considered to be simplified. How can we rewrite $\dfrac{4}{\sqrt{7}}$ as an equivalent expression that does not contain the $\sqrt{7}$ in the denominator? Since $\sqrt{7}\sqrt{7} = 7$, we can multiply the numerator and the denominator by the radical in the denominator.

$$\frac{4}{\sqrt{7}} \cdot \frac{\sqrt{7}}{\sqrt{7}} = \frac{4\sqrt{7}}{\sqrt{49}} = \frac{4\sqrt{7}}{7}$$

This expression is considered to be in simplest form. We call this process rationalizing the denominator.

Rationalizing the denominator is the process of transforming a fraction with one or more radicals in the denominator into an equivalent fraction without a radical in the denominator.

EXAMPLE 8 Simplify by rationalizing the denominator $\dfrac{3}{\sqrt{2}}$.

$$\frac{3}{\sqrt{2}} = \frac{3}{\sqrt{2}} \cdot \frac{\sqrt{2}}{\sqrt{2}} \qquad \text{Since } \frac{\sqrt{2}}{\sqrt{2}} = 1.$$

$$= \frac{3\sqrt{2}}{\sqrt{4}} \qquad \text{Product rule for radicals.}$$

$$= \frac{3\sqrt{2}}{2}$$

Practice Problem 8 Simplify by rationalizing the denominator $\dfrac{7}{\sqrt{3}}$.

We can rationalize the denominator either before or after we simplify the denominator.

EXAMPLE 9 Simplify $\frac{3}{\sqrt{12x}}$.

Method 1: First we simplify the radical in the denominator, and then we multiply in order to rationalize the denominator.

$$\frac{3}{\sqrt{12x}} = \frac{3}{\sqrt{4}\sqrt{3x}} = \frac{3}{2\sqrt{3x}} \cdot \frac{\sqrt{3x}}{\sqrt{3x}} = \frac{\cancel{3}\sqrt{3x}}{2(\cancel{3}x)} = \frac{\sqrt{3x}}{2x}$$

Method 2: We can multiply numerator and denominator by a value that will make the denominator a perfect square (i.e., rationalize the denominator).

$$\frac{3}{\sqrt{12x}} = \frac{3}{\sqrt{12x}} \cdot \frac{\sqrt{3x}}{\sqrt{3x}}$$

$$= \frac{3\sqrt{3x}}{\sqrt{36x^2}}$$ Since $\sqrt{12x}\sqrt{3x} = \sqrt{36x^2}$.

$$= \frac{3\sqrt{3x}}{6x} = \frac{\sqrt{3x}}{2x}$$

Practice Problem 9 Simplify $\frac{8}{\sqrt{20x}}$.

If the radicand has a fraction, it is not considered to be simplified. We can use the quotient rule for radicals and then rationalize the denominator to simplify the radical. We have already rationalized denominators when they contain square roots. Now we will rationalize denominators when they contain radical expressions that are cube roots or higher-order roots.

EXAMPLE 10 Simplify $\sqrt[3]{\frac{2}{3x^2}}$.

Method 1:

$$\sqrt[3]{\frac{2}{3x^2}} = \frac{\sqrt[3]{2}}{\sqrt[3]{3x^2}}$$ Quotient rule for radicals.

$$= \frac{\sqrt[3]{2}}{\sqrt[3]{3x^2}} \cdot \frac{\sqrt[3]{9x}}{\sqrt[3]{9x}}$$ Multiply the numerator and denominator by an appropriate value so that the new denominator will be a perfect cube.

$$= \frac{\sqrt[3]{18x}}{\sqrt[3]{27x^3}}$$ Observe that we can evaluate the cube root in the denominator.

$$= \frac{\sqrt[3]{18x}}{3x}$$

Method 2:

$$\sqrt[3]{\frac{2}{3x^2}} = \sqrt[3]{\frac{2}{3x^2} \cdot \frac{9x}{9x}}$$

$$= \sqrt[3]{\frac{18x}{27x^3}}$$

$$= \frac{\sqrt[3]{18x}}{\sqrt[3]{27x^3}}$$

$$= \frac{\sqrt[3]{18x}}{3x}$$

Practice Problem 10 Simplify $\sqrt[3]{\frac{6}{5x}}$.

If the denominator of a radical expression contains a sum or difference with radicals, we multiply the numerator and denominator by the *conjugate* of the denominator. For example, the conjugate of $x + \sqrt{y}$ is $x - \sqrt{y}$; similarly, the conjugate of $x - \sqrt{y}$ is $x + \sqrt{y}$. What is the conjugate of $3 + \sqrt{2}$? It is $3 - \sqrt{2}$. How about $\sqrt{11} + \sqrt{xyz}$? It is $\sqrt{11} - \sqrt{xyz}$.

Conjugates

The expressions $a + b$ and $a - b$, where a and b represent any algebraic term, are called **conjugates**. Each expression is the conjugate of the other expression.

Multiplying by conjugates is simply an application of the formula

$$(a + b)(a - b) = a^2 - b^2.$$

For example,

$$(\sqrt{x} + \sqrt{y})(\sqrt{x} - \sqrt{y}) = (\sqrt{x})^2 - (\sqrt{y})^2 = x - y.$$

EXAMPLE 11 Simplify $\dfrac{5}{3 + \sqrt{2}}$.

$$\frac{5}{3 + \sqrt{2}} = \frac{5}{3 + \sqrt{2}} \cdot \frac{3 - \sqrt{2}}{3 - \sqrt{2}}$$

Multiply the numerator and denominator by the conjugate of $3 + \sqrt{2}$.

$$= \frac{15 - 5\sqrt{2}}{(3)^2 - (\sqrt{2})^2}$$

$$= \frac{15 - 5\sqrt{2}}{9 - 2} = \frac{15 - 5\sqrt{2}}{7}$$

Practice Problem 11 Simplify $\dfrac{4}{2 + \sqrt{5}}$.

EXAMPLE 12 Simplify $\dfrac{\sqrt{7} + \sqrt{3}}{\sqrt{7} - \sqrt{3}}$.

The conjugate of $\sqrt{7} - \sqrt{3}$ is $\sqrt{7} + \sqrt{3}$.

$$\frac{\sqrt{7} + \sqrt{3}}{\sqrt{7} - \sqrt{3}} \cdot \frac{\sqrt{7} + \sqrt{3}}{\sqrt{7} + \sqrt{3}} = \frac{\sqrt{49} + 2\sqrt{21} + \sqrt{9}}{(\sqrt{7})^2 - (\sqrt{3})^2}$$

$$= \frac{7 + 2\sqrt{21} + 3}{7 - 3}$$

$$= \frac{10 + 2\sqrt{21}}{4}$$

$$= \frac{2(5 + \sqrt{21})}{2 \cdot 2}$$

$$= \frac{\cancel{2}(5 + \sqrt{21})}{\cancel{2} \cdot 2}$$

$$= \frac{5 + \sqrt{21}}{2}$$

Practice Problem 12 Simplify $\dfrac{\sqrt{11} + \sqrt{2}}{\sqrt{11} - \sqrt{2}}$.

7.4 Exercises

Multiply and simplify. Assume that all variables represent nonnegative numbers.

1. $(2\sqrt{6})(-3\sqrt{2})$

2. $(-4\sqrt{5})(2\sqrt{10})$

3. $(-3\sqrt{y})(\sqrt{5x})$

4. $(\sqrt{2x})(-7\sqrt{3y})$

5. $7\sqrt{x}(2\sqrt{3} - 5\sqrt{x})$

6. $3\sqrt{y}(4\sqrt{6} + 11\sqrt{y})$

7. $(3 - \sqrt{2})(8 + \sqrt{2})$

8. $(\sqrt{5} + 4)(\sqrt{5} - 1)$

9. $(2\sqrt{3} + \sqrt{2})(2\sqrt{3} - 4\sqrt{2})$

10. $(3\sqrt{3} + \sqrt{5})(\sqrt{3} - 2\sqrt{5})$

11. $(\sqrt{7} + 4\sqrt{5x})(2\sqrt{7} + 3\sqrt{5x})$

12. $(\sqrt{6} + 3\sqrt{3y})(5\sqrt{6} + 2\sqrt{3y})$

13. $(\sqrt{3} + 2\sqrt{2})(\sqrt{5} + \sqrt{3})$

14. $(3\sqrt{5} + \sqrt{3})(\sqrt{2} + 2\sqrt{5})$

15. $(\sqrt{x} - 2\sqrt{3x})(\sqrt{x} + 2\sqrt{3x})$

16. $(2\sqrt{x} + \sqrt{5x})(2\sqrt{x} - \sqrt{5x})$

17. $(\sqrt{5} - 2\sqrt{6})^2$

18. $(\sqrt{3} + 4\sqrt{7})^2$

19. $(\sqrt{3x + 4} + 3)^2$

20. $(\sqrt{2x + 1} - 2)^2$

21. $(6 - 5\sqrt{a})^2$

22. $(3\sqrt{b} + 4)^2$

23. $(\sqrt[3]{x^2})(3\sqrt[3]{4x} - 4\sqrt[3]{x^5})$

24. $(2\sqrt[3]{x})(\sqrt[3]{4x^2} - \sqrt[3]{14x})$

Divide and simplify. Assume that all variables represent positive numbers.

25. $\sqrt{\frac{49}{25}}$

26. $\sqrt{\frac{16}{36}}$

27. $\sqrt{\frac{12x}{49y^6}}$

28. $\sqrt{\frac{27a^4}{64x^2}}$

29. $\sqrt[3]{\frac{8x^5y^6}{27}}$

30. $\sqrt[3]{\frac{125a^3b^4}{64}}$

31. $\frac{\sqrt[3]{24x^3y^5}}{\sqrt[3]{3y^2}}$

32. $\frac{\sqrt[3]{250a^4b^6}}{\sqrt[3]{2a}}$

Simplify by rationalizing the denominator.

33. $\frac{3}{\sqrt{2}}$

34. $\frac{5}{\sqrt{7}}$

35. $\sqrt{\frac{4}{3}}$

36. $\sqrt{\frac{25}{2}}$

37. $\frac{1}{\sqrt{5y}}$

38. $\frac{1}{\sqrt{3x}}$

39. $\frac{x}{\sqrt{5} - \sqrt{2}}$

40. $\frac{y}{\sqrt{7} + \sqrt{3}}$

41. $\frac{\sqrt{3}}{\sqrt{5} - 2}$

42. $\frac{\sqrt{7}}{\sqrt{7} - 1}$

43. $\frac{\sqrt{x}}{\sqrt{3x} + \sqrt{2}}$

44. $\frac{\sqrt{x}}{\sqrt{5} + \sqrt{2x}}$

45. $\frac{\sqrt{5} + \sqrt{3}}{\sqrt{5} - \sqrt{3}}$

46. $\frac{\sqrt{11} - \sqrt{5}}{\sqrt{11} + \sqrt{5}}$

47. $\frac{\sqrt{3x} - 2\sqrt{y}}{\sqrt{3x} + \sqrt{y}}$

48. $\frac{\sqrt{x} + \sqrt{y}}{\sqrt{x} - 2\sqrt{y}}$

49. $\frac{x\sqrt{5} + 1}{\sqrt{5} + 2}$

50. $\frac{y\sqrt{2} - 1}{2\sqrt{2} + 1}$

51. $\frac{5}{\sqrt{2} - \sqrt{3}}$

52. $\frac{ab}{\sqrt{6} - \sqrt{7}}$

53. $\frac{\sqrt[3]{x^2}}{\sqrt[3]{7x^2}}$

54. $\frac{\sqrt[3]{6y^4}}{\sqrt[3]{4x^5}}$

To Think About

55. A student rationalized the denominator of $\frac{\sqrt{6}}{2\sqrt{3}-\sqrt{2}}$ and obtained $\frac{\sqrt{3}+3\sqrt{2}}{5}$. Find a decimal approximation of each expression. Are the decimals equal? Did the student do the work correctly?

56. A student rationalized the denominator of $\frac{\sqrt{5}}{\sqrt{5}+\sqrt{3}}$ and obtained $\frac{5-\sqrt{15}}{2}$. Find a decimal approximation of each expression. Are the decimals equal? Did the student do the work correctly?

In calculus, students are sometimes required to rationalize the numerator of an expression. In this case the numerator will not have a radical in the answer. Rationalize the numerator in each of the following:

57. $\frac{\sqrt{3}+2\sqrt{7}}{8}$

58. $\frac{\sqrt{5}-4\sqrt{3}}{6}$

Applications

The cost of fertilizing a lawn is $0.18 per square foot. Find the cost to fertilize each of the following triangular lawns. Round your answers to the nearest cent.

▲ **59.** The base of the triangle is $\sqrt{21}$ feet, and the altitude is $\sqrt{50}$ feet.

▲ **60.** The base of the triangle is $\sqrt{17}$ feet, and the altitude is $\sqrt{40}$ feet.

▲ **61.** A medical doctor has designed a pacemaker that has a rectangular control panel. This rectangle has a width of $\sqrt{x}+3$ millimeters and a length of $\sqrt{x}+5$ millimeters. Find the area in square millimeters of this rectangle.

▲ **62.** An FBI agent has designed a secret listening device that has a rectangular base. The rectangle has a width of $\sqrt{x}+7$ centimeters and a length of $\sqrt{x}+11$ centimeters. Find the area in square centimeters of this rectangle.

Cumulative Review Problems

Solve for x and y.

63. $2x + 3y = 13$
$5x - 2y = 4$

Solve for x, y, and z.

64. $3x - y - z = 5$
$2x + 3y - z = -16$
$x + 2y + 2z = -3$

65. A cup of strong coffee contains about 200 milligrams of caffeine. A cup of strong tea contains 80 milligrams of caffeine. Juanita used to drink 1 cup of each every day. However, she resolved on January 1 to reduce her intake of caffeine to less than 18 milligrams per day. On January 2 she cut her consumption of both coffee and tea in half. Three days later she again cut her consumption in half. If she continues this pattern of reduction, on what day will she reach her goal?

66. Juanita's husband, Carlos, has several cups of coffee and tea each day. On January 1, he had 11 cups in total and consumed a total of 1480 milligrams of caffeine. Using the information in Exercise 65, find out how many cups of coffee and how many cups of tea he consumed. If he cut his consumption of coffee and tea in half on January 2 and continues to cut his consumption of coffee and tea in half every 4 days after that, when will he reach his goal of fewer than 24 milligrams per day?

Tiffany & Co., one of the most famous diamond merchants, offers engagement rings in a variety of price ranges. These data are displayed in the bar graph to the right. The data indicate the price of all diamond rings sold during a recent year.

67. What percent of the rings sold for $23,000 or less?

68. If Tiffany & Co. sold 85,000 diamond engagement rings last year, what is the number of rings that cost more than $5,000?

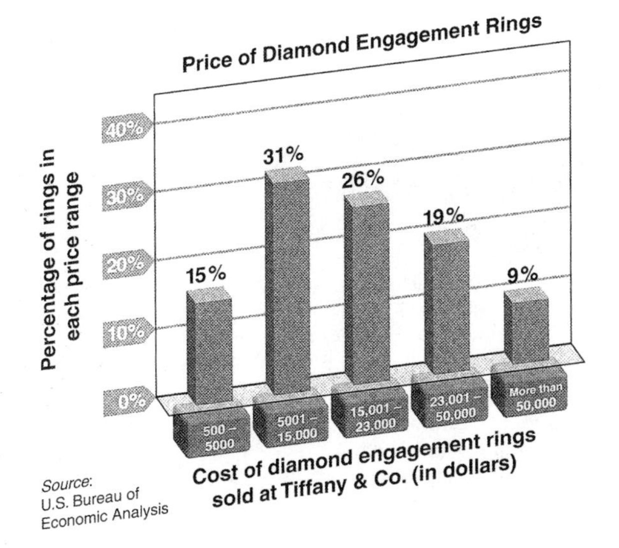

7.5 Radical Equations

Student Learning Objectives

After studying this section, you will be able to:

 Solve a radical equation that requires squaring each side once.

 Solve a radical equation that requires squaring each side twice.

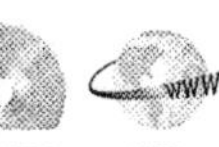

SSM PH TUTOR CENTER CD & VIDEO MATH PRO WEB

1 Solving a Radical Equation by Squaring Each Side Once

A **radical equation** is an equation with a variable in one or more of the radicals. $3\sqrt{x} = 8$ and $\sqrt{3x - 1} = 5$ are radical equations. We solve radical equations by raising each side of the equation to the appropriate power. In other words, we square both sides if the radicals are square roots, cube both sides if the radicals are cube roots, and so on. Once we have done this, solving for the unknown becomes routine.

Sometimes after we square each side, we obtain a quadratic equation. In this case we collect all terms on one side and use the zero factor method that we developed in Section 5.8. After solving the equation, *always* check your answers to see whether extraneous solutions have been introduced.

We will now generalize this rule because it is very useful in higher-level mathematics courses.

Raising Each Side of an Equation to a Power

If $y = x$, then $y^n = x^n$, for all natural numbers n.

EXAMPLE 1 Solve $\sqrt{2x + 9} = x + 3$.

$$(\sqrt{2x + 9})^2 = (x + 3)^2 \quad \text{Square each side.}$$
$$2x + 9 = x^2 + 6x + 9 \quad \text{Simplify.}$$
$$0 = x^2 + 4x \quad \text{Collect all terms on one side.}$$
$$0 = x(x + 4) \quad \text{Factor.}$$
$$x = 0 \quad \text{or} \quad x + 4 = 0$$
$$x = 0 \qquad x = -4 \quad \text{Solve for } x.$$

Check:

For $x = 0$: $\sqrt{2(0) + 9} \stackrel{?}{=} 0 + 3$, $\sqrt{9} \stackrel{?}{=} 3$, $3 = 3$ ✓

For $x = -4$: $\sqrt{2(-4) + 9} \stackrel{?}{=} -4 + 3$, $\sqrt{1} \stackrel{?}{=} -1$, $1 \neq -1$

Therefore, 0 is the only solution to this equation.

Practice Problem 1 Solve and check your solution(s). $\sqrt{3x - 8} = x - 2$

> **Graphing Calculator**
>
> **Solving Radical Equations**
>
> On a graphing calculator Example 1 can be solved in two ways. Let $y_1 = \sqrt{2x + 9}$ and let $y_2 = x + 3$. Use your graphing calculator to determine where y_1 intersects y_2. What value of x do you obtain? Now let $y = \sqrt{2x + 9} - x - 3$ and find the value of x when $y = 0$. What value of x do you obtain? Which method seems more efficient?
>
> Use the method above that you found most efficient to solve the following equations, and round your answers to the nearest tenth.
>
> $$\sqrt{x + 9.5} = x - 2.3$$
> $$\sqrt{6x + 1.3} = 2x - 1.5$$

As you begin to solve more complicated radical equations, it is important to make sure that one radical expression is alone on one side of the equation. This is often referred to as **isolating the radical term**.

EXAMPLE 2 Solve $\sqrt{10x + 5} - 1 = 2x$.

$$\sqrt{10x + 5} = 2x + 1 \quad \text{Isolate the radical term.}$$
$$(\sqrt{10x + 5})^2 = (2x + 1)^2 \quad \text{Square each side.}$$
$$10x + 5 = 4x^2 + 4x + 1 \quad \text{Simplify.}$$
$$0 = 4x^2 - 6x - 4 \quad \text{Collect all terms on one side.}$$
$$0 = 2(2x^2 - 3x - 2) \quad \text{Factor out the common factor.}$$
$$0 = 2(2x + 1)(x - 2) \quad \text{Factor completely.}$$
$$2x + 1 = 0 \quad \text{or} \quad x - 2 = 0 \quad \text{Solve for } x.$$
$$2x = -1 \qquad x = 2$$
$$x = -\frac{1}{2}$$

Check:

$x = -\frac{1}{2}$: $\sqrt{10\left(-\frac{1}{2}\right) + 5} - 1 \stackrel{?}{=} 2\left(-\frac{1}{2}\right)$ $\qquad$ $x = 2$: $\sqrt{10(2) + 5} - 1 \stackrel{?}{=} 2(2)$

$$\sqrt{-5 + 5} - 1 \stackrel{?}{=} -1 \qquad \sqrt{25} - 1 \stackrel{?}{=} 4$$

$$\sqrt{0} - 1 \stackrel{?}{=} -1 \qquad 5 - 1 \stackrel{?}{=} 4$$

$$-1 = -1 \checkmark \qquad 4 = 4 \checkmark$$

Both answers check, so $-\frac{1}{2}$ and 2 are roots of the equation.

Practice Problem 2 Solve and check your solution(s). $\sqrt{x + 4} = x + 4$

2 Solving a Radical Equation by Squaring Each Side Twice

In some exercises, we must square each side twice in order to remove all the radicals. It is important to isolate at least one radical before squaring each side.

EXAMPLE 3 Solve $\sqrt{5x + 1} - \sqrt{3x} = 1$.

$$\sqrt{5x + 1} = 1 + \sqrt{3x} \qquad \text{Isolate one of the radicals.}$$

$$\left(\sqrt{5x + 1}\right)^2 = \left(1 + \sqrt{3x}\right)^2 \qquad \text{Square each side.}$$

$$5x + 1 = \left(1 + \sqrt{3x}\right)\left(1 + \sqrt{3x}\right)$$

$$5x + 1 = 1 + 2\sqrt{3x} + 3x$$

$$2x = 2\sqrt{3x} \qquad \text{Isolate the remaining radical.}$$

$$x = \sqrt{3x} \qquad \text{Divide each side by 2.}$$

$$(x)^2 = \left(\sqrt{3x}\right)^2 \qquad \text{Square each side.}$$

$$x^2 = 3x$$

$$x^2 - 3x = 0 \qquad \text{Collect all terms on one side.}$$

$$x(x - 3) = 0$$

$$x = 0 \quad \text{or} \quad x - 3 = 0 \qquad \text{Solve for } x.$$

$$x = 3$$

Check:

$x = 0$: $\sqrt{5(0) + 1} - \sqrt{3(0)} \stackrel{?}{=} 1$ $\qquad$ $x = 3$: $\sqrt{5(3) + 1} - \sqrt{3(3)} \stackrel{?}{=} 1$

$$\sqrt{1} - \sqrt{0} \stackrel{?}{=} 1 \qquad \sqrt{16} - \sqrt{9} \stackrel{?}{=} 1$$

$$1 = 1 \checkmark \qquad 1 = 1 \checkmark$$

Both answers check. The solutions are 0 and 3.

Practice Problem 3 Solve and check your solution(s). $\sqrt{2x + 5} - 2\sqrt{2x} = 1$

We will now formalize the procedure for solving radical equations.

Procedure for Solving Radical Equations

1. Perform algebraic operations to obtain one radical by itself on one side of the equation.
2. If the equation contains square roots, square each side of the equation. Otherwise, raise each side to the appropriate power for third- and higher-order roots.
3. Simplify, if possible.
4. If the equation still contains a radical, repeat steps 1 to 3.
5. Collect all terms on one side of the equation.
6. Solve the resulting equation.
7. Check all apparent solutions. Solutions to radical equations must be verified.

EXAMPLE 4 Solve $\sqrt{2y+5} - \sqrt{y-1} = \sqrt{y+2}$.

$$(\sqrt{2y+5} - \sqrt{y-1})^2 = (\sqrt{y+2})^2$$

$$(\sqrt{2y+5} - \sqrt{y-1})(\sqrt{2y+5} - \sqrt{y-1}) = y+2$$

$$2y + 5 - 2\sqrt{(y-1)(2y+5)} + y - 1 = y + 2$$

$$-2\sqrt{(y-1)(2y+5)} = -2y - 2$$

$$\sqrt{(y-1)(2y+5)} = y + 1 \quad \text{Divide each side by } -2.$$

$$(\sqrt{2y^2 + 3y - 5})^2 = (y+1)^2 \quad \text{Square each side.}$$

$$2y^2 + 3y - 5 = y^2 + 2y + 1$$

$$y^2 + y - 6 = 0 \quad \text{Collect all terms on one side.}$$

$$(y+3)(y-2) = 0$$

$$y = -3 \quad \text{or} \quad y = 2$$

Check: Verify that 2 is a valid solution but −3 is not a valid solution.

Practice Problem 4 Solve and check your solution(s).

$$\sqrt{y-1} + \sqrt{y-4} = \sqrt{4y-11}$$

7.5 Exercises

Verbal and Writing Skills

1. Before squaring each side of a radical equation, what step should be taken first?

2. Why do we have to check the solutions when we solve radical equations?

Solve each radical equation. Check your solution(s).

3. $\sqrt{8x + 1} = 5$

4. $\sqrt{5x - 4} = 6$

5. $2x = \sqrt{x + 3}$

6. $3x = \sqrt{9x - 2}$

7. $y - \sqrt{y - 3} = 5$

8. $\sqrt{2y - 4} + 2 = y$

9. $\sqrt{y + 1} - 1 = y$

10. $5 + \sqrt{2y + 5} = y$

11. $x - 2\sqrt{x - 3} = 3$

12. $2\sqrt{4x + 1} + 5 = x + 9$

13. $\sqrt{3x^2 - x} = x$

14. $\sqrt{5x^2 - 3x} = 2x$

15. $\sqrt[3]{2x + 3} = 2$

16. $\sqrt[3]{3x - 6} = 3$

17. $\sqrt[3]{4x - 1} = 3$

18. $\sqrt[3]{3 - 5x} = 2$

19. $\sqrt{x + 4} = 1 + \sqrt{x - 3}$

20. $\sqrt{5x + 1} = 1 + \sqrt{3x}$

21. $\sqrt{x + 6} = 1 + \sqrt{x + 2}$

22. $\sqrt{3x + 1} - \sqrt{x - 4} = 3$

23. $\sqrt{6x + 6} = 1 + \sqrt{4x + 5}$

24. $\sqrt{8x + 17} = \sqrt{2x + 8} + 3$

25. $\sqrt{2x+9} - \sqrt{x+1} = 2$

26. $\sqrt{4x+6} = \sqrt{x+1} - \sqrt{x+5}$

27. $\sqrt{3x+4} + \sqrt{x+5} = \sqrt{7-2x}$

28. $\sqrt{2x+6} = \sqrt{7-2x} + 1$

29. $2\sqrt{x} - \sqrt{x-5} = \sqrt{2x-2}$

30. $\sqrt{3 - 2\sqrt{x}} = \sqrt{x}$

Optional Graphing Calculator Problems

Solve for x. Round your answer to four decimal places.

31. $x = \sqrt{5.326x - 1.983}$

32. $\sqrt[3]{5.62x + 9.93} = 1.47$

Applications

33. When a car traveling on wet pavement at a speed V in miles per hour stops suddenly, it will produce skid marks of length S feet according to the formula $V = 2\sqrt{3S}$.

(a) Solve the equation for S.

(b) Use your result from **(a)** to find the length of the skid mark S if the car is traveling at 18 miles per hour.

34. The volume V of a steel container inside a flight data recorder is defined by the equation

$$x = \sqrt{\frac{V}{5}},$$

where x is the sum of the length and the width of the container in inches and the height of the container is 5 inches.

(a) Solve the equation for V.

(b) Use the result from **(a)** to find the volume of the container whose length and width total 3.5 inches.

Recently an experiment was conducted relating the speed a car is traveling and the stopping distance. In this experiment, a car is traveling on dry pavement at a constant rate of speed. From the instant that a driver recognizes the need to stop, the number of feet it takes for him to stop the car is recorded. For example, for a driver traveling at 50 miles per hour, it requires a stopping distance of 190 feet. In general, the stopping distance x in feet is related to the speed of the car y in miles per hour by the equation

$$0.11y + 1.25 = \sqrt{3.7625 + 0.22x}.$$

Source: National Highway Traffic Safety Administration.

35. Solve this equation for x.

36. Use your answer from Exercise 35 to find what the stopping distance x would have been for a car traveling at $y = 60$ miles per hour.

To Think About

37. The solution to the equation

$$\sqrt{x^2 - 4x + c} = x - 1$$

is $x = 4$. What is the value of c?

38. The solution to the equation

$$\sqrt{x + b} - \sqrt{x} = -2$$

is $x = 16$. What is the value of b?

Cumulative Review Problems

Simplify.

39. $(4^3x^6)^{2/3}$

40. $(2^{-3}x^{-6})^{1/3}$

41. $\sqrt[3]{-216x^6y^9}$

42. $\sqrt[4]{64x^{12}y^{16}}$

▲ **43.** The area of the top of a solid rectangular coffee table measures $(4x^2 + 2x + 9)$ square centimeters. The height of the coffee table measures $(2x + 3)$ centimeters. Find the volume of the solid coffee table.

▲ **44.** A rectangular display case has $(2r^2 + 5r + 3)$ boxes of cereal on each shelf. The display case has $(2r + 4)$ shelves. Find the number of cereal boxes in the display case.

45. The Mississippi Magic paddleboat can travel 12 miles per hour in still water. After traveling for 3 hours downstream with the current, it takes 5 hours to get upstream with the current and return to its original starting point. What is the speed of the current?

46. Louise Elton rides the ski lift for 1.75 miles to the top of Mount Gray. Once she is there, she immediately skis directly down the mountain. The ski trail winding down the mountain is 2.5 miles long. If she skis five times as fast as the lift runs and the round trip takes 45 minutes, find the rate at which she skis.

7.6 Complex Numbers

Student Learning Objectives

After studying this section, you will be able to:

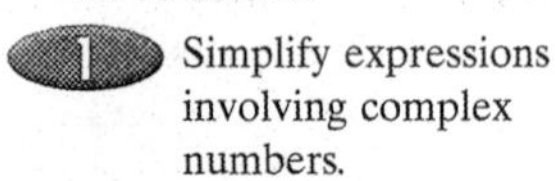
1. Simplify expressions involving complex numbers.

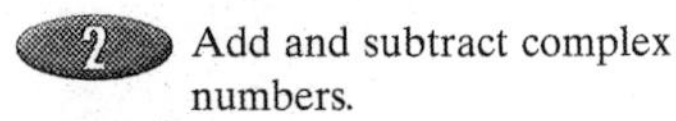
2. Add and subtract complex numbers.

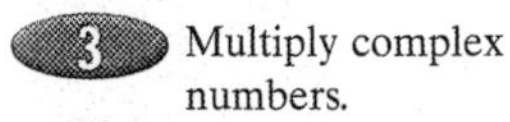
3. Multiply complex numbers.

4. Evaluate complex numbers of the form i^n.

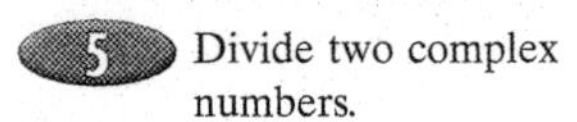
5. Divide two complex numbers.

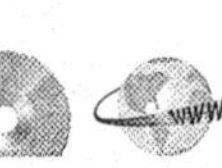

SSM PH TUTOR CENTER CD & VIDEO MATH PRO WEB

1 Simplifying Expressions Involving Complex Numbers

Until now we have not been able to solve an equation such as $x^2 = -4$ because there is no *real* number that satisfies this equation. However, this equation *does* have a nonreal solution. This solution is an *imaginary number*.

We define a new number:

$$i = \sqrt{-1} \text{ or } i^2 = -1.$$

Now let us use this procedure

$$\sqrt{-a} = \sqrt{-1}\sqrt{a}$$

and see if it is valid.

$$\text{Then } \sqrt{-4} = \sqrt{4(-1)} = \sqrt{4}\sqrt{-1} = \sqrt{4} \cdot i = 2i.$$

Thus, one solution to the equation $x^2 = -4$ is $2i$. Let's check it.

$$x^2 = -4$$
$$(2i)^2 \stackrel{?}{=} -4$$
$$4i^2 \stackrel{?}{=} -4$$
$$4(-1) \stackrel{?}{=} -4$$
$$-4 = -4 \quad \checkmark$$

The value $-2i$ is also a solution. You should verify this.

Now we formalize our definitions and give some examples of imaginary numbers.

Definition of Imaginary Number

The **imaginary number i** is defined as follows:

$$i = \sqrt{-1} \quad \text{and} \quad i^2 = -1.$$

The set of imaginary numbers consists of numbers of the form bi, where b is a real number and $b \neq 0$.

Definition

For all positive real numbers a,

$$\sqrt{-a} = \sqrt{-1}\sqrt{a} = i\sqrt{a}.$$

EXAMPLE 1 Simplify. **(a)** $\sqrt{-36}$ **(b)** $\sqrt{-17}$

(a) $\sqrt{-36} = \sqrt{-1}\sqrt{36} = (i)(6) = 6i$

(b) $\sqrt{-17} = \sqrt{-1}\sqrt{17} = i\sqrt{17}$

Practice Problem 1 Simplify. **(a)** $\sqrt{-49}$ **(b)** $\sqrt{-31}$

To avoid confusing $\sqrt{17i}$ with $\sqrt{17}i$, we write the i before the radical. That is, we write $i\sqrt{17}$.

EXAMPLE 2 Simplify $\sqrt{-45}$.

$$\sqrt{-45} = \sqrt{-1}\,\sqrt{45} = i\sqrt{45} = i\sqrt{9}\,\sqrt{5} = 3i\sqrt{5}$$

Practice Problem 2 Simplify $\sqrt{-98}$.

The rule $\sqrt{a}\,\sqrt{b} = \sqrt{ab}$ requires that $a \geq 0$ and $b \geq 0$. Therefore, we cannot use our product rule when the radicands are negative unless we first use the definition of $\sqrt{-1}$. Recall that

$$\sqrt{-1} \cdot \sqrt{-1} = i \cdot i = i^2 = -1.$$

EXAMPLE 3 Multiply $\sqrt{-16} \cdot \sqrt{-25}$.

First we must use the definition $\sqrt{-1} = i$. Thus, we have the following:

$$\begin{aligned}(\sqrt{-16})(\sqrt{-25}) &= (i\sqrt{16})(i\sqrt{25}) \\ &= i^2(4)(5) \\ &= -1(20) \qquad i^2 = -1. \\ &= -20\end{aligned}$$

Practice Problem 3 Multiply $\sqrt{-8} \cdot \sqrt{-2}$.

Now we formally define a complex number.

Definition

A number that can be written in the form $a + bi$, where a and b are real numbers, is a **complex number**. We say that a is the **real part** and bi is the **imaginary part**.

Under this definition, every real number is also a complex number. For example, the real number 5 can be written as $5 + 0i$. Therefore, 5 is a complex number. In a similar fashion, the imaginary number $2i$ can be written as $0 + 2i$. So $2i$ is a complex number. Thus, the set of complex numbers includes the set of real numbers and the set of imaginary numbers.

Definition

Two complex numbers $a + bi$ and $c + di$ are equal if and only if $a = c$ and $b = d$.

This definition means that two complex numbers are equal if and only if their real parts are equal *and* their imaginary parts are equal.

EXAMPLE 4 Find the real numbers x and y if $x + 3i\sqrt{7} = -2 + yi$.

By our definition, the real parts must be equal, so x must be -2; the imaginary parts must also be equal, so y must be $3\sqrt{7}$.

Practice Problem 4 Find the real numbers x and y if $-7 + 2yi\sqrt{3} = x + 6i\sqrt{3}$.

Graphing Calculator

Complex Numbers

Some graphing calculators, such as the TI-83, have a complex number mode. If your graphing calculator has this capability, you will be able to use it to do complex number operations. First you must use the Mode command to transfer selection from "Real" to "Complex" or "a + bi." To verify your status, try to find $\sqrt{-7}$ on your graphing calculator. If you obtain an approximate answer of "2.645751311 *i*," then your calculator is operating in the complex number mode. If you obtain "ERROR: NONREAL ANSWER," then your calculator is not operating in the complex number mode.

2 Adding and Subtracting Complex Numbers

Adding and Subtracting Complex Numbers

For all real numbers a, b, c, and d,

$$(a + bi) + (c + di) = (a + c) + (b + d)i \quad \text{and}$$
$$(a + bi) - (c + di) = (a - c) + (b - d)i.$$

In other words, to combine complex numbers we add (or subtract) the real parts, and we add (or subtract) the imaginary parts.

EXAMPLE 5 Subtract $(6 - 2i) - (3 - 5i)$.

$$(6 - 2i) - (3 - 5i) = (6 - 2i) + (-3 + 5i) = (6 - 3) + (-2 + 5)i = 3 + 3i$$

Practice Problem 5 Subtract $(3 - 4i) - (-2 - 18i)$.

3 Multiplying Complex Numbers

As we might expect, the procedure for multiplying complex numbers is similar to the procedure for multiplying polynomials. We will see that the complex numbers obey the associative, commutative, and distributive properties.

EXAMPLE 6 Multiply $(7 - 6i)(2 + 3i)$.

Use FOIL.

$$\begin{aligned}(7 - 6i)(2 + 3i) &= (7)(2) + (7)(3i) + (-6i)(2) + (-6i)(3i)\\ &= 14 + 21i - 12i - 18i^2\\ &= 14 + 21i - 12i - 18(-1)\\ &= 14 + 21i - 12i + 18\\ &= 32 + 9i\end{aligned}$$

Practice Problem 6 Multiply $(4 - 2i)(3 - 7i)$.

EXAMPLE 7 Multiply $3i(4 - 5i)$.

Use the distributive property.

$$\begin{aligned}3i(4 - 5i) &= (3)(4)i + (3)(-5)i^2\\ &= 12i - 15i^2\\ &= 12i - 15(-1)\\ &= 15 + 12i\end{aligned}$$

Practice Problem 7 Multiply $-2i(5 + 6i)$.

It is important to rewrite any square roots with negative radicands using i notation for complex numbers before attempting to do any multiplication.

EXAMPLE 8 Multiply and simplify your answers. $\sqrt{-25} \cdot \sqrt{-36}$

Before any other steps are taken, we must first rewrite the expression using i notation.

$$\sqrt{-25} \cdot \sqrt{-36} = (i\sqrt{25})(i\sqrt{36})$$

Now we can finish the calculations using the properties of complex numbers.

$$\begin{aligned}(i\sqrt{25})(i\sqrt{36}) &= (5i)(6i)\\ &= 30i^2\\ &= 30(-1)\\ &= -30\end{aligned}$$

Practice Problem 8 Multiply. Then simplify your answer. $\sqrt{-50} \cdot \sqrt{-4}$

4 Evaluating Complex Numbers of the Form i^n

How would you evaluate i^n, where n is any positive integer? What if n is a negative integer? We look for a pattern. We have defined

$$i^2 = -1.$$

We could write

$$i^3 = i^2 \cdot i = (-1)i = -i.$$

We also have the following:

$$i^4 = i^2 \cdot i^2 = (-1)(-1) = +1$$

$$i^5 = i^4 \cdot i = (+1)i = +i$$

We notice that $i^5 = i$. Let's look at i^6.

$$i^6 = i^4 \cdot i^2 = (+1)(-1) = -1$$

We begin to see a pattern that starts with i and repeats itself for i^5. Will $i^7 = -i$? Why or why not?

Values of i^n			
	$i = i$	$i^5 = i$	$i^9 = i$
	$i^2 = -1$	$i^6 = -1$	$i^{10} = -1$
	$i^3 = -i$	$i^7 = -i$	$i^{11} = -i$
	$i^4 = +1$	$i^8 = +1$	$i^{12} = +1$

We can use this pattern to evaluate powers of i.

EXAMPLE 9 Evaluate. **(a)** i^{36} **(b)** i^{27}

(a) $i^{36} = (i^4)^9 = (1)^9 = 1$

(b) $i^{27} = (i^{24+3}) = (i^{24})(i^3) = (i^4)^6(i^3) = (1)^6(-i) = -i$

This suggests a quick method for evaluating powers of i. Divide the exponent by 4. i^4 raised to any power will be 1. Then use the first column of the values of i^n chart above to evaluate the remainder.

Practice Problem 9 Evaluate. **(a)** i^{42} **(b)** i^{53}

Graphing Calculator

Complex Operations
When we perform complex number operations on a graphing calculator, the answer will usually be displayed as an approximate value in decimal form. Try Example 10 on your graphing calculator by entering $(7 + i) \div (3 - 2i)$. You should obtain an approximate answer of $1.461538462 + 1.307692308i$.

Dividing Two Complex Numbers

The complex numbers $a + bi$ and $a - bi$ are called **conjugates**. The product of two complex conjugates is always a real number.

$$\begin{aligned}(a + bi)(a - bi) &= a^2 - abi + abi - b^2i^2 \\ &= a^2 - b^2(-1) \\ &= a^2 + b^2\end{aligned}$$

When dividing two complex numbers, we want to remove any expression involving i from the denominator. So we multiply the numerator and denominator by the conjugate of the denominator. This is just what we did when we rationalized the denominator in a radical expression.

EXAMPLE 10 Divide $\dfrac{7 + i}{3 - 2i}$.

$$\begin{aligned}\frac{(7 + i)}{(3 - 2i)} \cdot \frac{(3 + 2i)}{(3 + 2i)} &= \frac{21 + 14i + 3i + 2i^2}{9 - 4i^2} = \frac{21 + 17i + 2(-1)}{9 - 4(-1)} = \frac{21 + 17i - 2}{9 + 4} \\ &= \frac{19 + 17i}{13} \quad \text{or} \quad \frac{19}{13} + \frac{17}{13}i\end{aligned}$$

Practice Problem 10 Divide $\dfrac{4 + 2i}{3 + 4i}$.

EXAMPLE 11 Divide $\dfrac{3 - 2i}{4i}$.

The conjugate of $0 + 4i$ is $0 - 4i$ or simply $-4i$.

$$\begin{aligned}&= \frac{(3 - 2i)}{(4i)} \cdot \frac{(-4i)}{(-4i)} = \frac{-12i + 8i^2}{-16i^2} = \frac{-12i + 8(-1)}{-16(-1)} \\ &= \frac{-8 - 12i}{16} = \frac{\cancel{4}(-2 - 3i)}{\cancel{4} \cdot 4} \\ &= \frac{-2 - 3i}{4} \quad \text{or} \quad -\frac{1}{2} - \frac{3}{4}i\end{aligned}$$

Practice Problem 11 Divide $\dfrac{5 - 6i}{-2i}$.

7.6 Exercises

Verbal and Writing Skills

1. Does $x^2 = -9$ have a real number solution? Why or why not?

2. Describe a complex number and give an example(s).

3. Are the complex numbers $2 + 3i$ and $3 + 2i$ equal? Why or why not?

4. Describe in your own words how to add or subtract complex numbers.

Simplify. Express in terms of i.

5. $\sqrt{-36}$

6. $\sqrt{-81}$

7. $\sqrt{-50}$

8. $\sqrt{-48}$

9. $\sqrt{-\frac{1}{4}}$

10. $\sqrt{-\frac{1}{9}}$

11. $-\sqrt{-81}$

12. $-\sqrt{-36}$

13. $2 + \sqrt{-3}$

14. $5 + \sqrt{-7}$

15. $-3 + \sqrt{-24}$

16. $-6 - \sqrt{-32}$

Find the real numbers x and y.

17. $x - 3i = 5 + yi$

18. $x - 6i = 7 + yi$

19. $1.3 - 2.5yi = x - 5i$

20. $3.4 - 0.8i = 2x - yi$

21. $23 + yi = 17 - x + 3i$

22. $2 + x - 11i = 19 + yi$

Perform the addition or subtraction.

23. $\left(-\frac{3}{2} + \frac{1}{2}i\right) + \left(\frac{5}{2} - \frac{3}{2}i\right)$

24. $\left(\frac{3}{4} - \frac{3}{4}i\right) + \left(\frac{9}{4} + \frac{5}{4}i\right)$

25. $(2.8 - 0.7i) - (1.6 - 2.8i)$

26. $(5.4 + 4.1i) - (4.8 + 2.6i)$

Multiply and simplify your answers. Place in i notation before doing any other operations.

27. $(2 + 3i)(2 - i)$

28. $(4 - 6i)(2 + i)$

29. $5i - 2(-4 + i)$

30. $12i - 6(3 + i)$

31. $2i(5i - 6)$

32. $4i(7 - 2i)$

33. $\left(\frac{1}{2} + i\right)^2$

34. $\left(\frac{1}{3} - i\right)^2$

35. $(i\sqrt{3})(i\sqrt{7})$

36. $(i\sqrt{2})(i\sqrt{6})$

37. $(\sqrt{-3})(\sqrt{-2})$

38. $(\sqrt{-5})(\sqrt{-3})$

39. $(\sqrt{-36})(\sqrt{-4})$

40. $(\sqrt{-25})(\sqrt{-9})$

41. $(3 + \sqrt{-2})(4 + \sqrt{-5})$

42. $(2 + \sqrt{-3})(6 + \sqrt{-2})$

Evaluate.

43. i^{17}

44. i^{21}

45. i^{24}

46. i^{16}

47. i^{46}

48. i^{83}

49. $i^{30} + i^{28}$

50. $i^{26} + i^{24}$

Divide.

51. $\frac{2 + i}{3 - i}$

52. $\frac{4 + 2i}{2 - i}$

53. $\frac{3i}{4 + 2i}$

54. $\frac{-2i}{3 + 5i}$

55. $\frac{5 - 2i}{6i}$

56. $\frac{7 + 10i}{3i}$

57. $\frac{7}{5 - 6i}$

58. $\frac{3}{4 + 2i}$

59. $\frac{5 - 2i}{3 + 2i}$

60. $\frac{6 + 3i}{6 - 3i}$

61. $\frac{2 - 3i}{2 + i}$

62. $\frac{4 - 3i}{5 + 2i}$

Optional Graphing Calculator Problems

Perform each operation to obtain approximate answers.

63. $(29.3 + 56.2i)^2$

64. $\frac{196 - 34.8i}{24.9 + 56.4i}$

Applications

The impedance Z in an alternating current circuit (like the one used in your home and in your classroom) is given by the formula $Z = V/I$, where V is the voltage and I is the current.

65. Find the value of Z if $V = 3 + 2i$ and $I = 3i$.

66. Find the value of Z if $V = 4 + 2i$ and $I = -3i$.

Cumulative Review Problems

67. A grape juice factory produces juice in three different types of containers. $x + 3$ hours per week are spent on producing juice in glass bottles. $2x - 5$ hours per week are spent on producing juice in cans. $4x + 2$ hours per week are spent on producing juice in plastic bottles. If the factory operates 105 hours per week, how much time is spent producing juice in each type of container?

68. Citizens Bank has decided to donate its older personal computers to the Boston Public Schools. Each computer donated is worth \$120 in tax-deductible dollars to the bank. In addition, the computer company supplying the bank with its new computers gives a 7% rebate to any customer donating used computers to schools. If sixty new computers are purchased at a list price of \$1850 each and sixty older computers are donated to the Boston Public Schools, what is the net cost to the bank for this purchase?

7.7 Variation

Student Learning Objectives

After studying this section, you will be able to:

 Solve problems requiring the use of direct variation.

 Solve problems requiring the use of inverse variation.

 Solve problems requiring the use of joint or combined variation.

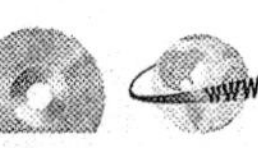
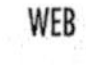

SSM PH TUTOR CENTER CD & VIDEO MATH PRO WEB

 Solving Problems Using Direct Variation

Many times in daily life we observe how a change in one quantity produces a change in another. If we order one large pepperoni pizza, we pay \$8.95. If we order two large pepperoni pizzas, we pay \$17.90. For three large pepperoni pizzas, it is \$26.85. The change in the number of pizzas we order results in a corresponding change in the price we pay.

Notice that the price we pay for each pizza stays the same. That is, each pizza costs \$8.95. The number of pizzas changes, and the corresponding price of the order changes. From our experience with functions and with equations, we see that the cost of the order is $y = \$8.95x$, where the price y depends on the number of pizzas x. We see that the variable y is a constant multiple of x. The two variables are said to *vary directly*. That is, y varies directly with x. We write a general equation that represents this idea as follows:

When we solve problems using direct variation, we usually are not given the value of the constant of variation k. This is something that we must find. Usually all we are given is a point of reference. That is, we are given the value of y for a specific value of x. Using this information, we can find k.

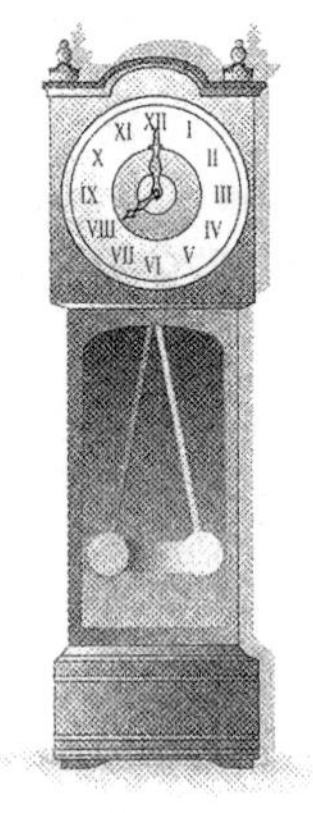

EXAMPLE 1 The time of a pendulum's swing varies directly with the square root of its length. If the pendulum is 1 foot long when the time is 0.2 second, find the time if the length is 4 feet.

Let t = the time and L = the length.

We then have the equation

$$t = k\sqrt{L}.$$

We can evaluate k by substituting $L = 1$ and $t = 0.2$ into the equation.

$$t = k\sqrt{L}$$
$$0.2 = k(\sqrt{1})$$
$$0.2 = k \qquad \text{Because } \sqrt{1} = 1.$$

Now we know the value of k and can write the equation more completely.

$$t = 0.2\sqrt{L}$$

When $L = 4$, we have the following:

$$t = 0.2\sqrt{4}$$
$$t = (0.2)(2)$$
$$t = 0.4 \text{ second}$$

Practice Problem 1 The maximum speed of a racing car varies directly with the square root of the horsepower of the engine. If the maximum speed of a car with 256 horsepower is 128 miles per hour, what is the maximum speed of a car with 225 horsepower?

 Solving Problems Using Inverse Variation

In some cases when one variable increases, another variable decreases. For example, as the amount of money you earn each year increases, the percentage of your income that you get to keep after taxes decreases. If one variable is a constant multiple of the reciprocal of the other, the two variables are said to *vary inversely*.

EXAMPLE 2 If y varies inversely with x, and $y = 12$ when $x = 5$, find the value of y when $x = 14$.

If y varies inversely with x, we can write the equation $y = \frac{k}{x}$. We can find the value of k by substituting the values $y = 12$ and $x = 5$.

$$12 = \frac{k}{5}$$

$$60 = k$$

We can now write the equation

$$y = \frac{60}{x}.$$

To find the value of y when $x = 14$, we substitute 14 for x in the equation.

$$y = \frac{60}{14}$$

$$y = \frac{30}{7}$$

Practice Problem 2 If y varies inversely with x, and $y = 45$ when $x = 16$, find the value of y when $x = 36$.

EXAMPLE 3 The amount of light from a light source varies inversely with the square of the distance to the light source. If an object receives 6.25 lumens when the light source is 8 meters away, how much light will the object receive if the light source is 4 meters away?

Let L = the amount of light and d = the distance to the light source.

Since the amount of light varies inversely with the *square of the distance* to the light source, we have

$$L = \frac{k}{d^2}.$$

Substituting the known values of $L = 6.25$ and $d = 8$, we can find the value of k.

$$6.25 = \frac{k}{8^2}$$

$$6.25 = \frac{k}{64}$$

$$400 = k$$

We are now able to write a more specific equation,

$$L = \frac{400}{d^2}.$$

We will use this to find L when $d = 4$ meters.

$$L = \frac{400}{4^2}$$

$$L = \frac{400}{16}$$

$$L = 25 \text{ lumens}$$

Check: Does this answer seem reasonable? Would we expect to have more light if we move closer to the light source? ✓

Practice Problem 3 If the amount of power in an electrical circuit is held constant, the resistance in the circuit varies inversely with the square of the amount of current. If the amount of current is 0.01 ampere, the resistance is 800 ohms. What is the resistance if the amount of current is 0.04 ampere?

3 Solving Problems Using Joint or Combined Variation

Sometimes a quantity depends on the variation of two or more variables. This is called joint or **combined variation.**

EXAMPLE 4 y varies directly with x and z and inversely with d^2. When $x = 7$, $z = 3$, and $d = 4$, the value of y is 20. Find the value of y when $x = 5$, $z = 6$, and $d = 2$.

We can write the equation

$$y = \frac{kxz}{d^2}.$$

To find the value of k, we substitute into the equation $y = 20$, $x = 7$, $z = 3$, and $d = 4$.

$$20 = \frac{k(7)(3)}{4^2}$$

$$20 = \frac{21k}{16}$$

$$320 = 21k$$

$$\frac{320}{21} = k$$

Now we substitute $\frac{320}{21}$ for k into our original equation.

$$y = \frac{\frac{320}{21}xz}{d^2} \quad \text{or} \quad y = \frac{320xz}{21d^2}$$

We use this equation to find y for the known values of x, z, and d. We want to find y when $x = 5$, $z = 6$, and $d = 2$.

$$y = \frac{320(5)(6)}{21(2)^2} = \frac{9600}{84}$$

$$y = \frac{800}{7}$$

Practice Problem 4 y varies directly with z and w^2 and inversely with x. $y = 20$ when $z = 3$, $w = 5$, and $x = 4$. Find y when $z = 4$, $w = 6$, and $x = 2$.

Many applied problems involve joint variation. For example, a cylindrical cement column has a safe load capacity that varies directly with the diameter raised to the fourth power and inversely with the square of its length.

Therefore, if d = diameter and l = length, the equation would be of the form

$$y = \frac{kd^4}{l^2}.$$

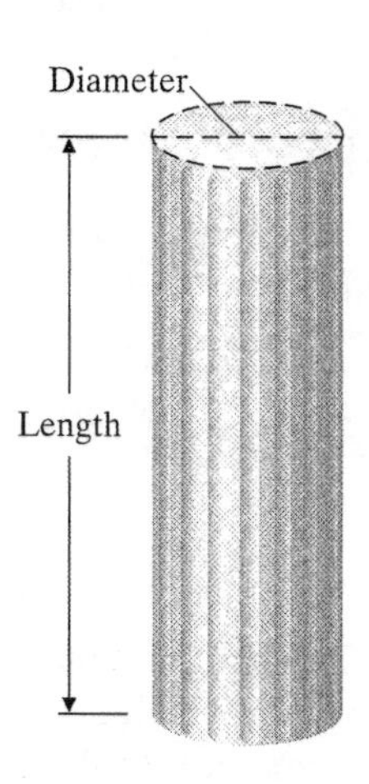

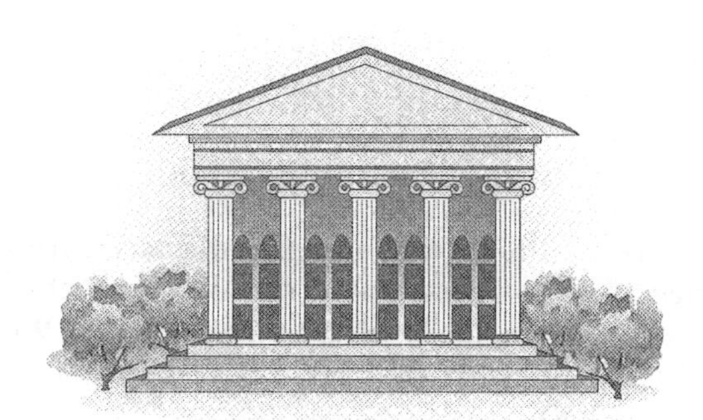

7.7 Exercises

Verbal and Writing Skills

1. Give an example in everyday life of direct variation and write an equation as a mathematical model.

2. The general equation $y = kx$ means that y varies ________ with x. k is called the ________ of variation.

3. If y varies inversely with x, we write the equation ________.

4. Write a mathematical model for the following situation: The strength of a rectangular beam varies directly with its width and the square of its depth.

Round all answers to the nearest tenth.

5. If y varies directly with x and $y = 15$ when $x = 40$, find y when $x = 64$.

6. If y varies directly with x and $y = 42$ when $x = 35$, find y when $x = 100$.

7. A marine biology submarine was searching the waters for blue whales at 50 feet below the surface, where it experienced a pressure of 21 pounds per square inch (psi). If the pressure of water on a submerged object varies directly with its distance beneath the surface, how much pressure would the submarine have experienced if it had to dive to 170 feet?

8. A car's stopping distance varies directly with the square of its speed. A car that is traveling 30 miles per hour can stop in 40 feet. What distance will it take to stop if it is traveling 60 miles per hour?

9. When an object is dropped, the distance it falls in feet varies directly with the square of the duration of the fall in seconds. An apple that falls from a tree falls 1 foot in $\frac{1}{4}$ second. How far will it fall in 1 second? How far will it fall in 2 seconds?

10. A veterinarian specializing in marine biology is faced with operating on a dolphin. A cube-shaped aquarium has been built, which will allow the doctor to operate while keeping most of the dolphin's body submerged. The time it takes to fill a tank with water varies directly with the cube of each length of the side of the container. If a cube 2 meters on each side can be filled in 7 minutes, how long will it take to fill the dolphin tank, which is 3.5 meters on each side?

11. If y varies inversely with the square of x, and $y = 10$ when $x = 2$, find y when $x = 0.5$.

12. If y varies inversely with the square root of x, and $y = 1.8$ when $x = 0.04$, find y when $x = 0.3$.

13. Engineers have decided that part of the structure that houses certain elements of a satellite will use 9 inches of special insulation. The heat lost through a certain type of insulation varies inversely as the thickness of the insulation. If the heat lost through 6 inches of insulation is 2000 Btu per hour, how much heat will be lost with the 9 inches on the satellite?

14. The weight of an object on the Earth's surface varies inversely with the square of its distance from the center of the Earth. An object weighs 1000 pounds on the Earth's surface. This is approximately 4000 miles from the center of the Earth. How much would an object weigh 4500 miles from the center of the Earth?

15. Police officers can detect speeding by using variation. The speed of a car varies inversely with the time it takes to cover a certain fixed distance. Between two points on a highway, a car travels 45 miles per hour in 6 seconds. What is the speed of a car that travels the same distance in 9 seconds?

16. If the voltage in an electric circuit is kept at the same level, the current varies inversely with the resistance. The current measures 40 amperes when the resistance is 270 ohms. Find the current when the resistance is 100 ohms.

17. The weight that can be safely supported by a 2- by 6-inch support beam varies inversely with its length. A builder finds that a support beam that is 8 feet long will support 900 pounds. Find the weight that can be safely supported by a beam that is 18 feet long.

18. The speed that is required to maintain a satellite in a circular orbit around the Earth varies directly with the square root of the distance of the satellite from the center of the Earth. We will assume that the radius of the Earth is approximately 4000 miles. A satellite that is 100 miles above the surface of the Earth is orbiting at approximately 18,000 miles per hour. What speed would be necessary for the satellite to orbit 500 miles above the surface of the Earth? Round to nearest mile per hour.

19. The field intensity of a magnetic field varies directly with the force acting on it and inversely with the strength of the pole. If the intensity of the magnetic field is 4 oersteds when the force is 700 dynes and the strength of the pole is 200, find the intensity of the field if the force is 500 dynes and the strength of the pole is 250.

20. The attraction F of two masses m_1 and m_2 varies directly with the product of m_1 and m_2 and inversely with the square of the distance between the two bodies. If a force of 10 pounds attracts two bodies weighing 80 tons and 100 tons that are 100 miles apart, how great would the force be if the two bodies weighed 8 tons and 15 tons and were 20 miles apart?

21. Atmospheric drag tends to slow down moving objects. Atmospheric drag varies jointly with an object's surface area A and velocity v. If a Dodge Intrepid, traveling at a speed of 45 mph with a surface area of 37.8 square feet, experiences a drag of 222 newtons, how fast must a Dodge Caravan, with a surface area of 55 square feet, travel in order to experience a drag force of 450 newtons?

22. The force on a blade of a wind generator varies jointly with the product of the blade's area and the square of the wind velocity. The force of the wind is 20 pounds when the area is 3 square feet and the velocity is 30 feet per second. Find the force when the area is increased to 5 square feet and the velocity is reduced to 25 feet per second.

Cumulative Review Problems

Solve each of the following equations or word problems.

23. $3x^2 - 8x + 4 = 0$

24. $4x^2 = -28x + 32$

25. In Champaign, Illinois, the sales tax is 6.25%. Donny bought an amplifier for his stereo that cost $488.75 after tax. What was the original price of the amplifier?

26. It takes 7.5 gallons of white paint to properly paint lines on three tennis courts. How much paint is needed to paint twenty-two tennis courts?

27. Craig Emanuel has a photography studio in Los Angeles. He wants to frame his collection of 110 antique photographs in special gold leaf and silver frames. The price of each gold leaf frame is $140, and the price of each silver frame is $95. If Craig has $13,375 for the frames, how many of each frame can he buy to decorate his studio?

▲ **28.** A triangular New Year's noisemaking toy has a perimeter of 50 centimeters. The first side is $\frac{4}{5}$ as long as the second side. The third side is 2 centimeters shorter than the first side. Find the length of each side.

Math in the Media

The Pythagorean Winning Percentage Formula

The Pythagorean winning percentage formula, developed by Bill James, is used to predict the record of a team based on its runs scored and runs allowed. The formula is:

$$\frac{(\text{Runs Scored})^2}{(\text{Runs Scored})^2 + (\text{Runs Allowed})^2}$$

In each part of the formula, an exponent of 1.83 is sometimes used instead of 2 because it provides a slightly more precise calculation.

The Pythagorean winning percentage formula was put to just such a use in a recent article, *So Who Would Win?* by Devin Clancy in USATODAY.com.

To get some hands on experience with this formula try the following exercises.

EXERCISES

1. The Cincinnati Reds scored 865 runs and allowed 711 runs in the 1999 season. Using the Pythagorean winning percentage formula (with the exponent of 2), calculate the team's predicted winning percent. Round to 3 decimal places.

2. The Cincinnati Reds ended the 1999 season with a 0.589 win percentage. Calculate exercise 1 again and use 1.83 rather than an exponent of 2 in the winning percentage formula. What is the predicted winning percent? Did the accuracy of the prediction improve?

3. The New York Yankees ended the 2000 season with a 0.540 win percentage. The team scored 871 runs and allowed 814 runs in the 2000 season. Using the Pythagorean winning percentage formula, with an exponent of 2, calculate the team's predicted winning percentage. Repeat the formula with an exponent of 1.83. Which calculation is closer to the exact value?

Chapter 7 Organizer

Topic	Procedure	Examples
Multiplication of variables with rational exponents, p. 362.	$x^m x^n = x^{m+n}$	$(3x^{1/5})(-2x^{3/5}) = -6x^{4/5}$
Division of variables with rational exponents, p. 362.	$\dfrac{x^m}{x^n} = x^{m-n}, \quad n \neq 0, x \neq 0$	$\dfrac{-16x^{3/20}}{24x^{5/20}} = -\dfrac{2x^{-1/10}}{3}$
Removing negative exponents, p. 361.	$x^{-n} = \dfrac{1}{x^n}, \quad m \text{ and } n \neq 0, x \text{ and } y \neq 0$ $\dfrac{x^{-n}}{y^{-m}} = \dfrac{y^m}{x^n}$	Write with positive exponents. $3x^{-4} = \dfrac{3}{x^4}$ $\dfrac{2x^{-6}}{5y^{-8}} = \dfrac{2y^8}{5x^6}$ $4^{-2} = \dfrac{1}{4^2} = \dfrac{1}{16}$
Zero exponent, p. 364.	$x^0 = 1 \quad (\text{if } x \neq 0)$	$(3x^{1/2})^0 = 1$
Raising a variable with an exponent to a power, p. 361.	$(x^m)^n = x^{mn}$ $(xy)^n = x^n y^n$ $\left(\dfrac{x}{y}\right)^n = \dfrac{x^n}{y^n}, \quad y \neq 0$	$(x^{-1/2})^{-2/3} = x^{1/3}$ $(3x^{-2}y^{-1/2})^{2/3} = 3^{2/3}x^{-4/3}y^{-1/3}$ $\left(\dfrac{4x^{-2}}{3^{-1}y^{-1/2}}\right)^{1/4} = \dfrac{4^{1/4}x^{-1/2}}{3^{-1/4}y^{-1/8}}$
Multiplication of expressions with rational exponents, p. 362.	Add exponents whenever expressions with the same base are multiplied.	$x^{2/3}(x^{1/3} - x^{1/4}) = x^{3/3} - x^{2/3+1/4} = x - x^{11/12}$
Higher-order roots, p. 368.	If x is a nonnegative real number, $\sqrt[n]{x}$ is a nonnegative nth root and has the property that $(\sqrt[n]{x})^n = x.$ If x is a negative real number, $(\sqrt[n]{x})^n = x$ when n is an odd integer. If x is a negative real number, $(\sqrt[n]{x})^n$ is not a real number when n is an even integer. $\sqrt[3]{27} = 3$ because $3^3 = 27$.	$\sqrt[5]{-32} = -2$ because $(-2)^5 = -32$. $\sqrt[4]{-16}$ is *not* a real number.
Rational exponents and radicals, p. 369.	For positive integers m and n and any real number x for which $x^{1/n}$ is defined, $x^{m/n} = (\sqrt[n]{x})^m = \sqrt[n]{x^m}.$ If it is also true that $x \neq 0$, then $x^{1/n} = \sqrt[n]{x}.$	Write as a radical: $x^{3/7} = \sqrt[7]{x^3}, 3^{1/5} = \sqrt[5]{3}$ Write as an expression with a fractional exponent: $\sqrt[4]{w^3} = w^{3/4}$ Evaluate. $25^{3/2} = (\sqrt{25})^3 = (5)^3 = 125$
Higher-order roots and absolute value, p. 372.	$\sqrt[n]{x^n} = \|x\|$ when n is an even positive integer. $\sqrt[n]{x^n} = x$ when n is an odd positive integer.	$\sqrt[6]{x^6} = \|x\|$ $\sqrt[5]{x^5} = x$
Evaluation of higher-order roots, p. 372.	Use exponent notation.	$\sqrt[5]{-32x^{15}} = \sqrt[5]{(-2)^5x^{15}}$ $= [(-2)^5x^{15}]^{1/5} = (-2)^1x^3 = -2x^3$

Topic	Procedure	Examples
Simplification of radicals with the product rule, p. 376.	For nonnegative real numbers a and b and positive integers n, $\sqrt[n]{a}\sqrt[n]{b} = \sqrt[n]{ab}$.	Simplify when $x \geq 0$, $y \geq 0$. $\sqrt{75x^3} = \sqrt{25x^2}\sqrt{3x}$ $= 5x\sqrt{3x}$ $\sqrt[3]{16x^5y^6} = \sqrt[3]{8x^3y^6}\sqrt[3]{2x^2}$ $= 2xy^2\sqrt[3]{2x^2}$
Combining radicals, p. 377.	Simplify radicals and combine them if they have the same index and the same radicand.	Combine. $2\sqrt{50} - 3\sqrt{98} = 2\sqrt{25}\sqrt{2} - 3\sqrt{49}\sqrt{2}$ $= 2(5)\sqrt{2} - 3(7)\sqrt{2}$ $= 10\sqrt{2} - 21\sqrt{2} = -11\sqrt{2}$
Multiplying radicals, p. 381.	**1.** Multiply coefficients outside the radical and then multiply the radicands. **2.** Simplify your answer.	$(2\sqrt{3})(4\sqrt{5}) = 8\sqrt{15}$ $2\sqrt{6}(\sqrt{2} - 3\sqrt{12}) = 2\sqrt{12} - 6\sqrt{72}$ $= 2\sqrt{4}\sqrt{3} - 6\sqrt{36}\sqrt{2}$ $= 4\sqrt{3} - 36\sqrt{2}$ $(\sqrt{2} + \sqrt{3})(2\sqrt{2} - \sqrt{3})$ By the FOIL method. $= 2\sqrt{4} - \sqrt{6} + 2\sqrt{6} - \sqrt{9}$ $= 4 + \sqrt{6} - 3$ $= 1 + \sqrt{6}$
Simplifying quotients of radicals with the quotient rule, p. 382.	For nonnegative real numbers a, positive real numbers b, and positive integers n, $\sqrt[n]{\frac{a}{b}} = \frac{\sqrt[n]{a}}{\sqrt[n]{b}}$.	$\sqrt[3]{\frac{5}{27}} = \frac{\sqrt[3]{5}}{\sqrt[3]{27}} = \frac{\sqrt[3]{5}}{3}$
Rationalizing denominators, p. 383.	Multiply numerator and denominator by a value that eliminates the radical in the denominator.	$\frac{2}{\sqrt{7}} = \frac{2}{\sqrt{7}} \cdot \frac{\sqrt{7}}{\sqrt{7}} = \frac{2\sqrt{7}}{7}$ $\frac{3}{\sqrt{5}+\sqrt{2}} = \frac{3}{\sqrt{5}+\sqrt{2}} \cdot \frac{\sqrt{5}-\sqrt{2}}{\sqrt{5}-\sqrt{2}} = \frac{3\sqrt{5}-3\sqrt{2}}{(\sqrt{5})^2-(\sqrt{2})^2}$ $= \frac{3\sqrt{5} - 3\sqrt{2}}{5 - 2}$ $= \frac{3\sqrt{5} - 3\sqrt{2}}{3}$ $= \sqrt{5} - \sqrt{2}$
Solving radical equations, p. 390.	**1.** Perform algebraic operations to obtain one radical by itself on one side of the equation. **2.** If the equation contains square roots, square each side of the equation. Otherwise, raise each side to the appropriate power for third- and higher-order roots. **3.** Simplify, if possible. **4.** If the equation still contains a radical, repeat steps 1 to 3. **5.** Collect all terms on one side of the equation. **6.** Solve the resulting equation. **7.** Check all apparent solutions. Solutions to radical equations must be verified.	Solve. $x = \sqrt{2x + 9} - 3$ $x + 3 = \sqrt{2x + 9}$ $(x + 3)^2 = (\sqrt{2x + 9})^2$ $x^2 + 6x + 9 = 2x + 9$ $x^2 + 6x - 2x + 9 - 9 = 0$ $x^2 + 4x = 0$ $x(x + 4) = 0$ $x = 0$ or $x = -4$ *Check:* $x = 0$: $0 \stackrel{?}{=} \sqrt{2(0) + 9} - 3$ $0 \stackrel{?}{=} \sqrt{9} - 3$ $0 = 3 - 3$ ✓ $x = -4$: $-4 \stackrel{?}{=} \sqrt{2(-4) + 9} - 3$ $-4 \stackrel{?}{=} \sqrt{1} - 3$ $-4 \neq -2$ The only solution is 0.

Topic	Procedure	Examples
Simplifying imaginary numbers, p. 396.	Use $i = \sqrt{-1}$ and $i^2 = -1$ and $\sqrt{-a} = \sqrt{a}\sqrt{-1}$.	$\sqrt{-16} = \sqrt{-1}\sqrt{16} = 4i$ $\sqrt{-18} = \sqrt{-1}\sqrt{18} = i\sqrt{9}\sqrt{2} = 3i\sqrt{2}$
Adding and subtracting complex numbers, p. 398.	Combine real parts and imaginary parts separately.	$(5 + 6i) + (2 - 4i) = 7 + 2i$ $(-8 + 3i) - (4 - 2i) = -8 + 3i - 4 + 2i$ $= -12 + 5i$
Multiplying complex numbers, p. 398.	Use the FOIL method and $i^2 = -1$.	$(5 - 6i)(2 - 4i) = 10 - 20i - 12i + 24i^2$ $= 10 - 32i + 24(-1)$ $= 10 - 32i - 24$ $= -14 - 32i$
Dividing complex numbers, p. 400.	Multiply the numerator and denominator by the conjugate of the denominator.	$\frac{5 + 2i}{4 - i} = \frac{5 + 2i}{4 - i} \cdot \frac{4 + i}{4 + i} = \frac{20 + 5i + 8i + 2i^2}{16 - i^2}$ $= \frac{20 + 13i + 2(-1)}{16 - (-1)}$ $= \frac{20 + 13i - 2}{16 + 1}$ $= \frac{18 + 13i}{17}$ or $\frac{18}{17} + \frac{13}{17}i$
Raising i to a power, p. 399.	$i^1 = i$ $i^2 = -1$ $i^3 = -i$ $i^4 = 1$	Evaluate. $i^{27} = i^{24} \cdot i^3$ $= (i^4)^6 \cdot i^3$ $= (1)^6(-i)$ $= -i$
Direct variation, p. 404.	If y varies directly with x, there is a constant of variation k such that $y = kx$. After k is determined, other values of y or x can easily be computed.	y varies directly with x. When $x = 2$, $y = 7$. $y = kx$ $7 = k(2)$ Substitute. $k = \frac{7}{2}$ Solve. $y = \frac{7}{2}x$ What is y when $x = 18$? $y = \frac{7}{2}x = \frac{7}{2} \cdot 18 = 63$
Inverse variation, p. 405.	If y varies inversely with x, the constant k is such that $y = \frac{k}{x}$.	y varies inversely with x. When x is 5, y is 12. What is y when x is 30? $y = \frac{k}{x}$ $12 = \frac{k}{5}$ Substitute. $k = 60$ Solve. $y = \frac{60}{x}$ Substitute. When $x = 30$, $y = \frac{60}{30} = 2$.

Putting Your Skills to Work

The Sailor's Observation Formula

For centuries sailors have used a formula to determine how many miles they can see in the distance D given the number of feet they are above sea level H. The formula is

$$D = \sqrt{\frac{3H}{2}}.$$

Use this formula to answer the following questions. Round your answers to the nearest tenth.

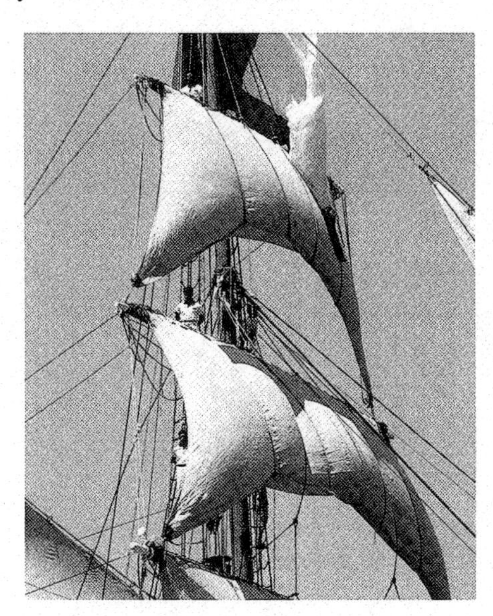

Problems for Individual Investigation and Analysis

1. Find the distance in miles that a sailor can see if he is 10 feet above sea level, 50 feet above sea level, and 100 feet above sea level.

2. Find the distance a sailor can see if he is 150 feet and 250 feet above sea level. Use these answers as well as the answers obtained in Question 1 to graph the equation.

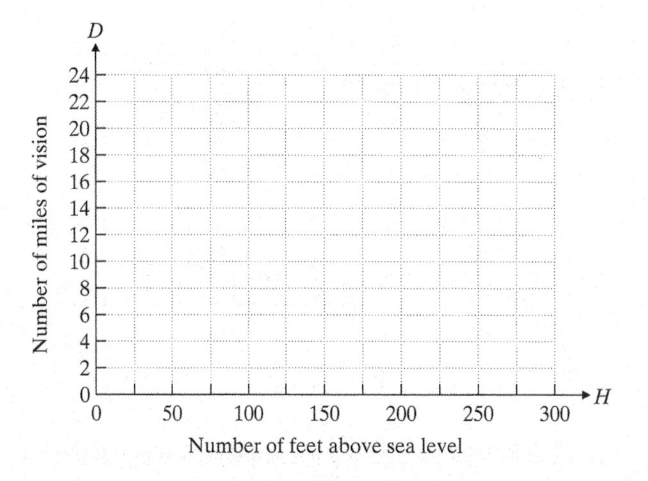

Problems for Group Investigation and Cooperative Learning

3. Solve the equation for H. Use the result to find the height H that a sailor must be above sea level in order to see a distance of 20 miles.

4. On the USS *Constitution*, sailors were normally stationed 150 feet above sea level in order to serve as lookouts. However, it was possible to climb higher in order to obtain a better view. How much was the viewing distance increased if a sailor climbed from 150 feet to 210 feet above sea level?

Internet Connections

Netsite: http://www.prenhall.com/tobey_intermediate

Site: USS Constitution site

This site provides you with history and data regarding the oldest ship in the U.S. Navy.

5. Determine the height of the tallest mast on the USS *Constitution*. If a sailor stood on the top of the tallest mast with his head level with the top of the mast, how far would he be able to see into the distance?

6. How much further would a sailor on top of the main mast be able to see than one on top of the mizzenmast?

Chapter 7 Review Problems

In all exercises assume that the variables represent positive real numbers unless otherwise stated. Simplify using only positive exponents in your answers.

1. $(3xy^{1/2})(5x^2y^{-3})$

2. $\dfrac{3x^{2/3}}{6x^{1/6}}$

3. $(25a^3b^4)^{1/2}$

4. $5^{1/4} \cdot 5^{1/2}$

5. $(2a^{1/3}b^{1/4})(-3a^{1/2}b^{1/2})$

6. $\dfrac{6x^{2/3}y^{1/10}}{12x^{1/6}y^{-1/5}}$

7. $(2x^{-1/5}y^{1/10}z^{4/5})^{-5}$

8. $\left(\dfrac{49a^3b^6}{a^{-7}b^4}\right)^{1/2}$

9. $\dfrac{(x^{3/4}y^{2/5})^{1/2}}{x^{-1/8}}$

10. $\left(\dfrac{27x^{5n}}{x^{2n-3}}\right)^{1/3}$

11. $(5^{6/5})^{10/7}$

12. Combine as one fraction containing only positive exponents. $2x^{1/3} + x^{-2/3}$

13. Factor out a common factor of $3x$ from $6x^{3/2} - 9x^{1/2}$.

In Exercises 14–23, assume that all variables are positive real numbers.

14. Write in exponential form $\sqrt{\sqrt[5]{2x}}$.

15. Write in radical form $(2x + 3y)^{4/9}$.

16. Evaluate $\sqrt[3]{125} + \sqrt[4]{81}$.

17. Explain the difference between $-\sqrt[6]{64}$ and $\sqrt[6]{-64}$.

Evaluate or simplify each expression.

18. $27^{-4/3}$

19. $\left(\dfrac{4}{9}\right)^{3/2}$

20. $\sqrt{99x^3y^6z^{10}}$

21. $\sqrt[3]{-56a^8b^{10}c^{12}}$

22. $\sqrt{144x^{10}y^{12}z^0}$

23. $\sqrt[3]{125a^9b^6c^{300}}$

In Exercises 24–29, assume that x and y can be any **positive** *or* **negative** *real number.*

Simplify the following:

24. $\sqrt[3]{y^3}$

25. $\sqrt{y^2}$

26. $\sqrt[4]{x^4y^4}$

27. $\sqrt[5]{x^{10}}$

28. $\sqrt[3]{x^{21}}$

29. $\sqrt{x^8}$

Combine where possible.

30. $\sqrt{50} + 2\sqrt{32} - \sqrt{8}$

31. $\sqrt{28} - 4\sqrt{7} + 5\sqrt{63}$

32. $\sqrt[3]{8} + 3\sqrt[3]{16} - 4\sqrt[3]{54}$

33. $2\sqrt{32x} - 5x\sqrt{2} + \sqrt{18x} + 2\sqrt{8x^2}$

Multiply and simplify.

34. $(5\sqrt{12})(3\sqrt{6})$

35. $3\sqrt{x}(2\sqrt{8x} - 3\sqrt{48})$

36. $(5\sqrt{2} + \sqrt{3})(\sqrt{2} - 2\sqrt{3})$

37. $(5\sqrt{6} - 2\sqrt{2})(\sqrt{6} - \sqrt{2})$

38. $(2\sqrt{5} - 3\sqrt{6})^2$

39. $(\sqrt[3]{2x} + \sqrt[3]{6})(\sqrt[3]{4x^2} - \sqrt[3]{y})$

40. Let $f(x) = \sqrt{5x + 20}$.
(a) Find $f(16)$.
(b) What is the domain of $f(x)$?

41. Let $f(x) = \sqrt{36 - 4x}$.
(a) Find $f(5)$.
(b) What is the domain of $f(x)$?

42. Let $f(x) = \sqrt{\frac{3}{4}x - \frac{1}{2}}$.

(a) Find $f(1)$.

(b) What is the domain of $f(x)$?

Rationalize the denominator and simplify the expression.

43. $\sqrt{\dfrac{3x^2}{y}}$

44. $\dfrac{2}{\sqrt{3y}}$

45. $\dfrac{3\sqrt{7x}}{\sqrt{21x}}$

46. $\dfrac{2}{\sqrt{6} - \sqrt{5}}$

47. $\dfrac{\sqrt{x}}{3\sqrt{x} + \sqrt{y}}$

48. $\dfrac{\sqrt{5}}{\sqrt{7} - 3}$

49. $\dfrac{2\sqrt{3} + \sqrt{6}}{\sqrt{3} + 2\sqrt{6}}$

50. $\dfrac{5\sqrt{2} - \sqrt{3}}{\sqrt{6} - \sqrt{3}}$

51. $\dfrac{3\sqrt{x} + \sqrt{y}}{\sqrt{x} - \sqrt{y}}$

52. $\dfrac{2xy}{\sqrt[3]{16xy^5}}$

53. Simplify $\sqrt{-16} + \sqrt{-45}$.

54. Find x and y. $2x - 3i + 5 = yi - 2 + \sqrt{6}$

Simplify by performing the operation indicated.

55. $(-12 - 6i) + (3 - 5i)$ **56.** $(2 - i) - (12 - 3i)$ **57.** $(7 + 3i)(2 - 5i)$ **58.** $(8 - 4i)^2$

59. $2i(3 + 4i)$ **60.** $3 - 4(2 + i)$ **61.** Evaluate i^{34}. **62.** i^{65}

Divide.

63. $\frac{7 - 2i}{3 + 4i}$ **64.** $\frac{5 - 2i}{1 - 3i}$ **65.** $\frac{4 - 3i}{5i}$ **66.** $\frac{12}{3 - 5i}$ **67.** $\frac{10 - 4i}{2 + 5i}$

Solve and check your solution(s).

68. $2\sqrt{6x + 1} = 10$

69. $\sqrt[3]{3x - 1} = \sqrt[3]{5x + 1}$

70. $\sqrt{2x + 1} = 2x - 5$

71. $1 + \sqrt{3x + 1} = x$

72. $\sqrt{3x + 1} - \sqrt{2x - 1} = 1$

73. $\sqrt{7x + 2} = \sqrt{x + 3} + \sqrt{2x - 1}$

Round all answers to the nearest tenth.

74. If y varies directly with x, and $y = 16$ when $x = 5$, find the value of y when $x = 3$.

75. If y varies directly with x, and $y = 5$ when $x = 20$, find the value of y when $x = 50$.

76. A car's stopping distance varies directly with the square of its speed. A car traveling on wet pavement can stop in 50 feet when traveling at 30 miles per hour. What distance will it take the car to stop if it is traveling at 55 miles per hour?

77. The time it takes a falling object to drop a given distance varies directly with the square root of the distance traveled. A steel ball takes 2 seconds to drop a distance of 64 feet. How many seconds will it take to drop a distance of 196 feet?

78. If y varies inversely with x, and $y = 8$ when $x = 3$, find the value of y when $x = 48$.

79. The volume of a gas varies inversely with the pressure of the gas on its container. If a pressure of 24 pounds per square inch corresponds to a volume of 70 cubic inches, what pressure corresponds to a volume of 100 cubic inches?

80. Suppose that y varies directly with x and inversely with the square of z. When $x = 8$ and $z = 4$, then $y = 1$. Find y when $x = 6$ and $z = 3$.

81. The capacity of a cylinder varies directly with the height and the square of the radius. A cylinder with a radius of 3 centimeters and a height of 5 centimeters has a capacity of 50 cubic centimeters. What is the capacity of a cylinder with a height of 9 centimeters and a radius of 4 centimeters?

Chapter 7 Test

Simplify.

1. $(2x^{1/2}y^{1/3})(-3x^{1/3}y^{1/6})$

2. $\dfrac{7x^3}{4x^{3/4}}$

3. $(8x^{1/3})^{3/2}$

4. $6^{1/5} \cdot 6^{3/5}$

Evaluate.

5. $8^{-2/3}$

6. $16^{5/4}$

Simplify. Assume that all variables are nonnegative.

7. $\sqrt{75a^4b^9}$

8. $\sqrt{64x^6y^5}$

9. $\sqrt[3]{250x^4y^6}$

Combine like terms where possible.

10. $3\sqrt{48} - \sqrt[3]{54x^5} + 2\sqrt{27} + 2x\sqrt[3]{16x^2}$

11. $\sqrt{32} - 3\sqrt{8} + 2\sqrt{72}$

Multiply and simplify.

12. $2\sqrt{3}(3\sqrt{6} - 5\sqrt{2})$

13. $(5\sqrt{3} - \sqrt{6})(2\sqrt{3} + 3\sqrt{6})$

Rationalize the denominator.

14. $\dfrac{8}{\sqrt{20x}}$

15. $\sqrt{\dfrac{xy}{3}}$

16. $\dfrac{5 + 2\sqrt{3}}{4 - \sqrt{3}}$

Solve and check your solution(s).

17. $\sqrt{3x - 2} = x$

18. $5 + \sqrt{x + 15} = x$

19. $5 - \sqrt{x - 2} = \sqrt{x + 3}$

1. ______
2. ______
3. ______
4. ______
5. ______
6. ______
7. ______
8. ______
9. ______
10. ______
11. ______
12. ______
13. ______
14. ______
15. ______
16. ______
17. ______
18. ______
19. ______

20. ______

Simplify by using the properties of complex numbers.

20. $(8 + 2i) - 3(2 - 4i)$

21. ______

21. $i^{18} + \sqrt{-16}$

22. ______

22. $(3 - 2i)(4 + 3i)$

23. ______

23. $\dfrac{2 + 5i}{1 - 3i}$

24. ______

24. $(6 + 3i)^2$

25. ______

25. i^{43}

26. ______

26. If y varies inversely with x, and $y = 9$ when $x = 2$, find the value of y when $x = 6$.

27. ______

27. Suppose y varies directly with x and inversely with the square of z. When $x = 8$ and $z = 4$, then $y = 3$. Find y when $x = 5$ and $z = 6$.

28. ______

28. A car's stopping distance varies directly with the square of its speed. A car traveling on pavement can stop in 30 feet when traveling at 30 miles per hour. What distance will it take the car to stop if it is traveling at 50 miles per hour?

Cumulative Test for Chapters 1–7

Approximately one half of this test covers the content of Chapters 1–6. The remainder covers the content of Chapter 7.

1. Identify what property of real numbers is illustrated by the equation $7 + (2 + 3) = (7 + 2) + 3$.

2. Remove parentheses and collect like terms. $2a(3a^3 - 4) - 3a^2(a - 5)$

3. Simplify. $7(12 - 14)^3 - 7 + 3 \div (-3)$

4. Solve for x. $y = -\frac{3}{4}x + 2$

5. Graph $3x - 5y = 15$.

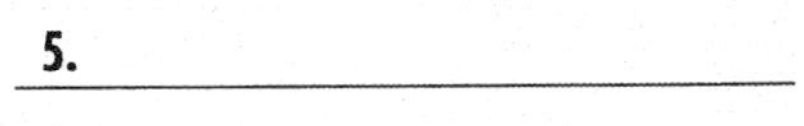

6. Factor completely $16x^2 + 24x - 16$.

7. Solve for x, y, and z.

$$\begin{aligned} x + 4y - z &= 10 \\ 3x + 2y + z &= 4 \\ 2x - 3y + 2z &= -7 \end{aligned}$$

8. Combine $\frac{7x}{x^2 - 2x - 15} - \frac{2}{x - 5}$.

▲ **9.** The length of a rectangle is 3 meters longer than twice its width. The perimeter of the rectangle is 48 meters. Find the dimensions of the rectangle.

10. Solve for b. $56x + 2 = 8b + 4x$

1. ______
2. ______
3. ______
4. ______
5. ______
6. ______
7. ______
8. ______
9. ______
10. ______

11. ____________________

12. ____________________

13. ____________________

14. ____________________

15. ____________________

16. ____________________

17. ____________________

18. ____________________

19. ____________________

20. ____________________

21. ____________________

22. ____________________

23. ____________________

24. ____________________

Simplify.

11. $\dfrac{2x^{-3}y^{-4}}{4x^{-5/2}y^{7/2}}$

12. $(3x^{-1/2}y^{2})^{-1/3}$

13. Evaluate $64^{-1/3}$.

14. Simplify $\sqrt[3]{40x^5y^9}$.

15. Combine like terms. $\sqrt{80x} + 2\sqrt{45x} - 3\sqrt{20x}$

16. Multiply and simplify. $(2\sqrt{3} - 5\sqrt{2})(\sqrt{3} + 4\sqrt{2})$

17. Rationalize the denominator. $\dfrac{\sqrt{3} + 2}{2\sqrt{3} - 5}$

18. Simplify $i^{21} + \sqrt{-16} + \sqrt{-49}$.

19. Simplify $(3 - 4i)^2$.

20. Simplify $\dfrac{1 + 4i}{1 + 3i}$.

Solve for x and check your solutions.

21. $x - 3 = \sqrt{3x + 1}$

22. $1 + \sqrt{x + 1} = \sqrt{x + 2}$

23. If y varies directly with the square of x, and $y = 12$ when $x = 2$, find the value of y if $x = 5$.

24. The amount of light provided by a lightbulb varies inversely with the square of the distance from the lightbulb. A lightbulb provides 120 lumens at a distance of 10 feet from the light. How many lumens are provided if the distance from the light is 15 feet?

Chapter 8

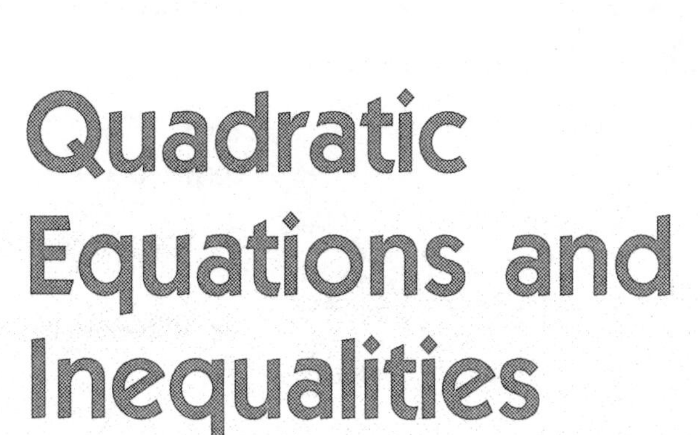

Quadratic Equations and Inequalities

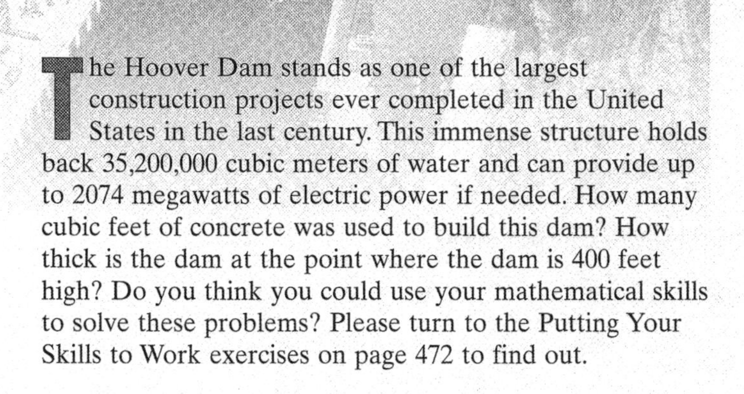

The Hoover Dam stands as one of the largest construction projects ever completed in the United States in the last century. This immense structure holds back 35,200,000 cubic meters of water and can provide up to 2074 megawatts of electric power if needed. How many cubic feet of concrete was used to build this dam? How thick is the dam at the point where the dam is 400 feet high? Do you think you could use your mathematical skills to solve these problems? Please turn to the Putting Your Skills to Work exercises on page 472 to find out.

Pretest Chapter 8

1. ____

2. ____

3. ____

4. ____

5. ____

6. ____

7. ____

8. ____

9. ____

10. ____

If you are familiar with the topics in this chapter, take this test now. Check your answers with those in the back of the book. If an answer is wrong or you can't do an exercise, study the appropriate section of the chapter.

If you are not familiar with the topics in this chapter, don't take this test now. Instead, study the examples, work the practice exercises, and then take the test.

This test will help you to identify those concepts that you have mastered and those that need more study.

Section 8.1

1. Solve by the square root property: $2x^2 + 3 = 39$

2. Solve by completing the square: $2x^2 - 4x - 3 = 0$

Section 8.2

Solve by the quadratic formula.

3. $8x^2 - 2x - 7 = 0$

4. $(x - 1)(x + 5) = 2$

5. Solve for the *nonreal* complex roots of the equation: $4x^2 = -12x - 17$

Sections 8.1 and 8.2

Solve by any method.

6. $5x^2 + 4x - 12 = 0$

7. $7x^2 + 9x = 14x^2 - 3x$

8. $\dfrac{18}{x} + \dfrac{12}{x + 1} = 9$

Section 8.3

Solve for any real roots and check your answers.

9. $x^6 - 7x^3 - 8 = 0$

10. $w^{4/3} - 6w^{2/3} + 8 = 0$

Section 8.4

11. Solve for x. Assume that w is a positive constant.

$$3x^2 + 2wx + 8w = 0$$

11. ______

▲ **12.** The area of a rectangle is 52 square meters. The length of the rectangle is 1 meter longer than three times its width. Find the length and width of the rectangle.

12. ______

Section 8.5

13. Find the vertex and the intercepts of the quadratic function $f(x) = 3x^2 + 6x - 9$.

14. Draw a graph of the quadratic function $g(x) = -x^2 + 6x - 5$. Label the vertex and intercepts.

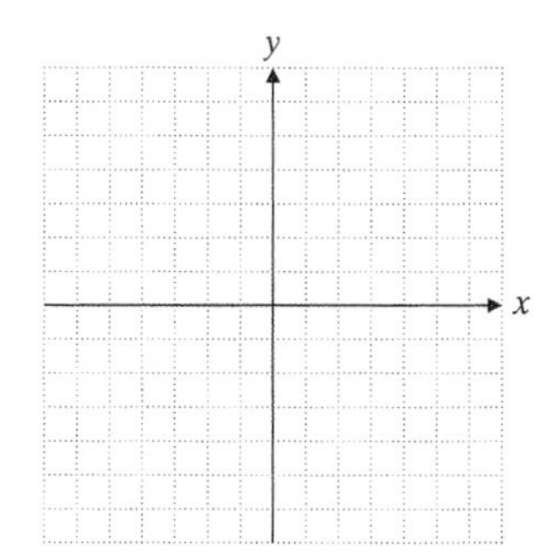

13. ______

14. ______

Section 8.6

Solve each quadratic inequality and graph your solutions.

15. ______

15. $x^2 - x - 6 > 0$

−5 −4 −3 −2 −1 0 1 2 3 4 5

16. $2x^2 + 9x \leq -9$

16. ______

−5 −4 −3 −2 −1 0 1 2 3 4 5 x

17. Use a square root table or a calculator to approximate to the nearest tenth the solution for the quadratic inequality.

$$4x^2 - 3x - 5 < 0$$

17. ______

8.1 Quadratic Equations

Student Learning Objectives

After studying this section, you will be able to:

1. Solve quadratic equations by the square root property.
2. Solve quadratic equations by completing the square.

SSM PH TUTOR CENTER CD & VIDEO MATH PRO WEB

1 Solving Quadratic Equations by the Square Root Property

Recall that an equation written in the form $ax^2 + bx + c = 0$, where a, b, and c are real numbers and $a \neq 0$, is called a **quadratic equation**. Recall also that we call this the **standard form** of a quadratic equation. We have previously solved quadratic equations using the zero-factor property. This has allowed us to factor the left side of an equation such as $x^2 - 7x + 12 = 0$ and obtain $(x - 3)(x - 4) = 0$ and then solve to find that $x = 3$ and $x = 4$. In this chapter we develop new methods of solving quadratic equations.

The first method is often called the **square root property**.

The Square Root Property

If $x^2 = a$, then $x = \pm\sqrt{a}$ for all real numbers a.

The notation $\pm\sqrt{a}$ is a shorthand way of writing "$+\sqrt{a}$ or $-\sqrt{a}$." The symbol $\pm$ is read "plus or minus." We can justify this property by using the zero-factor property. If we write $x^2 = a$ in the form $x^2 - a = 0$, we can factor it to obtain $(x + \sqrt{a})(x - \sqrt{a}) = 0$ and thus, $x = -\sqrt{a}$ or $x = +\sqrt{a}$. This can be written more compactly as $x = \pm\sqrt{a}$.

EXAMPLE 1 Solve and check: $x^2 - 36 = 0$

If we add 36 to each side, we have $x^2 = 36$.

$$\begin{aligned} x &= \pm\sqrt{36} \\ &= \pm 6 \end{aligned}$$

Thus, the two roots are 6 and -6.

Check: $6^2 = 36$ and $(-6)^2 = 36$

Practice Problem 1 Solve and check: $x^2 - 121 = 0$

EXAMPLE 2 Solve $x^2 = 48$.

$$\begin{aligned} x &= \pm\sqrt{48} = \pm\sqrt{16 \cdot 3} \\ x &= \pm 4\sqrt{3} \end{aligned}$$

The roots are $4\sqrt{3}$ and $-4\sqrt{3}$.

Practice Problem 2 Solve $x^2 = 18$.

EXAMPLE 3 Solve and check: $3x^2 + 2 = 77$

$$\begin{aligned} 3x^2 + 2 &= 77 \\ 3x^2 &= 75 \\ x^2 &= 25 \\ x &= \pm\sqrt{25} \\ x &= \pm 5 \end{aligned}$$

The roots are 5 and -5.

Check:

$$\begin{aligned} 3(5)^2 + 2 &\stackrel{?}{=} 77 \\ 3(25) + 2 &\stackrel{?}{=} 77 \\ 75 + 2 &\stackrel{?}{=} 77 \\ 77 &= 77 \checkmark \end{aligned} \qquad \begin{aligned} 3(-5)^2 + 2 &\stackrel{?}{=} 77 \\ 3(25) + 2 &\stackrel{?}{=} 77 \\ 75 + 2 &\stackrel{?}{=} 77 \\ 77 &= 77 \checkmark \end{aligned}$$

Practice Problem 3 Solve $5x^2 + 1 = 46$.

Sometimes we obtain roots that are complex numbers.

EXAMPLE 4 Solve and check: $4x^2 = -16$

$$x^2 = -4$$
$$x = \pm\sqrt{-4}$$
$$x = \pm 2i \qquad \text{Simplify using } \sqrt{-1} = i.$$

The roots are $2i$ and $-2i$.

Check:

$$4(2i)^2 \stackrel{?}{=} -16 \qquad 4(-2i)^2 \stackrel{?}{=} -16$$
$$4(4i^2) \stackrel{?}{=} -16 \qquad 4(4i^2) \stackrel{?}{=} -16$$
$$4(-4) \stackrel{?}{=} -16 \qquad 4(-4) \stackrel{?}{=} -16$$
$$-16 = -16 \checkmark \qquad -16 = -16 \checkmark$$

Practice Problem 4 Solve and check: $3x^2 = -27$

EXAMPLE 5 Solve $(4x - 1)^2 = 5$.

$$4x - 1 = \pm\sqrt{5}$$
$$4x = 1 \pm \sqrt{5}$$
$$x = \frac{1 \pm \sqrt{5}}{4}$$

The roots are $\frac{1 + \sqrt{5}}{4}$ and $\frac{1 - \sqrt{5}}{4}$.

Practice Problem 5 Solve $(2x + 3)^2 = 7$.

2 Solving Quadratic Equations by Completing the Square

Often, a quadratic equation cannot be factored (or it may be difficult to factor). So we use another method of solving the equation, called **completing the square**. When we complete the square, we are changing the polynomial to a perfect square trinomial. The form of the equation then becomes $(x + d)^2 = e$.

We already know that

$$(x + d)^2 = x^2 + 2dx + d^2.$$

Notice three things about the quadratic equation on the right-hand side.

1. The coefficient of the quadratic term (x^2) is 1.
2. The coefficient of the linear (x) term is $2d$.
3. The constant term (d^2) is the square of *half* the coefficient of the linear term.

For example, in the trinomial $x^2 + 6x + 9$, the coefficient of the linear term is 6 and the constant term is $\left(\frac{6}{2}\right)^2 = (3)^2 = 9$.

For the trinomial $x^2 - 10x + 25$, the coefficient of the linear term is -10 and the constant term is $\left(\frac{-10}{2}\right)^2 = (-5)^2 = 25$.

What number n makes the trinomial $x^2 + 12x + n$ a perfect square?

$$n = \left(\frac{12}{2}\right)^2 = 6^2 = 36$$

Hence, the trinomial $x^2 + 12x + 36$ is a perfect square trinomial and can be written as $(x + 6)^2$.

Now let's solve some equations.

EXAMPLE 6 Solve and check: $x^2 + 6x + 1 = 0$

Step 1 First we rewrite the equation in the form $ax^2 + bx = c$ by adding -1 to each side of the equation. Thus, we obtain

$$x^2 + 6x = -1.$$

Step 2 We want to complete the square of $x^2 + 6x$. That is, we want to add a constant term to $x^2 + 6x$ so that we get a perfect square trinomial. We do this by taking half the coefficient of x and squaring it.

$$\left(\frac{6}{2}\right)^2 = 3^2 = 9$$

Adding 9 to $x^2 + 6x$ gives the perfect square trinomial $x^2 + 6x + 9$, which we factor to $(x + 3)^2$. But we cannot just add 9 to the left side of our equation unless we also add 9 to the right side. (Why?) We now have

$$x^2 + 6x + 9 = -1 + 9.$$

Step 3 Now we factor.

$$(x + 3)^2 = 8$$

Step 4 We now use the square root property.

$$(x + 3) = \pm\sqrt{8}$$
$$x + 3 = \pm 2\sqrt{2}$$

Step 5 Next we solve for x by adding -3 to each side of the equation.

$$x = -3 \pm 2\sqrt{2}$$

The roots are $-3 + 2\sqrt{2}$ and $-3 - 2\sqrt{2}$.

Step 6 We *must* check our solution in the *original* equation (not the perfect square trinomial we constructed).

$$x^2 + 6x + 1 = 0$$
$$(-3 + 2\sqrt{2})^2 + 6(-3 + 2\sqrt{2}) + 1 \stackrel{?}{=} 0$$
$$9 - 12\sqrt{2} + 8 - 18 + 12\sqrt{2} + 1 \stackrel{?}{=} 0$$
$$18 - 18 - 12\sqrt{2} + 12\sqrt{2} \stackrel{?}{=} 0$$
$$0 = 0 \checkmark$$

$$x^2 + 6x + 1 = 0$$
$$(-3 - 2\sqrt{2})^2 + 6(-3 - 2\sqrt{2}) + 1 \stackrel{?}{=} 0$$
$$9 + 12\sqrt{2} + 8 - 18 - 12\sqrt{2} + 1 \stackrel{?}{=} 0$$
$$18 - 18 + 12\sqrt{2} - 12\sqrt{2} \stackrel{?}{=} 0$$
$$0 = 0 \checkmark$$

Practice Problem 6 Solve by completing the square: $x^2 + 8x + 3 = 0$

Let us summarize for future reference the six steps we have performed to solve a quadratic equation by completing the square.

Completing the Square

1. Put the equation in the form $ax^2 + bx = -c$.
2. If $a \neq 1$, divide each term of the equation by a.
3. Square half of the numerical coefficient of the linear term. Add the result to both sides of the equation.
4. Factor the left side; then take the square root of both sides of the equation.
5. Solve each resulting equation for x.
6. Check the solutions in the original equation.

EXAMPLE 7 Solve: $3x^2 - 8x + 1 = 0$

$$3x^2 - 8x = -1 \qquad \text{Add } -1 \text{ to each side.}$$

$$\frac{3x^2}{3} - \frac{8x}{3} = -\frac{1}{3}$$

Divide each term by 3. (Remember that the coefficient of the quadratic term must be 1.)

$$x^2 - \frac{8}{3}x + \frac{16}{9} = -\frac{1}{3} + \frac{16}{9}$$

$$\left(x - \frac{4}{3}\right)^2 = \frac{13}{9}$$

$$x - \frac{4}{3} = \pm\sqrt{\frac{13}{9}}$$

$$x - \frac{4}{3} = \pm\frac{\sqrt{13}}{3}$$

$$x = \frac{4}{3} \pm \frac{\sqrt{13}}{3}$$

$$x = \frac{4 \pm \sqrt{13}}{3}$$

Check: For $x = \dfrac{4 + \sqrt{13}}{3}$,

$$3\left(\frac{4 + \sqrt{13}}{3}\right)^2 - 8\left(\frac{4 + \sqrt{13}}{3}\right) + 1 \stackrel{?}{=} 0$$

$$\frac{16 + 8\sqrt{13} + 13}{3} - \frac{32 + 8\sqrt{13}}{3} + 1 \stackrel{?}{=} 0$$

$$\frac{16 + 8\sqrt{13} + 13 - 32 - 8\sqrt{13}}{3} + 1 \stackrel{?}{=} 0$$

$$\frac{29 - 32}{3} + 1 \stackrel{?}{=} 0$$

$$-\frac{3}{3} + 1 \stackrel{?}{=} 0$$

$$-1 + 1 = 0 \quad \checkmark$$

See whether you can check the solution $\dfrac{4 - \sqrt{13}}{3}$.

Practice Problem 7 Solve by completing the square: $2x^2 + 4x + 1 = 0$

8.1 Exercises

Solve the equations by using the square root property. Express any complex numbers using i notation.

1. $x^2 = 100$ **2.** $x^2 = 49$ **3.** $x^2 + 81 = 0$ **4.** $x^2 + 144 = 0$ **5.** $3x^2 - 45 = 0$

6. $4x^2 - 68 = 0$ **7.** $5x^2 - 10 = 0$ **8.** $2x^2 - 14 = 0$ **9.** $x^2 = -81$ **10.** $x^2 = -64$

11. $6x^2 + 4 = 4x^2$ **12.** $(x - 3)^2 = 12$ **13.** $(x + 2)^2 = 18$ **14.** $(2x + 1)^2 = 7$ **15.** $(3x + 2)^2 = 5$

16. $(4x - 3)^2 = 36$ **17.** $(5x - 2)^2 = 25$ **18.** $\left(\frac{x}{2} + 5\right)^2 = 8$ **19.** $\left(\frac{x}{3} - 1\right)^2 = 45$

Solve the equations by completing the square. Simplify your answers. Express any complex numbers using i notation.

20. $x^2 + 10x + 5 = 0$ **21.** $x^2 + 6x + 2 = 0$ **22.** $x^2 - 8x = 17$ **23.** $x^2 - 12x = 4$

24. $\frac{x^2}{2} + \frac{5}{2}x = 2$ **25.** $\frac{x^2}{3} - \frac{x}{3} = 3$ **26.** $2y^2 + 10y = -11$ **27.** $7x^2 + 4x - 5 = 0$

28. $3x^2 + 10x - 2 = 0$ **29.** $5x^2 + 4x - 3 = 0$ **30.** $2y^2 - y = 6$ **31.** $2y^2 - y = 15$

32. $x^2 + 1 = x$

33. $2x^2 + 2 = 3x$

34. $3x^2 + 8x + 3 = 2$

35. Check the solution $x = -1 + \sqrt{6}$ in the equation $x^2 + 2x - 5 = 0$.

36. Check the solution $x = 2 + \sqrt{3}$ in the equation $x^2 - 4x + 1 = 0$.

Applications

The sides of the box shown are labeled with the dimensions in feet.

▲ **37.** What is the value of x if the volume of the box is 648 cubic feet?

▲ **38.** What is the value of x if the volume of the box is 1800 cubic feet?

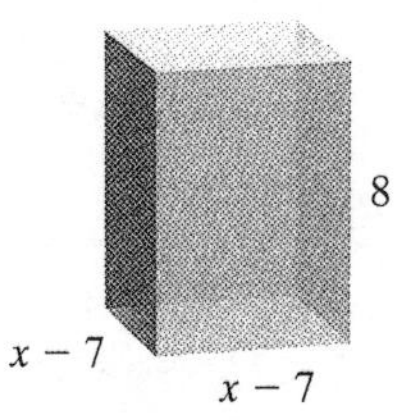

The time a basketball player spends in the air when shooting a basket is called "the hang time." The vertical leap L measured in feet is related to the hang time t measured in seconds by the equation $L = 4t^2$.

39. During his career as a Boston Celtics player, Larry Bird often displayed a leap of 3.1 feet. Find the hang time for that leap.

40. Shaquille O'Neal of the Los Angeles Lakers has often shown a vertical leap of 3.3 feet. Find the hang time for that leap.

The formula $D = 16t^2$ is used to approximate the distance in feet that an object falls in t seconds.

41. A parachutist jumps from an airplane, falls 3600 feet, and then opens her parachute. For how many seconds was the parachutist falling before she opened the parachute?

42. How long would it take an object to fall to the ground from a helicopter hovering at 1936 feet above the ground?

Cumulative Review Problems

Evaluate the expressions for the given values.

43. $\sqrt{b^2 - 4ac}$; $b = 4, a = 3, c = -4$

44. $\sqrt{b^2 - 4ac}$; $b = -5, a = 2, c = -3$

45. $5x^2 - 6x + 8$; $x = -2$

46. $2x^2 + 3x - 5$; $x = -3$

8.2 The Quadratic Formula and Solutions to Quadratic Equations

Student Learning Objectives

After studying this section, you will be able to:

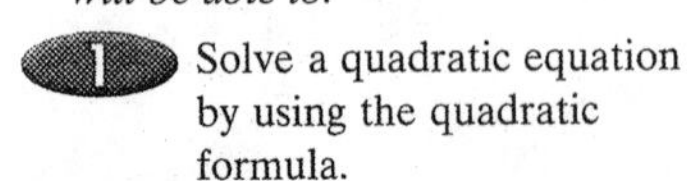
Solve a quadratic equation by using the quadratic formula.

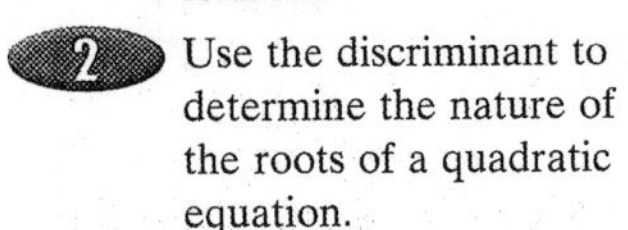
Use the discriminant to determine the nature of the roots of a quadratic equation.

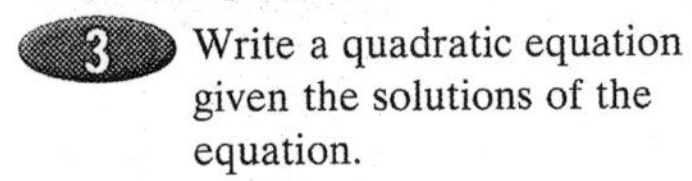
Write a quadratic equation given the solutions of the equation.

1 *Solving a Quadratic Equation by Using the Quadratic Formula*

The last method we'll study for solving quadratic equations is the **quadratic formula.** This method works for *any* quadratic equation.

The quadratic formula is developed from completing the square. We begin with the **standard form** of the quadratic equation.

$$ax^2 + bx + c = 0$$

To complete the square, we want the equation to be in the form $x^2 + dx = e$. Thus, we divide by a.

$$\frac{ax^2}{a} + \frac{b}{a}x + \frac{c}{a} = 0$$

$$x^2 + \frac{b}{a}x = -\frac{c}{a}$$

Now we complete the square by adding $\left(\frac{b}{2a}\right)^2$ to each side.

$$x^2 + \frac{b}{a}x + \left(\frac{b}{2a}\right)^2 = -\frac{c}{a} + \left(\frac{b}{2a}\right)^2$$

We factor the left side and write the right side as one fraction.

$$\left(x + \frac{b}{2a}\right)^2 = \frac{b^2 - 4ac}{4a^2}$$

Now we use the square root property.

$$x + \frac{b}{2a} = \pm\sqrt{\frac{b^2 - 4ac}{4a^2}}$$

We solve for x and simplify.

$$x = -\frac{b}{2a} \pm \sqrt{\frac{b^2 - 4ac}{4a^2}}$$

$$= \frac{-b \pm \sqrt{b^2 - 4ac}}{2a}$$

This is the quadratic formula.

Quadratic Formula

For all equations $ax^2 + bx + c = 0$,

$$x = \frac{-b \pm \sqrt{b^2 - 4ac}}{2a}, \qquad \text{where } a \neq 0.$$

EXAMPLE 1 Solve by using the quadratic formula: $x^2 + 8x = -3$

The standard form is $x^2 + 8x + 3 = 0$. We substitute $a = 1$, $b = 8$, and $c = 3$.

$$x = \frac{-b \pm \sqrt{b^2 - 4ac}}{2a}$$

$$= \frac{-8 \pm \sqrt{8^2 - 4(1)(3)}}{2(1)}$$

$$= \frac{-8 \pm \sqrt{64 - 12}}{2} = \frac{-8 \pm \sqrt{52}}{2} = \frac{-8 \pm \sqrt{4}\sqrt{13}}{2}$$

$$= \frac{-8 \pm 2\sqrt{13}}{2} = \frac{\cancel{2}(-4 \pm \sqrt{13})}{\cancel{2}}$$

$$= -4 \pm \sqrt{13}$$

Practice Problem 1 Solve by using the quadratic formula: $x^2 + 5x = -1 + 2x$

EXAMPLE 2 Solve by using the quadratic formula: $3x^2 - x - 2 = 0$

Here $a = 3$, $b = -1$, and $c = -2$.

$$x = \frac{-b \pm \sqrt{b^2 - 4ac}}{2a}$$

$$= \frac{-(-1) \pm \sqrt{(-1)^2 - 4(3)(-2)}}{2(3)}$$

$$= \frac{1 \pm \sqrt{1 + 24}}{6} = \frac{1 \pm \sqrt{25}}{6}$$

$$x = \frac{1 + 5}{6} = \frac{6}{6} \quad \text{or} \quad x = \frac{1 - 5}{6} = -\frac{4}{6}$$

$$x = 1 \qquad\qquad x = -\frac{2}{3}$$

Practice Problem 2 Solve by using the quadratic formula: $2x^2 + 7x + 6 = 0$

EXAMPLE 3 Solve by using the quadratic formula: $2x^2 - 48 = 0$

This equation is equivalent to $2x^2 - 0x - 48 = 0$. Therefore, we know that $a = 2$, $b = 0$, and $c = -48$.

$$x = \frac{-b \pm \sqrt{b^2 - 4ac}}{2a}$$

$$= \frac{-0 \pm \sqrt{(0)^2 - 4(2)(-48)}}{2(2)}$$

$$= \frac{\pm\sqrt{384}}{4}$$

$$= \frac{\pm\sqrt{64}\sqrt{6}}{4} = \frac{\pm 8\sqrt{6}}{4}$$

$$= \pm 2\sqrt{6}$$

Practice Problem 3 Solve by using the quadratic formula: $2x^2 - 26 = 0$

EXAMPLE 4 A small company that manufactures canoes makes a daily profit p according to the equation $p = -100x^2 + 3400x - 26{,}196$, where p is measured in dollars and x is the number of canoes made per day. Find the number of canoes that must be made each day to produce a zero profit for the company. Round your answer to the nearest whole number.

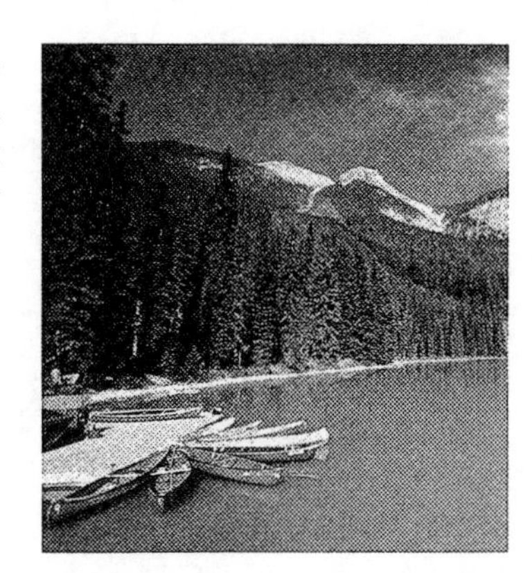

Since $p = 0$, we are solving the equation $0 = -100x^2 + 3400x - 26{,}196$.

In this case we have $a = -100$, $b = 3400$, and $c = -26{,}196$.

Now we substitute these into the quadratic formula.

$$x = \frac{-b \pm \sqrt{b^2 - 4ac}}{2a}$$

$$= \frac{-3400 \pm \sqrt{(3400)^2 - 4(-100)(-26{,}196)}}{2(-100)}$$

We will use a calculator to assist us with computation in this problem.

$$= \frac{-3400 \pm \sqrt{11{,}560{,}000 - 10{,}478{,}400}}{-200}$$

$$= \frac{-3400 \pm \sqrt{1{,}081{,}600}}{-200}$$

$$= \frac{-3400 \pm 1040}{-200}$$

We now obtain two answers.

$$x = \frac{-3400 + 1040}{-200} = \frac{-2360}{-200} = 11.8 \approx 12$$

$$x = \frac{-3400 - 1040}{-200} = \frac{-4440}{-200} = 22.2 \approx 22$$

A zero profit is obtained when approximately twelve canoes are produced or when approximately twenty-two canoes are produced. Actually a slight profit of $204 is made when these numbers of canoes are produced. The discrepancy is due to the round-off error that occurs when we approximate. By methods that we will learn later in this chapter, the maximum profit is produced when seventeen canoes are made at the factory. We will investigate exercises of this kind later.

Practice Problem 4 A company that manufactures modems makes a daily profit p according to the equation $p = -100x^2 + 4800x - 52{,}559$, where p is measured in dollars and x is the number of modems made per day. Find the number of modems that must be made each day to produce a zero profit for the company. Round your answer to the nearest whole number.

When a quadratic equation contains fractions, eliminate them by multiplying each term by the LCD. Then rewrite the equation in standard form before using the quadratic formula.

EXAMPLE 5 Solve by using the quadratic formula: $\frac{2x}{x + 2} = 1 - \frac{3}{x + 4}$

The LCD is $(x + 2)(x + 4)$.

$$\frac{2}{x + 2} = 1 - \frac{3}{x + 4}$$

$$\frac{2x}{\cancel{x + 2}}\cancel{(x + 2)}(x + 4) = 1(x + 2)(x + 4) - \frac{3}{\cancel{x + 4}}(x + 2)\cancel{(x + 4)}$$

$$2x(x + 4) = (x + 2)(x + 4) - 3(x + 2)$$

$$2x^2 + 8x = x^2 + 6x + 8 - 3x - 6$$ Now we have an equation that is quadratic.

$$2x^2 + 8x = x^2 + 3x + 2$$

$$x^2 + 5x - 2 = 0$$

Now the equation is in standard form, and we can use the quadratic formula with $a = 1, b = 5$, and $c = -2$.

$$x = \frac{-5 \pm \sqrt{5^2 - 4(1)(-2)}}{2(1)} = \frac{-5 \pm \sqrt{25 + 8}}{2}$$

$$x = \frac{-5 \pm \sqrt{33}}{2}$$

Practice Problem 5 Solve by using the quadratic formula: $\frac{1}{x} + \frac{1}{x - 1} = \frac{5}{6}$

Some quadratic equations will have solutions that are not real numbers. You should use i notation to simplify the solutions of nonreal complex numbers.

EXAMPLE 6 Solve and simplify your answer: $8x^2 - 4x + 1 = 0$

$a = 8, b = -4$, and $c = 1$.

$$x = \frac{-(-4) \pm \sqrt{(-4)^2 - 4(8)(1)}}{2(8)}$$

$$= \frac{4 \pm \sqrt{16 - 32}}{16} = \frac{4 \pm \sqrt{-16}}{16}$$

$$= \frac{4 \pm 4i}{16} = \frac{4(1 \pm i)}{16} = \frac{1 \pm i}{4}$$

Practice Problem 6 Solve by using the quadratic formula: $2x^2 - 4x + 5 = 0$

You may have noticed that complex roots come in pairs. In other words, if $a + bi$ is a solution of a quadratic equation, its conjugate $a - bi$ is also a solution.

Using the Discriminant to Determine the Nature of the Roots of a Quadratic Equation

So far we have used the quadratic formula to solve quadratic equations that had two real roots. Sometimes the roots were rational, and sometimes they were irrational. We have also solved equations like Example 6 with nonreal complex numbers. Such solutions occur when the expression $b^2 - 4ac$, the radicand in the quadratic formula, is negative.

$$x = \frac{-b \pm \sqrt{b^2 - 4ac}}{2a},$$

The expression $b^2 - 4ac$ is called the **discriminant**. Depending on the value of the discriminant and whether the discriminant is positive, zero, or negative, the roots of the quadratic equation will be rational, irrational, or complex. We summarize the types of solutions in the following table.

If the Discriminant $b^2 - 4ac$ is:	Then the Quadratic Equation $ax^2 + bx + c = 0$, Where a, b, and c are integers, will have:
A positive number that is also a perfect square	Two different rational solutions (Such an equation can always be factored.)
A positive number that is not a perfect square	Two different irrational solutions
Zero	One rational solution
Negative	Two complex solutions containing i (They will be complex conjugates.)

EXAMPLE 7 What type of solutions does the equation $2x^2 - 9x - 35 = 0$ have? Do not solve the equation.

$a = 2, b = -9$, and $c = -35$. Thus,

$$b^2 - 4ac = (-9)^2 - 4(2)(-35) = 361.$$

Since the discriminant is positive, the equation has two real roots.

Since $(19)^2 = 361$, 361 is a perfect square. Thus, the equation has two different rational solutions. This type of quadratic equation can always be factored.

Practice Problem 7 Use the discriminant to find what type of solutions the equation $9x^2 + 12x + 4 = 0$ has. Do not solve the equation.

EXAMPLE 8 Use the discriminant to determine the type of solutions each of the following equations has.

(a) $3x^2 - 4x + 2 = 0$ **(b)** $5x^2 - 3x - 5 = 0$

(a) Here $a = 3$, $b = -4$, and $c = 2$. Thus,

$$\begin{aligned} b^2 - 4ac &= (-4)^2 - 4(3)(2) \\ &= 16 - 24 = -8 \end{aligned}$$

Since the discriminant is negative, the equation will have two complex solutions containing i.

(b) Here $a = 5$, $b = -3$, and $c = -5$. Thus,

$$\begin{aligned} b^2 - 4ac &= (-3)^2 - 4(5)(-5) \\ &= 9 + 100 = 109 \end{aligned}$$

Since this positive number is not a perfect square, the equation will have two different irrational solutions.

Practice Problem 8 Use the discriminant to determine the type of solutions each of the following equations has.

(a) $x^2 - 4x + 13 = 0$ **(b)** $9x^2 + 6x + 7 = 0$

3 Writing a Quadratic Equation Given the Solutions of the Equation

By using the zero-product rule in reverse, we can find a quadratic equation that contains two given solutions. To illustrate, if 3 and 7 are the two solutions, then we could write the equation $(x - 3)(x - 7) = 0$, and therefore, a quadratic equation that has these two solutions is $x^2 - 10x + 21 = 0$. This answer is not unique. Any constant multiple of $x^2 - 10x + 21 = 0$ would also have roots of 3 and 7. Thus, $2x^2 - 20x + 42 = 0$ also has roots of 3 and 7.

EXAMPLE 9 Find a quadratic equation whose roots are 5 and -2.

$$\begin{aligned} x &= 5 \qquad\qquad x = -2 \\ x - 5 &= 0 \qquad\qquad x + 2 = 0 \\ (x - 5)(x + 2) &= 0 \\ x^2 - 3x - 10 &= 0 \end{aligned}$$

Practice Problem 9 Find a quadratic equation whose roots are -10 and -6.

EXAMPLE 10 Find a quadratic equation whose solutions are $3i$ and $-3i$. First we write the two equations.

$$\begin{aligned} x - 3i = 0 \quad \text{and} \quad x + 3i &= 0 \\ (x - 3i)(x + 3i) &= 0 \\ x^2 + 3ix - 3ix - 9i^2 &= 0 \\ x^2 - 9(-1) &= 0 \qquad \text{Use } i^2 = -1. \\ x^2 + 9 &= 0 \end{aligned}$$

Practice Problem 10 Find a quadratic equation whose solutions are $2i\sqrt{3}$ and $-2i\sqrt{3}$.

8.2 Exercises

Verbal and Writing Skills

1. How is the quadratic formula used to solve a quadratic equation?

2. The discriminant in the quadratic formula is the expression __________.

3. If the discriminant in the quadratic formula is zero, then the quadratic equation will have __________ solution(s).

4. If the discriminant in the quadratic formula is a perfect square, then the quadratic equation will have ____________________ solution(s).

Solve by the quadratic formula. Simplify your answers. Use i notation for nonreal complex numbers.

5. $x^2 - x - 3 = 0$

6. $x^2 + 5x + 2 = 0$

7. $2x^2 + x - 4 = 0$

8. $5x^2 - x - 1 = 0$

9. $x^2 = \frac{2}{3}x$

10. $\frac{4}{5}x^2 = x$

11. $6x^2 - x - 1 = 0$

12. $4x^2 + 11x - 3 = 0$

13. $4x^2 + 3x - 2 = 0$

14. $6x^2 - 2x - 1 = 0$

15. $3x^2 + 1 = 8$

16. $5x^2 - 1 = 5$

17. $2x(x + 3) - 3 = 4x - 2$

18. $5 + 3x(x - 2) = 4$

19. $3x^2 + 5x + 1 = 5x + 4$

20. $2x^2 - 7x - 3 = 9 - 7x$

21. $(x - 2)(x + 1) = \frac{2x + 3}{2}$

22. $3x(x + 1) = \frac{7x + 1}{3}$

23. $\frac{1}{x + 2} + \frac{1}{x} = \frac{1}{3}$

24. $y + \frac{3}{y + 3} = \frac{5}{2}$

25. $\frac{1}{y} - y = \frac{5}{3}$

26. $\frac{1}{15} + \frac{3}{y} = \frac{4}{y + 1}$

27. $\frac{1}{4} + \frac{6}{y + 2} = \frac{6}{y}$

28. $x^2 - 4x + 8 = 0$

29. $x^2 - 2x + 4 = 0$

30. $2x^2 + 15 = 0$

31. $5x^2 = -3$

32. $3x^2 - 8x + 7 = 0$

Use the discriminant to find what type of solutions (two rational, two irrational, one rational, or two nonreal complex) each of the following equations has. Do not solve the equation.

33. $3x^2 + 4x = 2$

34. $4x^2 - 20x + 25 = 0$

35. $2x^2 + 10x + 8 = 0$

36. $2x^2 - 7x - 4 = 0$

37. $9x^2 + 4 = 12x$

38. $5x^2 - 8x - 2 = 0$

Write a quadratic equation having the given solutions.

39. $13, -2$

40. $5, -11$

41. $-5, -12$

42. $-6, -10$

43. $4i, -4i$

44. $6i, -6i$

45. $3, -\frac{5}{2}$

46. $-2, \frac{5}{6}$

Solve for x by using the quadratic formula. Approximate your answers to four decimal places.

47. $3x^2 + 5x - 9 = 0$

48. $1.2x^2 - 12.3x - 4.2 = 0$

49. $20.6x^2 - 73.4x + 41.8 = 0$

50. $0.162x^2 + 0.094x - 0.485 = 0$

Applications

51. A company that manufactures sport parachutes makes a daily profit p according to the equation $p = -100x^2 + 4200x - 39{,}476$, where p is measured in dollars and x is the number of parachutes made per day. Find the number of parachutes that must be made each day to produce a zero profit for the company. Round your answer to the nearest whole number.

52. A company that manufactures mountain bikes makes a daily profit p according to the equation $p = -100x^2 + 4800x - 54{,}351$, where p is measured in dollars and x is the number of mountain bikes made per day. Find the number of mountain bikes that must be made each day to produce a zero profit for the company. Round your answer to the nearest whole number.

To Think About

53. The company described in Exercise 51 earns a maximum profit when $x = 21$. What profit does the company make per day if it produces twenty-one parachutes? Speculate how you could have predicted that the maximum profit occurs when $x = 21$ based on the answers you obtained in the Exercise 51.

54. The company described in Exercise 52 earns a maximum profit when $x = 24$. What profit does the company make per day if it produces twenty-four mountain bikes? Speculate how you could have predicted that the maximum profit occurs when $x = 24$ based on the answers you obtained in Exercise 52.

Cumulative Review Problems

Simplify.

55. $9x^2 - 6x + 3 - 4x - 12x^2 + 8$

56. $3y(2 - y) + \frac{1}{5}(10y^2 - 15y)$

▲ **57.** Music Galaxy sells compact discs, cassettes, and everything else you could possibly want from a music supply superstore. The management plans to expand its compact disc section. Presently, it takes 50 feet of an inner security fence to enclose the rectangular section. The expansion plans call for tripling the width and doubling the length. The new CD section will need 118 feet of inner security fencing. What is the length and width of the current compact disc section?

58. Last year, Cecile, a professional mountain bike racer, purchased three new padded riding suits to protect her from injury and compress her muscles while riding. In addition, she purchased two pairs of racing goggles. The cost for these items was \$343. This year, suits cost \$10 more and goggles cost \$5 more than last year. This year she purchased two new suits and three pairs of goggles for \$312. How much did each suit cost last year? How much did each pair of goggles cost last year?

8.3 Equations That Can Be Transformed into Quadratic Form

Student Learning Objectives

After studying this section, you will be able to:

1. Solve equations of degree greater than 2 that can be transformed into quadratic form.

2. Solve equations with fractional exponents that can be transformed into quadratic form.

WEB

1 Solve Equations of Degree Greater than 2

Some higher-order equations can be solved by writing them in the form of a quadratic equation. An equation is **quadratic in form** if we can substitute a linear term for the variable raised to the lowest power and get an equation of the form $ay^2 + by + c = 0$.

EXAMPLE 1 Solve $x^4 - 13x^2 + 36 = 0$.

Let $y = x^2$. Then $y^2 = x^4$. Thus, we obtain a new equation and solve it as follows:

$$y^2 - 13y + 36 = 0 \quad \text{Replace } x^2 \text{ by } y \text{ and } x^4 \text{ by } y^2.$$

$$(y - 4)(y - 9) = 0 \quad \text{Factor.}$$

$$y - 4 = 0 \quad \text{or} \quad y - 9 = 0 \quad \text{Solve for } y.$$

$$y = 4 \qquad y = 9$$

These are *not* the roots to the original equation. We must replace y by x^2.

$$x^2 = 4 \qquad x^2 = 9$$

$$x = \pm\sqrt{4} \qquad x = \pm\sqrt{9}$$

$$x = \pm 2 \qquad x = \pm 3$$

Thus, there are *four* solutions to the original equation: $x = +2$, $x = -2$, $x = +3$, and $x = -3$. Check these values to verify that they are solutions.

Practice Problem 1 Solve $x^4 - 5x^2 - 36 = 0$.

EXAMPLE 2 Solve for all real roots: $2x^6 - x^3 - 6 = 0$

Let $y = x^3$. Then $y^2 = x^6$. Thus, we have the following:

$$2y^2 - y - 6 = 0 \quad \text{Replace } x^3 \text{ by } y \text{ and } x^6 \text{ by } y^2.$$

$$(2y + 3)(y - 2) = 0 \quad \text{Factor.}$$

$$2y + 3 = 0 \quad \text{or} \quad y - 2 = 0 \quad \text{Solve for } y.$$

$$y = -\frac{3}{2} \qquad y = 2$$

$$x^3 = -\frac{3}{2} \quad \text{or} \quad x^3 = 2 \quad \text{Replace } y \text{ by } x^3.$$

$$x = \sqrt[3]{-\frac{3}{2}} \qquad x = \sqrt[3]{2} \quad \text{Take the cube root of each side of the equation.}$$

$$x = \frac{\sqrt[3]{-12}}{2} \quad \text{Simplify } \sqrt[3]{-\frac{3}{2}} \text{ by rationalizing the denominator.}$$

Check these solutions.

Practice Problem 2 Solve for all real roots: $x^6 - 5x^3 + 4 = 0$

2 Solving Equations with Fractional Exponents

EXAMPLE 3 Solve and check your solutions: $x^{2/3} - 3x^{1/3} + 2 = 0$

Let $y = x^{1/3}$. Then $y^2 = x^{2/3}$.

$y^2 - 3y + 2 = 0$ — Replace $x^{1/3}$ by y and $x^{2/3}$ by y^2.

$(y - 2)(y - 1) = 0$ — Factor.

$y - 2 = 0$ or $y - 1 = 0$

$y = 2$ $\quad$ $y = 1$ — Solve for y.

$x^{1/3} = 2$ or $x^{1/3} = 1$ — Replace y by $x^{1/3}$.

$(x^{1/3})^3 = (2)^3$ $\quad$ $(x^{1/3})^3 = (1)^3$ — Cube each side of the equation.

$x = 8$ $\quad$ $x = 1$

Check:

$x = 8$: $(8)^{2/3} - 3(8)^{1/3} + 2 \stackrel{?}{=} 0$

$(\sqrt[3]{8})^2 - 3(\sqrt[3]{8}) + 2 \stackrel{?}{=} 0$

$(2)^2 - 3(2) + 2 \stackrel{?}{=} 0$

$4 - 6 + 2 \stackrel{?}{=} 0$

$0 = 0$ ✓

$x = 1$: $(1)^{2/3} - 3(1)^{1/3} + 2 \stackrel{?}{=} 0$

$(\sqrt[3]{1})^2 - 3(\sqrt[3]{1}) + 2 \stackrel{?}{=} 0$

$1 - 3 + 2 \stackrel{?}{=} 0$

$0 = 0$ ✓

The exercises that appear in this section are somewhat difficult to solve. Part of the difficulty lies in the fact that the equations have different numbers of solutions. A fourth-degree equation like the one in Example 1 has four different solutions. Whereas a sixth-degree equation such as the one in Example 2 has only two solutions, some sixth-degree equations will have as many as six solutions. Although the equation that we examined in Example 3 has only two solutions, other equations with fractional exponents may have one solution or even no solution at all. It is good to take some time to carefully examine your work to determine that you have obtained the correct number of solutions.

A graphing program on a computer such as TI Interactive, Derive, or Maple can be very helpful in determining or verifying the solutions to these types of problems. Of course a graphing calculator can be most helpful, particularly in verifying the value of a solution and the number of solutions.

Optional Graphing Calculation Exploration: If you have a graphing calculator, verify the solutions for Example 3 by graphing the equation

$$y = x^{2/3} - 3x^{1/3} + 2.$$

Determine from your graph whether the curve does in fact cross the x-axis (that is, $y = 0$ when $x = 1$ and $x = 8$). You will have to carefully select the window so that you can see the behavior of the curve clearly. For this equation a useful window is $[-1, 12, -1, 2]$. Remember that with most graphing calculators, you will need to surround the exponents with parentheses.

Practice Problem 3 Solve and check your solutions: $3x^{4/3} - 5x^{2/3} + 2 = 0$

EXAMPLE 4 Solve and check your solutions: $2x^{1/2} = 5x^{1/4} + 12$

$2x^{1/2} - 5x^{1/4} - 12 = 0$ — Place in standard form.

$2y^2 - 5y - 12 = 0$ — Replace $x^{1/4}$ by y and $x^{1/2}$ by y^2.

$(2y + 3)(y - 4) = 0$ — Factor.

$2y = -3$ or $y = 4$

$y = -\frac{3}{2}$ — Solve for y.

$x^{1/4} = -\frac{3}{2}$ or $x^{1/4} = 4$ — Replace y by $x^{1/4}$.

$(x^{1/4})^4 = \left(-\frac{3}{2}\right)^4$ $(x^{1/4})^4 = (4)^4$ — Solve for x.

$x = \frac{81}{16}$ $x = 256$

Check:

$$x = \frac{81}{16}: \quad 2\left(\frac{81}{16}\right)^{1/2} - 5\left(\frac{81}{16}\right)^{1/4} - 12 \stackrel{?}{=} 0$$

$$2\left(\frac{9}{4}\right) - 5\left(\frac{3}{2}\right) - 12 \stackrel{?}{=} 0$$

$$\frac{9}{2} - \frac{15}{2} - 12 \stackrel{?}{=} 0$$

$$-15 \neq 0$$

$$x = 256: \quad 2(256)^{1/2} - 5(256)^{1/4} - 12 \stackrel{?}{=} 0$$

$$2(16) - 5(4) - 12 \stackrel{?}{=} 0$$

$$32 - 20 - 12 \stackrel{?}{=} 0$$

$$0 = 0 \checkmark$$

$\frac{81}{16}$ is extraneous and not a valid solution. The only valid solution is 256.

Practice Problem 4 Solve and check your solutions: $3x^{1/2} = 8x^{1/4} - 4$

Although we have covered just four basic examples here, this substitution technique can be extended to other types of equations. In each case we substitute y for an appropriate expression in order to obtain a quadratic equation. The following table lists some substitutions that would be appropriate.

If You Want to Solve:	Then You Would Use the Substitution:
$x^4 - 13x^2 + 36 = 0$	$y = x^2$
$2x^6 - x^3 - 6 = 0$	$y = x^3$
$x^{2/3} - 3x^{1/3} + 2 = 0$	$y = x^{1/3}$
$6(x - 1)^{-2} + (x - 1)^{-1} - 2 = 0$	$y = (x - 1)^{-1}$
$(2x^2 + x)^2 + 4(2x^2 + x) + 3 = 0$	$y = 2x^2 + x$
$\left(\frac{1}{x - 1}\right)^2 + \frac{1}{x - 1} - 6 = 0$	$y = \frac{1}{x - 1}$
$2x - 5x^{1/2} + 2 = 0$	$y = x^{1/2}$

A collection of exercises like these is provided in the exercise set.

8.3 Exercises

Solve. Express any nonreal complex numbers with i notation.

1. $x^4 - 9x^2 + 20 = 0$

2. $x^4 - 11x^2 + 18 = 0$

3. $x^4 + x^2 - 12 = 0$

4. $x^4 - 2x^2 - 8 = 0$

5. $3x^4 = 10x^2 + 8$

6. $5x^4 = 4x^2 + 1$

In Exercises 7–10, find all valid real roots for each equation.

7. $x^6 - 7x^3 - 8 = 0$

8. $x^6 - 3x^3 - 4 = 0$

9. $x^6 - 5x^3 - 14 = 0$

10. $x^6 + 2x^3 - 15 = 0$

Solve for real roots.

11. $x^8 = 3x^4 - 2$

12. $x^8 = 7x^4 - 12$

13. $3x^8 + 13x^4 = 10$

14. $3x^8 - 10x^4 = 8$

15. $x^{2/3} + 2x^{1/3} - 8 = 0$ **16.** $x^{2/3} + x^{1/3} - 12 = 0$ **17.** $2x^{2/3} - 7x^{1/3} - 4 = 0$ **18.** $12x^{2/3} + 5x^{1/3} - 2 = 0$

19. $3x^{1/2} - 14x^{1/4} - 5 = 0$ **20.** $2x^{1/2} - 5x^{1/4} - 3 = 0$ **21.** $2x^{1/2} - x^{1/4} - 6 = 0$

22. $2x^{1/2} - x^{1/4} - 1 = 0$ **23.** $x^{2/5} + x^{1/5} - 2 = 0$ **24.** $2x^{2/5} + 7x^{1/5} + 3 = 0$

In each exercise make an appropriate substitution in order to obtain a quadratic equation. Find all complex values for x.

25. $(x^2 + x)^2 - 5(x^2 + x) = -6$ **26.** $(x^2 - 2x)^2 + 2(x^2 - 2x) = 3$ **27.** $x - 5x^{1/2} + 6 = 0$

28. $x - 5x^{1/2} - 36 = 0$

29. $10x^{-2} + 7x^{-1} + 1 = 0$

30. $20x^{-2} + 9x^{-1} + 1 = 0$

To Think About

Solve. Find all valid real roots for each equation.

31. $15 - \frac{2x}{x - 1} = \frac{x^2}{x^2 - 2x + 1}$

32. $4 - \frac{x^3 + 1}{x^3 + 6} = \frac{x^3 - 3}{x^3 + 2}$

Cumulative Review Problems

Simplify.

33. $\sqrt{8x} + 3\sqrt{2x} - 4\sqrt{50x}$

34. $\sqrt{27x} + 6\sqrt{3x} - 2\sqrt{48x}$

Multiply and simplify.

35. $3\sqrt{2}(\sqrt{5} - 2\sqrt{6})$

36. $(\sqrt{2} + \sqrt{6})(3\sqrt{2} - 2\sqrt{5})$

37. How much greater is the average annual salary of a man than a woman at each of the four levels of educational attainment shown in the graph? Express your answers to the nearest tenth of a percent.

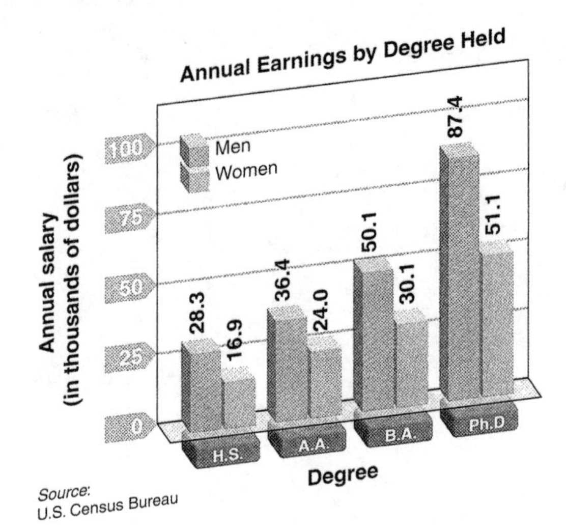

38. Approximately how many extra years would an average woman with an associate's degree have to work to earn the same lifetime earnings as a male counterpart who worked for 30 years? Round your answer to the nearest tenth of a year.

A Broadway musical called Miss Saigon closed in 2000. The musical was performed 4063 times, making it the sixth longest running show in Broadway history. The show cost $109 million, grossed $281.5 million, and was seen by about six million people. Cats, the longest running show in Broadway history, was performed 7451 times.

39. What was the average profit per performance for *Miss Saigon*?

40. What was the average cost for a person to see the performance?

41. If *Cats* had the same profit per performance as *Miss Saigon*, what was the total profit of *Cats*?

8.4 Formulas and Applications

 Solving a Quadratic Equation Containing Several Variables

Student Learning Objectives

After studying this section, you will be able to:

 Solve a quadratic equation containing several variables.

 Solve problems requiring the use of the Pythagorean theorem.

 Solve applied problems requiring the use of a quadratic equation.

In mathematics, physics, and engineering, we must often solve an equation for a variable in terms of other variables. You recall we solved linear equations in several variables in Section 2.2. We now examine several cases where the variable that we are solving for is squared. If the variable we are solving for is squared, and there is no other term containing that variable, then the equation can be solved using the square root property.

EXAMPLE 1 The surface area of a sphere is given by $A = 4\pi r^2$. Solve this equation for r. (You do not need to rationalize the denominator.)

$$A = 4\pi r^2$$

$$\frac{A}{4\pi} = r^2$$

$$\pm\sqrt{\frac{A}{4\pi}} = r \qquad \text{Use the square root property.}$$

$$\pm\frac{1}{2}\sqrt{\frac{A}{\pi}} = r \qquad \text{Simplify.}$$

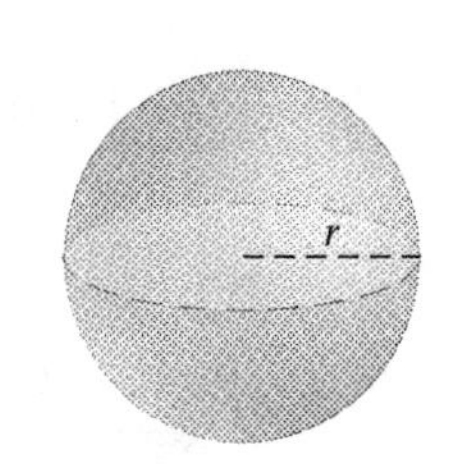

Since the radius of a sphere must be a positive value, we use only the principal root.

$$r = \frac{1}{2}\sqrt{\frac{A}{\pi}}$$

Practice Problem 1 The volume of a cylindrical cone is $V = \frac{1}{3}\pi r^2 h$. Solve this equation for r. (You do not need to rationalize the denominator.)

Some quadratic equations containing many variables can be solved for one variable by factoring.

EXAMPLE 2 Solve for y: $y^2 - 2yz - 15z^2 = 0$

$$(y + 3z)(y - 5z) = 0 \qquad \text{Factor.}$$

$$y + 3z = 0 \qquad y - 5z = 0 \qquad \text{Set each factor equal to 0.}$$

$$y = -3z \qquad y = 5z \qquad \text{Solve for } y.$$

Practice Problem 2 Solve for y: $2y^2 + 9wy + 7w^2 = 0$

Sometimes the quadratic formula is required in order to solve the equation.

EXAMPLE 3 Solve for x: $2x^2 + 3wx - 4z = 0$

We use the quadratic formula where the variable is considered to be x and the letters w and z are considered constants. Thus, $a = 2$, $b = 3w$, and $c = -4z$.

$$x = \frac{-b \pm \sqrt{b^2 - 4ac}}{2a}$$

$$= \frac{-3w \pm \sqrt{(3w)^2 - 4(2)(-4z)}}{2(2)} = \frac{-3w \pm \sqrt{9w^2 + 32z}}{4}$$

Note that this answer cannot be simplified any further.

Practice Problem 3 Solve for y: $3y^2 + 2fy - 7g = 0$

EXAMPLE 4 The formula for the curved surface area S of a right circular cone of altitude h and with base of radius r is $S = \pi r\sqrt{r^2 + h^2}$.

Solve for r^2.

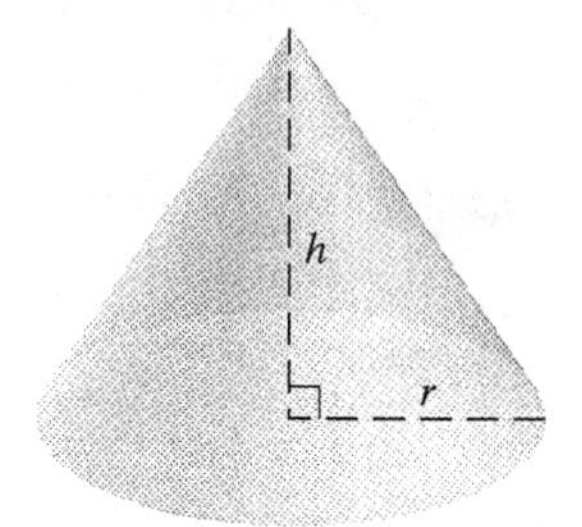

$$S = \pi r\sqrt{r^2 + h^2}$$

$$\frac{S}{\pi r} = \sqrt{r^2 + h^2} \qquad \text{Isolate the radical.}$$

$$\frac{S^2}{\pi^2 r^2} = r^2 + h^2 \qquad \text{Square both sides.}$$

$$\frac{S^2}{\pi^2} = r^4 + h^2r^2 \qquad \text{Multiply each term by } r^2.$$

$$0 = r^4 + h^2r^2 - \frac{S^2}{\pi^2} \qquad \text{Subtract } S^2/\pi^2.$$

This equation is quadratic in form. If we let $y = r^2$, then we have

$$0 = y^2 + h^2y - \frac{S^2}{\pi^2}.$$

By the quadratic formula we have the following:

$$y = \frac{-h^2 \pm \sqrt{(h^2)^2 - 4(1)\left(-\frac{S^2}{\pi^2}\right)}}{2}$$

$$= \frac{-h^2 \pm \sqrt{\frac{\pi^2h^4}{\pi^2} + \frac{4S^2}{\pi^2}}}{2}$$

$$= \frac{-h^2 \pm \frac{1}{\pi}\sqrt{\pi^2h^4 + 4S^2}}{2}$$

$$= \frac{-\pi h^2 \pm \sqrt{\pi^2h^4 + 4S^2}}{2\pi}$$

Since $y = r^2$, we have

$$r^2 = \frac{-\pi h^2 \pm \sqrt{\pi^2h^4 + 4S^2}}{2\pi}.$$

Practice Problem 4 The formula for the number of diagonals d in a polygon of n sides is $d = \frac{n^2 - 3n}{2}$. Solve for n.

2 Solving Problems Requiring the Use of the Pythagorean Theorem

A very useful formula is the Pythagorean theorem for right triangles.

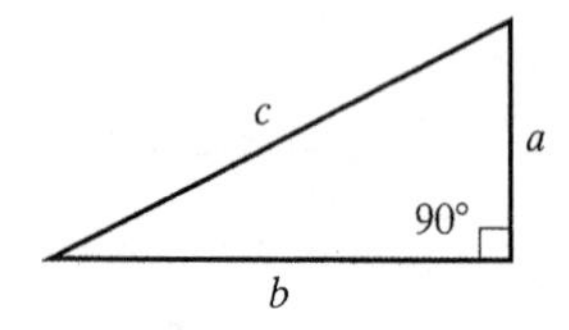

Pythagorean Theorem

If c is the length of the longest side of a right triangle and a and b are the lengths of the other two sides, then $a^2 + b^2 = c^2$.

The longest side of a right triangle is called the **hypotenuse**. The other two sides are called the **legs** of the triangle.

EXAMPLE 5

(a) Solve the Pythagorean theorem $a^2 + b^2 = c^2$ for a.

(b) Find the value of a if $c = 13$ and $b = 5$.

(a) $a^2 = c^2 - b^2$ Subtract b^2 from each side.

$a = \pm\sqrt{c^2 - b^2}$ Use the square root property.

Since a, b, and c must be positive numbers because they represent lengths, we use only the positive root, $a = \sqrt{c^2 - b^2}$.

(b) $a = \sqrt{c^2 - b^2}$

$= \sqrt{(13)^2 - (5)^2} = \sqrt{169 - 25} = \sqrt{144} = 12$

Thus, $a = 12$.

Practice Problem 5

(a) Solve the Pythagorean theorem for b.

(b) Find the value of b if $c = 26$ and $a = 24$.

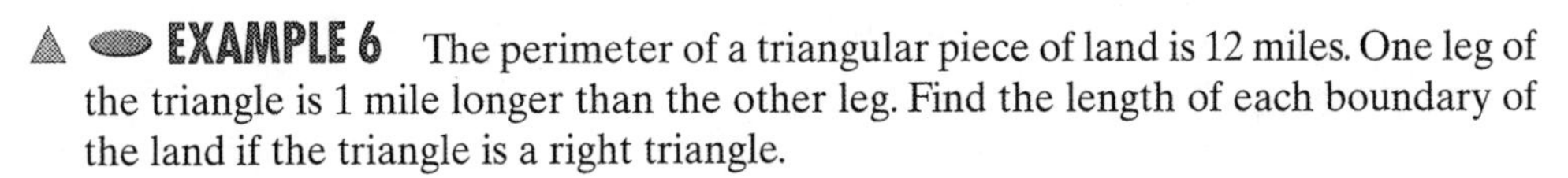

EXAMPLE 6 The perimeter of a triangular piece of land is 12 miles. One leg of the triangle is 1 mile longer than the other leg. Find the length of each boundary of the land if the triangle is a right triangle.

1. *Understand the problem.*
Draw a picture of the piece of land and label the side of the triangle.

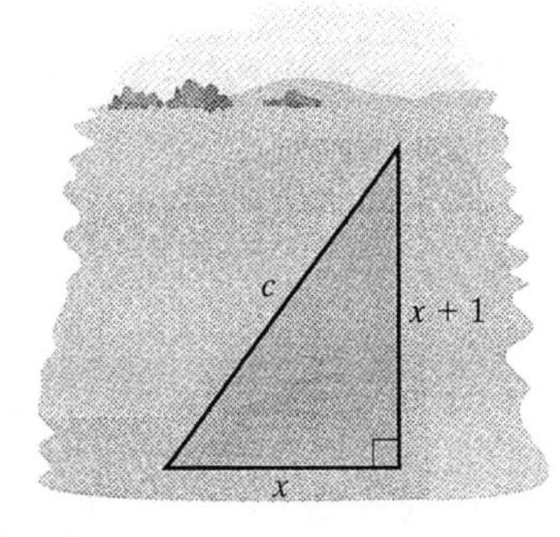

2. *Write an equation.*
We can use the Pythagorean theorem. First, we want only one variable in our equation. (Right now, both c and x are not known.)

We are given that the perimeter is 12 miles, so

$$x + (x + 1) + c = 12.$$

Thus,

$$c = -2x + 11.$$

By the Pythagorean theorem,

$$x^2 + (x + 1)^2 = (-2x + 11)^2.$$

3. *Solve the equation and state the answer.*

$$x^2 + (x + 1)^2 = (-2x + 11)^2$$
$$x^2 + x^2 + 2x + 1 = 4x^2 - 44x + 121$$
$$0 = 2x^2 - 46x + 120$$
$$0 = x^2 - 23x + 60$$

By the quadratic formula, we have the following:

$$x = \frac{-(-23) \pm \sqrt{(-23)^2 - 4(1)(60)}}{2(1)}$$

$$x = \frac{23 \pm \sqrt{289}}{2}$$

$$x = \frac{23 \pm 17}{2}$$

$$x = \frac{40}{2} = 20 \quad \text{or} \quad x = \frac{6}{2} = 3$$

The answer $x = 20$ cannot be right because the perimeter (the sum of *all* the sides) is only 12. The only answer that makes sense is $x = 3$. Thus, the sides of the triangle are $x = 3, x + 1 = 3 + 1 = 4$, and $-2x + 11 = -2(3) + 11 = 5$. The longest boundary of this triangular piece of land is 5 miles. The other two boundaries are 4 miles and 3 miles.

Notice that we could have factored the quadratic equation instead of using the quadratic formula. $x^2 - 23x + 60 = 0$ can be written as $(x - 20)(x - 3) = 0$.

4. ***Check.***
Is the perimeter 12 miles?

$$5 + 4 + 3 = 12 \quad ✓$$

Is one leg 1 mile longer than the other?

$$4 = 3 + 1 \quad ✓$$

Practice Problem 6 The perimeter of a triangular piece of land is 30 miles. One leg of the triangle is 7 miles shorter than the other leg. Find the length of each boundary of the land if the triangle is a right triangle.

3 *Solving Applied Problems Requiring the Use of a Quadratic Equation*

Many types of area problems can be solved with quadratic equations as shown in the next two examples.

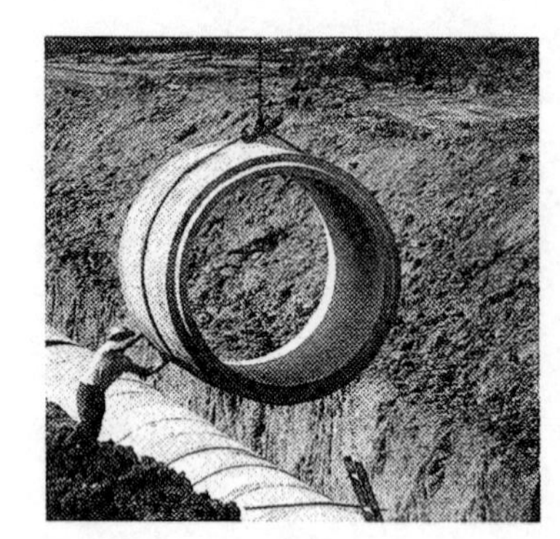

▲ **EXAMPLE 7** The radius of an old circular pipe under a roadbed is 10 inches. Designers want to replace it with a smaller pipe and have decided they can use one with a cross-sectional area that is 36π square inches smaller. What should the radius of the new pipe be?

First we need the formula for the area of a circle,

$$A = \pi r^2,$$

where A is the area and r is the radius. The area of the cross section of the old pipe is as follows:

$$A_{\text{old}} = \pi(10)^2$$
$$= 100\pi$$

10 inches radius

Cross section of old pipe

x inches radius

Cross section of new pipe

Let x = the radius of the new pipe.

$$(\text{area of old pipe}) - (\text{area of new pipe}) = 36\pi$$

$$100\pi \quad - \quad \pi x^2 \quad = 36\pi$$

$64\pi = \pi x^2$ Add πx^2 to each side and subtract 36π from each side.

$\dfrac{64\pi}{\pi} = \dfrac{\pi x^2}{\pi}$ Divide each side by π.

$64 = x^2$

$\pm 8 = x$ Use the square root property.

Since the radius must be positive, we select $x = 8$. The radius of the new pipe is 8 inches. Check to verify this solution.

Practice Problem 7 Redo Example 7 when the radius of the pipe under the roadbed is 6 inches and the designers want to replace it with a pipe that has a cross-sectional area that is 45π square inches larger. What should the radius of the new pipe be?

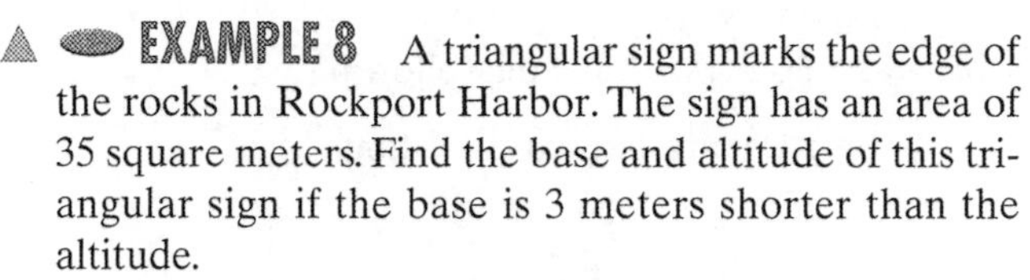

EXAMPLE 8 A triangular sign marks the edge of the rocks in Rockport Harbor. The sign has an area of 35 square meters. Find the base and altitude of this triangular sign if the base is 3 meters shorter than the altitude.

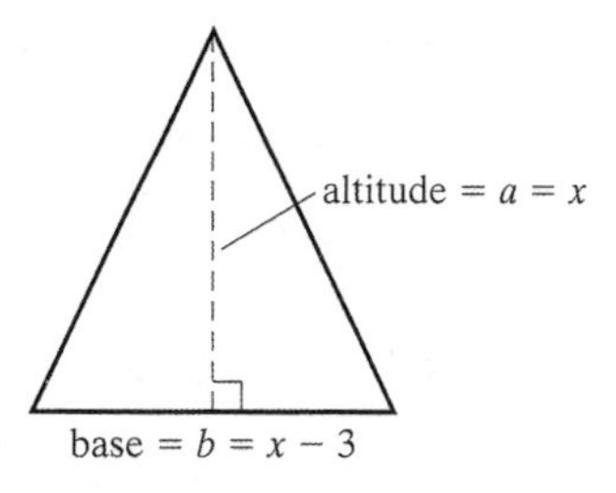

The area of a triangle is given by

$$A = \frac{1}{2}ab.$$

Let x = the length in meters of the altitude. Then $x - 3$ = the length in meters of the base.

$35 = \dfrac{1}{2}x(x - 3)$ Replace A (area) by 35, a (altitude) by x, and b (base) by $x - 3$.

$70 = x(x - 3)$ Multiply each side by 2.

$70 = x^2 - 3x$ Use the distributive property.

$0 = x^2 - 3x - 70$ Subtract 70 from each side.

$0 = (x - 10)(x + 7)$

$x = 10 \quad \text{or} \quad x = -7$

The length of a side of a triangle must be a positive number, so we disregard -7. Thus,

$$\text{altitude} = x = 10 \text{ meters and}$$
$$\text{base} = x - 3 = 7 \text{ meters.}$$

The check is left to the student.

Practice Problem 8 The length of a rectangle is 3 feet shorter than twice the width. The area of the rectangle is 54 square feet. Find the dimensions of the rectangle.

We will now examine a few word problems that require the use of the formula distance = (rate)(time) or $d = rt$.

EXAMPLE 9 When Barbara was training for a bicycle race, she rode a total of 135 miles on Monday and Tuesday. On Monday she rode for 75 miles in the rain. On Tuesday she rode 5 miles per hour faster because the weather was better. Her total cycling time for the 2 days was 8 hours. Find her speed for each day.

It would be helpful to organize a few basic facts.

We can find each distance. If Barbara rode 75 miles on Monday and a total of 135 miles during the 2 days, then she rode $135 - 75 = 60$ miles on Tuesday.

Let x = the cycling rate in miles per hour on Monday. Since Barbara rode 5 miles per hour faster on Tuesday, $x + 5$ = the cycling rate in miles per hour on Tuesday.

Since distance divided by rate is equal to time $\left(\frac{d}{r} = t\right)$, we can determine that the time Barbara cycled on Monday was $\frac{75}{x}$ and the time she cycled on Tuesday was $\frac{60}{x + 5}$.

We put these facts into a table.

Day	Distance	Rate	Time
Monday	75	x	$\frac{75}{x}$
Tuesday	60	$x + 5$	$\frac{60}{x + 5}$
Totals	135	(not used)	8

Since the total cycling time was 8 hours, we have the following:

$$\text{time cycling Monday} + \text{time cycling Tuesday} = 8 \text{ hours}$$

$$\frac{75}{x} + \frac{60}{x + 5} = 8$$

The LCD of this equation is $x(x + 5)$. Multiply each term by the LCD.

$$\cancel{x}(x + 5)\left(\frac{75}{\cancel{x}}\right) + x(\cancel{x + 5})\left(\frac{60}{\cancel{x + 5}}\right) = x(x + 5)(8)$$

$$75(x + 5) + 60x = 8x(x + 5)$$

$$75x + 375 + 60x = 8x^2 + 40x$$

$$0 = 8x^2 - 95x - 375$$

$$0 = (x - 15)(8x + 25)$$

$$x - 15 = 0 \quad \text{or} \quad 8x + 25 = 0$$

$$x = 15 \qquad\qquad x = \frac{-25}{8}$$

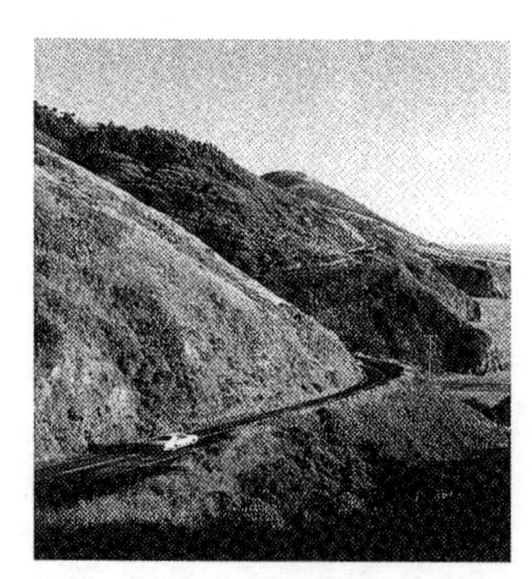

We disregard the negative answer. The cyclist did not have a negative rate of speed—unless she was pedaling backward! Thus, $x = 15$. So Barbara's rate of speed on Monday was 15 mph, and her rate of speed on Tuesday was $x + 5 = 15 + 5 = 20$ mph.

Practice Problem 9 Carlos traveled in his car at a constant speed on a secondary road for 150 miles. Then he traveled 10 mph faster on a better road for 240 miles. If Carlos drove for 7 hours, find the car's speed for each part of the trip.

8.4 Exercises

Solve for the variable specified. Assume that all other variables are nonzero.

1. $S = 16t^2$; for t

2. $E = mc^2$; for c

3. $A = \pi\left(\frac{d}{2}\right)^2$; for d

4. $V = \frac{1}{3}\pi r^2 h$; for r

5. $3H = \frac{1}{2}ax^2$; for x

6. $5B = \frac{2}{3}hx^2$; for x

7. $4(y^2 + w) - 5 = 7R$; for y

8. $9x^2 - 2 = 3B$; for x

9. $Q = \frac{3mwM^2}{2c}$; for M

10. $H = \frac{5abT^2}{7k}$; for T

11. $V = \pi(r^2 + R^2)h$; for r

12. $H = b(a^2 + w^2)$; for w

13. $x^2 + 3bx - 10b^2 = 0$; for x

14. $y^2 - 4yw - 45w^2 = 0$; for y

15. $P = EI - RI^2$; for I

16. $A = P(1 + r)^2$; for r

17. $10w^2 - 3qw - 4 = 0$; for w

18. $7w^2 + 5qw - 1 = 0$; for w

19. $S = 2\pi rh + \pi r^2$; for r

20. $B = 3abx^2 - 5x$; for x

21. $(a + 1)x^2 + 5x + 2w = 0$; for x

22. $(b - 2)x^2 - 3x + 5y = 0$; for x

In Exercises 23–32 use the Pythagorean theorem to find the missing side(s).

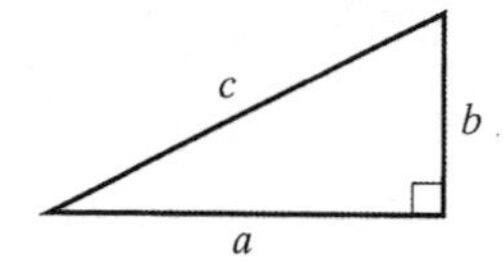

▲ **23.** $b = 7, a = \sqrt{3}$; find c

▲ **24.** $a = 2\sqrt{3}, b = 3$; find c

▲ **25.** $c = \sqrt{34}, b = \sqrt{19}$; find a

▲ **26.** $c = \sqrt{21}, a = \sqrt{5}$; find b

▲ **27.** $c = 12, b = 2a$; find b and a

▲ **28.** $c = 15, a = 2b$; find b and a

▲ **29.** A racing sailboat is traveling along a triangular course. The three straight line distances form a right triangle. One leg of the triangle represents a distance of 12 miles. The other leg of the triangle is 6 miles shorter than the hypotenuse. What is the length of the hypotenuse of this triangle? What is the length of the other leg?

▲ **30.** Tony Pitkin has a cornfield in South Dakota that is shaped like a right triangle. The hypotenuse of this triangle is 10 miles long. One leg of the triangular field is 2 miles shorter than the other leg. Find the length of the other two sides of the field.

31. An airplane flew from London a distance of 11 kilometers due north. The plane banked to the right and flew the second leg of the journey. Finally, the plane then banked to the right again and flew back to the starting point. The entire course was shaped like a right triangle with the 11-kilometer distance serving as the hypotenuse. The final leg of this journey was 3 miles longer than the second leg. How many miles were the second and third legs of the journey? Round your answers to the nearest hundredth of a mile.

32. A Norwegian freighter travels 12 miles due east toward the United States. Seeking to avoid an underwater obstruction, the vessel turns to the left abruptly and travels for a certain distance. Having discovered engine trouble, the captain turns abruptly again and heads for home port. The entire course is shaped like a right triangle, with the 12-mile distance serving as the hypotenuse and with the final leg of the trip being 4 miles longer than the second leg of the trip. What are the lengths of the second and third legs of the trip? Round your answers to the nearest hundredth of a mile.

33. The area of a rectangular wall of a barn is 126 square feet. Its length is 4 feet longer than twice its width. Find the length and width of the wall of the barn.

34. The area of a rectangular tennis court is 140 square meters. Its length is 6 meters shorter than twice its width. Find the length and width of the tennis court.

35. The area of a triangular flag is 72 square centimeters. Its altitude is 2 centimeters longer than twice its base. Find the lengths of the altitude and the base.

36. A children's playground is triangular in shape. Its altitude is 2 yards shorter than its base. The area of the playground is 60 square yards. Find the base and altitude of the playground.

37. Roberto drove at a constant speed in a rainstorm for 225 miles. He took a break, and the rain stopped. He then drove 150 miles at a speed that was 5 miles per hour faster than his previous speed. If he drove for 8 hours, find the car's speed for each part of the trip.

38. Benita traveled at a constant speed on an old road for 160 miles. She then traveled 5 miles per hour faster on a newer road for 90 miles. If she drove for 6 hours, find the car's speed for each part of the trip.

39. Bob drove from home to work at 50 mph. After work the traffic was heavier, and he drove home at 45 mph. His driving time to and from work was 1 hour and 16 minutes. How far does he live from his job?

40. A driver drove his heavily loaded truck from the company warehouse to a delivery point at 35 mph. He unloaded the truck and drove back to the warehouse at 45 mph. The total trip took 5 hours and 20 minutes. How far is the delivery point from the warehouse?

The number of inmates N (measured in thousands) in federal and state prisons in the United States can be approximated by the equation $N = 1.11x^2 + 33.39x + 304.09$, *where x is the number of years since 1980. For example, when* $x = 1$, $N = 338.59$. *This tells us that in 1981 there were approximately 338,590 inmates in federal and state prisons. Use this equation to answer the following questions. (Source: U.S. Bureau of Justice Statistics.)*

41. How many inmates does the equation predict there will be in the year 2003?

42. How many inmates does the equation predict there will be in the year 2006?

43. In what year is the number of inmates expected to be 1,744,800?

44. In what year is the number of inmates expected to be 1,832,600?

To Think About

45. Solve for w: $w = \dfrac{12b^2}{\frac{5}{2}w + \frac{7}{2}b + \frac{21}{2}}$

46. The formula $A = P(1 + r)^2$ gives the amount A in dollars that will be obtained in 2 years if P dollars are invested at an annual compound interest rate of r. If you invest $P = \$1400$ and it grows to $\$1514.24$ in 2 years, what is the annual interest rate r?

Cumulative Review Problems

Rationalize the denominators.

47. $\dfrac{4}{\sqrt{3x}}$

48. $\dfrac{5\sqrt{6}}{2\sqrt{5}}$

49. $\dfrac{3}{\sqrt{x} + \sqrt{y}}$

50. $\dfrac{2\sqrt{3}}{\sqrt{3} - \sqrt{6}}$

51. $\dfrac{3ab}{\sqrt[3]{8ab^2}}$

8.5 Quadratic Functions

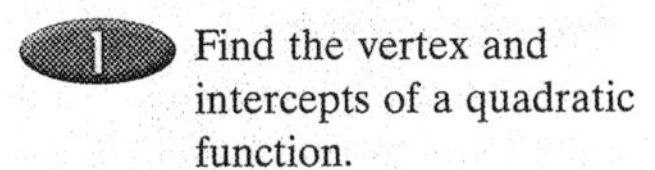

Student Learning Objectives

After studying this section, you will be able to:

1. Find the vertex and intercepts of a quadratic function.
2. Graph a quadratic function.

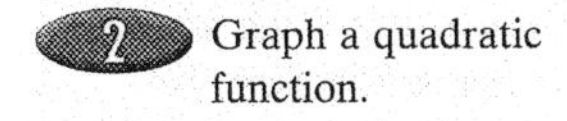

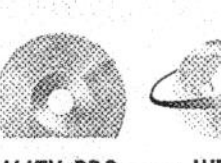

SSM PH TUTOR CENTER CD & VIDEO MATH PRO WEB

1 Finding the Vertex and the Intercepts of a Quadratic Function

In Section 3.6 we graphed functions such as $p(x) = x^2$ and $g(x) = (x + 2)^2$. We will now study quadratic functions in more detail.

Definition of a Quadratic Function

A **quadratic function** is a function of the form

$f(x) = ax^2 + bx + c$, where a, b, and c are real numbers and $a \neq 0$.

Graphs of quadratic functions written in this form will be parabolas opening upward if $a > 0$ or downward if $a < 0$. The **vertex** of a parabola is the lowest point on a parabola opening upward or the highest point on a parabola opening downward. The vertex will occur at $x = \frac{-b}{2a}$. To find the y-value, or $f(x)$, when $x = \frac{-b}{2a}$, we find $f\left(\frac{-b}{2a}\right)$. Therefore, we can say that a quadratic function has its vertex at $\left(\frac{-b}{2a}, f\left(\frac{-b}{2a}\right)\right)$.

It is helpful to know the x-intercept and the y-intercept when graphing a quadratic function.

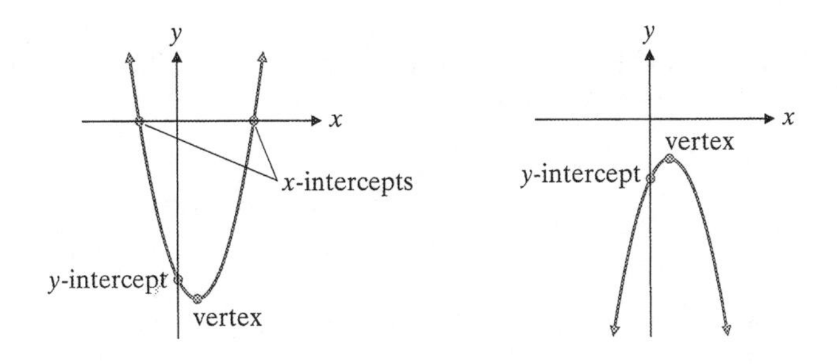

A quadratic function will always have exactly one y-intercept. However, it may have zero, one, or two x-intercepts. Why?

When Graphing Quadratic Functions of the Form $f(x) = ax^2 + bx + c, a \neq 0$

1. The coordinates of the vertex are $\left(\frac{-b}{2a}, f\left(\frac{-b}{2a}\right)\right)$.
2. The y-intercept is at $f(0)$.
3. The x-intercepts (if they exist) occur where $f(x) = 0$. They can always be found with the quadratic formula and can sometimes be found by factoring.

Since we may replace y by $f(x)$, the graph is equivalent to the graph of $y = ax^2 + bx + c$.

Graphing Calculator

Finding the x-intercepts and the vertex

You can use a graphing calculator to find the x-intercepts and vertex of a quadratic function. To find the intercepts of the quadratic function

$f(x) = x^2 - 4x + 3,$

graph $y = x^2 - 4x + 3$ on a graphing calculator using an appropriate window.

Display:

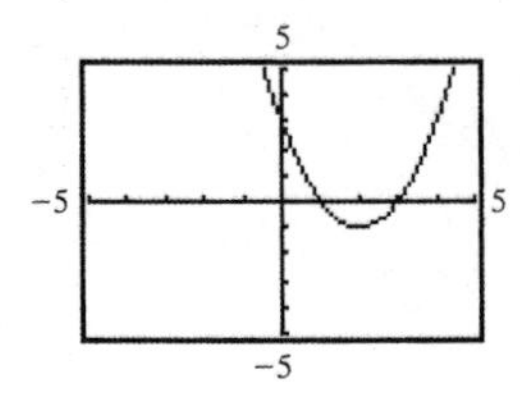

Next you can use the Trace and Zoom features or zero command of your calculator to find the x-intercepts.

You can also use the Trace and Zoom features to determine the vertex.

Some calculators have a feature that will calculate the maximum or minimum point on the graph. Use the feature that calculates the minimum point to find the vertex of $f(x) = x^2 - 4x + 3$.

Display:

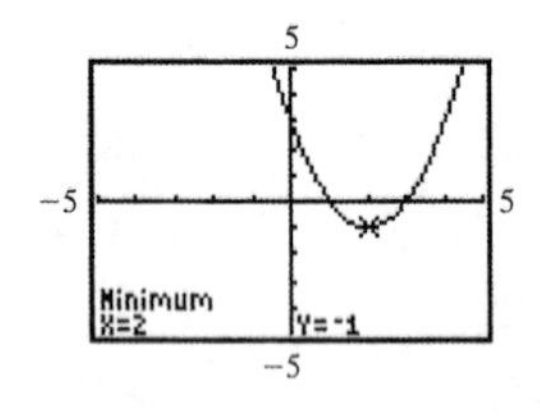

Thus, the vertex is at $(2, -1)$.

EXAMPLE 1 Find the coordinates of the vertex and the intercepts of the quadratic function $f(x) = x^2 - 8x + 15$.

For this function $a = 1$, $b = -8$, and $c = 15$.

Step 1 The vertex occurs at $x = \frac{-b}{2a}$. Thus,

$$x = \frac{-(-8)}{2(1)} = \frac{8}{2} = 4.$$

The vertex has an x-coordinate of 4. To find the y-coordinate, we evaluate $f(4)$.

$$f(4) = 4^2 - 8(4) + 15 = 16 - 32 + 15 = -1$$

Thus, the vertex is $(4, -1)$.

Step 2 The y-intercept is at $f(0)$. We evaluate $f(0)$ to find the y-coordinate when x is 0.

$$f(0) = 0^2 - 8(0) + 15 = 15$$

The y-intercept is $(0, 15)$.

Step 3 If there are x-intercepts, they will occur when $f(x) = 0$—that is, when $x^2 - 8x + 15 = 0$. We solve for x.

$$(x - 5)(x - 3) = 0$$

$$x - 5 = 0 \qquad x - 3 = 0$$

$$x = 5 \qquad x = 3$$

Thus, we conclude that the x-intercepts are $(5, 0)$ and $(3, 0)$. We list these four important points of the function in table form.

Name	x	$f(x)$
Vertex	4	−1
y-intercept	0	15
x-intercept	5	0
x-intercept	3	0

Practice Problem 1 Find the coordinates of the vertex and the intercepts of the quadratic function $f(x) = x^2 - 6x + 5$.

2 Graphing a Quadratic Function

It is helpful to find the vertex and the intercepts of a quadratic function before graphing it.

EXAMPLE 2 Find the vertex and the intercepts, and then graph the function $f(x) = x^2 + 2x - 4$.

Here $a = 1$, $b = 2$, and $c = -4$. Since $a > 0$, the parabola opens *upward*.

Step 1 We find the vertex.

$$x = \frac{-b}{2a} = \frac{-2}{2(1)} = \frac{-2}{2} = -1$$

$$f(-1) = (-1)^2 + 2(-1) - 4 = 1 + (-2) - 4 = -5$$

The vertex is $(-1, -5)$.

Step 2 We find the y-intercept. The y-intercept is at $f(0)$.

$$f(0) = (0)^2 + 2(0) - 4 = -4$$

The y-intercept is $(0, -4)$.

Step 3 We find the x-intercepts. The x-intercepts occur when $f(x) = 0$.

Thus, we solve $x^2 + 2x - 4 = 0$ for x. We cannot factor this equation, so we use the quadratic formula.

$$x = \frac{-b \pm \sqrt{b^2 - 4ac}}{2a} = \frac{-2 \pm \sqrt{2^2 - 4(1)(-4)}}{2(1)} = \frac{-2 \pm \sqrt{20}}{2} = -1 \pm \sqrt{5}$$

To aid our graphing, we will approximate the value of x to the nearest tenth by using a square root table or a scientific calculator.

1 [+/−] [+] 5 [√] [=] 1.236068

$x \approx 1.2$

1 [+/−] [−] 5 [√] [=] −3.236068

$x \approx -3.2$

The x-intercepts are approximately $(-3.2, 0)$ and $(1.2, 0)$.

We have found that the vertex is $(-1, -5)$; the y-intercept is $(0, -4)$; and the x-intercepts are approximately $(-3.2, 0)$ and $(1.2, 0)$. We connect these points by a smooth curve to graph the parabola.

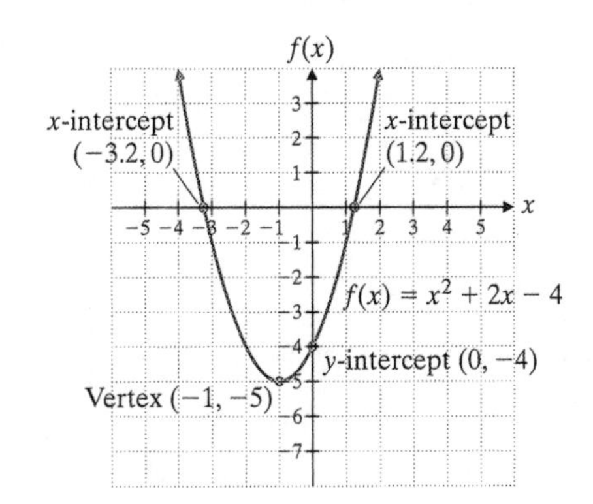

PRACTICE PROBLEM 2

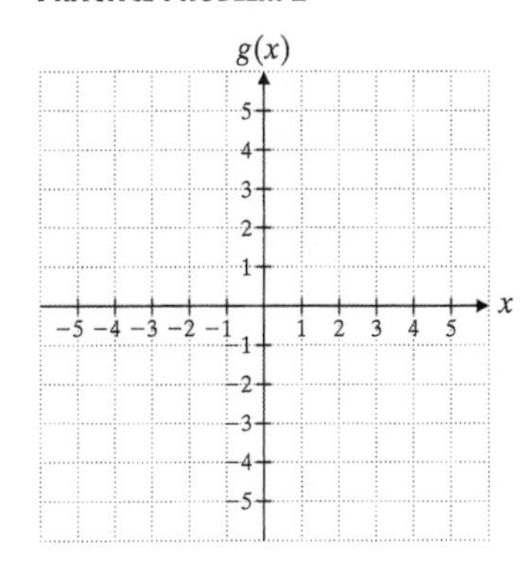

Practice Problem 2 Find the vertex and the intercepts, and then graph the function $g(x) = x^2 - 2x - 2$.

EXAMPLE 3 Find the vertex and the intercepts, and then graph the function $f(x) = -2x^2 + 4x - 3$.

Here $a = -2$, $b = 4$, and $c = -3$. Since $a < 0$, the parabola opens *downward*.

The vertex occurs at $x = \dfrac{-b}{2a}$.

$$x = \frac{-4}{2(-2)} = \frac{-4}{-4} = 1$$

$$f(1) = -2(1)^2 + 4(1) - 3 = -2 + 4 - 3 = -1$$

The vertex is $(1, -1)$.

The y-intercept is at $f(0)$.

$$f(0) = -2(0)^2 + 4(0) - 3 = -3$$

The y-intercept is $(0, -3)$.

If there are any x-intercepts, they will occur when $f(x) = 0$. We use the quadratic formula to solve $-2x^2 + 4x - 3 = 0$ for x.

$$x = \frac{-4 \pm \sqrt{4^2 - 4(-2)(-3)}}{2(-2)} = \frac{-4 \pm \sqrt{-8}}{-4}$$

Because $\sqrt{-8}$ yields an imaginary number, there are no real roots. Thus, there are no x-intercepts for the graph of the function. That is, the graph does not intersect the x-axis.

We know that the parabola opens *downward*. Thus, the vertex is a maximum value at $(1, -1)$. Since this graph has no x-intercepts, we will look for three additional points to help us in drawing the graph. We try $f(2)$, $f(3)$, and $f(-1)$.

$$f(2) = -2(2)^2 + 4(2) - 3 = -8 + 8 - 3 = -3$$
$$f(3) = -2(3)^2 + 4(3) - 3 = -18 + 12 - 3 = -9$$
$$f(-1) = -2(-1)^2 + 4(-1) - 3 = -2 - 4 - 3 = -9$$

We plot the vertex, the y-intercept, and the points $(2, -3)$, $(3, -9)$, and $(-1, -9)$.

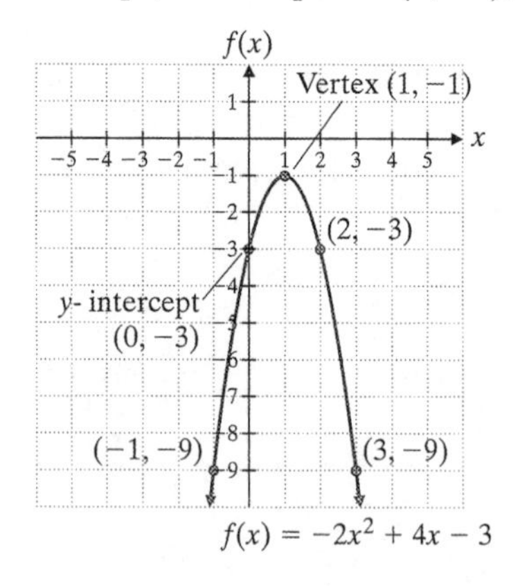

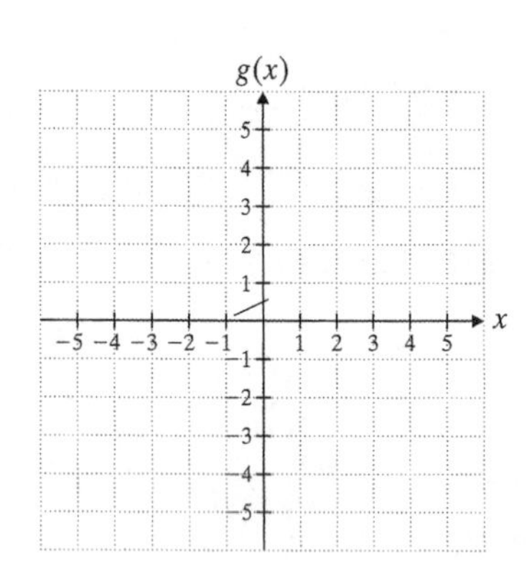

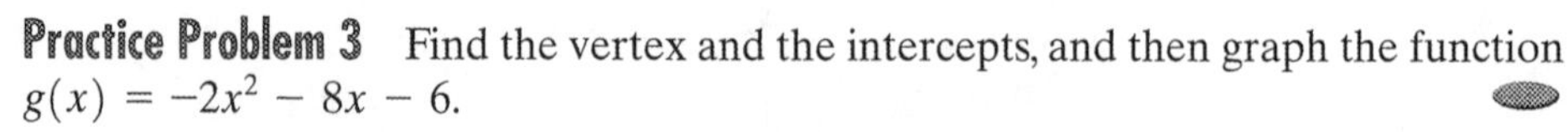

Practice Problem 3 Find the vertex and the intercepts, and then graph the function $g(x) = -2x^2 - 8x - 6$.

8.5 Exercises

Find the coordinates of the vertex and the intercepts of each of the following quadratic functions. When necessary, approximate the x-intercepts to the nearest tenth.

1. $f(x) = x^2 - 2x - 8$

2. $f(x) = x^2 - 4x - 5$

3. $g(x) = -x^2 - 4x + 12$

4. $g(x) = x^2 + 10x - 24$

5. $p(x) = 3x^2 + 12x + 3$

6. $p(x) = 2x^2 + 4x + 1$

7. $r(x) = -3x^2 - 2x - 6$

8. $s(x) = -2x^2 + 6x + 5$

9. $f(x) = 2x^2 + 2x - 4$

10. $f(x) = 5x^2 + 2x - 3$

In each of the following exercises, find the vertex, the y-intercept, and the x-intercepts (if any exist), and then graph the function.

11. $f(x) = x^2 - 6x + 8$

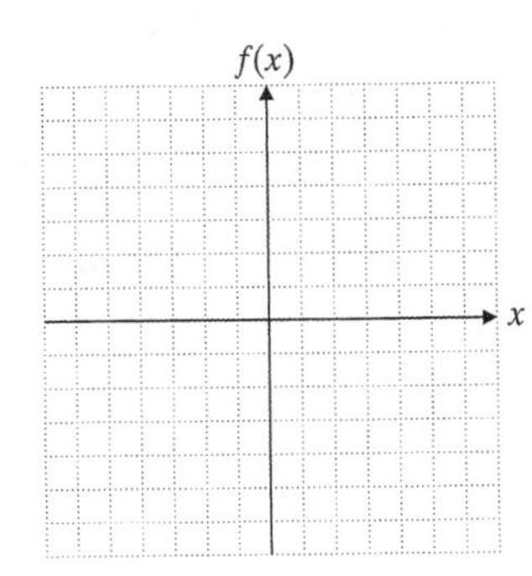

12. $f(x) = x^2 + 6x + 8$

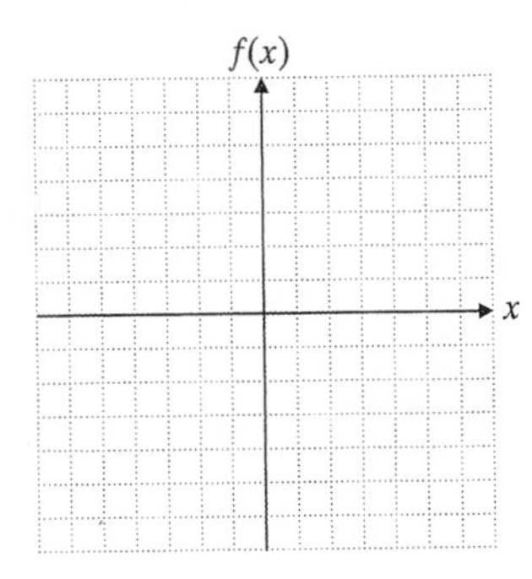

13. $g(x) = x^2 + 2x - 8$

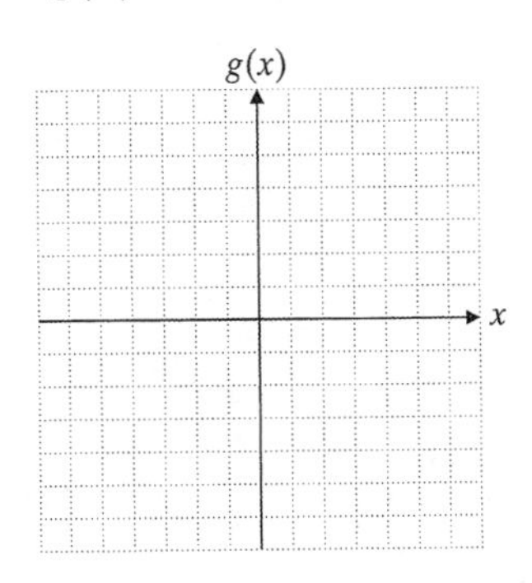

14. $g(x) = x^2 - 2x - 8$

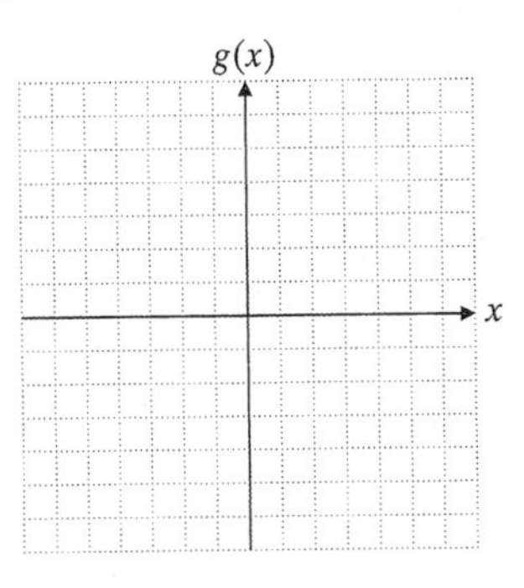

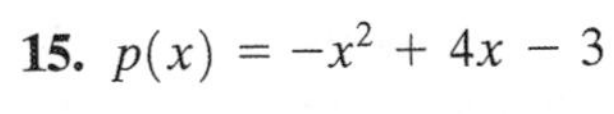

15. $p(x) = -x^2 + 4x - 3$

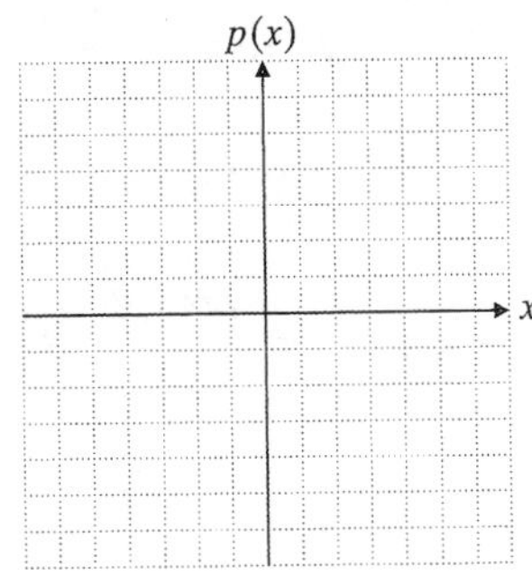

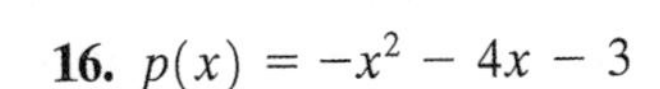

16. $p(x) = -x^2 - 4x - 3$

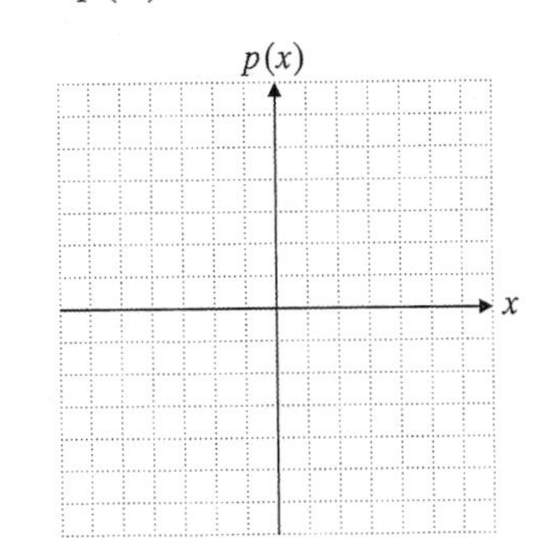

17. $r(x) = x^2 + 4x + 6$

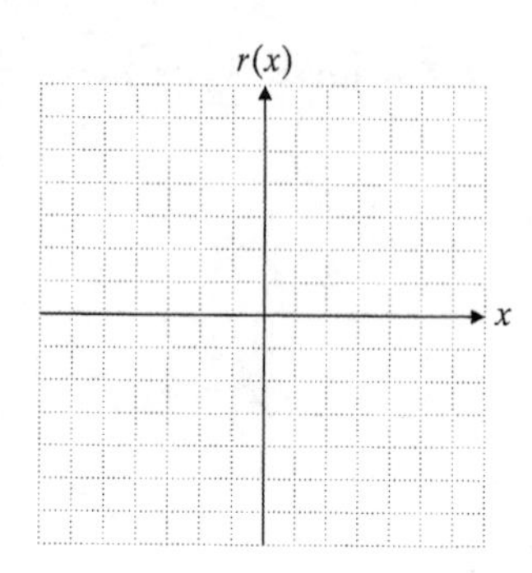

18. $r(x) = -x^2 + 4x - 5$

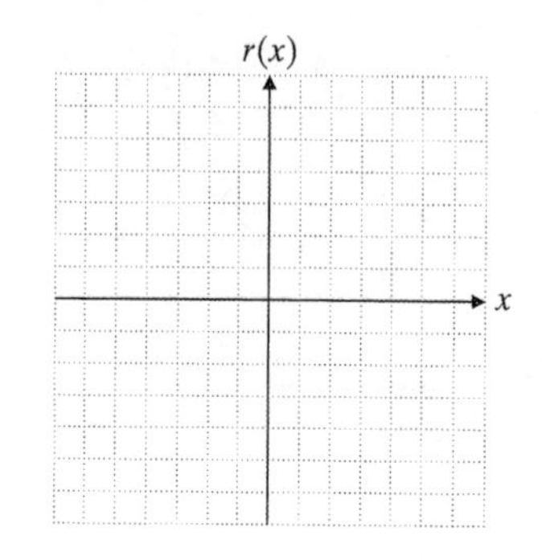

19. $f(x) = x^2 - 6x + 5$

20. $f(x) = x^2 - 4x + 4$

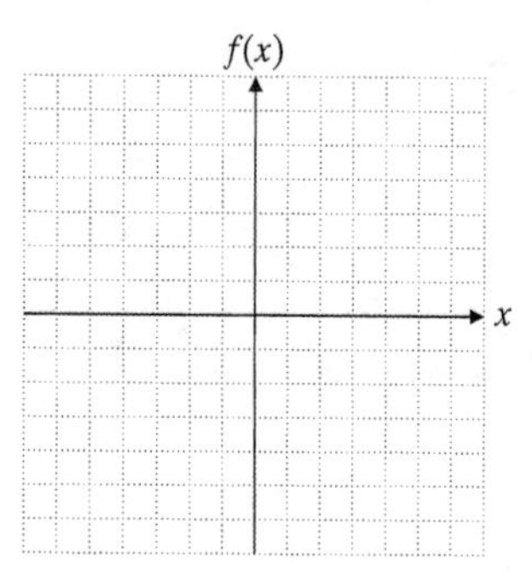

21. $g(x) = -x^2 + 6x - 9$

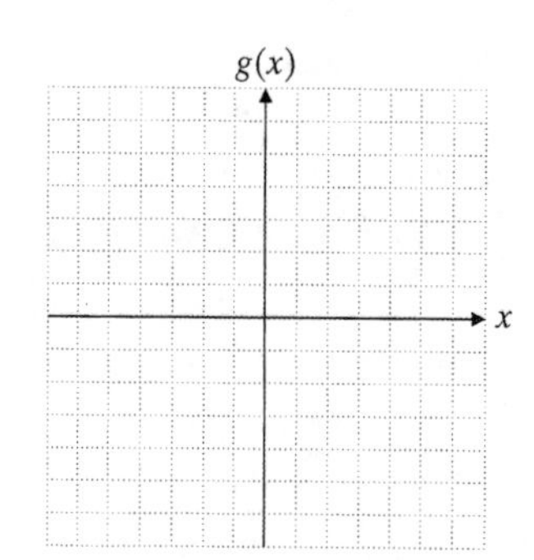

22. $g(x) = 2x^2 - 2x + 1$

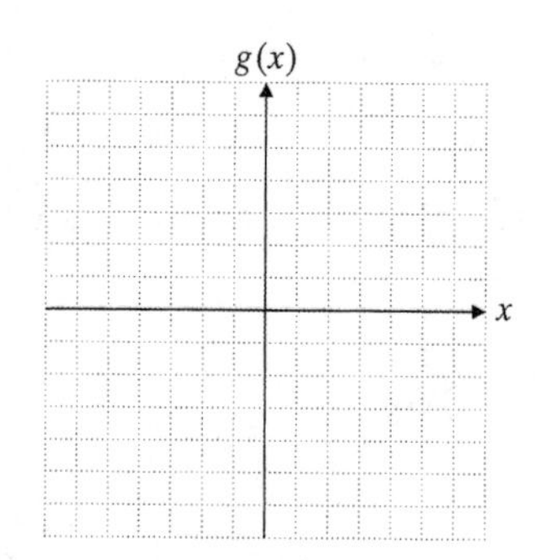

Applications

Some sports such as scuba diving are expensive. People with larger incomes are more likely to participate in such a sport. The number of people N (measured in thousands) who engage in scuba diving can be described by the function $N(x) = 0.18x^2 - 3.18x + 102.25$, *where x is the mean income (measured in thousands) and* $x \geq 20$. *Use this information to answer problems 23–27. (Source: U.S. Census Bureau.)*

23. Find $N(20)$, $N(40)$, $N(60)$, $N(80)$, and $N(100)$.

24. Use the results of Exercise 23 to graph the function from $x = 20$ to $x = 100$. You may use the graph grid provided on page 463.

25. Find $N(70)$ from your graph. Explain what $N(70)$ means.

26. Find $N(70)$ from the equation for $N(x)$. Compare your answers for Exercises 25 and 26.

27. Use your graph to determine for what value of x $N(x)$ is equal to 390. Explain what this means.

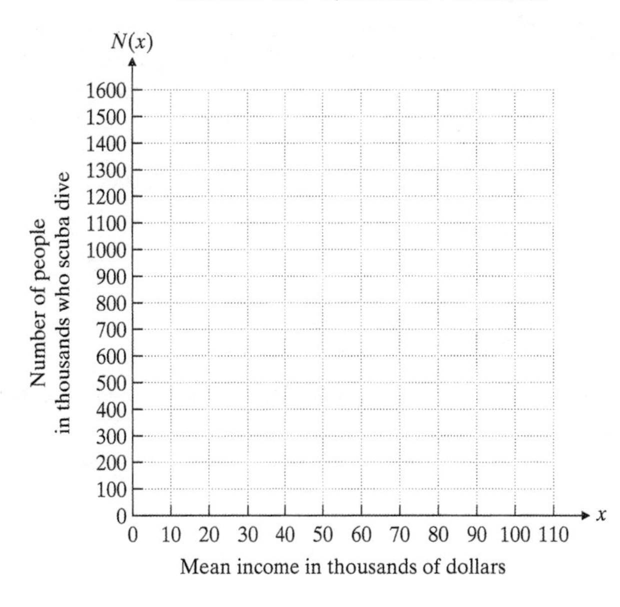

The daily profit P in dollars of the Pine Tree Table Company is described by the function $P(x) = -6x^2 + 312x - 3672$, *where x is the number of tables that are manufactured in 1 day. Use this information to answer Exercises 28–32.*

28. Find $P(16)$, $P(20)$, $P(24)$, $P(30)$, and $P(35)$.

29. Use the results of Exercise 28 to graph the function from $x = 16$ to $x = 35$.

30. The maximum profit of the company occurs at the vertex of the parabola. How many tables should be made per day in order to obtain the maximum profit for the company? What is the maximum profit?

31. How many tables per day should be made in order to obtain a daily profit of \$360? Why are there two answers to this question?

32. How many tables are made per day if the company has a daily profit of zero dollars?

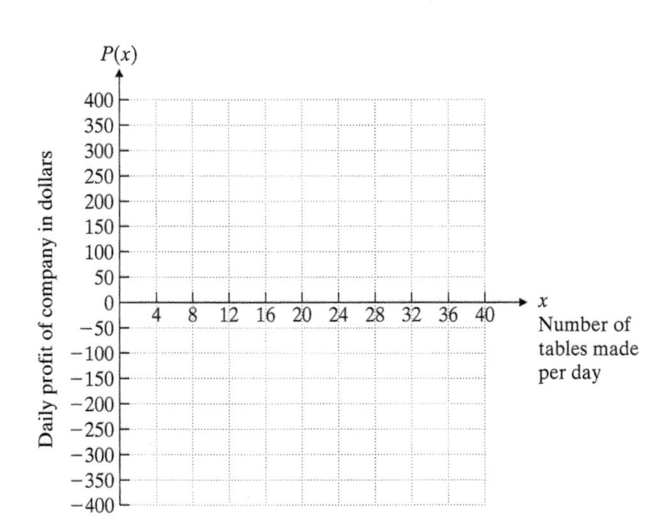

33. Susan throws a softball upward into the air at a speed of 32 feet per second from a 40-foot platform. The distance upward that the ball travels is given by the function $d(t) = -16t^2 + 32t + 40$. What is the maximum height of the softball? How many seconds does it take to reach the ground after first being thrown upward? (Round your answer to the nearest tenth.)

34. Henry is standing on a platform overlooking a baseball stadium. It is 160 feet above the playing field. When he throws a baseball upward at 64 feet per second, the distance d from the baseball to the ground is given by the function $d(t) = -16t^2 + 64t + 160$. What is the maximum height of the baseball if he throws it upward? How many seconds does it take until the ball finally hits the ground? (Round your answer to the nearest tenth.)

Optional Graphing Calculator Problems

Find the vertex and intercepts for each of the following. If your answers are not exact, round them to the nearest tenth.

35. $y = x^2 - 4.4x + 7.59$

36. $y = x^2 + 7.8x + 13.8$

37. Graph $y = 2.3x^2 - 5.4x - 1.6$. Find the x-intercepts to the nearest tenth.

38. Graph $y = -4.6x^2 + 7.2x - 2.3$. Find the x-intercepts to the nearest tenth.

Cumulative Review Problems

Solve each system.

39. $9x + 5y = 6$
$2x - 5y = -17$

40. $x + y = 16$
$95x + 143y = 1760$

41. $3x - y + 2z = 12$
$2x - 3y + z = 5$
$x + 3y + 8z = 22$

42. $7x + 3y - z = -2$
$x + 5y + 3z = 2$
$x + 2y + z = 1$

8.6 Quadratic Inequalities in One Variable

Student Learning Objectives

After studying this section, you will be able to:

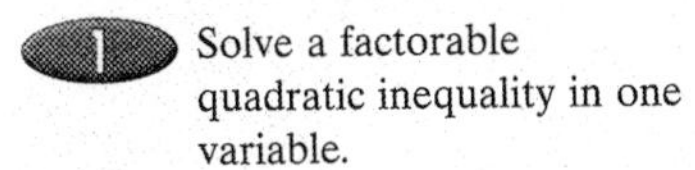

1. Solve a factorable quadratic inequality in one variable.

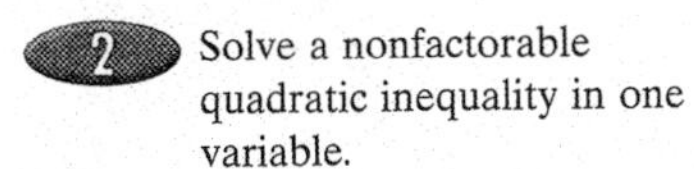

2. Solve a nonfactorable quadratic inequality in one variable.

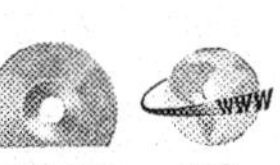

1 Solving a Factorable Quadratic Inequality in One Variable

We will now solve quadratic inequalities such as $x^2 - 2x - 3 > 0$ and $2x^2 + x - 15 < 0$. A **quadratic inequality** has the form $ax^2 + bx + c < 0$ (or replace $<$ by $>$, $\leq$, or $\geq$), where a, b, and c are real numbers $a \neq 0$. We use our knowledge of solving quadratic equations to solve quadratic inequalities.

Let's solve the inequality $x^2 - 2x - 3 > 0$. We want to find the two points where the expression on the left side is equal to zero. We call these the **critical points**. To do this, we replace the inequality symbol by an equal sign and solve the resulting equation.

$$x^2 - 2x - 3 = 0$$

$$(x + 1)(x - 3) = 0 \qquad \text{Factor.}$$

$$x + 1 = 0 \quad \text{or} \quad x - 3 = 0 \qquad \text{Zero-product rule}$$

$$x = -1 \qquad\qquad x = 3$$

These two solutions form critical points that divide the number line into three segments.

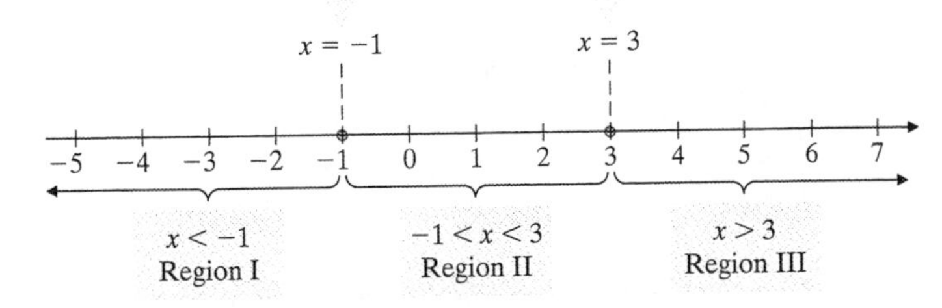

We will show as an exercise that all values of x in a given segment produce results that are greater than zero, or all values of x in a given segment produce results that are less than zero.

To solve the quadratic inequality, we pick an arbitrary test point in each region and then substitute it into the inequality to determine whether it satisfies the inequality. If one point in a region satisfies the inequality, then *all* points in the region satisfy the inequality. We will test three values of x in the expression $x^2 - 2x - 3$.

$x < -1$, *region I:* A sample point is $x = -2$.

$$(-2)^2 - 2(-2) - 3 = 4 + 4 - 3 = 5 > 0$$

$-1 < x < 3$, *region II:* A sample point is $x = 0$.

$$(0)^2 - 2(0) - 3 = 0 + 0 - 3 = -3 < 0$$

$x > 3$, *region III:* A sample point is $x = 4$.

$$(4)^2 - 2(4) - 3 = 16 - 8 - 3 = 5 > 0$$

Thus, we see that $x^2 - 2x - 3 > 0$ when $x < -1$ or $x > 3$. No points in region II satisfy the inequality. The graph of the solution is shown next.

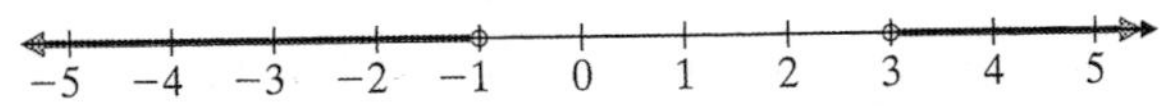

We summarize our method.

Solving a Quadratic Inequality

1. Replace the inequality symbol by an equal sign. Solve the resulting equation to find the critical points.
2. Use the critical points to separate the number line into three distinct regions.
3. Evaluate the quadratic expression at a test point in each region.
4. Determine which regions satisfy the original conditions of the quadratic inequality.

EXAMPLE 1 Solve and graph $x^2 - 10x + 24 > 0$.

1. We replace the inequality symbol by an equal sign and solve the resulting equation.

$$x^2 - 10x + 24 = 0$$
$$(x - 4)(x - 6) = 0$$
$$x - 4 = 0 \quad \text{or} \quad x - 6 = 0$$
$$x = 4 \qquad\qquad x = 6$$

2. We use the critical points to separate the number line into distinct regions.

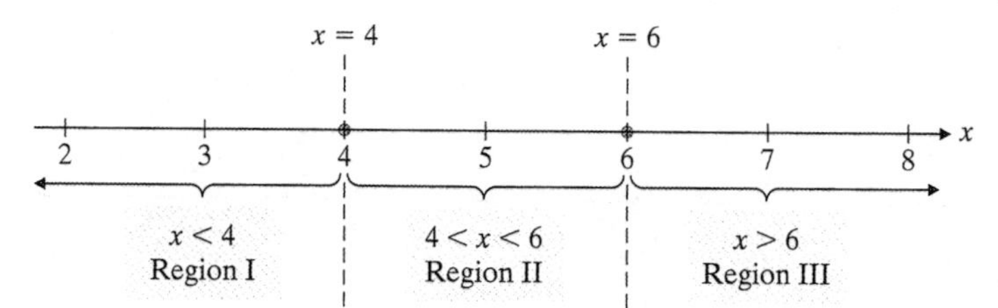

3. We evaluate the quadratic expression at a test point in each of the regions.

$$x^2 - 10x + 24$$

$x < 4$, *region I:* We pick the sample point $x = 1$.

$$(1)^2 - 10(1) + 24 = 1 - 10 + 24 = 15 > 0$$

$4 < x < 6$, *region II:* We pick the sample point $x = 5$.

$$(5)^2 - 10(5) + 24 = 25 - 50 + 24 = -1 < 0$$

$x > 6$, *region III:* We pick the sample point $x = 7$.

$$(7)^2 - 10(7) + 24 = 49 - 70 + 24 = 3 > 0$$

4. We determine which regions satisfy the original conditions of the quadratic inequality.

$x^2 - 10x + 24 > 0$ when $x < 4$ or when $x > 6$.

The graph of the solution is shown next.

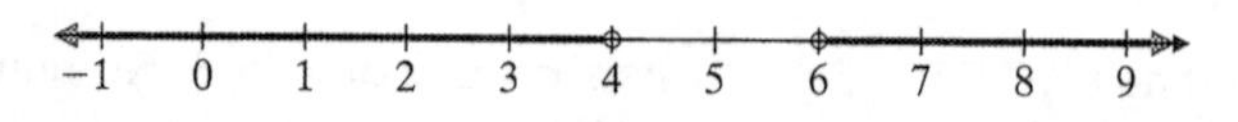

PRACTICE PROBLEM 1

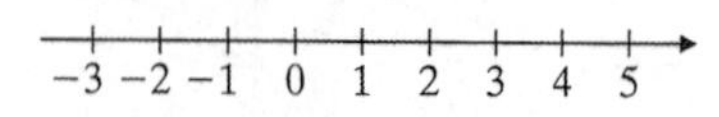

Practice Problem 1 Solve and graph $x^2 - 2x - 8 < 0$.

EXAMPLE 2 Solve and graph $2x^2 + x - 6 \le 0$.

We replace the inequality symbol by an equal sign and solve the resulting equation.

$$2x^2 + x - 6 = 0$$

$$(2x - 3)(x + 2) = 0$$

$$2x - 3 = 0 \quad \text{or} \quad x + 2 = 0$$

$$2x = 3 \qquad x = -2$$

$$x = \frac{3}{2} = 1.5$$

We use the critical points to separate the number line into distinct regions. The critical points are $x = -2$ and $x = 1.5$. Now we arbitrarily pick a test point in each region.

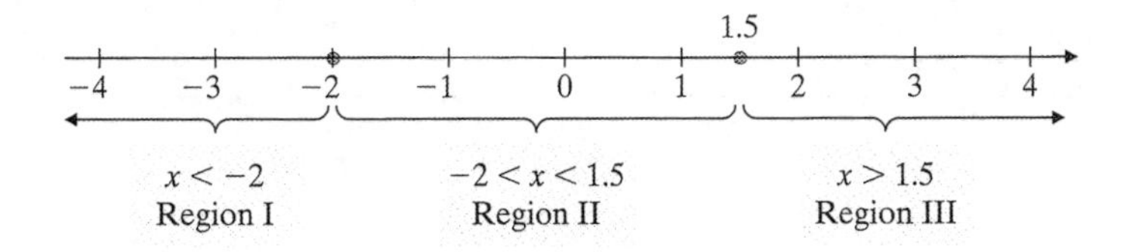

$$2x^2 + x - 6$$

Region I: We pick $x = -3$.

$$2(-3)^2 + (-3) - 6 = 18 - 3 - 6 = 9 > 0$$

Region II: We pick $x = 0$.

$$2(0)^2 + (0) - 6 = 0 + 0 - 6 = -6 < 0$$

Region III: We pick $x = 2$.

$$2(2)^2 + (2) - 6 = 8 + 2 - 6 = 4 > 0$$

Since our inequality is $\le$ and not just $<$, we need to include the critical points. Thus, $2x^2 + x - 6 \le 0$ when $-2 \le x \le 1.5$. The graph of our solution is shown next.

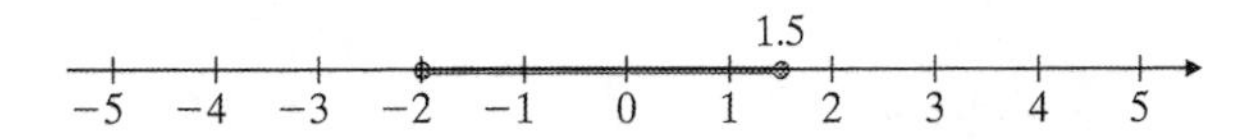

Practice Problem 2 Solve and graph $3x^2 - x - 2 \ge 0$.

Graphing Calculator

Solving Quadratic Inequalities

To solve Example 2 on a graphing calculator, graph $y = 2x^2 + x - 6$, zoom in on the two x-intercepts, and use the Trace feature to find the value of x where y changes from a negative value to a positive value or zero. You can use the Zero command if your calculator has it. Can you verify from your graph that the solution to Example 2 is $-2 \le x \le 1.5$? Use your graphing calculator and this method to solve the exercises below. Round your answers to the nearest hundredth.

1. $3x^2 - 3x - 60 \ge 0$
2. $2.1x^2 + 4.3x - 29.7 > 0$
3. $15.3x^2 - 20.4x + 6.8 \ge 0$
4. $16.8x^2 > -16.8x - 35.7$

If you are using a graphing calculator and you think there is no solution to a quadratic inequality, how can you *verify* this from the graph? Why is this possible?

PRACTICE PROBLEM 2

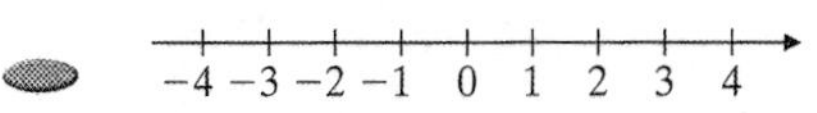

2 Solving a Nonfactorable Quadratic Inequality in One Variable

If the quadratic expression in a quadratic inequality cannot be factored, then we will use the quadratic formula to obtain the critical points.

EXAMPLE 3 Solve and graph $x^2 + 4x > 6$. Round your answer to the nearest tenth.

First we write $x^2 + 4x - 6 > 0$. Because we cannot factor $x^2 + 4x - 6$, we use the quadratic formula to find the critical points.

$$x = \frac{-4 \pm \sqrt{4^2 - 4(1)(-6)}}{2(1)} = \frac{-4 \pm \sqrt{16 + 24}}{2}$$

$$= \frac{-4 \pm \sqrt{40}}{2} = \frac{-4 \pm 2\sqrt{10}}{2} = -2 \pm \sqrt{10}$$

Using a calculator or our table of square roots, we find the following:

$$-2 + \sqrt{10} \approx -2 + 3.162 \approx 1.162 \text{ or about } 1.2$$

$$-2 - \sqrt{10} \approx -2 - 3.162 \approx -5.162 \text{ or about } -5.2$$

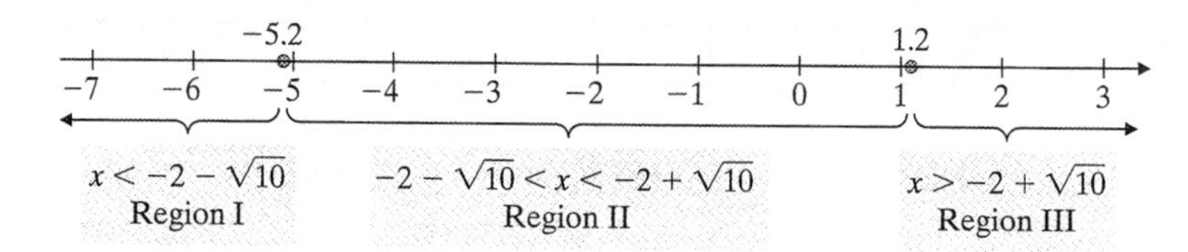

We will see where $x^2 + 4x - 6 > 0$.

Region I: $x = -6$

$$(-6)^2 + 4(-6) - 6 = 36 - 24 - 6 = 6 > 0$$

Region II: $x = 0$

$$(0)^2 + 4(0) - 6 = 0 + 0 - 6 = -6 < 0$$

Region III: $x = 2$

$$(2)^2 + 4(2) - 6 = 4 + 8 - 6 = 6 > 0$$

Thus, $x^2 + 4x > 6$ when $x^2 + 4x - 6 > 0$, and this occurs when $x < -2 - \sqrt{10}$ or $x > -2 + \sqrt{10}$. Rounding to the nearest tenth, our answer is

$$x < -5.2 \quad \text{or} \quad x > 1.2.$$

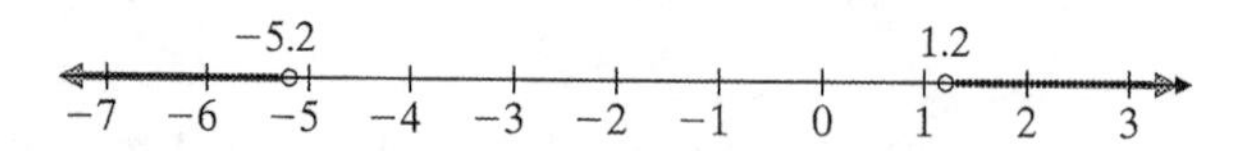

PRACTICE PROBLEM 3

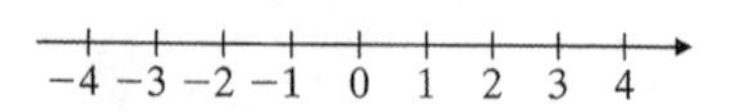

Practice Problem 3 Solve and graph $x^2 + 2x < 7$. Round your answer to the nearest tenth.

8.6 Exercises

Verbal and Writing Skills

1. When solving a quadratic inequality, why is it necessary to find the critical points?

2. What is the difference between solving an exercise like $ax^2 + bx + c > 0$ and an exercise like $ax^2 + bx + c \geq 0$?

Solve and graph.

3. $x^2 + x - 12 < 0$

4. $x^2 - x - 6 > 0$

5. $2x^2 + x - 3 < 0$

6. $6x^2 - 5x + 1 < 0$

7. $x^2 \geq 4$

8. $x^2 - 9 \leq 0$

Solve.

9. $5x^2 \leq 4x + 1$

10. $7x^2 \leq 5x + 2$

11. $20 - x - x^2 > 0$

12. $28 - 3x - x^2 > 0$

13. $6x^2 - 5x > 6$

14. $3x^2 + 17x > -10$

15. $-2x + 30 \geq x(x + 5)$
Hint: Put variables on the right and zero on the left in your first step.

16. $55 - x^2 \geq 6x$
Hint: Put variables on the right and zero on the left in your first step.

17. $x^2 - 4x \leq -4$

18. $x^2 - 6x \leq -9$

Solve each of the following quadratic inequalities if possible. Round your answers to the nearest tenth.

19. $x^2 - 2x > 4$

20. $x^2 + 6x > 8$

21. $x^2 - 6x < -7$

22. $x^2 < 2x + 1$

23. $2x^2 \geq x^2 - 4$

24. $4x^2 \geq 3x^2 - 9$

Applications

In Exercises 25 and 26, a projectile is fired vertically with an initial velocity of 640 feet per second. The distance s in feet above the ground after t seconds is given by the equation $s = -16t^2 + 640t$.

25. For what range of time (measured in seconds) will the height s be greater than 6000 feet?

26. For what range of time (measured in seconds) will the height s be less than 4800 feet?

In Exercises 27 and 28, the profit of a manufacturing company is determined by the number of units x manufactured each day according to the given equation. ***(a)*** *Find when the profit is greater than zero.* ***(b)*** *Find the daily profit when 50 units are manufactured.* ***(c)*** *Find the daily profit when 60 units are manufactured.*

27. Profit $= -20(x^2 - 220x + 2400)$

28. Profit $= -25(x^2 - 280x + 4000)$

Cumulative Review Problems

29. The university's synchronized swimming team will not let Mona participate unless she passes biology with a C (70 or better) average. There are six tests in the semester, and she failed the first one (with a score of 0). She decided to find a tutor. Since then, she received an 81, 92, and 80 on the next three tests. What must her minimum scores be on the last two tests to pass the course with a minimum grade of 70 and participate in synchronized swimming?

30. In a huge bowl at a college party, there are 360 ounces of mixed potato chips, peanuts, pretzels, and popcorn. There are 70 more ounces of peanuts than potato chips. There are twice as many ounces of pretzels as ounces of popcorn. There are 10 more ounces of popcorn than potato chips. How many ounces of each ingredient are in the snack mix?

The Circle Line Cruise is a 2-hour, 24-mile cruise around southern Manhattan (New York City). The charge for adults is $18; children 12 and under, $10; and the elderly, $16. For the 3-hour, 35-mile cruise around all of Manhattan, the charge for adults is $22; children 12 and under, $12; and the elderly, $19. The Yoffa family has come to New York for their family reunion and is planning family activities. The family has ten adults, fourteen children under 12, and five elderly members.

31. What would it cost for all of the family to take the 2-hour trip? The 3-hour trip?

32. Six people do not take a cruise. If the rest of the family takes a 2-hour cruise, it will cost $314. If the rest of the family takes a 3-hour cruise, it will cost $380. How many adults, how many children, and how many elderly members plan to take a cruise?

Putting Your Skills to Work

The Mathematics of the Hoover Dam

One of the most impressive construction projects completed in the United States in the twentieth century was the Hoover Dam. It weighs 6.6 million tons and contains 3.25 million cubic yards of concrete. The builders used so much concrete for this construction project that with it they could have built a two-lane highway from New York City to San Francisco.

During the construction of the dam, the water had to be diverted away from the project. This required the building of four diversion tunnels. The average length of the tunnels was 4000 feet.

Problems for Individual Investigation and Analysis

▲ **1.** Find the volume of rock that had to be removed for the four diversion tunnels if each tunnel was 56 feet in diameter. (Use $\pi \approx 3.14$.)

▲ **2.** Each diversion tunnel was lined with 3 feet of concrete. Thus, the outer shell of the tunnels was 56 feet in diameter, while the inside shaft of the tunnels was 50 feet in diameter. Find the volume of concrete that was used to build the four diversion tunnels. (Use $\pi \approx 3.14$.)

Problems for Group Investigation and Cooperative Learning

The Hoover Dam is 726.4 feet tall. It is 45 feet thick at the top and 660 feet thick at the bottom. The force of water on the bottom edge of the dam is 22.5 tons per square foot.

3. If the cross section of the center of the dam were superimposed on a rectangular coordinate system, its outside edges would be approximately defined by the equations $y = 0.00205x^2$, $y = 726$, $x = 660$, and $y = 0$, where x and y are measured in feet. Graph these four equations to show a cross-sectional view of the main wall of the center of the Hoover Dam.

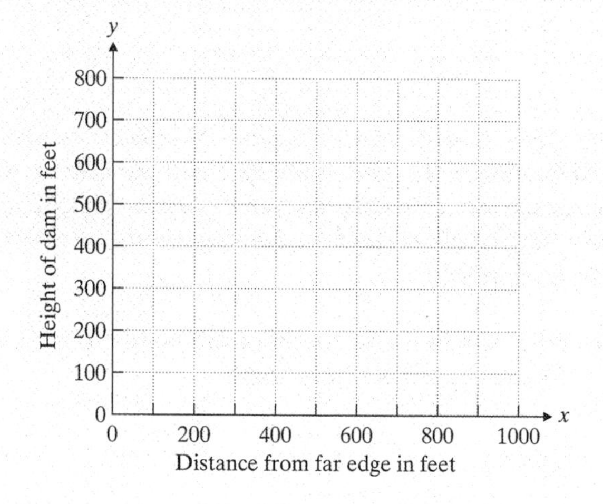

4. Use your graph to estimate the thickness of the Hoover Dam at the point where the dam is 400 feet high. Find the exact answer using the equations in Exercise 3. Compare your answers.

Internet Connections

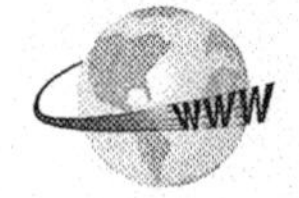

Netsite:  http://www.prenhall.com/tobey_intermediate 

Site: Hoover Dam Visitor Site

5. Of all the excavation that took place in the construction of the Hoover Dam, what percent was to dig the earth and rockfill needed for the cofferdams, the temporary dams that held back the water while the construction took place?

6. With the same number of cubic yards of concrete in the Hoover dam, power plant, and other structures on the site, how many monuments could be built with a cross-section of 100 square feet and a height of 30 feet?

Math in the Media

Stopping Distances

A USA TODAY.com Snapshot, Quick Stops, reported that increased speeds on U.S. highways were accompanied by increased stopping distances.

Stopping distances are an important and universal element in highway safety. For this reason, this data is widely collected by many different highway safety agencies throughout the world.

To get some hands-on experience examining the relationship between speed and stopping distance, try answering the questions that follow which are based on data from the Traffic Board of Western Australia.

EXERCISES

While driving, you suddenly see the brake lights of the car in front of you come on. If you assume the car ahead is going to stop and you then apply the brakes, how far will your car travel before it comes to a complete stop? In other words, what is the stopping distance from the moment your brain receives the signal to stop until the car is no longer moving?

The table below contains data for stopping distance in this situation. Note that the total stopping distance is the sum of the reaction distance (the distance traveled from the time you realize that you must brake unitl your foot hits the brake pedal) and the braking distance (distance traveled after the brake pedal is pressed).

V Speed miles/hour	x Speed feet/second	R (reaction time: 0.7 sec) Reaction distance feet	B Braking Distance feet	y Total Stopping Distance feet
55	81	57	219	276
65	95	67	301	368
75	110	77	403	480

Source: Based on data from the Traffic Board of Western Australia. *converted from Metric to US units.

1. Notice the pattern between the second and third columns and find an equation that gives the reaction distance R as a function of the speed x. R is rounded to the nearest foot.

2. The model for braking distance B as a function of the speed x is $B = 0.032512x^2 + 0.134975x - 5.24631$. Use this equation and the equation from your answer to question 1, to find an equation for total stopping distance y as a function of the speed x. Write the equation for total stopping distance in simplest form by combining like terms.

Chapter 8 Organizer

Topic	Procedure	Examples
Solving a quadratic equation by using the square root property, p. 426.	If $x^2 = a$, then $x = \pm\sqrt{a}$.	Solve. $2x^2 - 50 = 0$ $2x^2 = 50$ $x^2 = 25$ $x = \pm\sqrt{25}$ $x = \pm 5$
Solving a quadratic equation by completing the square, p. 427.	**1.** Rewrite the equation in the form $ax^2 + bx = c$. If $a \neq 1$, divide each term of the equation by a. **2.** Square half of the numerical coefficient of the linear term. Add the result to both sides of the equation. **3.** Factor the left side. **4.** Take the square root of both sides of the equation. **5.** Solve the resulting equation for x. **6.** Check the solutions in the original equation.	Solve. $2x^2 - 4x - 1 = 0$ $2x^2 - 4x = 1$ $\frac{2x^2}{2} - \frac{4x}{2} = \frac{1}{2}$ $x^2 - 2x + \_\_\_\_ = \frac{1}{2} + \_\_\_\_$ $x^2 - 2x + 1 = \frac{1}{2} + 1$ $(x - 1)^2 = \frac{3}{2}$ $x - 1 = \pm\sqrt{\frac{3}{2}}$ $x - 1 = \frac{\pm\sqrt{6}}{2}$ $x = 1 \pm \frac{1}{2}\sqrt{6}$
Placing a quadratic equation in standard form, p. 434.	A quadratic equation in standard form is an equation of the form $ax^2 + bx + c = 0$, where a, b, and c are real numbers and $a \neq 0$. It is often necessary to remove parentheses and clear away fractions by multiplying each term of the equation by the LCD to obtain the standard form.	Rewrite in quadratic form: $\frac{2}{x-3} + \frac{x}{x+3} = \frac{5}{x^2-9}$ $(x+3)(x-3)\left[\frac{2}{x-3}\right]$ $+ (x+3)(x-3)\left[\frac{x}{x+3}\right]$ $= (x+3)(x-3)\left[\frac{5}{(x+3)(x-3)}\right]$ $2(x+3) + x(x-3) = 5$ $2x + 6 + x^2 - 3x = 5$ $x^2 - x + 1 = 0$
Solve a quadratic equation by using the quadratic formula, p. 432.	If $ax^2 + bx + c = 0$, where $a \neq 0$, $x = \frac{-b \pm \sqrt{b^2 - 4ac}}{2a}$. **1.** Rewrite the equation in standard form. **2.** Determine the values of a, b, and c. **3.** Substitute the values of a, b, and c into the formula. **4.** Simplify the result to obtain the values of x. **5.** Any imaginary solutions to the quadratic equation should be simplified by using the definition $\sqrt{-a} = i\sqrt{a}$, where $a > 0$.	Solve. $2x^2 = 3x - 2$ $2x^2 - 3x + 2 = 0$ $a = 2, b = -3, c = 2$ $x = \frac{-(-3) \pm \sqrt{(-3)^2 - 4(2)(2)}}{2(2)}$ $= \frac{3 \pm \sqrt{9 - 16}}{4}$ $= \frac{3 \pm \sqrt{-7}}{4}$ $= \frac{3 \pm i\sqrt{7}}{4}$

Topic	Procedure	Examples
Equations that can be transformed into quadratic form, p. 440.	**1.** Find the variable with the smallest exponent. Let this quantity be replaced by y. **2.** Continue to make substitutions for the remaining variable terms based on the first substitution. (You should be able to replace the variable with the largest exponent by y^2.) **3.** Solve the resulting equation for y. **4.** Reverse the substitution used in step 1. **5.** Solve the resulting equation for x. **6.** Check your solution in the *original* equation.	Solve: $x^{2/3} - x^{1/3} - 2 = 0$ Let $y = x^{1/3}$. Then $y^2 = x^{2/3}$. $y^2 - y - 2 = 0$ $(y - 2)(y + 1) = 0$ $y = 2$ or $y = -1$ $x^{1/3} = 2$ or $x^{1/3} = -1$ $(x^{1/3})^3 = 2^3$ $\quad (x^{1/3})^3 = (-1)^3$ $x = 8$ $\quad x = -1$
Checking solutions for equations in quadratic form (continued), p. 442		*Check.* $x = 8$: $(8)^{2/3} - (8)^{1/3} - 2 \stackrel{?}{=} 0$ $2^2 - 2 - 2 \stackrel{?}{=} 0$ $4 - 4 = 0$ ✓ $x = -1$: $(-1)^{2/3} - (-1)^{1/3} - 2 \stackrel{?}{=} 0$ $(-1)^2 - (-1) - 2 \stackrel{?}{=} 0$ $1 + 1 - 2 = 0$ ✓ Both 8 and -1 are solutions.
Solving quadratic equations containing two or more variables, p. 447.	Treat the letter to be solved for as a variable, but treat all other letters as constants. Solve the equation by factoring, by using the square root property, or by using the quadratic formula.	Solve for x. **(a)** $6x^2 - 11xw + 4w^2 = 0$ **(b)** $4x^2 + 5b = 2w^2$ **(c)** $2x^2 + 3xz - 10z = 0$ **(a)** By factoring: $(3x - 4w)(2x - w) = 0$ $3x - 4w = 0$ or $2x - w = 0$ $x = \frac{4w}{3}$ $\quad x = \frac{w}{2}$ **(b)** Using the square root property: $4x^2 = 2w^2 - 5b$ $x^2 = \frac{2w^2 - 5b}{4}$ $x = \pm\sqrt{\frac{2w^2 - 5b}{4}} = \pm\frac{1}{2}\sqrt{2w^2 - 5b}$ **(c)** By the quadratic formula, with $a = 2$, $b = 3z$, $c = -10z$: $x = \frac{-3z \pm \sqrt{9z^2 + 80z}}{4}$
The Pythagorean theorem, p. 448.	In any right triangle, if c is the length of the hypotenuse and a and b are the lengths of the two legs, then $c^2 = a^2 + b^2$.	Find a if $c = 7$ and $b = 5$. $49 = a^2 + 25$ $49 - 25 = a^2$ $24 = a^2$ $\sqrt{24} = a$ $2\sqrt{6} = a$

Topic	Procedure	Examples
Graphing quadratic functions, p. 459.	Graph quadratic functions of the form $f(x) = ax^2 + bx + c$ with $a \neq 0$ as follows: **1.** Find the vertex at $\left(\frac{-b}{2a}, f\left(\frac{-b}{2a}\right)\right)$. **2.** Find the y-intercept, which occurs at $f(0)$. **3.** Find the x-intercepts if they exist. Solve $f(x) = 0$ for x.	Graph $f(x) = x^2 + 6x + 8$. Vertex: $x = \frac{-6}{2} = -3$ $f(-3) = (-3)^2 + 6(-3) + 8 = -1$ The vertex is $(-3, -1)$. Intercepts: $f(0) = (0)^2 + 6(0) + 8 = 8$ The y-intercept is $(0, 8)$. $x^2 + 6x + 8 = 0$ $(x + 2)(x + 4) = 0$ $x = -2, x = -4$ The x-intercepts are $(-2, 0)$ and $(-4, 0)$. 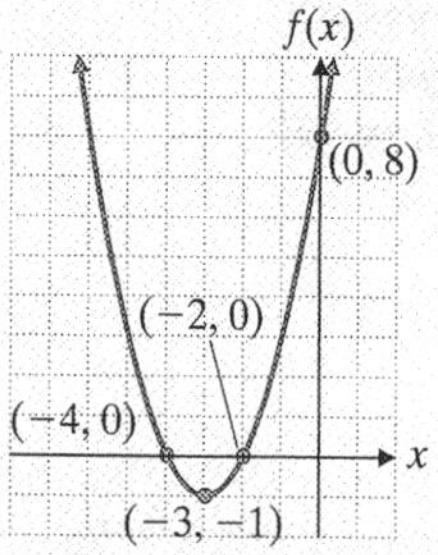 $f(x) = x^2 + 6x + 8$
Solving quadratic inequalities in one variable, p. 466.	**1.** Replace the inequality symbol by an equal sign. Solve the resulting equation to find the critical points. **2.** Use the critical points to separate the number line into distinct regions. **3.** Evaluate the quadratic expression at a test point in each region. **4.** Determine which regions satisfy the original conditions of the quadratic inequality.	Solve and graph: $3x^2 + 5x - 2 > 0$ **1.** $3x^2 + 5x - 2 = 0$ $(3x - 1)(x + 2) = 0$ $3x - 1 = 0 \qquad x + 2 = 0$ $x = \frac{1}{3} \qquad x = -2$ Critical points are -2 and $\frac{1}{3}$. **2.** 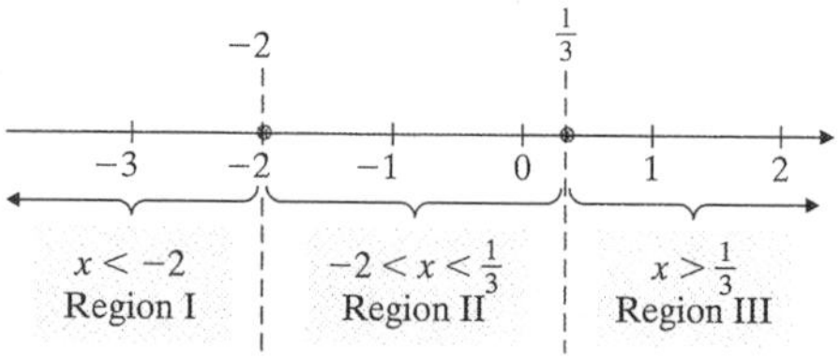 $x < -2$ Region I; $-2 < x < \frac{1}{3}$ Region II; $x > \frac{1}{3}$ Region III **3.** $3x^2 + 5x - 2$ *Region I:* Pick $x = -3$. $3(-3)^2 + 5(-3) - 2 = 27 - 15 - 2 = 10 > 0$ *Region II:* Pick $x = 0$. $3(0)^2 + 5(0) - 2 = 0 + 0 - 2 = -2 < 0$ *Region III:* Pick $x = 3$. $3(3)^2 + 5(3) - 2 = 27 + 15 - 2 = 40 > 0$ **4.** We know that the expression is greater than zero (that is, $3x^2 + 5x - 2 > 0$) when $x < -2$ or $x > \frac{1}{3}$. 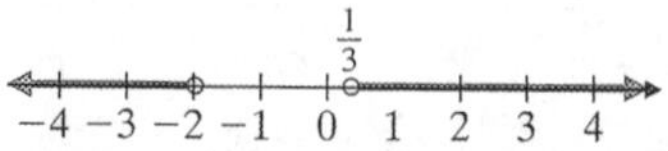

Chapter 8 Review Problems

Solve each of the following exercises by the specified method. Simplify all answers.

Solve by the square root property.

1. $5x^2 = 100$

2. $(x + 8)^2 = 81$

Solve by completing the square.

3. $x^2 + 8x + 13 = 0$

4. $4x^2 - 8x + 1 = 0$

Solve by the quadratic formula.

5. $3x^2 - 10x + 6 = 0$

6. $x^2 - 6x - 4 = 0$

Solve by any appropriate method and simplify your answers. Express any nonreal complex solutions using i notation.

7. $4x^2 - 12x + 9 = 0$

8. $3x^2 - 8x + 6 = 0$

9. $6x^2 - 23x = 4x$

10. $12x^2 - 29x + 15 = 0$

11. $x^2 - 3x - 23 = 5$

12. $3x^2 + 7x + 13 = 13$

13. $3x^2 - 2x = 15x - 10$

14. $6x^2 + 12x - 24 = 0$

15. $4x^2 - 3x + 2 = 0$

16. $3x^2 + 5x + 1 = 0$

17. $3x(3x + 2) - 2 = 3x$

18. $10x(x - 2) + 10 = 2x$

19. $\frac{5}{6}x^2 - x + \frac{1}{3} = 0$

20. $\frac{4}{5}x^2 + x + \frac{1}{5} = 0$

21. $y + \frac{5}{3y} + \frac{17}{6} = 0$

22. $\frac{19}{y} - \frac{15}{y^2} + 10 = 0$

23. $\frac{15}{y^2} - \frac{2}{y} = 1$

24. $y - 18 + \frac{81}{y} = 0$

25. $(3y + 2)(y - 1) = 7(-y + 1)$

26. $y(y + 1) + (y + 2)^2 = 4$

27. $\frac{2x}{x + 3} + \frac{3x - 1}{x + 1} = 3$

28. $\frac{4x + 1}{2x + 5} + \frac{3x}{x + 4} = 2$

Determine the nature of each of the following quadratic equations. Do not solve the equation. Find the discriminant in each case and determine whether the equation has (a) one rational solution, (b) two rational solutions, (c) two irrational solutions, or (d) two nonreal complex solutions.

29. $2x^2 + 5x - 3 = 0$

30. $3x^2 - 7x - 12 = 0$

31. $4x^2 - 6x + 5 = 0$

32. $25x^2 - 20x + 4 = 0$

Write a quadratic equation having the given numbers as solutions.

33. $5, -5$

34. $3i, -3i$

35. $4\sqrt{2}, -4\sqrt{2}$

36. $-3/4, -1/2$

Solve for any valid real roots.

37. $x^4 - 6x^2 + 8 = 0$

38. $2x^6 - 5x^3 - 3 = 0$

39. $x^{2/3} + 9x^{1/3} = -8$

40. $3x^{1/2} - 11x^{1/4} = 4$

41. $(2x - 5)^2 + 4(2x - 5) + 3 = 0$

42. $1 + 4x^{-8} = 5x^{-4}$

Solve for the variable specified. Assume that all radical expressions obtained have a positive radicand.

43. $A = \dfrac{2B^2C}{3H}$; for B

44. $2H = 3g(a^2 + b^2)$; for b

45. $20d^2 - xd - x^2 = 0$; for d

46. $yx^2 - 3x - 7 = 0$; for x

47. $3y^2 - 4ay + 2a = 0$; for y

48. $PV = 5x^2 + 3y^2 + 2x$; for x

Use the Pythagorean theorem to find the missing side. Assume that c is the length of the hypotenuse of a right triangle and that a and b are the lengths of the legs. Leave your answers as a radical in simplified form.

49. $c = 16, b = 4$; find a

50. $a = 3\sqrt{2}, b = 2$; find c

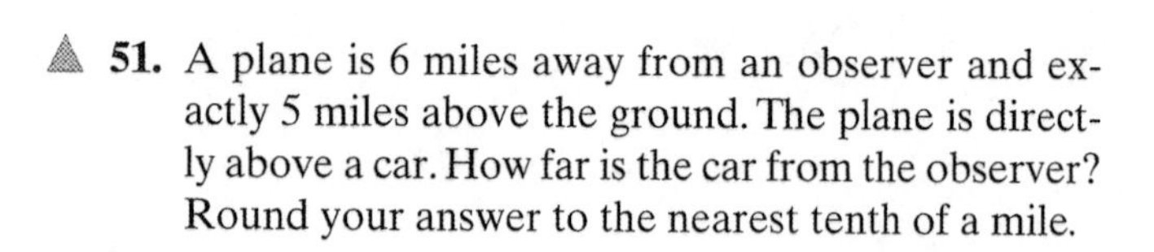

51. A plane is 6 miles away from an observer and exactly 5 miles above the ground. The plane is directly above a car. How far is the car from the observer? Round your answer to the nearest tenth of a mile.

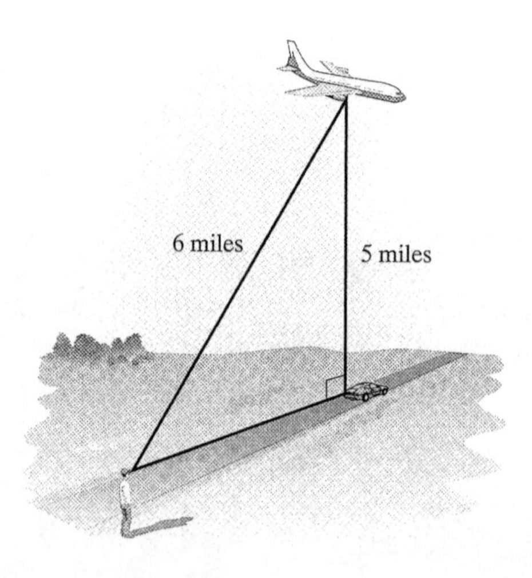

▲ **52.** The area of a rectangle is 203 square meters. Its length is 1 meter longer than four times its width. Find the length and width of the rectangle.

▲ **53.** The area of a triangle is 70 square centimeters. Its altitude is 6 meters longer than twice the length of the base. Find the dimensions of the altitude and base.

54. Jessica drove at a constant speed for 200 miles. Then it started to rain. So for the next 90 miles she traveled 5 miles per hour slower. The entire trip took 6 hours of driving time. Find her speed for each part of the trip.

55. John rode in a motorboat for 60 miles at constant cruising speed to get to his fishing grounds. Then for 5 miles he trolled to catch fish. His trolling speed was 15 miles per hour slower than his cruising speed. The trip took 4 hours. Find his speed for each part of the trip.

▲ **56.** Mr. and Mrs. Gomez are building a rectangular garden that is 10 feet by 6 feet. Around the outside of the garden, they will build a brick walkway. They have 100 square feet of brick. How wide should they make the brick walkway? Round your answer to the nearest tenth of a foot.

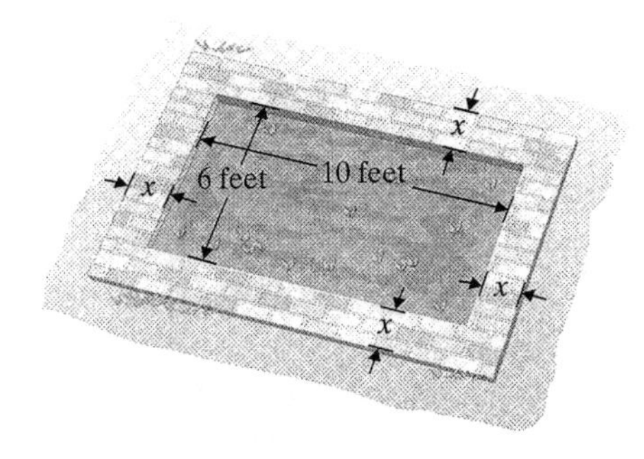

▲ **57.** The local YMCA is building a rectangular swimming pool that is 40 feet by 30 feet. The builders want to make a walkway around the pool with a nonslip cement surface. They have enough material to make 296 square feet of nonslip cement surface. How wide should the walkway be?

Find the vertex and the intercepts of the following quadratic functions.

58. $g(x) = -x^2 + 6x - 11$

59. $f(x) = x^2 + 10x + 25$

In each of the following exercises, find the vertex, the y-intercept, and the x-intercepts (if any exist) and then graph the function.

60. $f(x) = x^2 + 4x + 3$

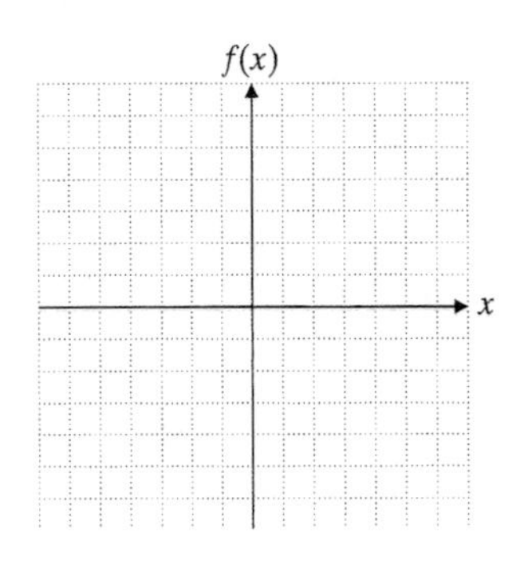

61. $f(x) = x^2 + 6x + 5$

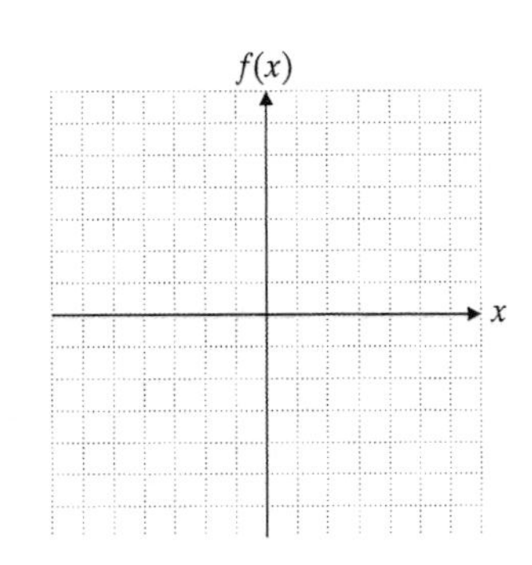

62. $f(x) = -x^2 + 6x - 5$

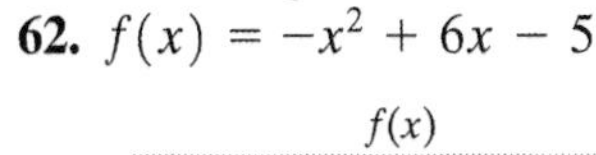

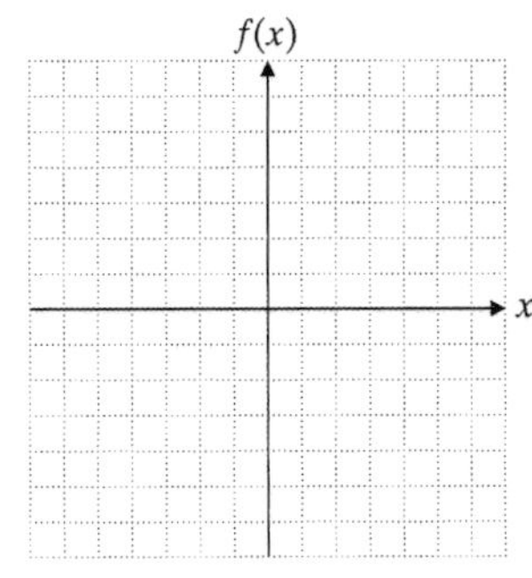

63. A model rocket is launched upward from a platform 40 feet above the ground. The height of the rocket h is given at any time t in seconds by the function $h(t) = -16t^2 + 400t + 40$. Find the maximum height of the rocket. How long will it take the rocket to go through its complete flight and then hit the ground? (Assume that the rocket does *not* have a parachute.) Round your answer to the nearest tenth.

64. A salesman for an electronics store finds that in 1 month he can sell $(1200 - x)$ compact disc players that each sell for x dollars. Write a function for the revenue. What is the price x that will result in the maximum revenue for the store?

Solve and graph your solutions.

65. $x^2 + 7x - 18 < 0$

66. $x^2 + 4x - 21 < 0$

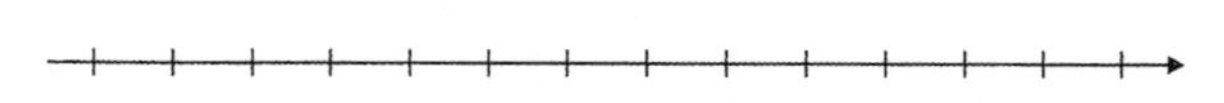

67. $x^2 - 9x + 20 > 0$

68. $x^2 - 11x + 28 > 0$

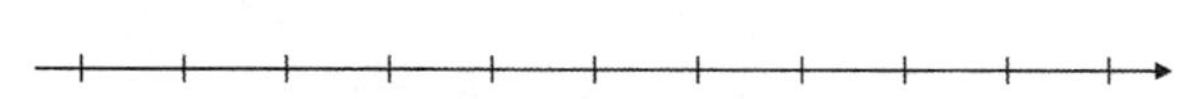

Solve each of the following if possible. Approximate, if necessary, any irrational solutions to the nearest tenth.

69. $2x^2 - 5x - 3 \leq 0$

70. $3x^2 - 5x - 2 \leq 0$

71. $16x^2 - 25 > 0$

72. $9x^2 - 4 > 0$

73. $x^2 - 9x > 4 - 7x$

74. $4x^2 - 8x \leq 12 + 5x^2$

75. $x^2 + 13x > 16 + 7x$

76. $3x^2 - 12x > -11$

77. $-2x^2 + 7x + 12 \leq -3x^2 + x$

78. $4x^2 + 12x + 9 < 0$

To Think About

79. $(x + 4)(x - 2)(3 - x) > 0$

80. $(x + 1)(x + 4)(2 - x) < 0$

Chapter 8 Test

Solve the quadratic equations and simplify your answers. Use i notation for any imaginary numbers.

1. $8x^2 + 9x = 0$

2. $8x^2 + 10x = 3$

3. $\frac{3x}{2} - \frac{8}{3} = \frac{2}{3x}$

4. $x(x - 3) - 30 = 5(x - 2)$

5. $7x^2 - 4 = 52$

6. $\frac{2x}{2x + 1} - \frac{6}{4x^2 - 1} = \frac{x + 1}{2x - 1}$

7. $2x^2 - 6x + 5 = 0$

8. $2x(x - 3) = -3$

Solve for any valid real roots.

9. $x^4 - 9x^2 + 14 = 0$

10. $3x^{-2} - 11x^{-1} - 20 = 0$

11. $x^{2/3} - 2x^{1/3} - 12 = 0$

1. ______________
2. ______________
3. ______________
4. ______________
5. ______________
6. ______________
7. ______________
8. ______________
9. ______________
10. ______________
11. ______________

Solve for the variable specified.

12. ______

12. $B = \frac{xyw}{z^2}$; for z

13. ______

13. $5y^2 + 2by + 6w = 0$; for y

14. The area of a rectangle is 80 square miles. Its length is 1 mile longer than three times its width. Find its length and width.

14. ______

15. Find the hypotenuse of a right triangle if the lengths of its legs are 6 and $2\sqrt{3}$.

15. ______

16. Shirley and Bill paddled a canoe at a constant speed for 6 miles. They rested, had lunch, and then paddled 1 mile per hour faster for an additional 3 miles. The travel time for the entire trip was 4 hours. How fast did they paddle during each part of the trip?

16. ______

17. Find the vertex and the intercepts for $f(x) = -x^2 - 6x - 5$. Then graph the function.

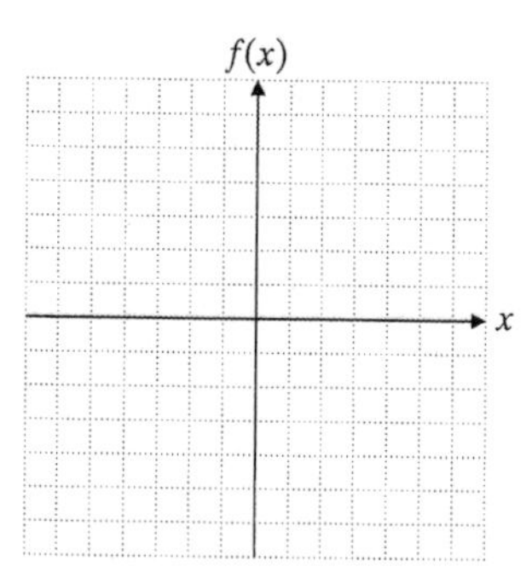

17. ______

18. ______

Solve.

19. ______

18. $2x^2 + 3x \geq 27$

19. $-3x^2 + 10x + 8 \geq 0$

20. ______

20. Use a calculator or square root table to approximate to the nearest tenth a solution to $x^2 + 3x - 7 > 0$.

Cumulative Test for Chapters 1–8

Approximately one half of this test is based on the content of Chapters 1–7. The remainder is based on the content of Chapter 8.

1. Simplify: $(-3x^{-2}y^3)^4$

2. Collect like terms.
$\frac{1}{2}a^3 - 2a^2 + 3a - \frac{1}{4}a^3 - 6a + a^2$

3. Solve for y: $a(2y + b) = 3ay - 4$

4. Graph: $6x - 3y = -12$

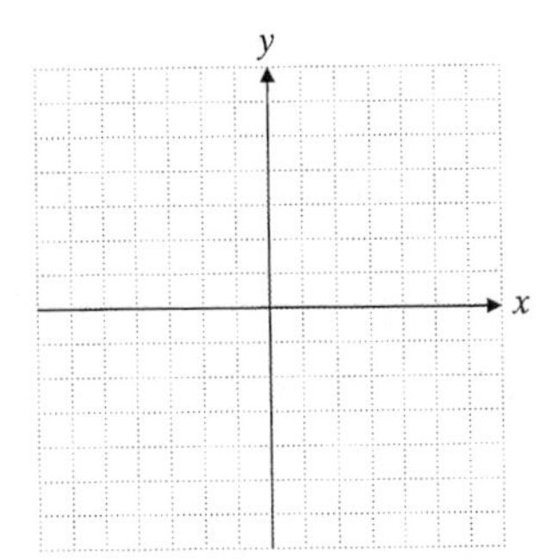

5. Write the equation of the line parallel to $2y + x = 8$ and passing through $(6, -1)$.

6. Find the volume of a sphere of radius 2 inches.

7. Factor: $125x^3 - 27y^3$

8. Simplify: $\sqrt{72x^3y^6}$

9. Multiply: $(3 + \sqrt{2})(\sqrt{6} + \sqrt{3})$

10. Rationalize the denominator. $\frac{3}{\sqrt{11}}$

Solve and simplify your answers. Use i notation for imaginary numbers.

11. $3x^2 + 12x = 26x$

12. $12x^2 = 11x - 2$

13. $44 = 3(2x - 3)^2 + 8$

14. $3 - \frac{4}{x} + \frac{5}{x^2} = 0$

1. ______
2. ______
3. ______
4. ______
5. ______
6. ______
7. ______
8. ______
9. ______
10. ______
11. ______
12. ______
13. ______
14. ______

15. ______

Solve and check.

15. $\sqrt{x-12} = \sqrt{x} - 2$

16. $x^{2/3} + 9x^{1/3} + 18 = 0$

16. ______

Solve for y.

17. $2y^2 + 5wy - 7z = 0$

18. $3y^2 + 16z^2 = 5w$

17. ______

19. The hypotenuse of a right triangle is $\sqrt{31}$. One leg of the triangle is 4. Find the length of the other leg.

18. ______

20. A triangle has an area of 45 square meters. The altitude is 3 meters longer than three times the length of the base. Find each dimension.

19. ______

Exercises 21 and 22 refer to the quadratic function $f(x) = -x^2 + 8x - 12$.

20. ______

21. Find the vertex and the intercepts of the function.

22. Graph the function.

21. ______

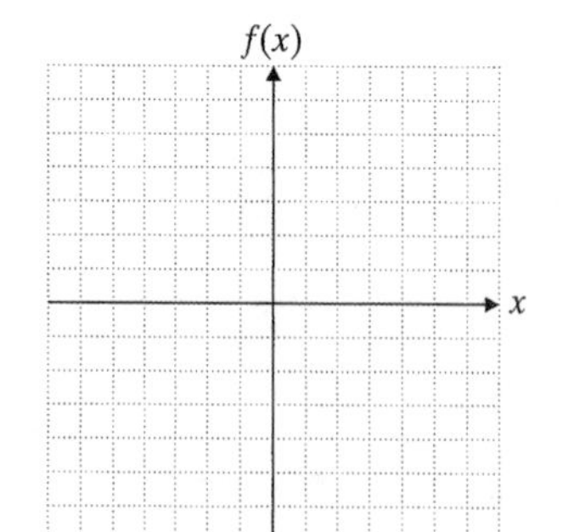

22. ______

23. ______

Solve each of the following quadratic inequalities.

24. ______

23. $6x^2 - x \leq 2$

24. $x^2 > -2x + 15$

Chapter 9

The Conic Sections

Suppose a major earthquake takes place. Shock waves radiate from the epicenter, which is the center of where an earthquake occurs. These shock waves travel out across the Earth as concentric circles. How could these patterns of circles be used to locate the exact epicenter of the earthquake? Could you use your knowledge of mathematics to determine these locations? Turn to the Putting Your Skills to Work exercises on page 530 to find out.

Pretest Chapter 9

1. ______

If you are familiar with the topics in this chapter, take this test now. Check your answers with those in the back of the book. If an answer is wrong or you can't do an exercise, study the appropriate section of the chapter.

If you are not familiar with the topics in this chapter, don't take this test now. Instead, study the examples, work the practice exercises, and then take the test.

This test will help you identify those concepts that you have mastered and those that need more study.

Section 9.1

2. ______

1. Write the standard form of the equation of a circle with center at $(8, -2)$ and a radius of $\sqrt{7}$.

2. Find the distance between $(-6, -2)$ and $(-3, 4)$.

3. Rewrite the equation $x^2 + y^2 - 2x - 4y + 1 = 0$ in standard form. Find the circle's center and radius and sketch its graph.

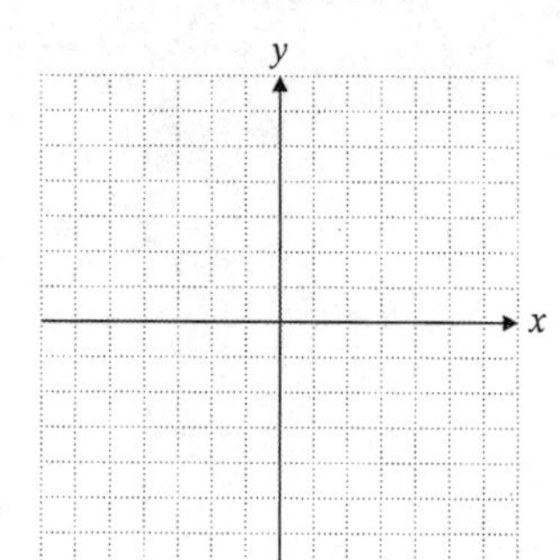

3. ______

Section 9.2

4. ______

Graph each parabola. Write the equation in standard form.

4. $x = (y + 1)^2 + 2$

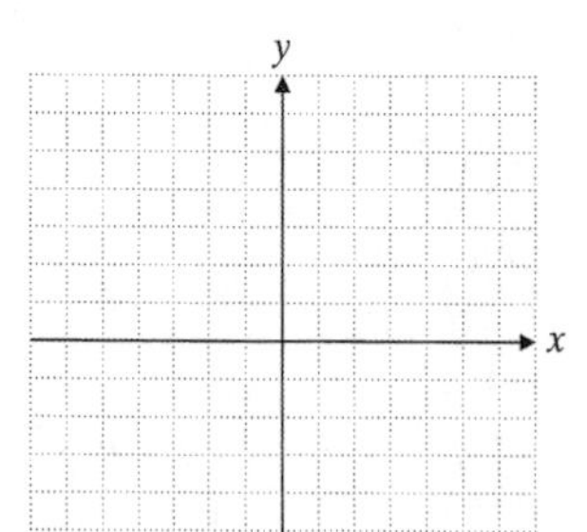

5. $x^2 = y - 4x - 1$

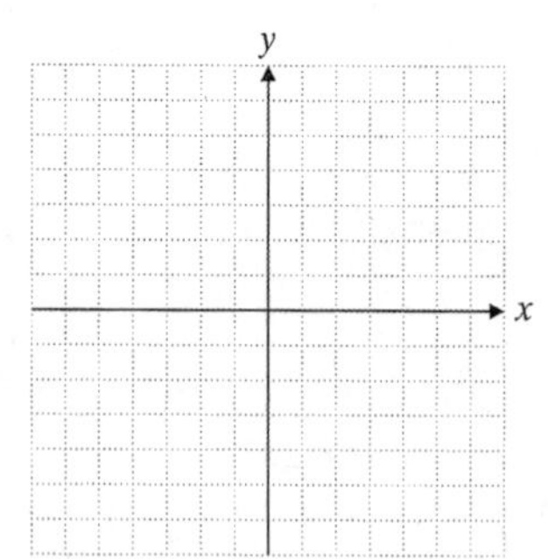

5. ______

Section 9.3

Graph each ellipse. Write the equations in standard form.

6. ______
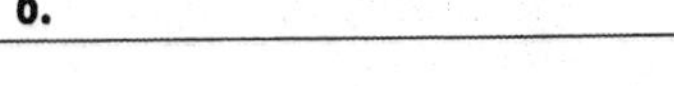

6. $4x^2 + y^2 - 36 = 0$

7. $\dfrac{(x+3)^2}{25} + \dfrac{(y-1)^2}{16} = 1$

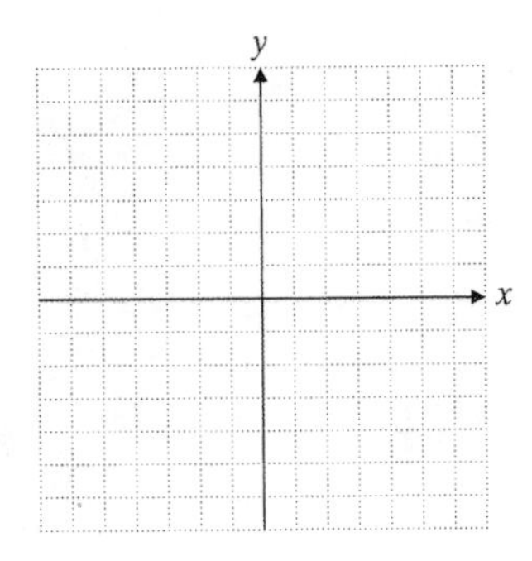

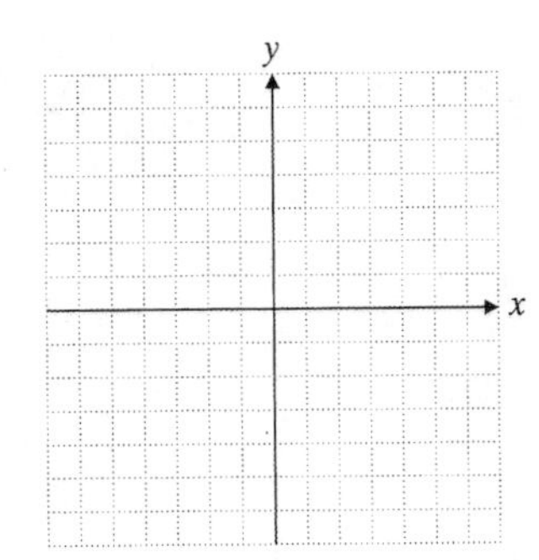

7. ______

Section 9.4

8. ______

Graph each hyperbola. Write the equations in standard form.

8. $25y^2 - 9x^2 = 225$

9. $\dfrac{(x-2)^2}{4} - \dfrac{(y+1)^2}{9} = 1$

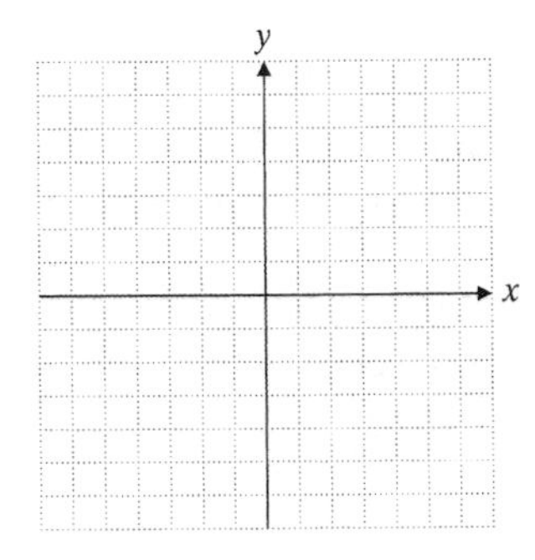

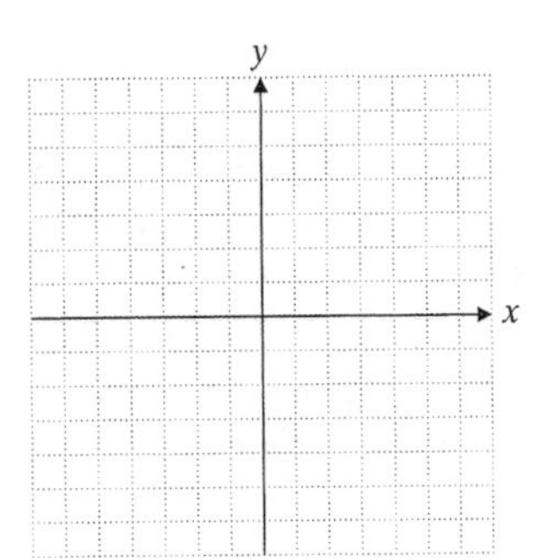

9. ______

10. ______

Section 9.5

Solve each nonlinear system.

10. $x^2 + y^2 = 25$
$3x + 4y = 0$

11. $y = x^2 + 1$
$4y^2 = 4 - x^2$

11. ______

9.1 The Distance Formula and the Circle

Student Learning Objectives

After studying this section, you will be able to:

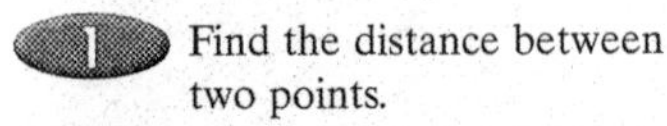
1. Find the distance between two points.

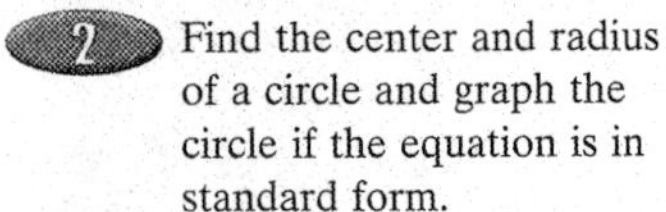
2. Find the center and radius of a circle and graph the circle if the equation is in standard form.

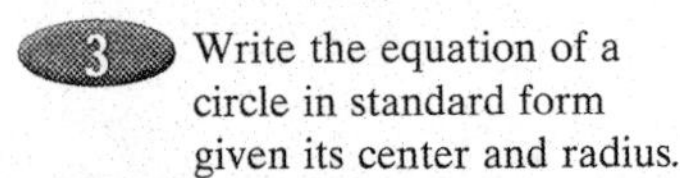
3. Write the equation of a circle in standard form given its center and radius.

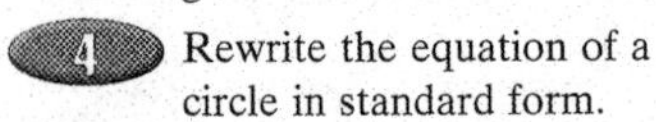
4. Rewrite the equation of a circle in standard form.

SSM PH TUTOR CENTER | CD & VIDEO | MATH PRO | WEB

In this chapter we'll talk about the equations and graphs of four special geometric figures—the circle, the parabola, the ellipse, and the hyperbola. These shapes are called **conic sections** because they can be formed by slicing a cone with a plane. The equation of any conic section is of degree 2.

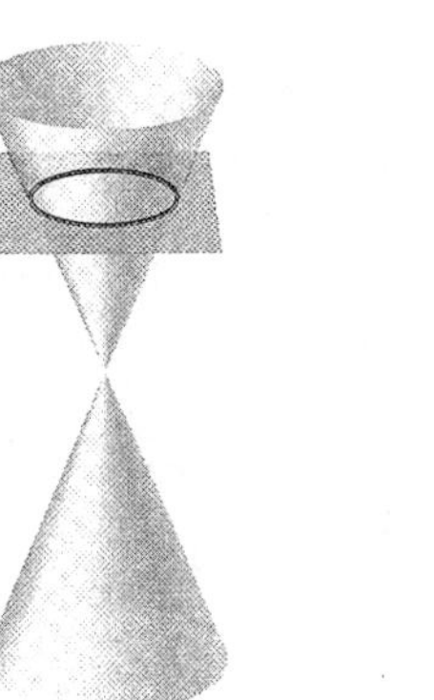
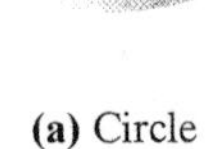

(a) Circle

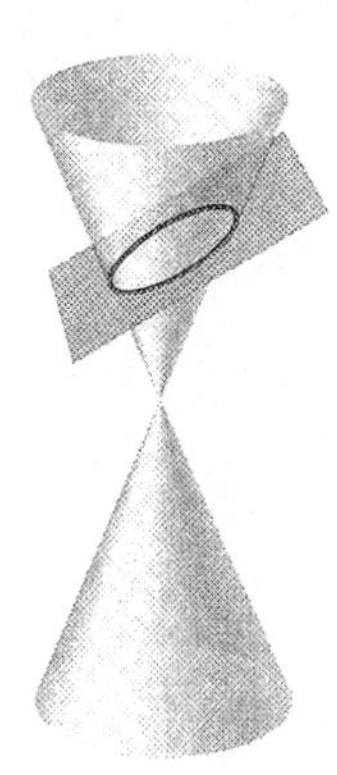

(b) Ellipse

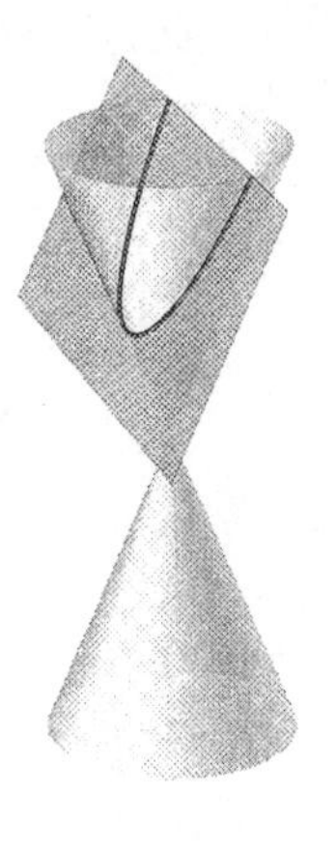

(c) Parabola

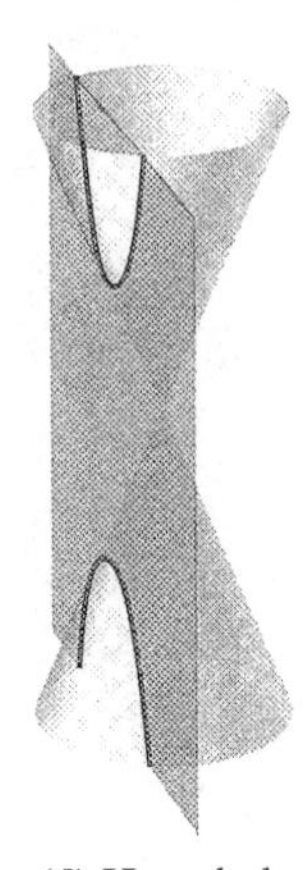

(d) Hyperbola

Conic sections are an important and interesting subject. They are studied along with many other things in a branch of mathematics called *analytic geometry.* Conic sections can be found in applications of physics and engineering. Satellite transmission dishes have parabolic shapes; the orbits of planets are ellipses, and the orbits of comets are hyperbolas; the path of a ball, rocket, or bullet is a parabola (if we neglect air resistance).

1 *Finding the Distance Between Two Points*

Before we investigate the conic sections, we need to know how to find the distance between two points in the xy-plane. We will derive a *distance formula* and use it to find the equations for the conic sections.

Recall from Chapter 1 that to find the distance between two points on the real number line, we simply find the absolute value of the difference of the values of the points. For example, the distance from -3 to 5 on the x-axis is

$$|5 - (-3)| = |5 + 3| = 8.$$

Remember that absolute value is another name for distance. We could have written

$$|-3 - (5)| = |-8| = 8.$$

Similarly, the distance from -3 to 5 on the y-axis is

$$|5 - (-3)| = 8.$$

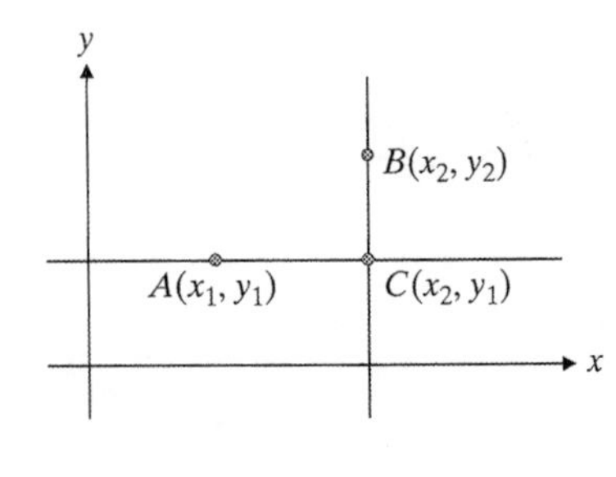

We use this simple fact to find the distance between two points in the xy-plane. Let $A(x_1, y_1)$ and $B(x_2, y_2)$ be points on a graph. First we draw a horizontal line through A, and then we draw a vertical line through B. (We could have drawn a horizontal line through B and a vertical line through A.) The lines intersect at point $C(x_2, y_1)$. Why are the coordinates x_2, y_1? The distance from A to C is $|x_2 - x_1|$ and from B to C $|y_2 - y_1|$.

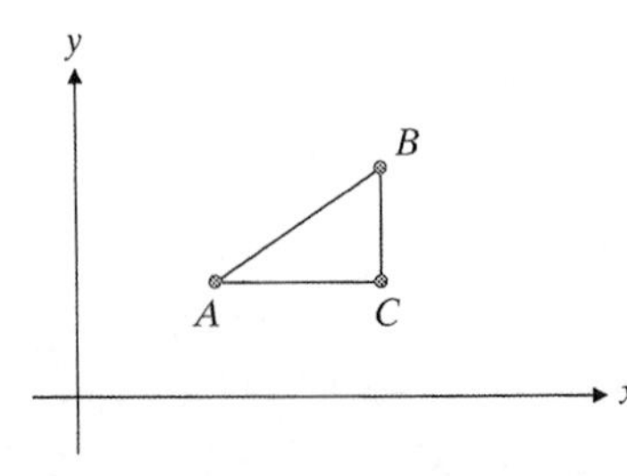

Now, if we draw a line from A to B, we have a right triangle ABC. We can use the Pythagorean theorem to find the length (distance) of the line from A to B. By the Pythagorean theorem,

$$(AB)^2 = (AC)^2 + (BC)^2.$$

Let's rename the distance AB as d. Then

$$d^2 = \left(|x_2 - x_1|\right)^2 + \left(|y_2 - y_1|\right)^2$$

and

$$d = \sqrt{(x_2 - x_1)^2 + (y_2 - y_1)^2}.$$

This is the **distance formula**.

Distance Formula

The distance between two points (x_1, y_1) and (x_2, y_2) is

$$d = \sqrt{(x_2 - x_1)^2 + (y_2 - y_1)^2}.$$

EXAMPLE 1 Find the distance between $(3, -4)$ and $(-2, -5)$.

To use the formula, we arbitrarily let $(x_1, y_1) = (3, -4)$ and $(x_2, y_2) = (-2, -5)$.

$$\begin{aligned} d &= \sqrt{(x_2 - x_1)^2 + (y_2 - y_1)^2} \\ &= \sqrt{[-2 - 3]^2 + [-5 - (-4)]^2} \\ &= \sqrt{(-5)^2 + (-5 + 4)^2} \\ &= \sqrt{(-5)^2 + (-1)^2} \\ &= \sqrt{25 + 1} = \sqrt{26} \end{aligned}$$

Practice Problem 1 Find the distance between $(-6, -2)$ and $(3, 1)$.

The choice of which point is (x_1, y_1) and which point is (x_2, y_2) is up to you. We would obtain exactly the same answer in Example 1 if $(x_1, y_1) = (-2, -5)$ and if $(x_2, y_2) = (3, -4)$. Try it for yourself and see whether you obtain the same result.

2 Finding the Center and Radius of a Circle and Graphing the Circle

A **circle** is defined as the set of all points in a plane that are at a fixed distance from a point in that plane. The fixed distance is called the **radius**, and the point is called the **center** of the circle.

We can use the distance formula to find the equation of a circle. Let a circle of radius r have its center at (h, k). For any point (x, y) on the circle, the distance formula tells us that

$$\sqrt{(x - h)^2 + (y - k)^2} = r.$$

Squaring each side gives

$$(x - h)^2 + (y - k)^2 = r^2.$$

This is the equation of a circle with center at (h, k) and radius r.

Graphing Calculator

Graphing Circles

A graphing calculator is designed to graph *functions*. In order to graph a circle, you need to separate it into two halves, each of which is a function. Thus, in order to graph the circle in Example 2 on the next page, first solve for y.

$$\begin{aligned} (y - 3)^2 &= 25 - (x - 2)^2 \\ y - 3 &= \pm\sqrt{25 - (x - 2)^2} \\ y &= 3 \pm \sqrt{25 - (x - 2)^2} \end{aligned}$$

Now graph the two functions

$y_1 = 3 + \sqrt{25 - (x - 2)^2}$
(the upper half of the circle)

and

$y_2 = 3 - \sqrt{25 - (x - 2)^2}$
(the lower half of the circle).

To get a proper-looking circle, use a "square" window setting. Window settings will vary depending on the calculator. Display:

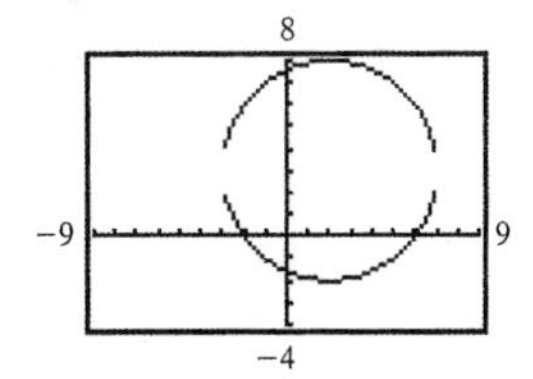

Notice that due to limitations in the calculator, it is not a perfect circle and two small gaps appear.

Standard Form of the Equation of a Circle

The standard form of the equation of a circle with center at (h, k) and radius r is

$$(x - h)^2 + (y - k)^2 = r^2.$$

EXAMPLE 2 Find the center and radius of the circle $(x - 2)^2 + (y - 3)^2 = 25$. Then sketch its graph.

From the equation of a circle,

$$(x - h)^2 + (y - k)^2 = r^2,$$

we see that $(h, k) = (2, 3)$. Thus, the center of the circle is at $(2, 3)$. Since $r^2 = 25$, the radius of the circle is $r = 5$.

The graph of this circle is shown on the right.

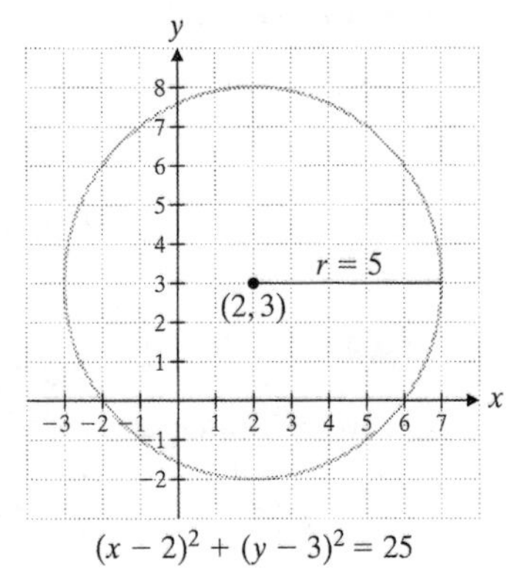

$(x - 2)^2 + (y - 3)^2 = 25$

PRACTICE PROBLEM 2

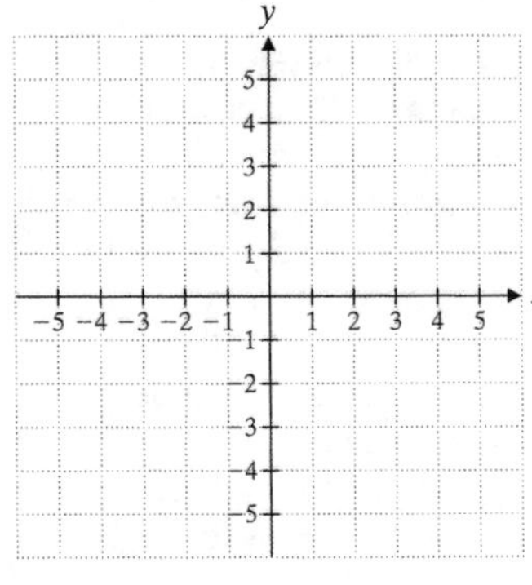

Practice Problem 2 Find the center and radius of the circle

$$(x + 1)^2 + (y + 2)^2 = 9.$$

Then sketch its graph.

3 Writing the Equation of a Circle in Standard Form Given the Center and Radius

We can write the standard form of the equation of a specific circle if we are given the center and the radius. We use the definition of the standard form of the equation of a circle to write the equation we want.

EXAMPLE 3 Write the equation of the circle with center $(-1, 3)$ and radius $\sqrt{5}$. Put your answer in standard form.

We are given that $(h, k) = (-1, 3)$ and $r = \sqrt{5}$. Thus,

$$(x - h)^2 + (y - k)^2 = r^2$$

becomes the following:

$$[x - (-1)]^2 + [y - 3]^2 = (\sqrt{5})^2$$

$$(x + 1)^2 + (y - 3)^2 = 5$$

Be careful of the signs. It is easy to make a sign error in these steps.

Practice Problem 3 Write the equation of the circle with center $(-5, 0)$ and radius $\sqrt{3}$. Put your answer in standard form.

Rewriting the Equation of a Circle in Standard Form

The standard form of the equation of a circle helps us sketch the graph of the circle. Sometimes the equation of a circle is not given in standard form, and we need to rewrite the equation.

EXAMPLE 4 Write the equation of the circle $x^2 + 2x + y^2 + 6y + 6 = 0$ in standard form. Find the radius and center of the circle and sketch its graph.

The standard form of the equation of a circle is

$$(x - h)^2 + (y - k)^2 = r^2.$$

If we multiply out the terms in the equation, we get

$$(x^2 - 2hx + h^2) + (y^2 - 2ky + k^2) = r^2.$$

Comparing this with the equation we were given,

$$(x^2 + 2x) + (y^2 + 6y) = -6,$$

suggests that we can complete the square to put the equation in standard form.

$$x^2 + 2x + \_\_\_\_\_ + y^2 + 6y + \_\_\_\_\_ = -6$$

$$x^2 + 2x + 1 \quad + y^2 + 6y + 9 \quad = -6 + 1 + 9$$

$$x^2 + 2x + 1 + y^2 + 6y + 9 = 4$$

$$(x + 1)^2 + (y + 3)^2 = 4$$

Thus, the center is at $(-1, -3)$, and the radius is 2. The sketch of the circle is shown.

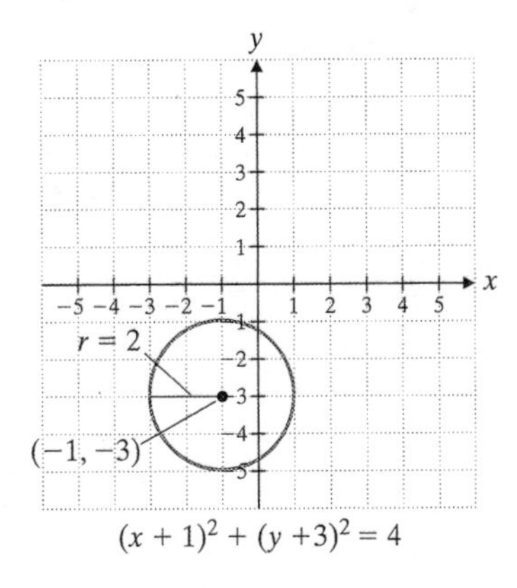

$(x + 1)^2 + (y + 3)^2 = 4$

Practice Problem 4 Write the equation of the circle $x^2 + 4x + y^2 + 2y - 20 = 0$ in standard form. Find its radius and center and sketch its graph.

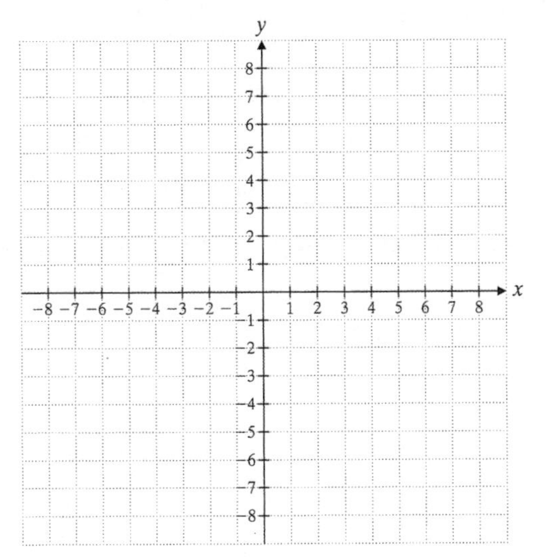

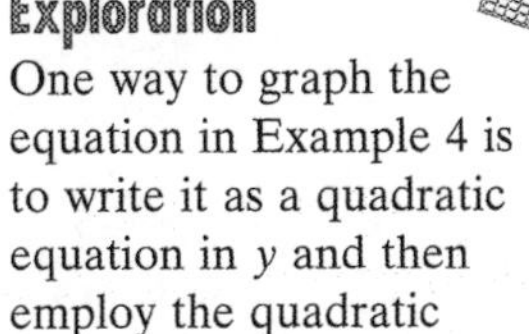

Graphing Calculator

Exploration

One way to graph the equation in Example 4 is to write it as a quadratic equation in y and then employ the quadratic formula.

$$y^2 + 6y + (x^2 + 2x + 6) = 0$$

$$ay^2 + by + c = 0$$

$a = 1$, $b = 6$, and
$c = x^2 + 2x + 6$

$$y = \frac{-6 \pm \sqrt{36 - 4(1)(x^2 + 2x + 6)}}{2(1)}$$

$$y = \frac{-6 \pm \sqrt{12 - 8x - 4x^2}}{2}$$

Thus, we have the two halves of the circle.

$$y_1 = \frac{-6 + \sqrt{12 - 8x - 4x^2}}{2}$$

$$y_2 = \frac{-6 - \sqrt{12 - 8x - 4x^2}}{2}$$

We can graph these on one coordinate system to obtain the graph. Use the quadratic formula to obtain the graph of the following circle.

$$x^2 + y^2 + 6x - 4y - 12 = 0$$

From your graph, estimate the value of the radius and the coordinates of the center. Some graphing calculators have a feature for getting a background grid for your graph. If you have this feature, use it to find the coordinates of the center.

9.1 Exercises

Verbal and Writing Skills

1. Explain how you would find the distance from -2 to 4 on the y-axis.

2. Explain how you would find the distance between $(3, -1)$ and $(-4, 0)$ in the xy-plane.

3. $(x - 1)^2 + (y + 2)^2 = 9$ is the equation of a circle. Explain how to determine the center and the radius of the circle.

4. $x^2 - 6x + y^2 - 2y = 6$ is the equation of a circle. Explain how you would rewrite the equation in standard form.

Find the distance between each pair of points. Simplify your answers.

5. $(1, 6)$ and $(2, 4)$

6. $(4, 6)$ and $(7, 5)$

7. $\left(\frac{1}{2}, \frac{5}{2}\right)$ and $\left(\frac{3}{4}, \frac{3}{2}\right)$

8. $\left(\frac{2}{3}, \frac{7}{4}\right)$ and $\left(\frac{5}{6}, \frac{3}{4}\right)$

9. $(3, 9)$ and $(-2, -3)$

10. $(8, 4)$ and $(-4, -1)$

11. $(0, -3)$ and $(4, 1)$

12. $(-5, -6)$ and $(2, 0)$

13. $\left(\frac{1}{3}, \frac{3}{5}\right)$ and $\left(\frac{7}{3}, \frac{1}{5}\right)$

14. $\left(-\frac{1}{4}, \frac{1}{7}\right)$ and $\left(\frac{3}{4}, \frac{6}{7}\right)$

15. $(1.3, 2.6)$ and $(-5.7, 1.6)$

16. $(8.2, 3.5)$ and $(6.2, -0.5)$

Find the value of the unknown coordinate so that the distance between the points is as given.

17. $(7, 2)$ and $(1, y)$; distance is 10

18. $(3, y)$ and $(3, -5)$; distance is 9

19. $(1.5, 2)$ and $(0, y)$; distance is 2.5

20. $\left(1, \frac{15}{2}\right)$ and $\left(x, -\frac{1}{2}\right)$; distance is 10

21. $(7, 3)$ and $(x, 6)$; distance is $\sqrt{10}$

22. $(4, 5)$ and $(2, y)$; distance is $\sqrt{5}$

Applications

Use the following information to solve Exercises 23 and 24. An airport is located at point O. A short-range radar tower is located at point R. The maximum range at which the radar can detect a plane is 4 miles from point R.

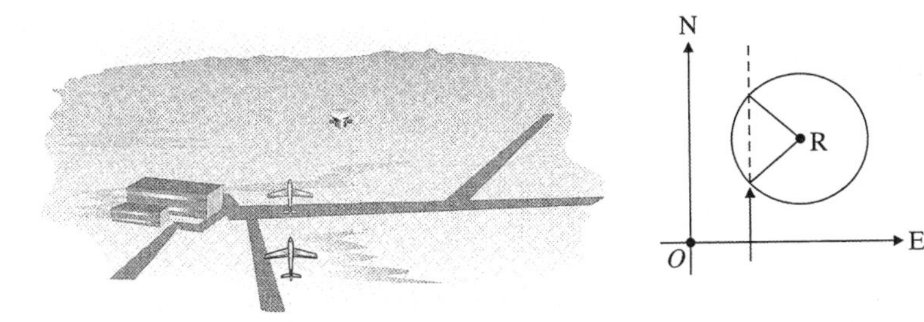

23. Assume that R is 6 miles east of O and 6 miles north of O. In other words, R is located at the point $(6, 6)$. An airplane is flying parallel to and 4 miles east of the north axis. (In other words, the plane is flying along the path $x = 4$.) What is the *greatest distance* north of the airport at which the plane can still be detected by the radar tower at R? Round your answer to the nearest tenth of a mile.

24. Assume that R is 5 miles east of O and 7 miles north of O. In other words, R is located at the point $(5, 7)$. An airplane is flying parallel to and 2 miles east of the north axis. (In other words, the plane is flying along the path $x = 2$.) What is the *shortest distance* north of the airport at which the plane can be detected by the radar tower at R? Round your answer to the nearest tenth of a mile.

Write in standard form the equation of the circle with the given center and radius.

25. center $(-1, -7)$; $r = \sqrt{5}$

26. center $(-3, -5)$; $r = \sqrt{2}$

27. center $(-3.5, 0)$; $r = 6$

28. center $\left(0, \frac{3}{2}\right)$; $r = \frac{1}{2}$

29. center $\left(\frac{7}{4}, 0\right)$; $r = \frac{1}{3}$

30. center $(0, -4.5)$; $r = 4$

Give the center and radius of each circle. Then sketch its graph.

31. $x^2 + y^2 = 25$

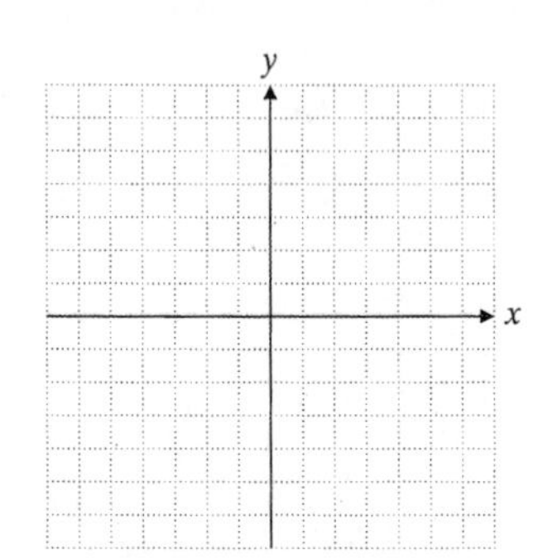

32. $x^2 + y^2 = 9$

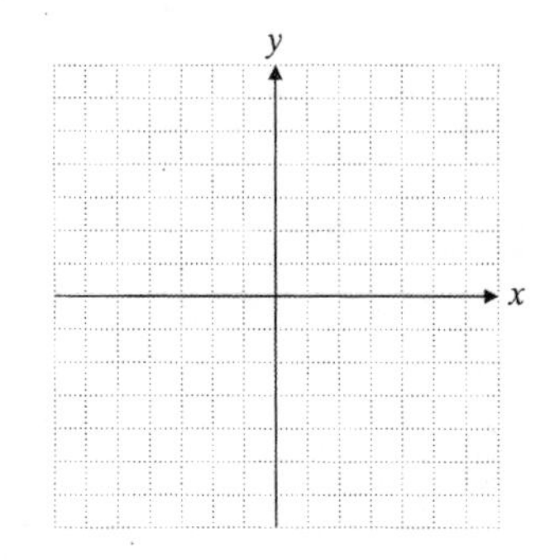

33. $(x - 3)^2 + (y - 2)^2 = 4$

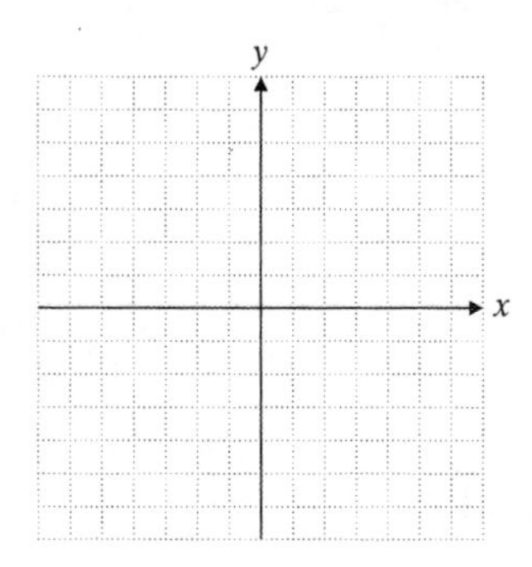

34. $(x - 5)^2 + (y - 3)^2 = 16$

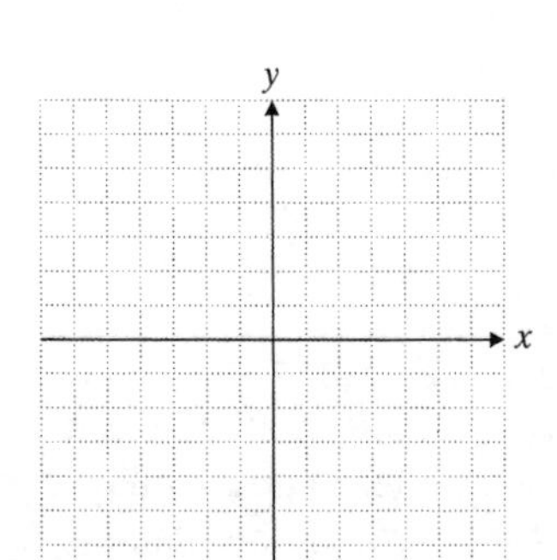

35. $(x + 2)^2 + (y - 3)^2 = 25$

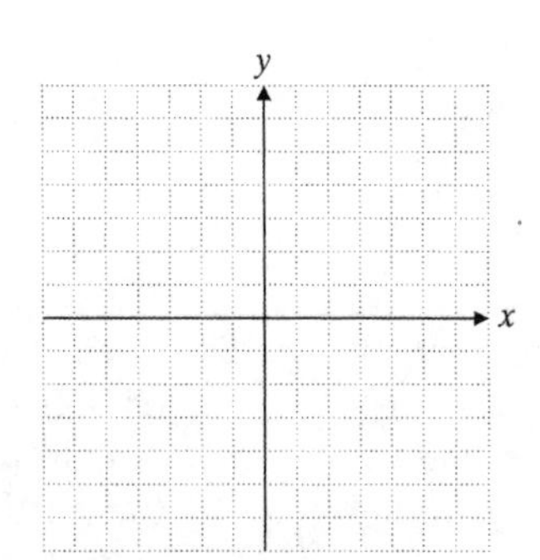

36. $\left(x - \frac{3}{2}\right)^2 + (y + 2)^2 = 9$

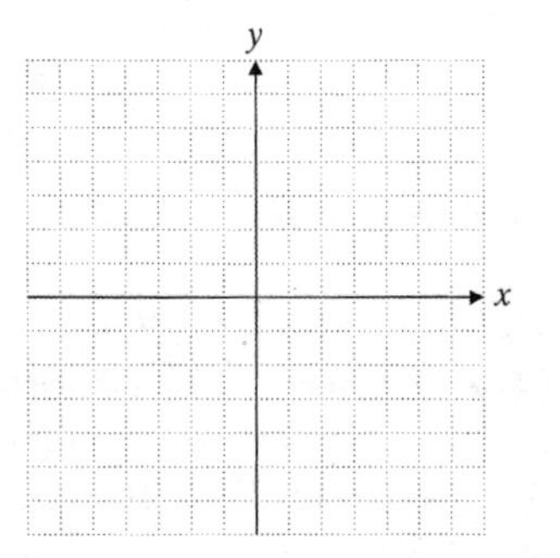

Rewrite each equation in standard form, using the approach of Example 4. Find the center and radius of each circle.

37. $x^2 + y^2 + 6x - 4y - 3 = 0$

38. $x^2 + y^2 + 8x - 6y - 24 = 0$

39. $x^2 + y^2 - 12x + 2y - 12 = 0$

40. $x^2 + y^2 + 4x - 4y + 7 = 0$

41. $x^2 + y^2 + 3x - 2 = 0$

42. $x^2 + y^2 - 5x - 1 = 0$

43. A Ferris wheel has a radius r of 25.1 feet. The height of the tower t is 29.7 feet. The distance d from the origin to the base of the tower is 42.7 feet. Find the standard form of the equation of the circle represented by the Ferris wheel.

44. A Ferris wheel has a radius r of 25.3 feet. The height of the tower t is 31.8 feet. The distance d from the origin to the base of the tower is 44.8 feet. Find the standard form of the equation of the circle represented by the Ferris wheel.

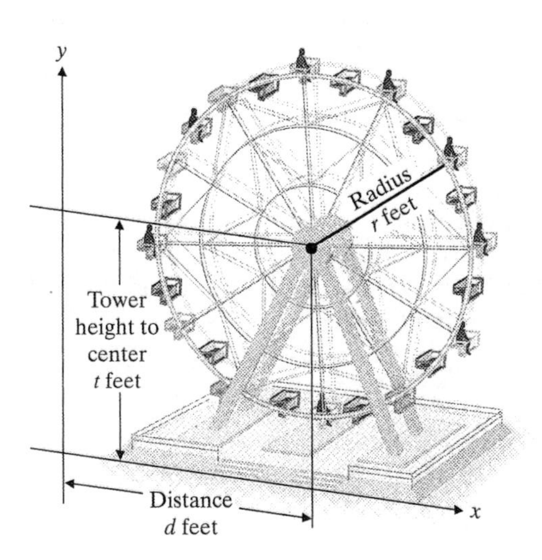

Optional Graphing Calculator Problems

Graph each circle with your graphing calculator.

45. $(x - 5.32)^2 + (y + 6.54)^2 = 47.28$

46. $x^2 + 9.56x + y^2 - 7.12y + 8.9995 = 0$

Cumulative Review Problems

Solve the following quadratic equations by factoring.

47. $9 + \frac{3}{x} = \frac{2}{x^2}$

48. $3x^2 - 5x + 2 = 0$

Solve the following quadratic equations by using the quadratic formula.

49. $5x^2 - 6x - 7 = 0$

50. $4x^2 + 2x = 1$

▲ **51.** The 1980 eruptions of Mount Saint Helens blew down or scorched 230 square miles of forest. A deposit of rock and sediments soon filled up a 20-square-mile area to an average depth of 150 feet. How many cubic feet of rock and sediments settled in this region?

52. Within a 15-mile radius north of Mt. Saint Helens, the blast of its 1980 eruption traveled at up to 670 miles per hour. If an observer 15 miles north of the volcano saw the blast and attempted to run for cover, how many seconds did he have to run before the blast reached his original location?

9.2 The Parabola

Student Learning Objectives

After studying this section, you will be able to:

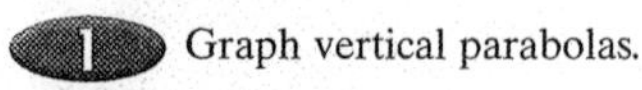
1 Graph vertical parabolas.

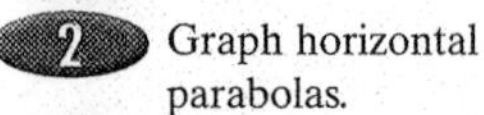
2 Graph horizontal parabolas.

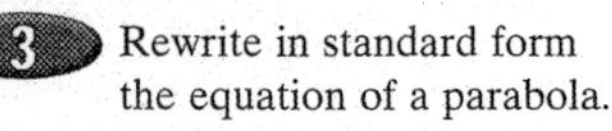
3 Rewrite in standard form the equation of a parabola.

If we pass a plane through a cone so that the plane is parallel to but not touching a side of the cone, we form a **parabola**. A **parabola** is defined as the set of points that are the same distance from some fixed line (called the **directrix**) and some fixed point (called the **focus**) that is *not* on the line.

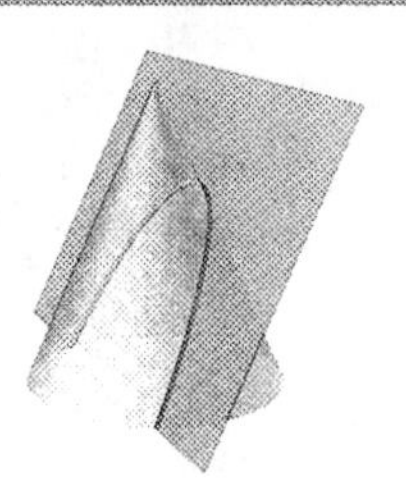

The shape of a parabola is a common one. For example, the cables that are used to support the weight of a bridge are in the shape of parabolas.

The simplest form for the equation is one variable = (another variable)^2. That is, $y = x^2$ or $x = y^2$. We will make a table of values for each equation, plot the points, and draw a graph. For the first equation we choose values for x and find y. For the second equation we choose values for y and find x.

$y = x^2$

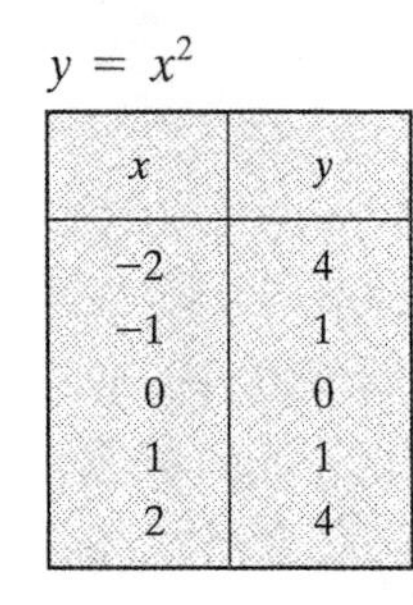

x	y
−2	4
−1	1
0	0
1	1
2	4

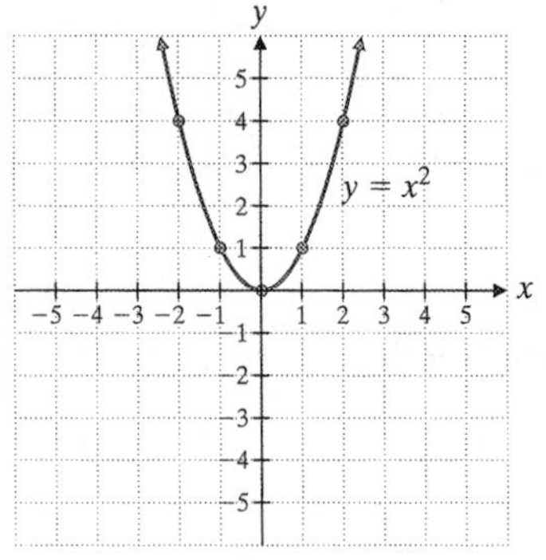

Vertical Parabola

$x = y^2$

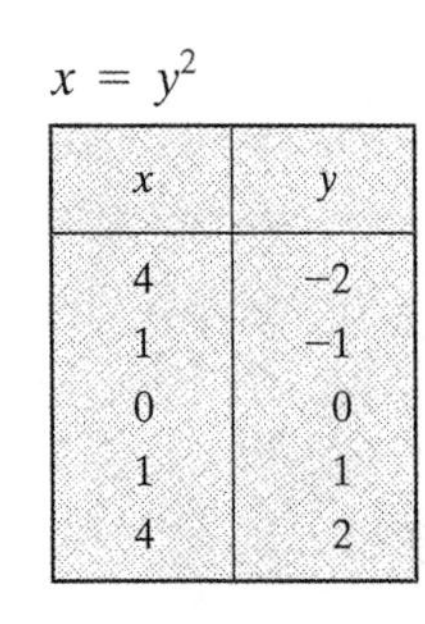

x	y
4	−2
1	−1
0	0
1	1
4	2

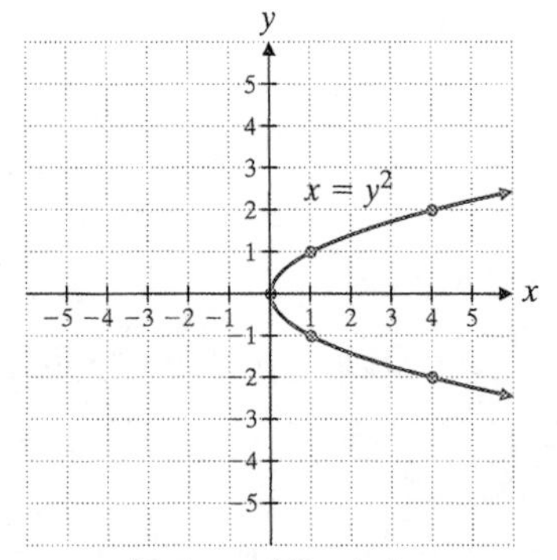

Horizontal Parabola

Notice that the graph of $y = x^2$ is symmetric about the y-axis. That is, if you folded the graph along the y-axis, the two parts of the curve would coincide. For this parabola, the y-axis is the **axis of symmetry**.

What is the axis of symmetry for the parabola $x = y^2$? Every parabola has an axis of symmetry. This axis can be *any* line; it depends on the location and orientation of the parabola in the rectangular coordinate system. The point at which the parabola crosses the axis of symmetry is the **vertex**. What are the coordinates of the vertex for $y = x^2$? For $x = y^2$?

1 Graphing Vertical Parabolas

EXAMPLE 1 Graph $y = (x - 2)^2$. Identify the vertex and the axis of symmetry.

We make a table of values. We begin with $x = 2$ in the middle of the table of values because $(2 - 2)^2 = 0$. That is, when $x = 2$, $y = 0$. We then fill in the x- and y-values above and below $x = 2$. We plot the points and draw the graph.

$y = (x - 2)^2$

x	y
4	4
3	1
2	0
1	1
0	4

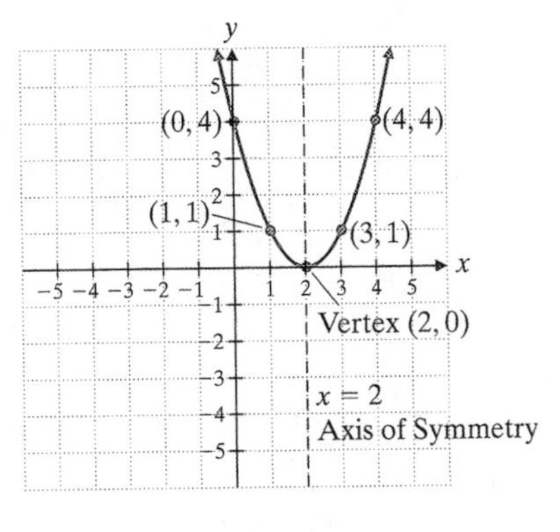

The vertex is $(2, 0)$, and the axis of symmetry is the line $x = 2$.

Practice Problem 1 Graph $y = -(x + 3)^2$. Identify the vertex and the axis of symmetry.

PRACTICE PROBLEM 1

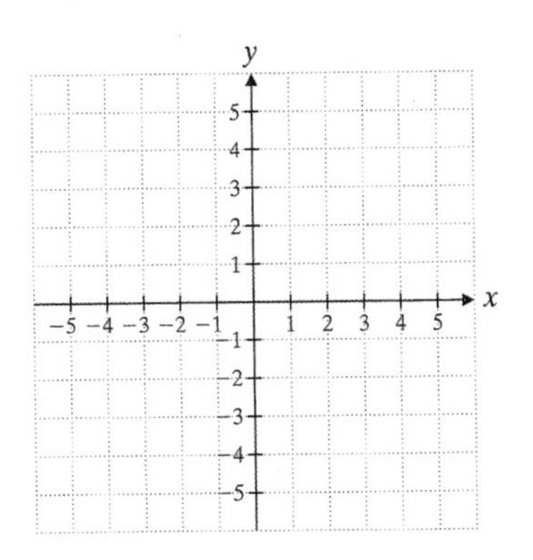

EXAMPLE 2 Graph $y = (x - 2)^2 + 3$. Find the vertex, the axis of symmetry, and the y-intercept.

This graph looks just like the graph of $y = x^2$, except that it is shifted 2 units to the right and 3 units up. The vertex is $(2, 3)$. The axis of symmetry is $x = 2$. We can find the y-intercept by letting $x = 0$ in the equation. We get

$$y = (0 - 2)^2 + 3 = 4 + 3 = 7.$$

Thus, the y-intercept is $(0, 7)$.

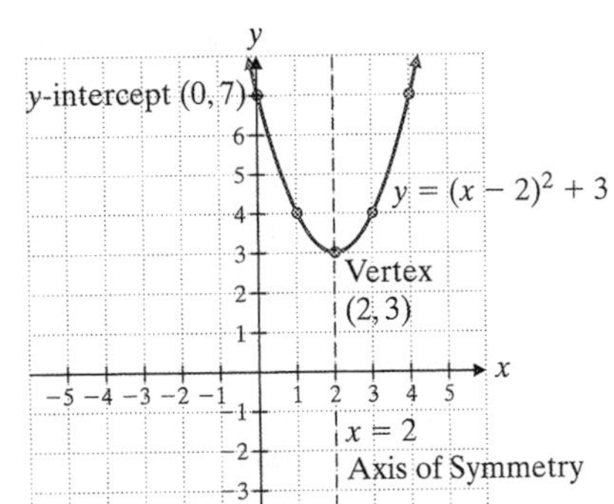

Practice Problem 2 Graph the parabola $y = (x - 6)^2 + 4$.

PRACTICE PROBLEM 2

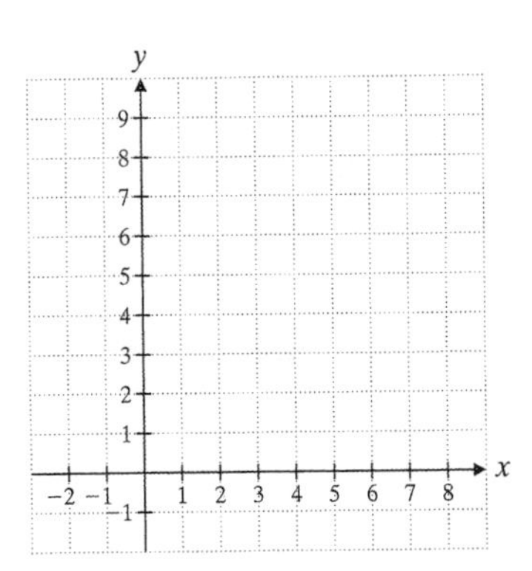

The examples we have studied illustrate the following properties of the standard form of the equation of a vertical parabola.

Standard Form of the Equation of a Vertical Parabola

1. The graph of $y = a(x - h)^2 + k$, where $a \neq 0$, is a vertical parabola.
2. The parabola opens upward ↖‿↗ if $a > 0$ and downward ↙⁀↘ if $a < 0$.
3. The vertex of the parabola is (h, k).
4. The axis of symmetry is the line $x = h$.
5. The y-intercept is the point where the parabola crosses the y-axis (i.e., where $x = 0$).

We can use these properties as steps to graph a parabola. If we want greater accuracy, we should also plot a few other points.

EXAMPLE 3 Graph $y = -\frac{1}{2}(x + 3)^2 - 1$.

Step 1 The equation has the form $y = a(x - h)^2 + k$, where $a = -\frac{1}{2}$, $h = -3$, and $k = -1$, so it is a vertical parabola.

$$y = a(x - h)^2 + k$$

$$y = -\frac{1}{2}[x - (-3)]^2 + (-1)$$

Step 2 $a < 0$; so the parabola opens downward.

Step 3 We have $h = -3$ and $k = -1$.
Therefore, the vertex of the parabola is $(-3, -1)$.

Step 4 The axis of symmetry is the line $x = -3$.

We plot a few points on either side of the axis of symmetry. We try $x = -1$ because $(-1 + 3)^2$ is 4 and $-\frac{1}{2}(4)$ is an integer. We avoid fractions. When $x = -1$, $y = -\frac{1}{2}(-1 + 3)^2 - 1 = -3$. Thus, the point is $(-1, -3)$. The image of this point on the other side of the axis of symmetry is $(-5, -3)$. We now try $x = 1$. When $x = 1$, $y = -\frac{1}{2}(1 + 3)^2 - 1 = -9$. Thus, the point is $(1, -9)$. The image of this point on the other side of the axis of symmetry is $(-7, -9)$.

Step 5 When $x = 0$, we have the following:

$$y = -\frac{1}{2}(0 + 3)^2 - 1$$

$$= -\frac{1}{2}(9) - 1$$

$$= -4.5 - 1 = -5.5$$

Thus, the y-intercept is $(0, -5.5)$.

The graph is shown on the right.

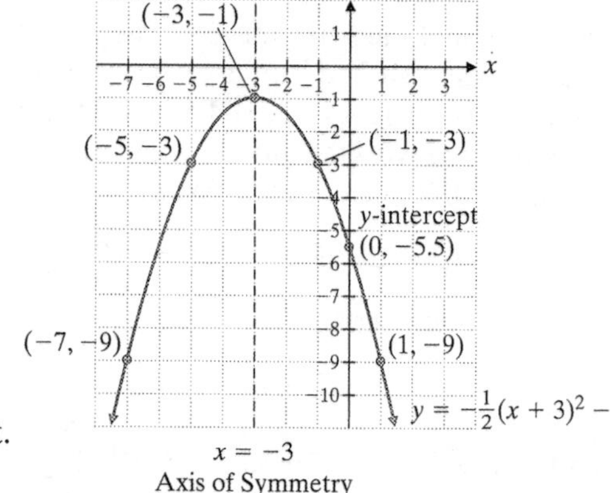

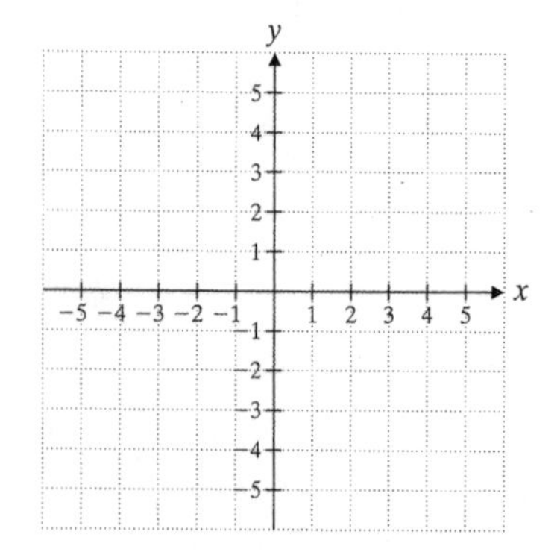

Practice Problem 3 Graph $y = \frac{1}{4}(x - 2)^2 + 3$.

2 Graphing Horizontal Parabolas

Recall that the equation $x = y^2$, in which the squared term is the y-variable, describes a horizontal parabola. Horizontal parabolas open to the left or right. They are symmetric about the x-axis or about a line parallel to the x-axis. We now look at examples of horizontal parabolas.

EXAMPLE 4 Graph $x = -2y^2$.

Notice that the y-term is squared. This means that the parabola is horizontal. We make a table of values, plot points, and draw the graph. To make the table of values, we choose values for y and find x. We begin with $y = 0$.

$x = -2y^2$

x	y
−8	−2
−2	−1
0	0
−2	1
−8	2

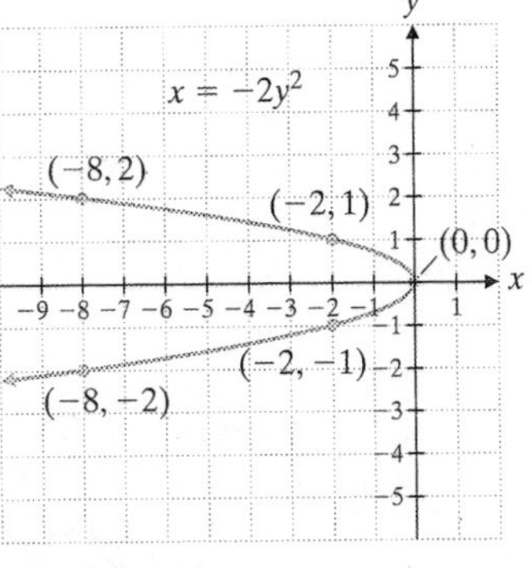

PRACTICE PROBLEM 4

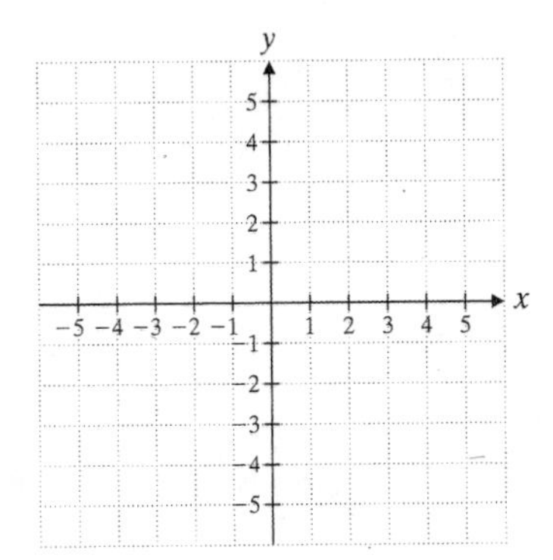

The parabola $x = -2y^2$ has its vertex at $(0, 0)$. The axis of symmetry is the x-axis.

Practice Problem 4 Graph the parabola $x = -2y^2 + 4$.

To Think About Compare the graphs in Example 4 and Practice Problem 4 to the graph of $x = y^2$. How are they different? How are they the same? What does the coefficient −2 in the equation $x = -2y^2$ do to the graph of the equation $x = y^2$? What does the constant 4 in $x = -2y^2 + 4$ do to the graph of $x = -2y^2$?

Now we can make the same type of observations for horizontal parabolas as we did for vertical ones.

Standard Form of the Equation of a Horizontal Parabola

1. The graph of $x = a(y - k)^2 + h$, where $a \neq 0$, is a horizontal parabola.
2. The parabola opens to the right if $a > 0$ and opens to the left if $a < 0$.
3. The vertex of the parabola is (h, k).
4. The axis of symmetry is the line $y = k$.
5. The x-intercept is the point where the parabola crosses the x-axis (i.e., where $y = 0$).

EXAMPLE 5 Graph $x = (y - 3)^2 - 5$. Find the vertex, the axis of symmetry, and the x-intercept.

Step 1 The equation has the form $x = a(y - k)^2 + h$, where $a = 1, k = 3$, and $h = -5$, so it is a horizontal parabola.

$$x = a(y - k)^2 + h$$

$$x = 1(y - 3)^2 + (-5)$$

Step 2 $a > 0$; so the parabola opens to the right.

Step 3 We have $k = 3$ and $h = -5$. Therefore, the vertex is $(-5, 3)$.

Step 4 The line $y = 3$ is the axis of symmetry.

We look for a few points on either side of the axis of symmetry. We will try y-values close to the vertex $(-5, 3)$. We try $y = 4$ and $y = 2$. When $y = 4$, $x = (4 - 3)^2 - 5 = -4$. When $y = 2$, $x = (2 - 3)^2 - 5 = -4$. Thus, the points are $(-4, 4)$ and $(-4, 2)$. (Remember to list the x-value first in a coordinate pair.) We try $y = 5$ and $y = 1$. When $y = 5$, $x = (5 - 3)^2 - 5 = -1$. When $y = 1$, $x = (1 - 3)^2 - 5 = -1$. Thus, the points are $(-1, 5)$ and $(-1, 1)$. You may prefer to find one point, graph it, and find its image on the other side of the axis of symmetry, as was done in Example 3. We decided to look for both pairs of points using the equation.

Step 5 When $y = 0$,

$$x = (0 - 3)^2 - 5 = 9 - 5 = 4.$$

Thus, the x-intercept is $(4, 0)$. We plot the points and draw the graph.

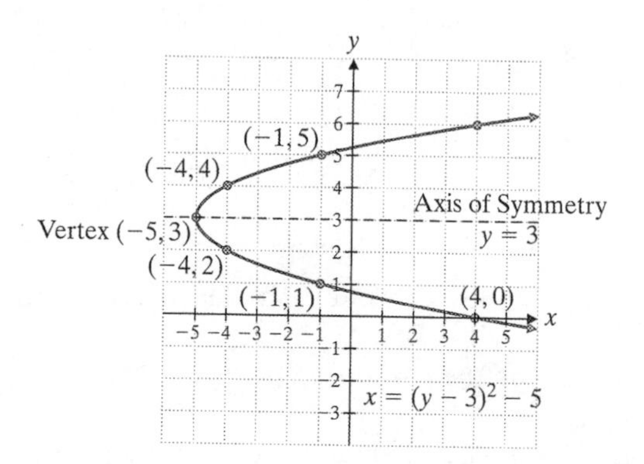

Notice that the graph also crosses the y-axis. You can find the y-intercepts by setting x equal to 0 and solving the resulting quadratic equation. Try it.

PRACTICE PROBLEM 5

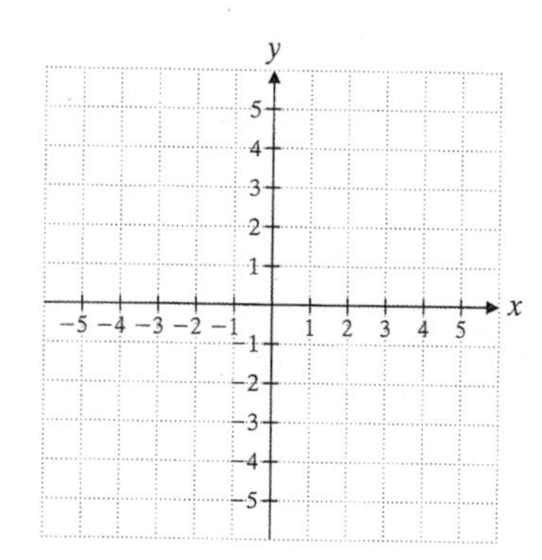

Practice Problem 5 Graph the parabola $x = -(y + 1)^2 - 3$. Find the vertex, the axis of symmetry, and the x-intercept.

3 Rewriting in Standard Form the Equation of a Parabola

So far, all the equations we have graphed have been in standard form. This rarely happens in the real world. How do you suppose we put the quadratic equation $y = ax^2 + bx + c$ in the standard form $y = a(x - h)^2 + k$? We do so by completing the square.

EXAMPLE 6 Place the equation $x = y^2 + 4y + 1$ in standard form. Then graph it.

Since the y-term is squared, we have a horizontal parabola. So the standard form is

$$x = a(y - k)^2 + h.$$

Now we have the following:

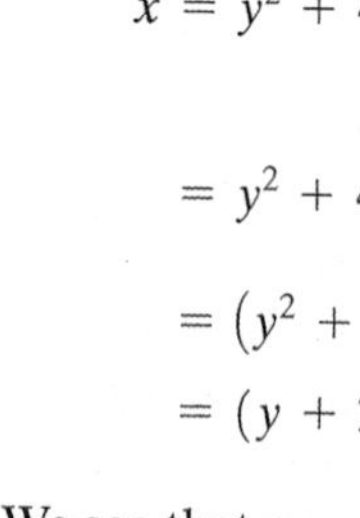

$x = y^2 + 4y + \_\_\_\_ - \_\_\_\_ + 1$	Whatever we add to the right side we must also subtract from the right side.
$= y^2 + 4y + \left(\frac{4}{2}\right)^2 - \left(\frac{4}{2}\right)^2 + 1$	Complete the square.
$= (y^2 + 4y + 4) - 3$	Simplify.
$= (y + 2)^2 - 3$	Standard form.

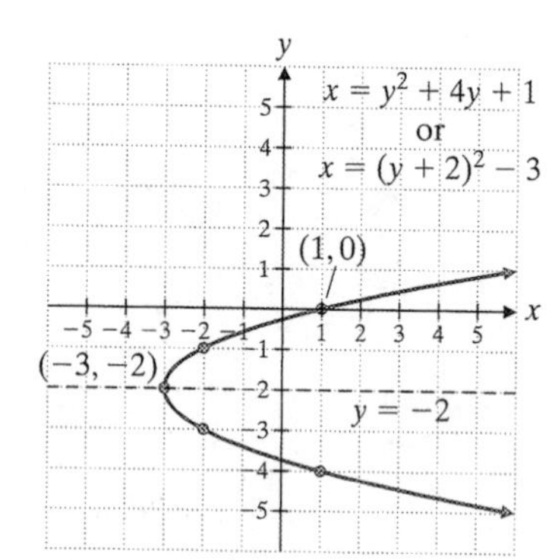

We see that $a = 1$, $k = -2$, and $h = -3$. Since a is positive, the parabola opens to the right. The vertex is $(-3, -2)$. The axis of symmetry is $y = -2$. If we let $y = 0$, we find that the x-intercept is $(1, 0)$. The graph is in the margin on the left.

Practice Problem 6 Place the equation $x = y^2 - 6y + 13$ in standard form and graph it.

PRACTICE PROBLEM 6

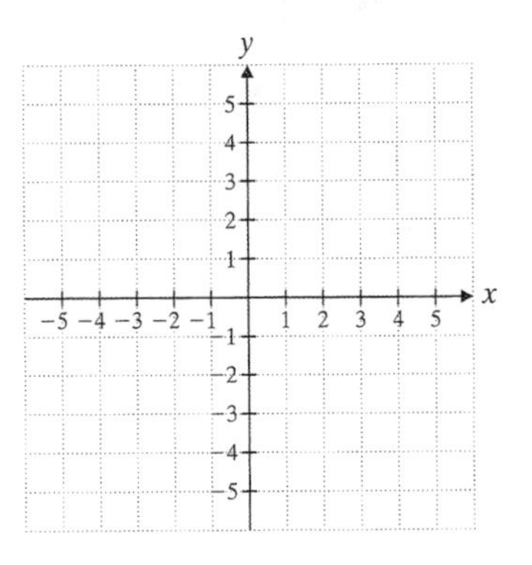

EXAMPLE 7 Place the equation $y = 2x^2 - 4x - 1$ in standard form. Then graph it.

This time the x-term is squared, so we have a vertical parabola. The standard form is

$$y = a(x - h)^2 + k.$$

We need to complete the square.

$$\begin{aligned} y &= 2(x^2 - 2x + \underline{\qquad}) - \underline{\qquad} - 1 \\ &= 2[x^2 - 2x + (1)^2] - 2(1)^2 - 1 \\ &= 2(x - 1)^2 - 3 \end{aligned}$$

The parabola opens upward $(a > 0)$, the vertex is $(1, -3)$, the axis of symmetry is $x = 1$, and the y-intercept is $(0, -1)$.

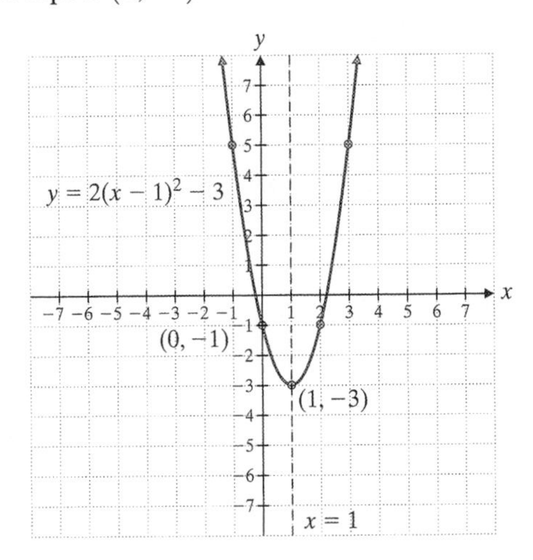

Practice Problem 7 Place $y = 2x^2 + 8x + 9$ in standard form and graph it.

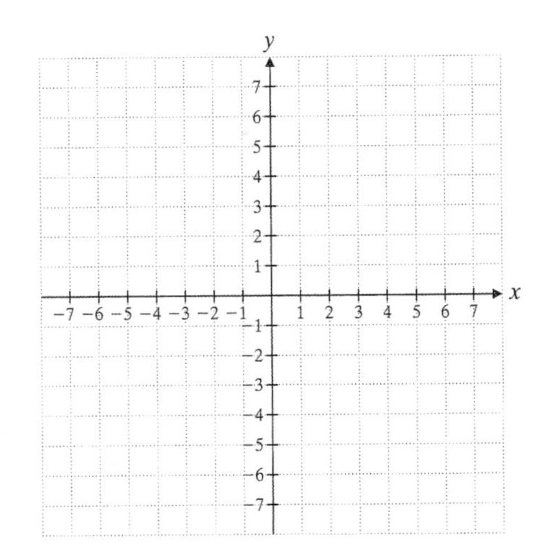

Graphing Calculator

Graphing Parabolas

Graphing horizontal parabolas such as the one in Example 6 on a graphing calculator requires dividing the curve into two halves. In this case the halves would be

$$y_1 = -2 + \sqrt{x + 3}$$

and

$$y_2 = -2 - \sqrt{x + 3}$$

Vertical parabolas can be graphed immediately on a graphing calculator. Why is this? How can you tell whether it is necessary to divide a curve into two halves? Graph the equations below on a graphing calculator. Use the quadratic formula when needed.

1. $y^2 + 8x - 4y = 28$
2. $4x^2 - 4x + 32y = 47$

9.2 Exercises

Verbal and Writing Skills

1. The graph of $y = x^2$ is symmetric about the ________. The graph of $x = y^2$ is symmetric about the ________.

2. Explain how to determine the axis of symmetry of the parabola $x = \frac{1}{2}(y + 5)^2 - 1$.

3. Explain how to determine the vertex of the parabola $y = 2(x - 3)^2 + 4$.

4. How does the coefficient -6 affect the graph of the parabola $y = -6x^2$?

Graph each parabola and label the vertex. Find the y-intercept. Place the x- and y-axes on the grid at a convenient place for your graphs.

5. $y = -4x^2$

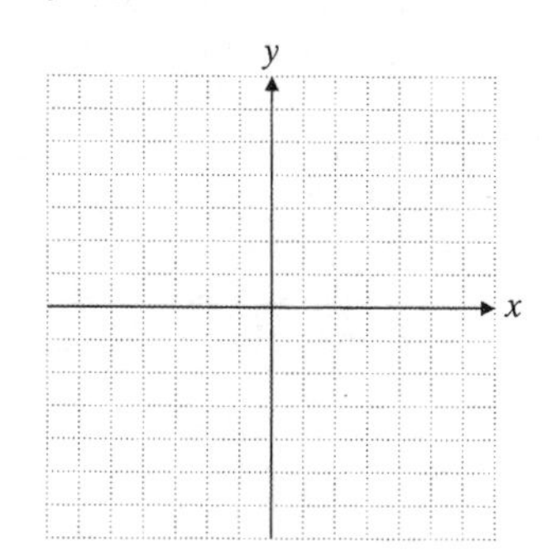

6. $y = -3x^2$

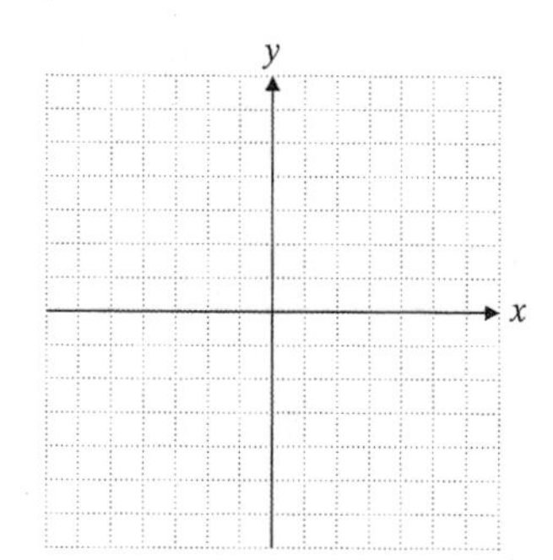

7. $y = x^2 - 6$

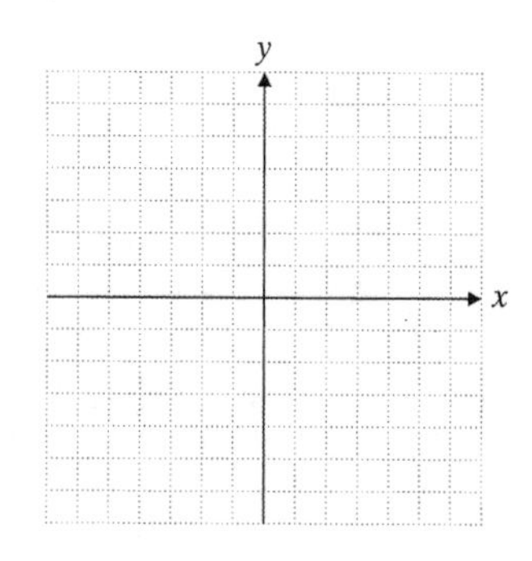

8. $y = x^2 + 2$

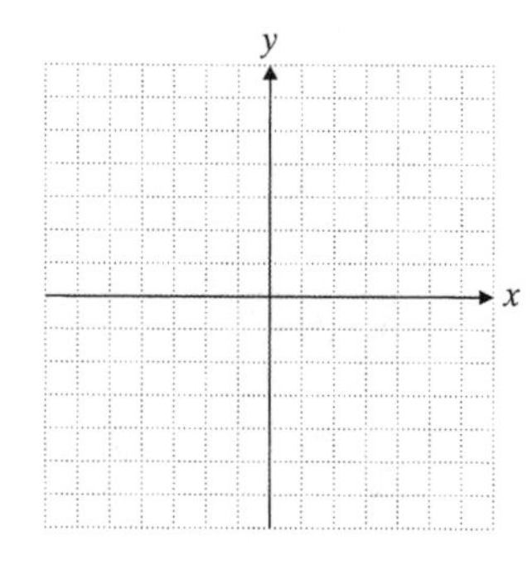

9. $y = -2x^2 + 4$

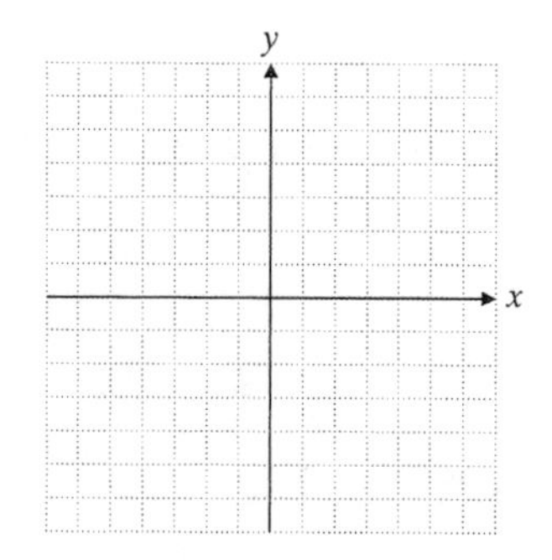

10. $y = -3x^2 + 1$

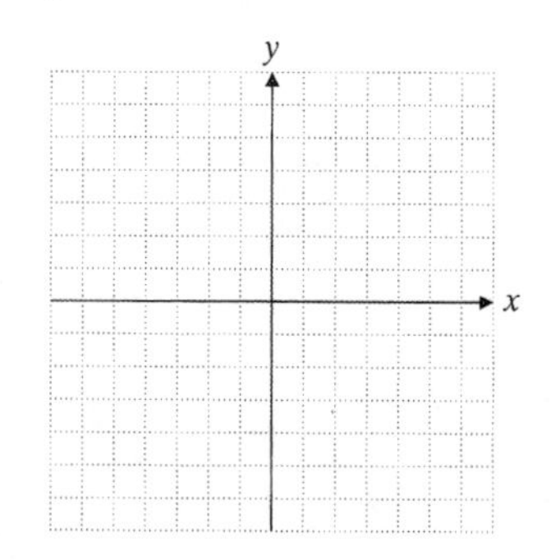

11. $y = (x - 3)^2 - 2$

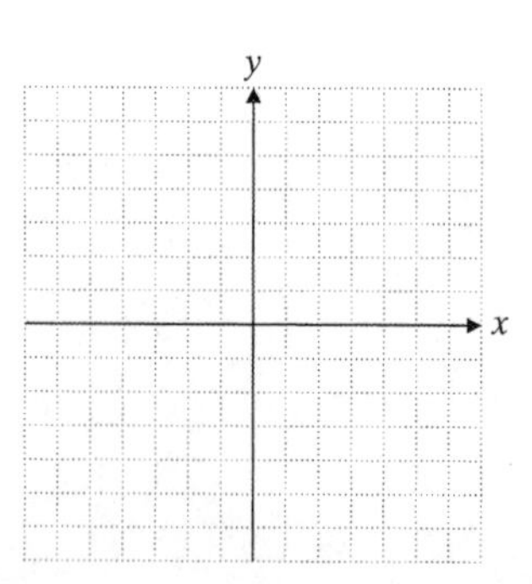

12. $y = (x - 2)^2 - 4$

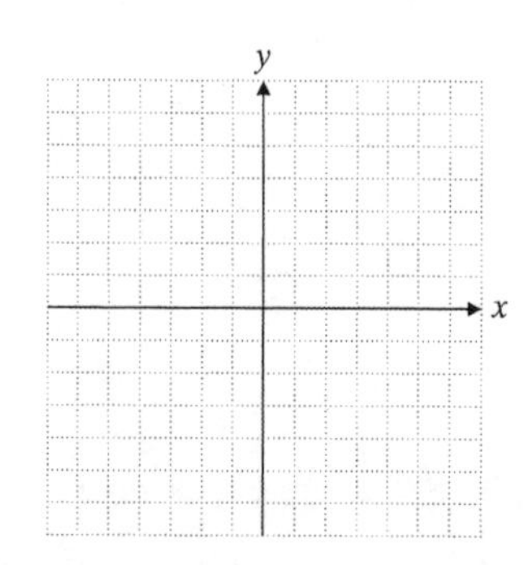

13. $y = 2(x - 1)^2 + \dfrac{3}{2}$

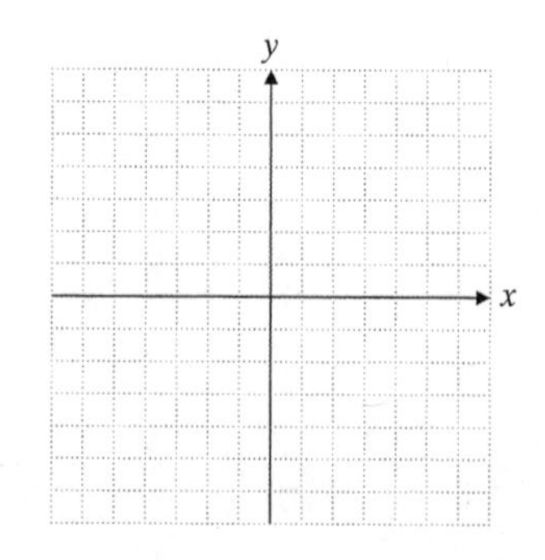

14. $y = 2(x - 2)^2 + \frac{5}{2}$

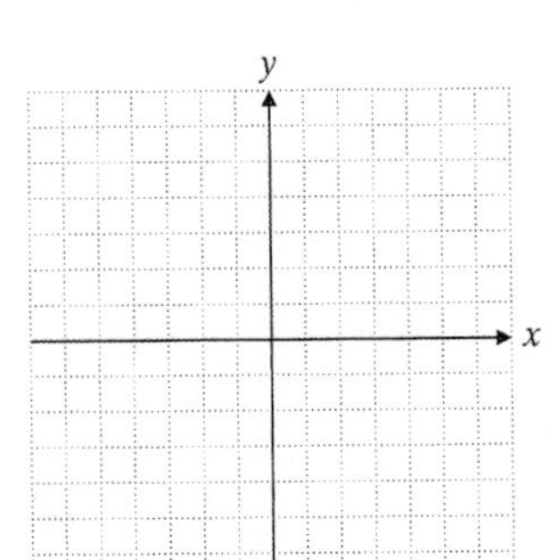

15. $y = -4\left(x + \frac{3}{2}\right)^2 + 5$

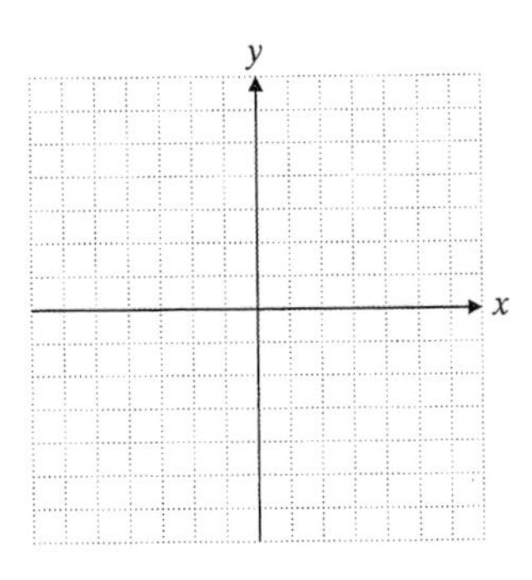

16. $y = -2\left(x + \frac{1}{2}\right)^2 - 1$

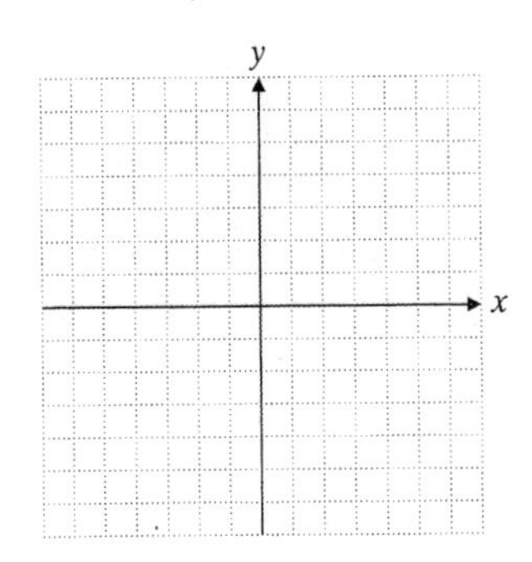

Graph each parabola and label the vertex. Find the x-intercept.

17. $x = \frac{1}{4}y^2 - 2$

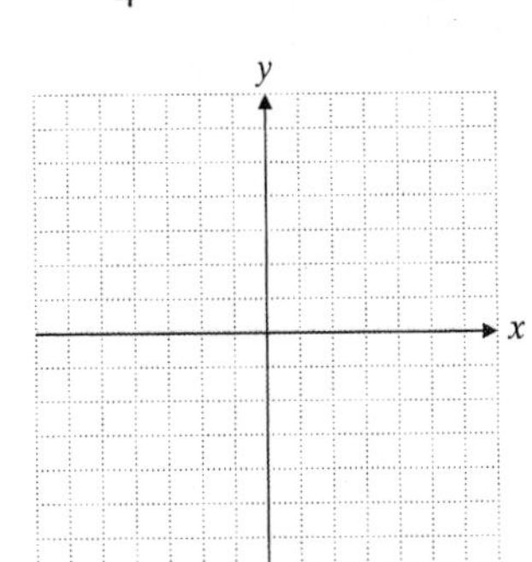

18. $x = \frac{1}{3}y^2 + 1$

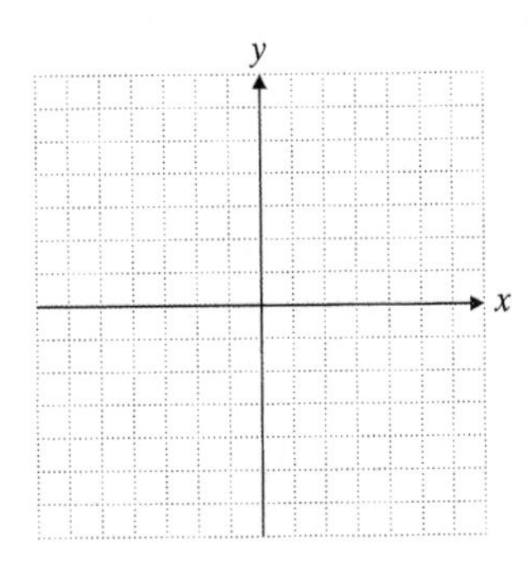

19. $x = (y - 2)^2 + 3$

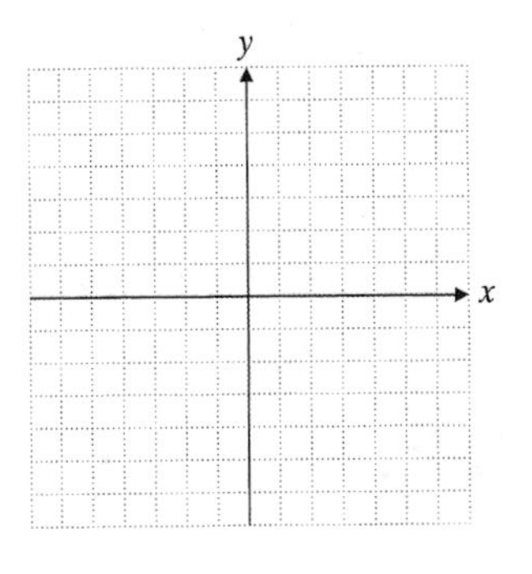

20. $x = (y - 4)^2 + 1$

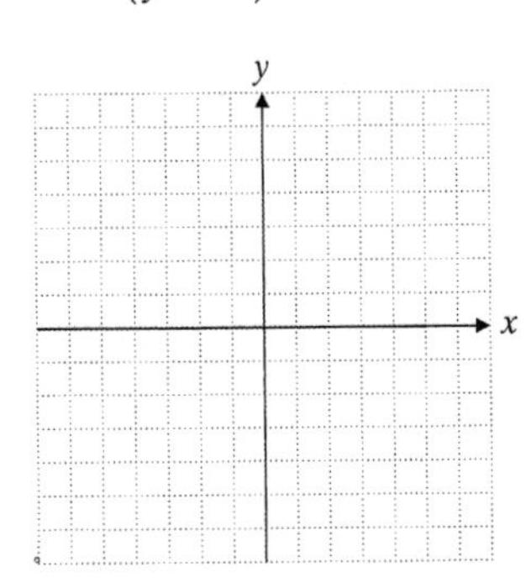

21. $x = -3(y + 1)^2 - 2$

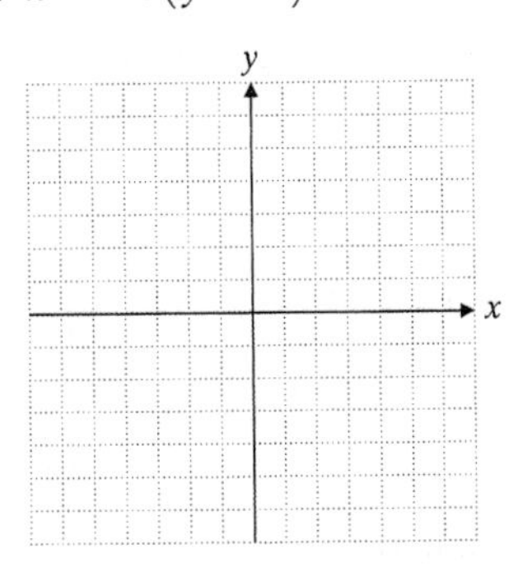

22. $x = -2(y + 3)^2 - 1$

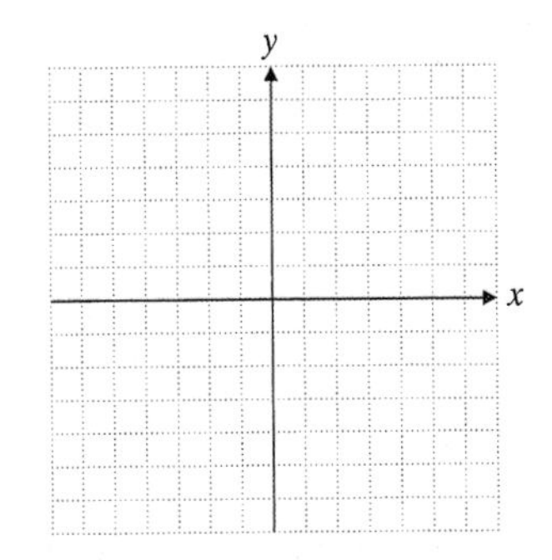

23. $x = \frac{1}{2}(y + 1)^2 + 2$

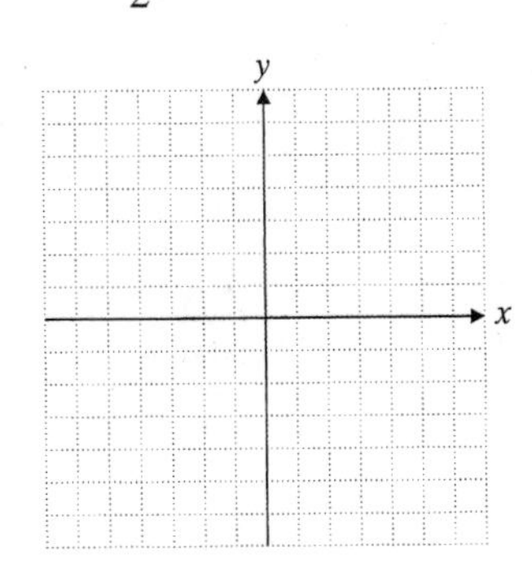

24. $x = \frac{1}{2}(y + 2)^2 + 1$

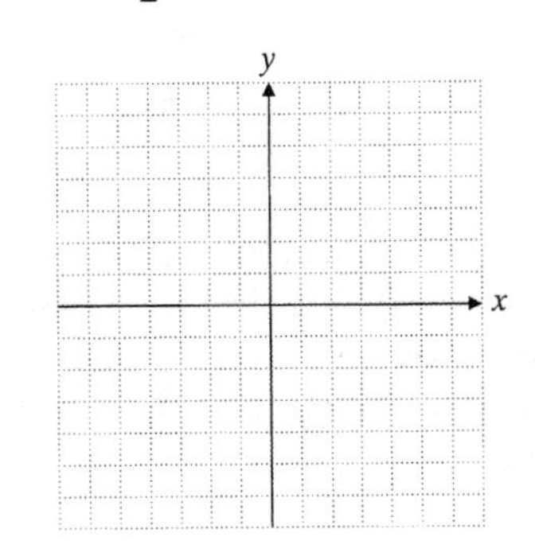

25. $x = -(y - 2)^2 + \frac{1}{2}$

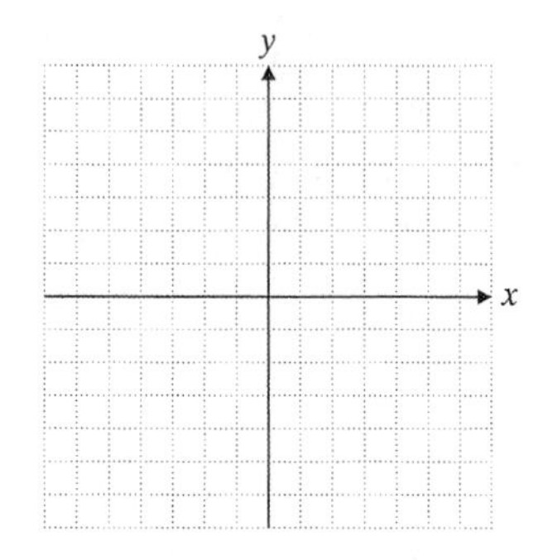

26. $x = -(y - 3)^2 + \frac{9}{2}$

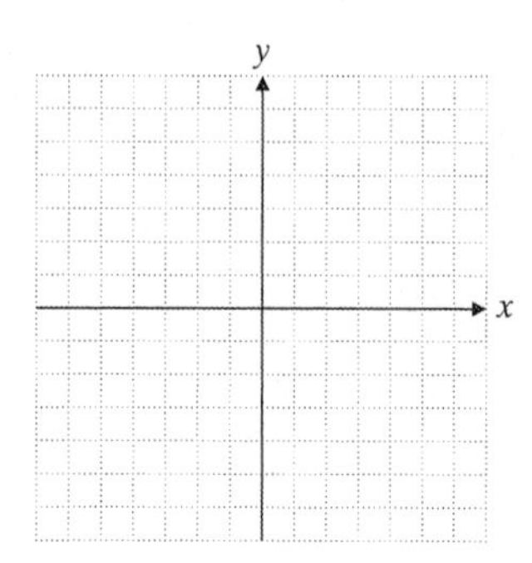

Rewrite in standard form each equation. Determine ***(a)*** *whether the parabola is horizontal or vertical,* ***(b)*** *the direction it opens, and* ***(c)*** *the vertex.*

27. $y = x^2 + 12x + 25$

28. $y = x^2 - 4x - 1$

29. $y = -2x^2 + 4x - 3$

30. $y = -2x^2 + 4x + 5$

31. $x = y^2 + 8y + 9$

32. $x = y^2 + 10y + 23$

Applications

33. Find an equation of the form $y = ax^2$ that describes the outline of a satellite dish such that the bottom of the dish passes through (0, 0), the diameter of the dish is 32 inches, and the depth of the dish is 8 inches.

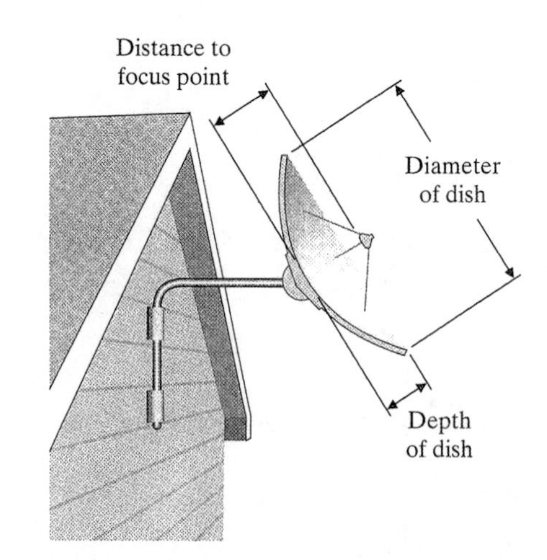

34. Find an equation of the form $y = ax^2$ that describes the outline of a satellite dish such that the bottom of the dish passes through (0, 0), the diameter of the dish is 24 inches, and the depth of the dish is 4 inches.

35. If the outline of a satellite dish is described by the equation $y = ax^2$, then the distance p from the center of the dish to the focus point of the dish is given by the equation $a = \frac{1}{4p}$. Find the distance p for the dish in Exercise 33.

36. If the outline of a satellite dish is described by the equation $y = ax^2$, then the distance p from the center of the dish to the focus point of the dish is given by the equation $a = \frac{1}{4p}$. Find the distance p for the dish in Exercise 34.

Optional Graphing Calculator Problems

Find the vertex and y-intercept of each parabola. Find the two x-intercepts.

37. $y = 2x^2 + 6.48x - 0.1312$

38. $y = -3x^2 + 33.66x - 73.5063$

Applications

By writing a quadratic equation in the form $y = a(x - h)^2 + k$, we can find the maximum or minimum value of the equation and the value of x at which it occurs. Remember that the equation $y = a(x - h)^2 + k$ is a vertical parabola. For $a > 0$, the parabola opens upward. Thus, the y-coordinate of the vertex is the smallest (or minimum) value of x. Similarly, when $a < 0$, the parabola opens downward, so the y-coordinate of the vertex is the maximum value of the equation. Since the vertex occurs at (h, k), the maximum value of the equation occurs when $x = h$. Then

$$y = -a(x - h)^2 + k = a(0) + k = k.$$

For example, suppose the weekly profit of a manufacturing company in dollars is $P = -2(x - 45)^2 + 2300$ for x units manufactured. By looking at the equation, we see that the maximum profit per week is \$2300 and is attained when 45 units are manufactured. Use this approach for Exercises 39–42.

39. A company's monthly profit equation is

$$P = -2x^2 + 200x + 47,000,$$

where x is the number of items manufactured. Find the maximum monthly profit and the number of items that must be produced each month to attain maximum profit?

40. A company's monthly profit equation is

$$P = -3x^2 + 240x + 31,200,$$

where x is the number of items manufactured. Find the maximum monthly profit and the number of items that must be produced each month to attain maximum profit.

41. A research pharmacologist has determined that sensitivity S to a drug depends on the dosage d in milligrams, according to the equation $S = 650d - 2d^2$. What is the maximum sensitivity that will occur? What dosage will produce that maximum sensitivity?

42. The effective yield from a grove of orange trees is described by the equation $E = x(900 - x)$, where x is the number of orange trees per acre. What is the maximum effective yield? How many orange trees per acre should be planted to achieve the maximum yield?

Cumulative Review Problems

Simplify.

43. $\sqrt{50x^3}$

44. $\sqrt[3]{40x^3y^4}$

Add.

45. $\sqrt{98x} + x\sqrt{8} - 3\sqrt{50x}$

46. $\sqrt[3]{16x^4} + 4x\sqrt[3]{2} - 8x\sqrt[3]{54}$

47. Matthew drives from work to his home at 40 mph. One morning, an accident on the road delayed him for 15 minutes. The driving time including the delay was 56 minutes. How far does Matthew live from his job?

48. A driver delivering eggs drove from the farm to a supermarket warehouse at 30 mph. He unloaded the eggs and drove back to the farm at 50 mph. The total trip took 2 hours and 15 minutes. How far is the farm from the supermarket warehouse?

49. Sir George Tipkin of Sussex has a collection of eight large English rose bushes, each having approximately 1050 buds. In normal years this type of bush produces blooms from 73% of its buds. During years of drought this figure drops to 44%. During years of heavy rainfall the figure rises to 88%. How many blooms can Sir George expect on these bushes if there is heavy rainfall this year?

50. Last year Sir George had only six of the type of bushes described in Exercise 49. It was a drought year, and he counted 2900 blooms. Using the bloom rates given in Exercise 49, determine approximately how many buds appeared on each of these six bushes. (Round your answer to the nearest whole number.)

9.3 The Ellipse

Suppose a plane cuts a cone at an angle so that the plane intersects all sides of the cone. If the plane is not perpendicular to the axis of the cone, the conic section that is formed is called an ellipse.

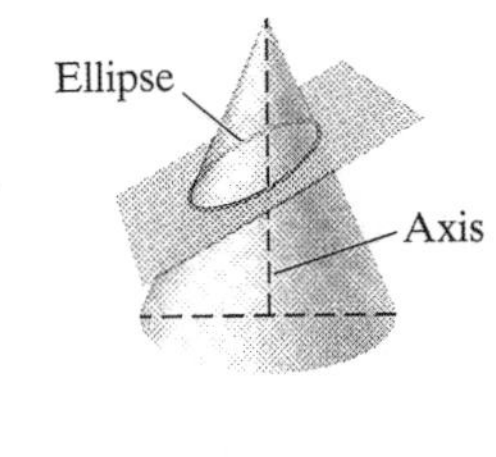

Student Learning Objectives

After studying this section, you will be able to:

 Graph an ellipse whose center is at the origin.

 Graph an ellipse whose center is at (h, k).

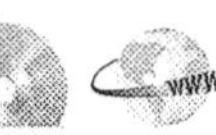

We define an **ellipse** as the set of points in a plane such that for each point in the set, the *sum* of its distances to two fixed points is constant. The fixed points are called **foci** (plural of *focus*).

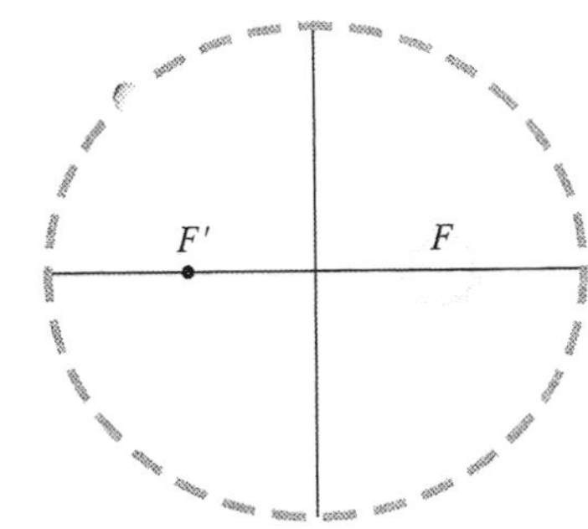

We can use this definition to draw an ellipse using a piece of string tied at each end to a thumbtack. Place a pencil as shown in the drawing and draw the curve, keeping the pencil pushed tightly against the string. The two thumbtacks are the foci of the ellipse that results.

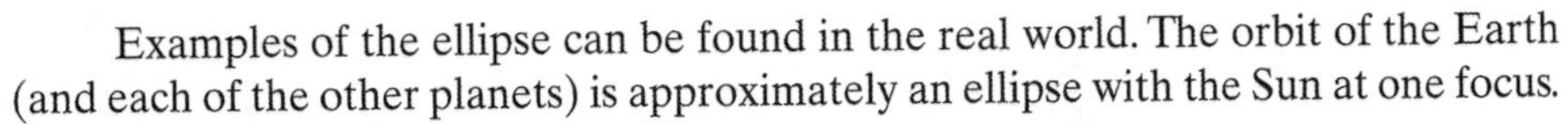

Examples of the ellipse can be found in the real world. The orbit of the Earth (and each of the other planets) is approximately an ellipse with the Sun at one focus.

An elliptical surface has a special reflecting property. When sound, light, or some other object originating at one focus reaches the ellipse, it is reflected in such a way that it passes through the other focus. This property can be found in the United States Capitol in a famous room known as the Statuary Hall. If a person whispers at the focus of one end of this elliptically shaped room, a person at the other focus can easily hear him or her.

 Graphing an Ellipse Whose Center is at the Origin

The equation of an ellipse is similar to the equation of a circle. The standard form of the equation of an ellipse centered at the origin is given next.

Standard Form of the Equation of an Ellipse

An ellipse with center at the origin has the equation

$$\frac{x^2}{a^2} + \frac{y^2}{b^2} = 1, \qquad \text{where } a \text{ and } b > 0.$$

The **vertices** of this ellipse are at $(a, 0)$, $(-a, 0)$, $(0, b)$, and $(0, -b)$.

To plot the ellipse, we need the x- and y-intercepts.

$$\frac{x^2}{a^2} + \frac{y^2}{b^2} = 1$$

If $x = 0$, then $\frac{y^2}{b^2} = 1$.

$$y^2 = b^2$$
$$\pm\sqrt{y^2} = \pm\sqrt{b^2}$$
$$\pm y = \pm b \text{ or } y = \pm b$$

If $y = 0$, then $\frac{x^2}{a^2} = 1$.

$$x^2 = a^2$$
$$\pm\sqrt{x^2} = \pm\sqrt{a^2}$$
$$\pm x = \pm a \text{ or } x = \pm a$$

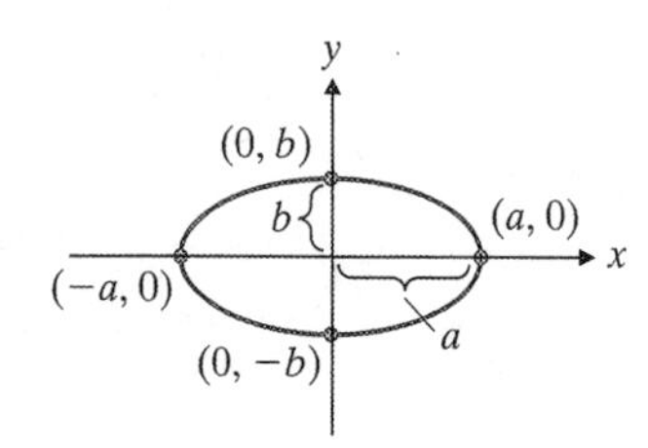

So the x-intercepts are $(a, 0)$ and $(-a, 0)$, and the y-intercepts are $(0, b)$ and $(0, -b)$ for an ellipse of the form $\frac{x^2}{a^2} + \frac{y^2}{b^2} = 1$.

A circle is a special case of an ellipse. If $a = b$, we get the following:

$$\frac{x^2}{a^2} + \frac{y^2}{a^2} = 1$$
$$x^2 + y^2 = a^2$$

This is the equation of a circle of radius a.

EXAMPLE 1 Graph $x^2 + 3y^2 = 12$. Label the intercepts.

Before we can graph this ellipse, we need to rewrite the equation in standard form.

$$\frac{x^2}{12} + \frac{3y^2}{12} = \frac{12}{12} \quad \text{Divide each side by 12.}$$
$$\frac{x^2}{12} + \frac{y^2}{4} = 1 \quad \text{Simplify.}$$

Thus, we have the following:

$$a^2 = 12 \quad \text{so} \quad a = 2\sqrt{3}$$
$$b^2 = 4 \quad \text{so} \quad b = 2$$

The x-intercepts are $(-2\sqrt{3}, 0)$ and $(2\sqrt{3}, 0)$, and the y-intercepts are $(0, 2)$ and $(0, -2)$. We plot these points and draw the ellipse.

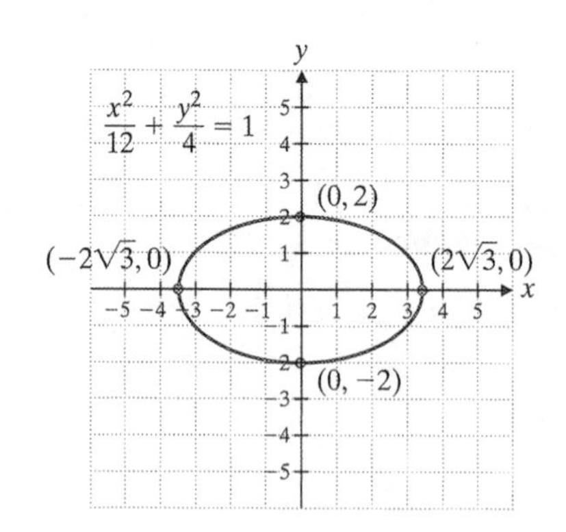

PRACTICE PROBLEM 1

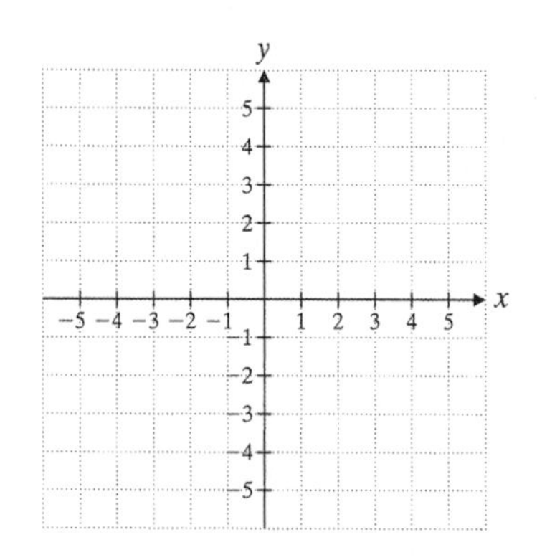

Practice Problem 1 Graph $4x^2 + y^2 = 16$. Label the intercepts.

 Graphing an Ellipse Whose Center Is at (h, k)

If the center of the ellipse is not at the origin but at some point whose coordinates are (h, k), then the standard form of the equation is changed.

An ellipse with center at (h, k) has the equation

$$\frac{(x-h)^2}{a^2}+\frac{(y-k)^2}{b^2}=1,$$

where a and $b > 0$.

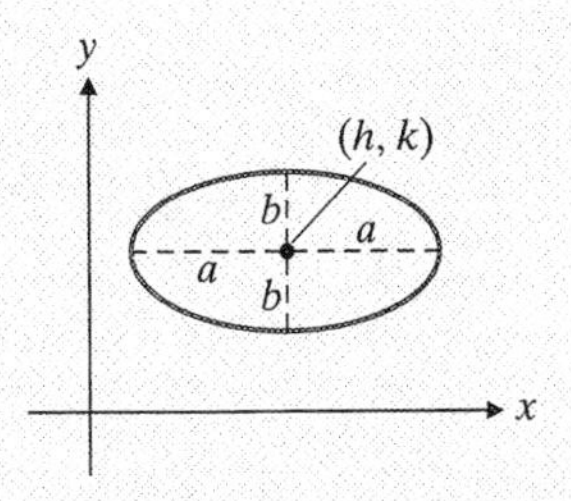

Note that a and b are *not* the x-intercepts now. Why is this? Look at the sketch. You'll see that a is the horizontal distance from the center of the ellipse to a point on the ellipse. Similarly, b is the vertical distance. Hence, when the center of the ellipse is not at the origin, the ellipse may not even cross either axis.

EXAMPLE 2 Graph $\frac{(x-5)^2}{9}+\frac{(y-6)^2}{4}=1.$

The center of the ellipse is $(5, 6)$, $a = 3$, and $b = 2$. Therefore, we begin at $(5, 6)$. We plot points 3 units to the left, 3 units to the right, 2 units up, and 2 units down from $(5, 6)$.

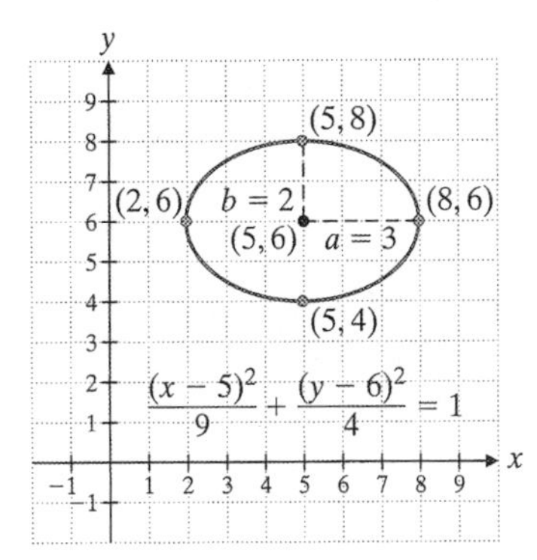

Practice Problem 2 Graph $\frac{(x-2)^2}{16}+\frac{(y+3)^2}{9}=1.$

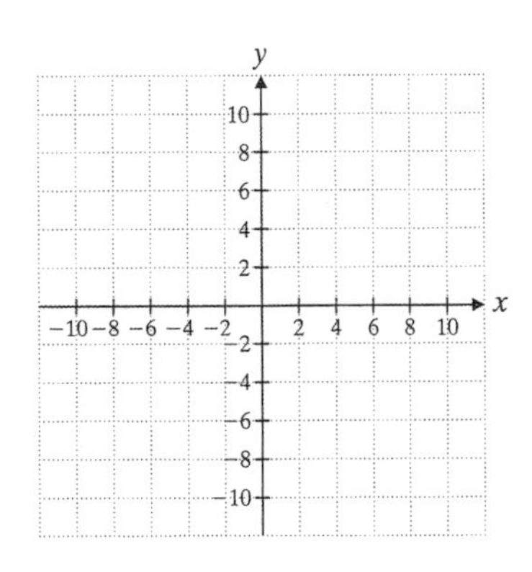

Graphing Calculator

Graphing Ellipses

In order to graph the ellipse in Example 2 on a graphing calculator, we first need to solve for y.

$$\frac{(y-6)^2}{4}=1-\frac{(x-5)^2}{9}$$

$$(y-6)^2=4\left[1-\frac{(x-5)^2}{9}\right]$$

$$y=6\pm 2\sqrt{1-\frac{(x-5)^2}{9}}$$

Is it necessary to break up the curve into two halves in order to graph the ellipse? Why or why not?

Use the above concepts to graph

$$\frac{(x-2)^2}{9}+\frac{(y-1)^2}{4}=1.$$

Using the Trace feature, determine from your graph the coordinates of the two x-intercepts and the two y-intercepts. Express your answers to the nearest hundredth.

9.3 Exercises

Verbal and Writing Skills

1. Explain how to determine the center of the ellipse $\frac{(x+2)^2}{4} + \frac{(y-3)^2}{9} = 1$.

2. Explain how to determine the x- and y-intercepts of the ellipse $\frac{x^2}{9} + \frac{y^2}{16} = 1$.

Graph each ellipse. Label the intercepts. You may need to use a scale other than 1 square = 1 unit.

3. $\frac{x^2}{36} + \frac{y^2}{4} = 1$

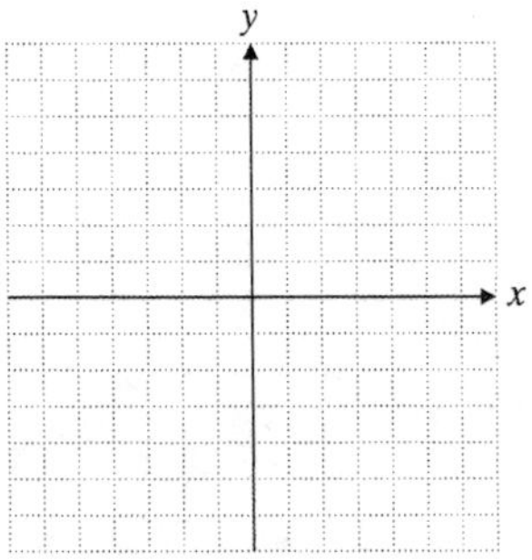

4. $\frac{x^2}{49} + \frac{y^2}{25} = 1$

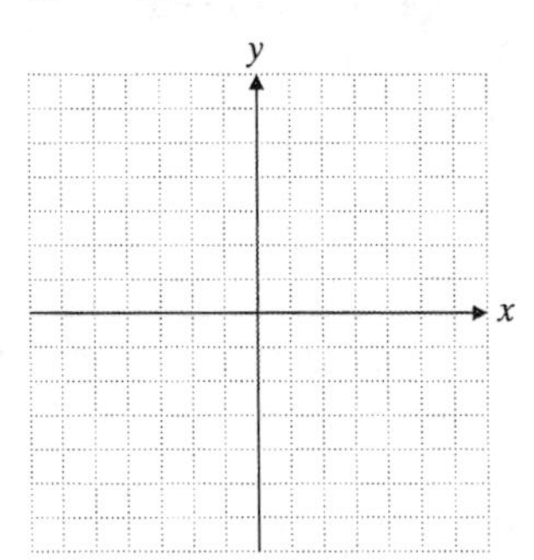

5. $\frac{x^2}{81} + \frac{y^2}{100} = 1$

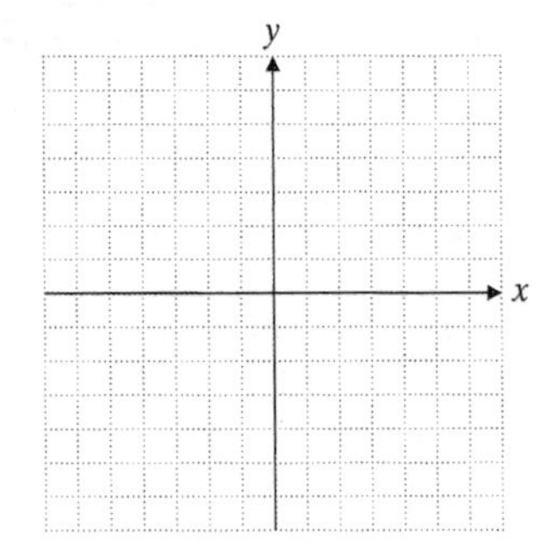

6. $\frac{x^2}{121} + \frac{y^2}{144} = 1$

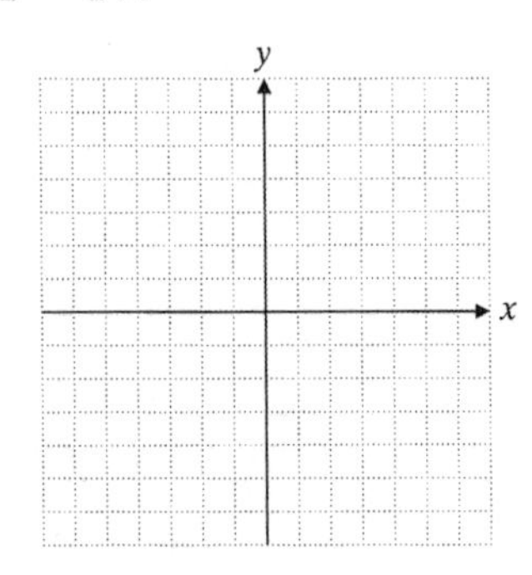

7. $4x^2 + y^2 - 36 = 0$

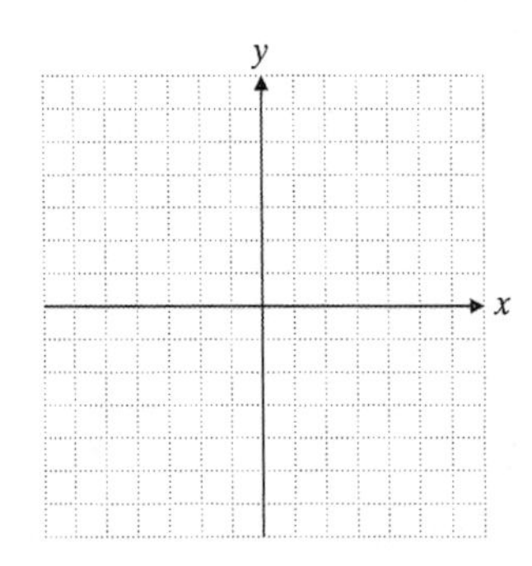

8. $x^2 + 25y^2 - 25 = 0$

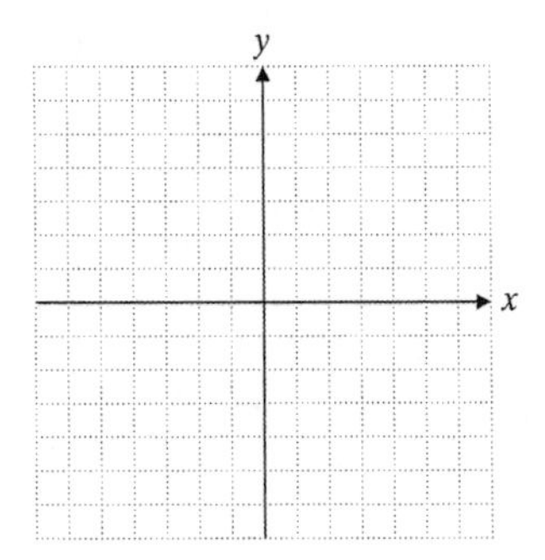

9. $x^2 + 9y^2 = 81$

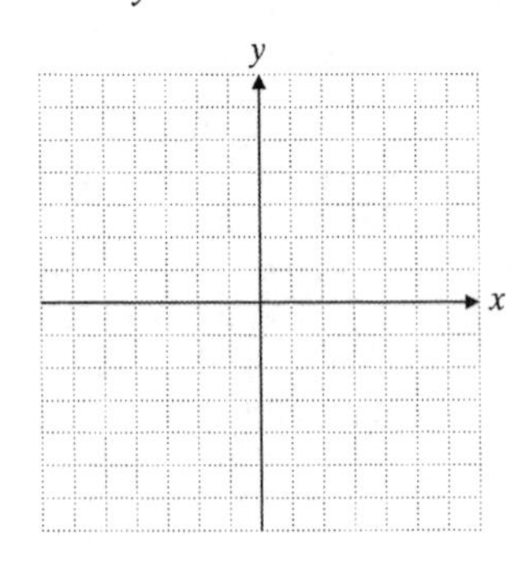

10. $4x^2 + 25y^2 = 100$

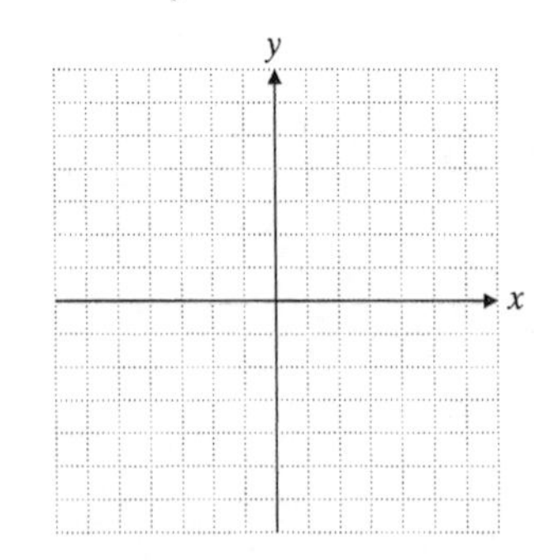

11. $x^2 + 12y^2 = 36$

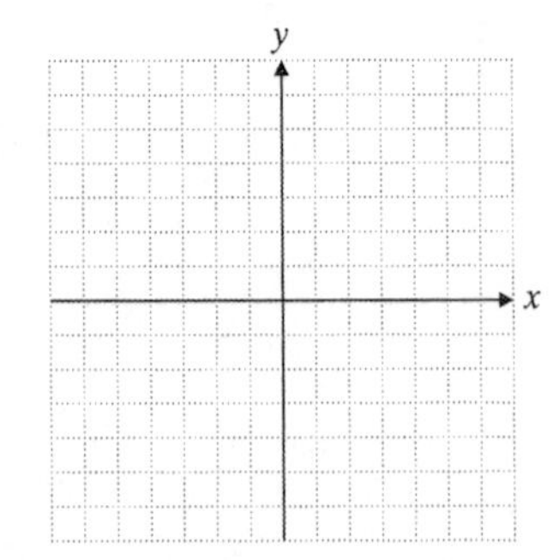

12. $8x^2 + y^2 = 16$

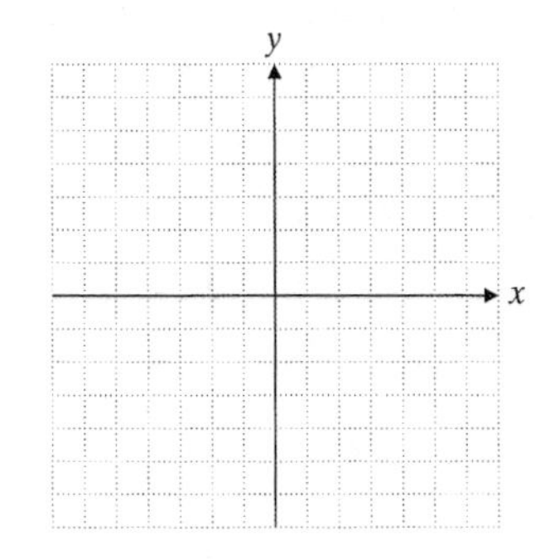

13. $\dfrac{x^2}{\frac{9}{4}} + \dfrac{y^2}{\frac{25}{4}} = 1$

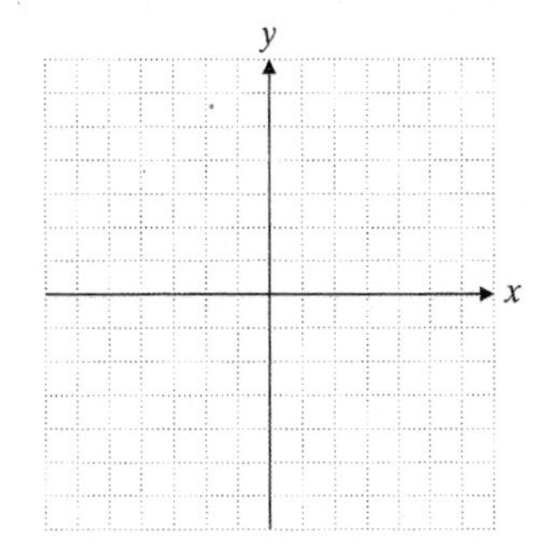

14. $\dfrac{x^2}{\frac{81}{4}} + \dfrac{y^2}{\frac{25}{16}} = 1$

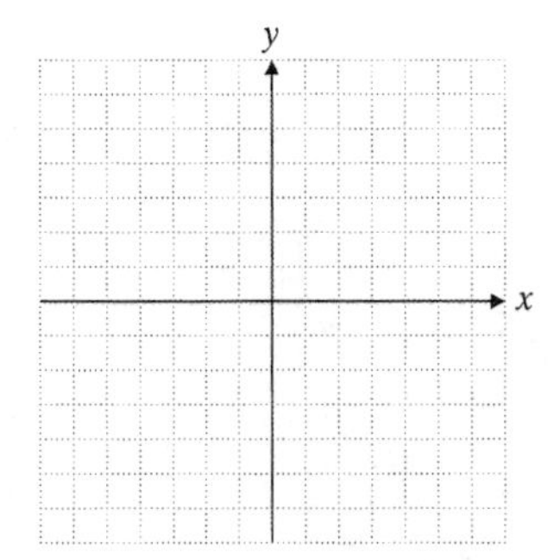

15. $121x^2 + 64y^2 = 7744$

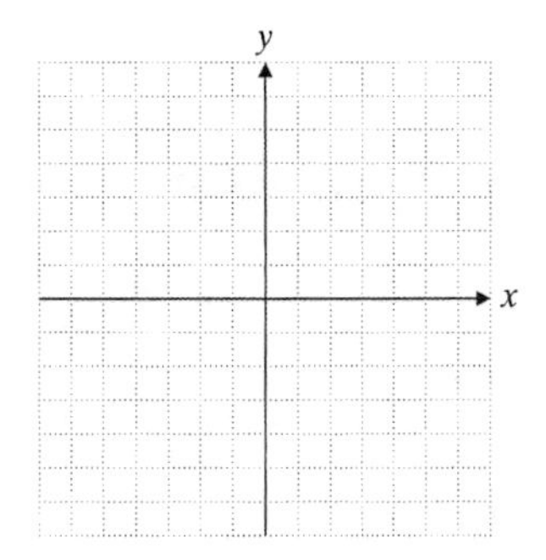

16. Write in standard form the equation of an ellipse with center at the origin, an x-intercept at $(8, 0)$, and a y-intercept at $(0, 10)$.

17. Write in standard form the equation of an ellipse with center at the origin, an x-intercept at $(9, 0)$, and a y-intercept at $(0, -2)$.

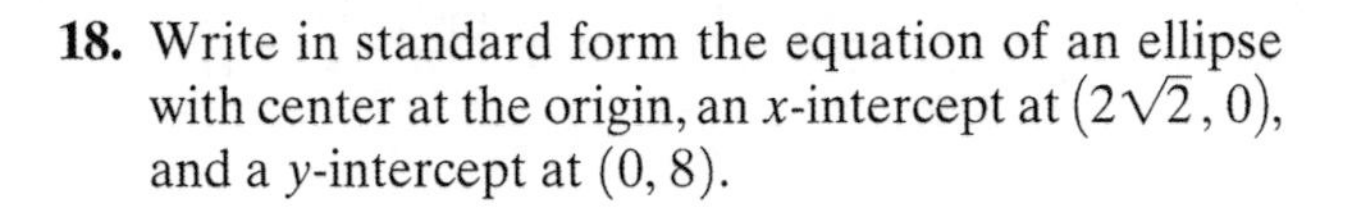

18. Write in standard form the equation of an ellipse with center at the origin, an x-intercept at $(2\sqrt{2}, 0)$, and a y-intercept at $(0, 8)$.

19. Write in standard form the equation of an ellipse with center at the origin, an x-intercept at $(9, 0)$, and a y-intercept at $(0, 3\sqrt{2})$.

Applications

20. The orbit of Venus is an ellipse with the Sun as a focus. If we say that the center of the ellipse is at the origin, an approximate equation for the orbit is

$$\frac{x^2}{5013} + \frac{y^2}{4970} = 1,$$

where x and y are measured in millions of miles. Find the largest possible distance across the ellipse. Round your answer to the nearest million miles.

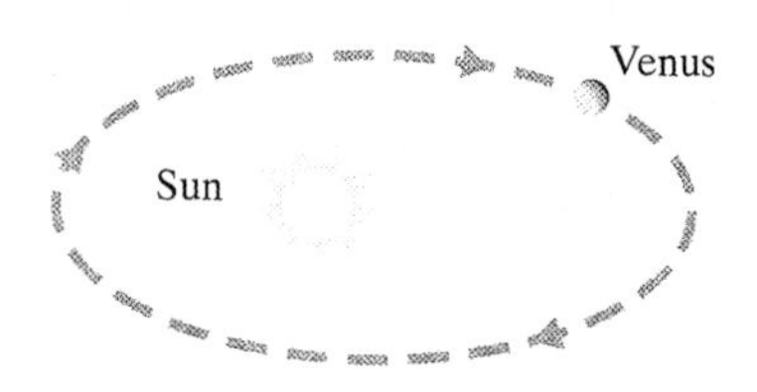

21. The window shown in the sketch is in the shape of half of an ellipse. Find the equation for the ellipse if the center of the ellipse is at point $A = (0, 0)$.

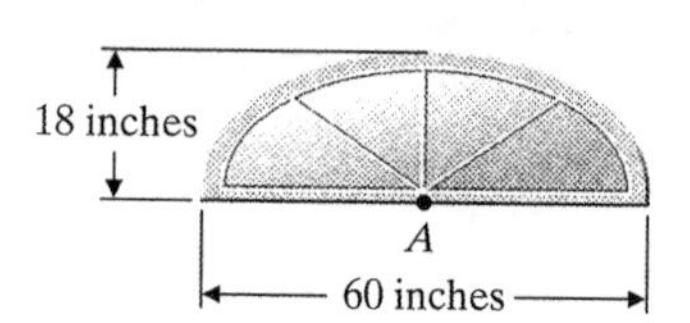

Graph each ellipse, Label the center. Place the x- and y-axes on the grid at a convenient location for each graph. You may need to use a scale other than 1 square = 1 unit.

22. $\frac{(x-7)^2}{4} + \frac{(y-6)^2}{9} = 1$

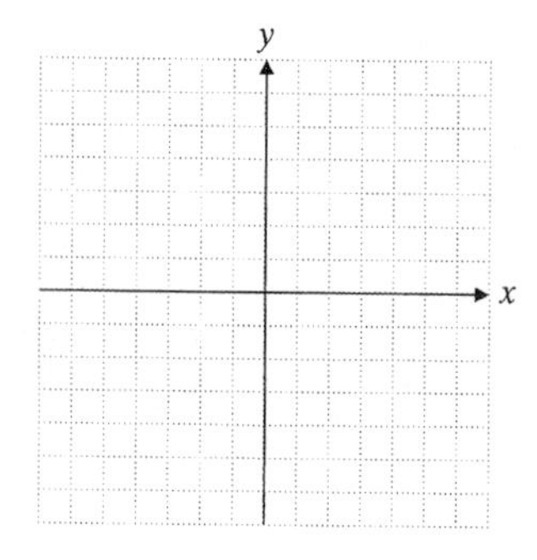

23. $\frac{(x-5)^2}{9} + \frac{(y-2)^2}{1} = 1$

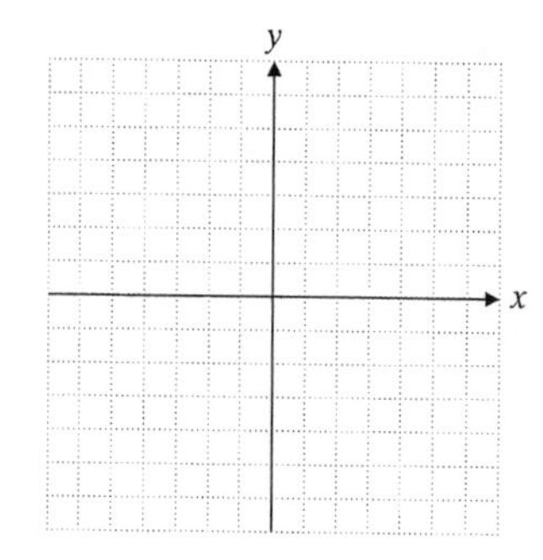

24. $\frac{x^2}{25} + \frac{(y-4)^2}{16} = 1$

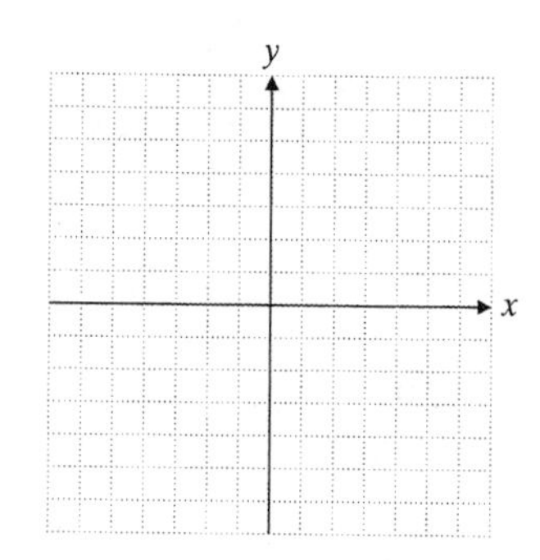

25. $\frac{(x+2)^2}{49} + \frac{y^2}{25} = 1$

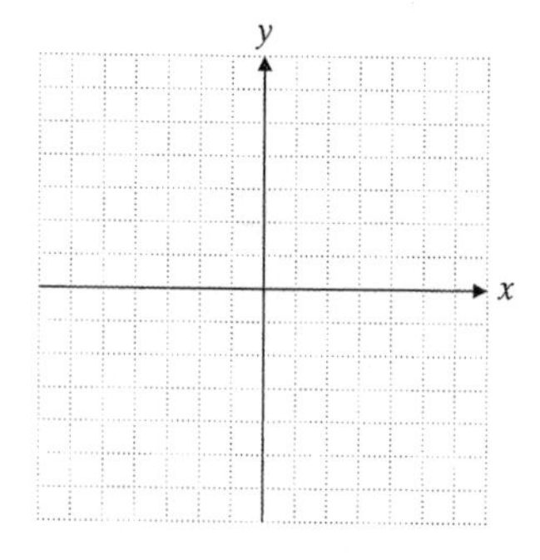

26. $\frac{(x+5)^2}{16} + \frac{(y+2)^2}{36} = 1$

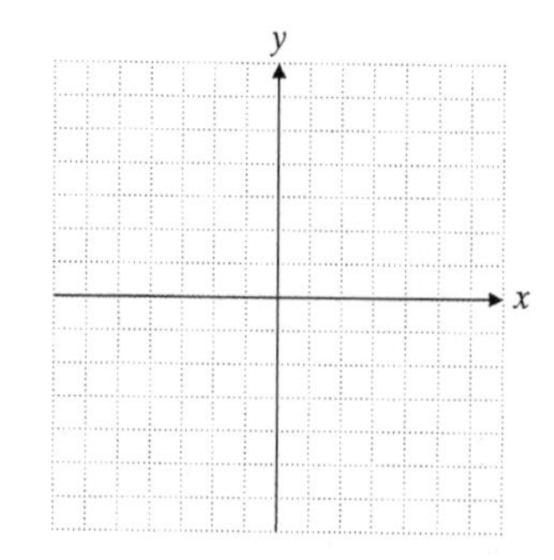

27. $\frac{(x+1)^2}{36} + \frac{(y+4)^2}{16} = 1$

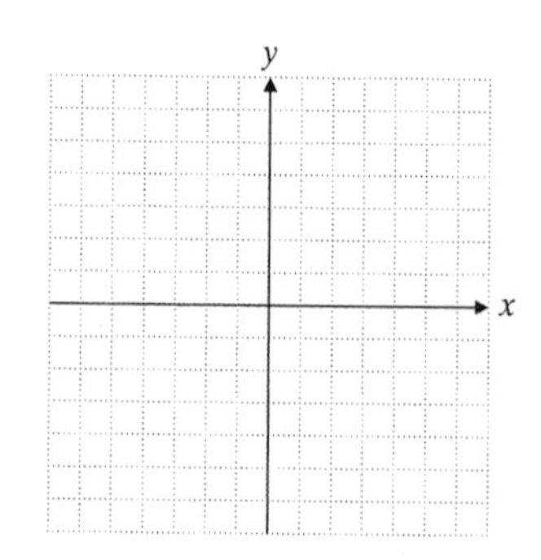

28. Write in standard form the equation of an ellipse whose vertices are $(-3, -2)$, $(5, -2)$, $(1, 1)$, and $(1, -5)$.

29. Write in standard form the equation of an ellipse whose vertices are $(2, 3)$, $(6, 3)$, $(4, 7)$, and $(4, -1)$.

30. Bob's backyard is a rectangle 40 meters by 60 meters. He drove two posts into the ground and fastened a rope to each post, passing the rope through the metal ring on his dog's collar. When the dog pulls on the rope while running, its path is an ellipse. (See the figure.) If the dog can just reach all four sides of the rectangle, find the equation of the elliptical path.

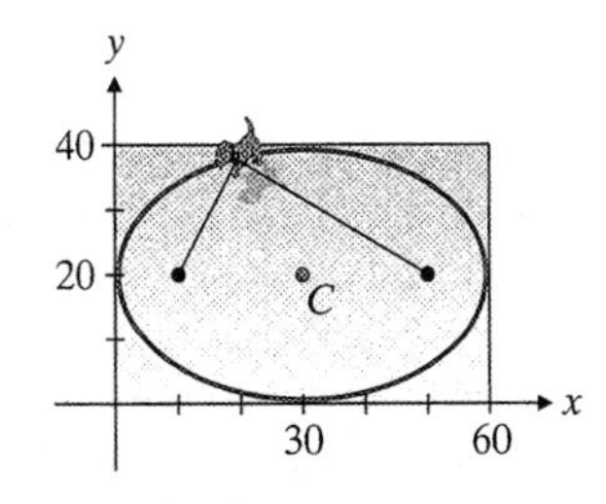

31. For what value of a does the ellipse

$$\frac{(x + 5)^2}{4} + \frac{(y + a)^2}{9} = 1$$

pass through the point $(-4, 4)$?

Optional Graphing Calculator Problems

Find the four intercepts, accurate to four decimal places, for each ellipse.

32. $\dfrac{x^2}{12} + \dfrac{y^2}{19} = 1$

33. $\dfrac{(x - 3.6)^2}{14.98} + \dfrac{(y - 5.3)^2}{28.98} = 1$

To Think About

The area enclosed by the ellipse $\frac{x^2}{a^2} + \frac{y^2}{b^2} = 1$ *is given by the equation* $A = \pi ab$. *Use the value* $\pi \approx 3.1416$ *to find an approximate value for each of the following answers.*

34. An oval mirror has an outer boundary in the shape of an ellipse. The width of the mirror is 20 inches, and the length of the mirror is 45 inches. Find the area of the mirror. Round your answer to the nearest tenth.

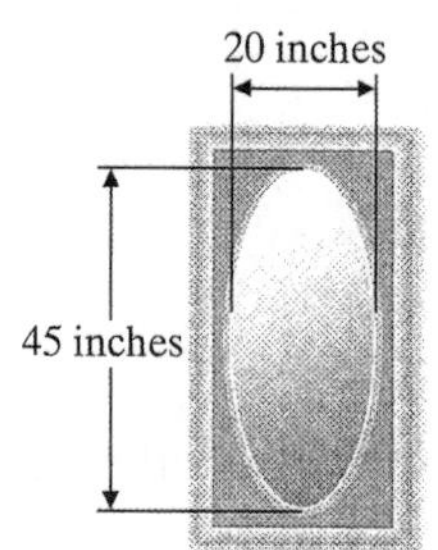

35. In Australia a type of football is played on Aussie Rules fields. These fields are in the shape of an ellipse. Suppose the distance from A to B for the field shown is 185 meters and the distance from C to D is 154 meters. Find the area of the playing field. Round your answer to the nearest tenth.

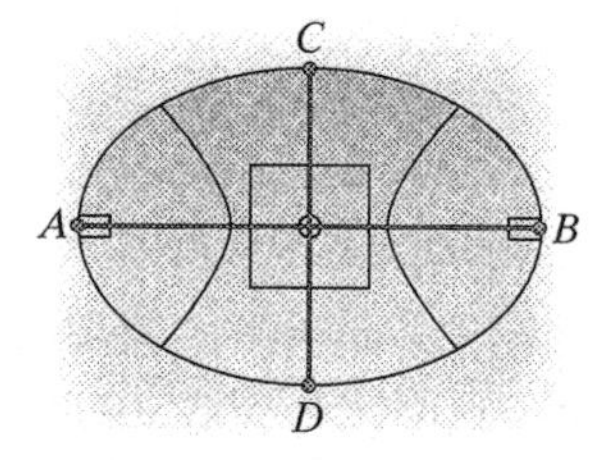

Cumulative Review Problems

Multiply and simplify.

36. $(2\sqrt{3} + 4\sqrt{2})(5\sqrt{6} - \sqrt{2})$

Rationalize the denominator.

37. $\frac{5}{\sqrt{2x} - \sqrt{y}}$

38. The Empire State Building was the tallest building in the world for many years. Construction began on March 17, 1930, and the framework rose at a rate of 4.5 stories per week. How many weeks did it take to complete the framework for all 102 stories?

39. The top floor (the observatory on the 102nd floor) of the Empire State Building is 1224 feet above street level. To walk up the stairway of the building from street level to the 102nd floor requires climbing 1850 steps. (Once a year an official race is held to see who is the fastest to climb the stairs to the observatory.) What is the average height of one step at the Empire State Building? Round your answer to the nearest tenth of an inch.

9.4 The Hyperbola

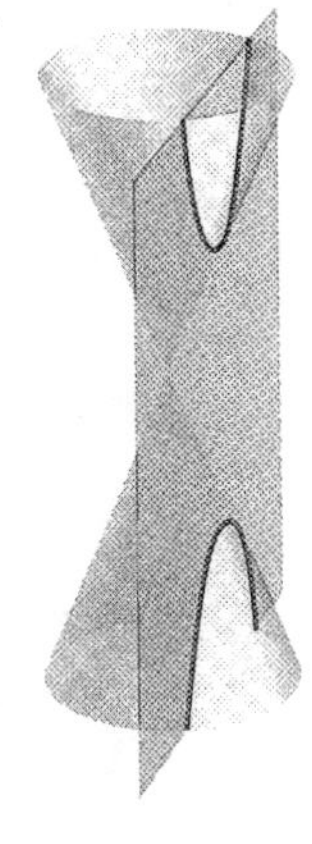

By cutting two branches of a cone by a plane as shown in the sketch, we obtain the two branches of a hyperbola. A comet moving with more than enough kinetic energy to escape the Sun's gravitational pull will travel in a hyperbolic path. Similarly, a rocket traveling with more than enough velocity to escape the Earth's gravitational field will follow a hyperbolic path.

We define a **hyperbola** as the set of points in a plane such that for each point in the set, the absolute value of the *difference* of its distances to two fixed points (called **foci**) is constant.

Student Learning Objectives

After studying this section, you will be able to:

1. Graph a hyperbola whose center is at the origin.

2. Graph a hyperbola whose center is at (h, k).

SSM · PH TUTOR CENTER · CD & VIDEO · MATH PRO · WEB

1 Graphing a Hyperbola Whose Center is at the Origin

Notice the similarity of the definition of a hyperbola to the definition of an ellipse. If we replace the word *difference* by *sum*, we have the definition of an ellipse. Hence, we should expect that the equation of a hyperbola will be that of an ellipse with the plus sign replaced by a minus sign. And it is. If the hyperbola has its center at the origin, its equation is

$$\frac{x^2}{a^2} - \frac{y^2}{b^2} = 1 \quad \text{or} \quad \frac{y^2}{b^2} - \frac{x^2}{a^2} = 1.$$

The hyperbola has two branches. If the center of the hyperbola is at the origin and the two branches have two x-intercepts but no y-intercepts, the hyperbola is a horizontal hyperbola, and its **axis** is the x-axis. If the center of the hyperbola is at the origin and the two branches have two y-intercepts but no x-intercepts, the hyperbola is a vertical hyperbola, and its axis is the y-axis.

The points where the hyperbola intersects its axis are called the **vertices** of the hyperbola.

For hyperbolas centered at the origin, the vertices are also the intercepts.

Standard Form of the Equation of a Hyperbola with Center at the Origin

Let a and b be any positive real numbers. A hyperbola with center at the origin and vertices $(-a, 0)$ and $(a, 0)$ has the equation

$$\frac{x^2}{a^2} - \frac{y^2}{b^2} = 1.$$

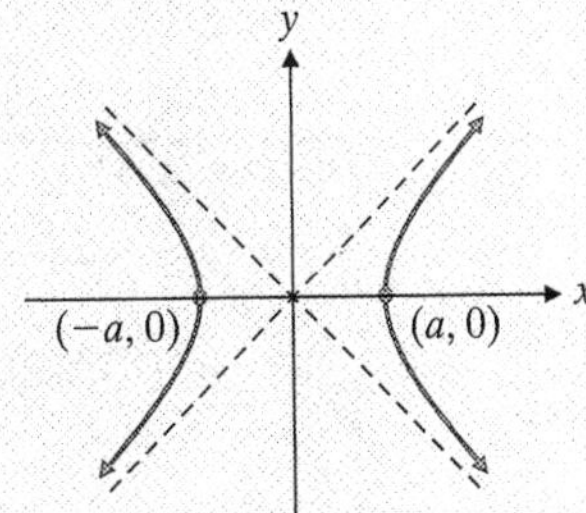

This is called a *horizontal hyperbola*.

A hyperbola with center at the origin and vertices $(0, b)$ and $(0, -b)$ has the equation

$$\frac{y^2}{b^2} - \frac{x^2}{a^2} = 1.$$

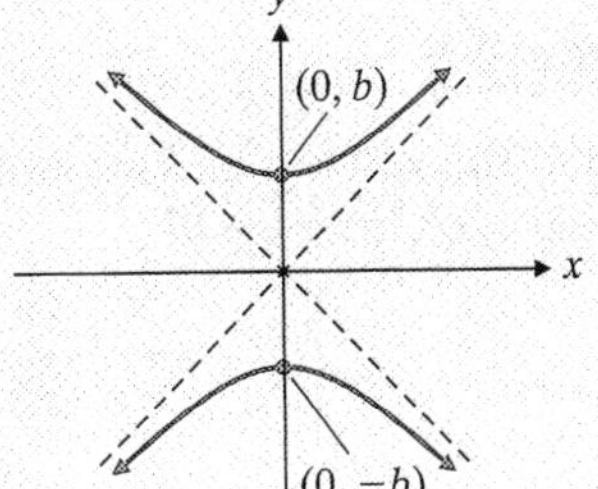

This is called a *vertical hyperbola*.

Notice that the two equations are slightly different. Be aware of this difference so that when you look at an equation you will be able to tell whether the hyperbola is horizontal or vertical.

Notice also the diagonal lines that we've drawn on the graphs of the hyperbolas. These lines are called **asymptotes**. The two branches of the hyperbola come increasingly closer to the asymptotes as the value of $|x|$ gets very large. By drawing the asymptotes and plotting the vertices, we can easily graph a hyperbola.

Asymptotes of Hyperbolas

The asymptotes of the hyperbolas $\dfrac{x^2}{a^2} - \dfrac{y^2}{b^2} = 1$ and $\dfrac{y^2}{b^2} - \dfrac{x^2}{a^2} = 1$ are

$$y = \frac{b}{a}x \text{ and } y = -\frac{b}{a}x.$$

Note that $\dfrac{b}{a}$ and $-\dfrac{b}{a}$ are the slopes of the asymptotes.

An easy way to find the asymptotes is to draw extended diagonal lines through the rectangle whose center is at the origin and whose corners are at (a, b), $(a, -b)$, $(-a, b)$, and $(-a, -b)$. (This rectangle is sometimes called the **fundamental rectangle**.) We draw the fundamental rectangle and the asymptotes with a dashed line because they are not part of the curve.

EXAMPLE 1 Graph $\dfrac{x^2}{25} - \dfrac{y^2}{16} = 1$.

The equation has the form $\dfrac{x^2}{a^2} - \dfrac{y^2}{b^2} = 1$, so it is a horizontal hyperbola. $a^2 = 25$, so $a = 5$; $b^2 = 16$, so $b = 4$. Since the hyperbola is horizontal, it has vertices at $(a, 0)$ and $(-a, 0)$ or $(5, 0)$ and $(-5, 0)$.

To draw the asymptotes, we construct a fundamental rectangle with corners at $(5, 4)$, $(5, -4)$, $(-5, 4)$, and $(-5, -4)$. We draw extended diagonal lines through the rectangle as the asymptotes. We construct each branch of the curve so that it passes through a vertex and gets closer to the asymptotes as it moves away from the origin.

PRACTICE PROBLEM 1

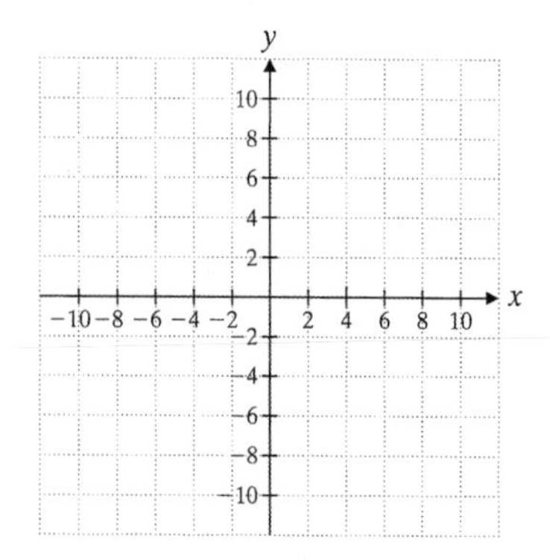

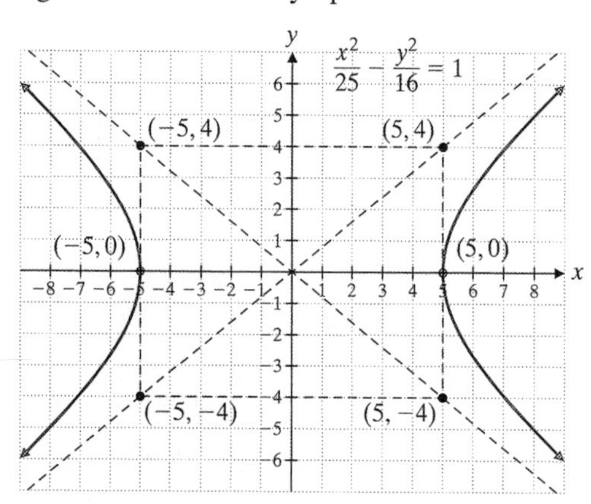

Practice Problem 1 Graph $\dfrac{x^2}{16} - \dfrac{y^2}{25} = 1$.

EXAMPLE 2 Graph $4y^2 - 7x^2 = 28$.

To find the vertices and asymptotes, we must rewrite the equation in standard form. Divide each term by 28.

$$\frac{4y^2}{28} - \frac{7x^2}{28} = \frac{28}{28}$$

$$\frac{y^2}{} - \frac{x^2}{} = 1$$

Thus, we have the standard form of a vertical hyperbola with center at the origin. Here $b^2 = 7$, so $b = \sqrt{7}$; $a^2 = 4$, so $a = 2$. The hyperbola has vertices at $(0, \sqrt{7})$ and $(0, -\sqrt{7})$. The fundamental rectangle has corners at $(2, \sqrt{7})$, $(2, -\sqrt{7})$, $(-2, \sqrt{7})$, and $(-2, -\sqrt{7})$. To aid us in graphing, we measure the distance $\sqrt{7}$ as approximately 2.6.

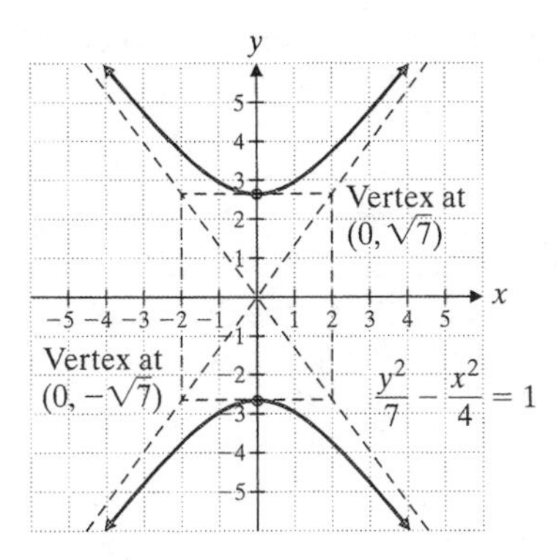

Practice Problem 2 Graph $y^2 - 4x^2 = 4$.

PRACTICE PROBLEM 2

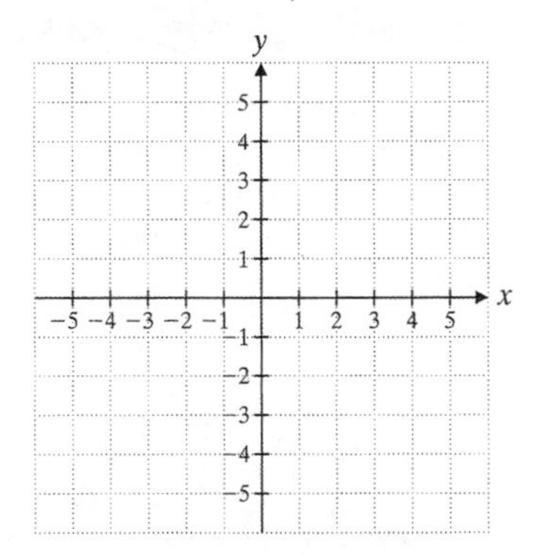

Graphing Calculator

Graphing Hyperbolas

Graph on your graphing calculator the hyperbola in Example 2 using

$$y_1 = \frac{\sqrt{28 + 7x^2}}{2}$$

and

$$y_2 = -\frac{\sqrt{28 + 7x^2}}{2}.$$

Do you see how we obtained y_1 and y_2?

2 Graphing a Hyperbola Whose Center Is at (h, k)

If a hyperbola does not have its center at the origin but is shifted h units to the right or left and k units up or down, its equation is one of the following:

Standard Form of the Equation of a Hyperbola with Center at (h, k)

Let a and b be any positive real numbers. A horizontal hyperbola with center at (h, k) and vertices $(h - a, k)$ and $(h + a, k)$ has the equation

$$\frac{(x - h)^2}{a^2} - \frac{(y - k)^2}{b^2} = 1.$$

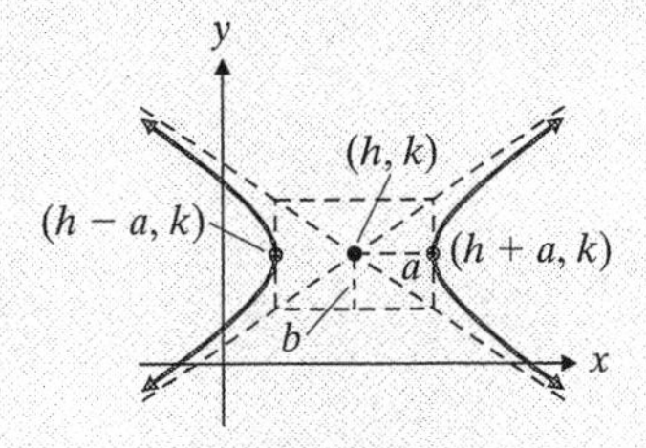

Horizontal Hyperbola

A vertical hyperbola with center at (h, k) and vertices $(h, k + b)$ and $(h, k - b)$ has the equation

$$\frac{(y - k)^2}{b^2} - \frac{(x - h)^2}{a^2} = 1.$$

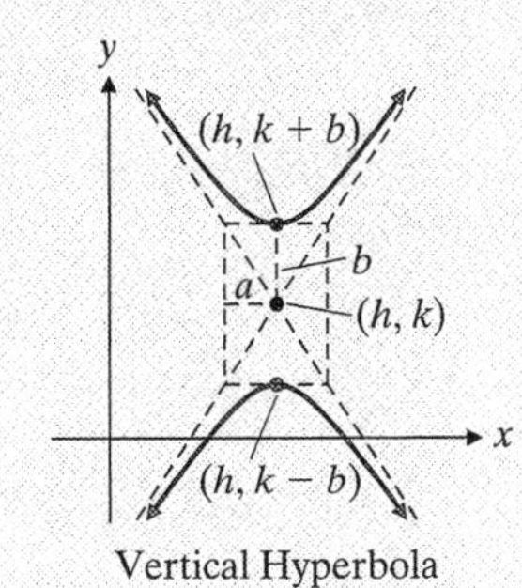

Vertical Hyperbola

Graphing Calculator

Exploration

Graph the hyperbola in Example 3 using

$$y_1 = 5 + \sqrt{\frac{4(x-4)^2}{9} - 4}$$

and

$$y_2 = 5 - \sqrt{\frac{4(x-4)^2}{9} - 4}.$$

Do you see how we obtained y_1 and y_2?

EXAMPLE 3 Graph $\frac{(x-4)^2}{9} - \frac{(y-5)^2}{4} = 1$.

The center is at (4, 5), and the hyperbola is horizontal. We have $a = 3$ and $b = 2$, so the vertices are $(4 \pm 3, 5)$, or (7, 5) and (1, 5). We can sketch the hyperbola more readily if we can draw a fundamental rectangle. Using (4, 5) as the center, we construct a rectangle $2a$ units wide and $2b$ units high. We then draw and extend the diagonals of the rectangle. The extended diagonals are the asymptotes for the branches of the hyperbola.

In this example, since $a = 3$ and $b = 2$, we draw a rectangle $2a = 6$ units wide and $2b = 4$ units high with a center at (4, 5). We draw extended diagonals through the rectangle. From the vertex at (7, 5), we draw a branch of the hyperbola opening to the right. From the vertex at (1, 5), we draw a branch of the hyperbola opening to the left. The graph of the hyperbola is shown.

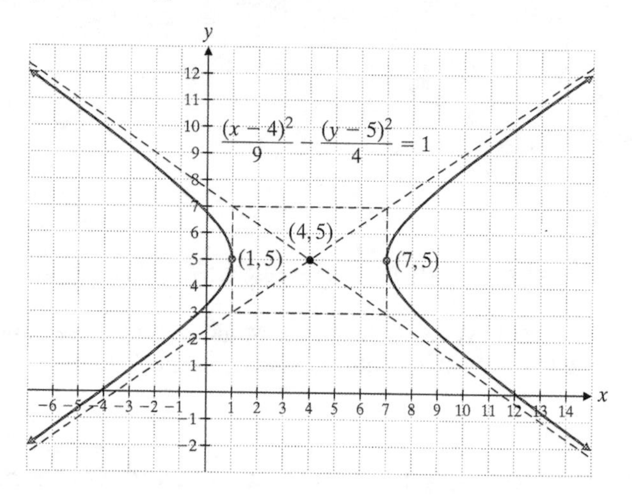

Practice Problem 3 Graph $\frac{(y+2)^2}{9} - \frac{(x-3)^2}{16} = 1$.

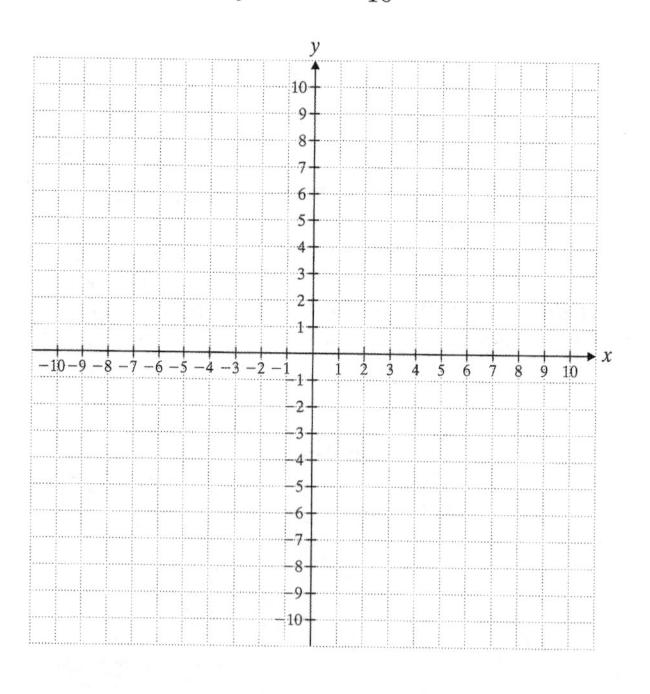

9.4 Exercises

Verbal and Writing Skills

1. What is the standard form of the equation of a horizontal hyperbola centered at the origin?

2. What are the vertices of the hyperbola $\frac{y^2}{9} - \frac{x^2}{4} = 1$? Is this a horizontal hyperbola or a vertical hyperbola? Why?

3. Explain in your own words how you would draw the graph of the hyperbola $\frac{x^2}{16} - \frac{y^2}{4} = 1$.

4. Explain how you determine the center of the hyperbola $\frac{(x-2)^2}{4} - \frac{(y+3)^2}{25} = 1$?

Find the vertices and graph each hyperbola. If the equation is not in standard form, write it as such.

5. $\frac{x^2}{4} - \frac{y^2}{25} = 1$

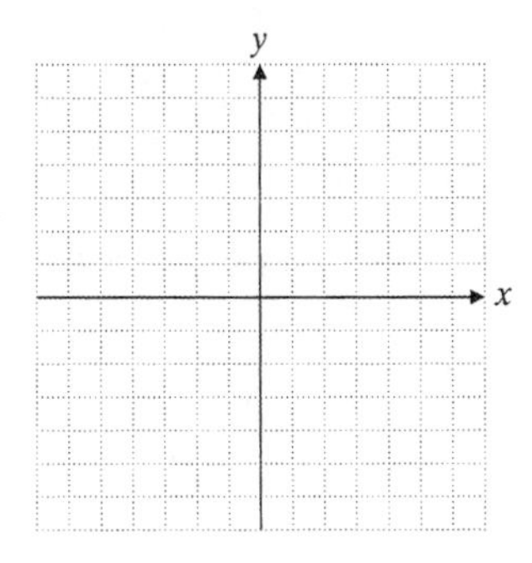

6. $\frac{x^2}{9} - \frac{y^2}{36} = 1$

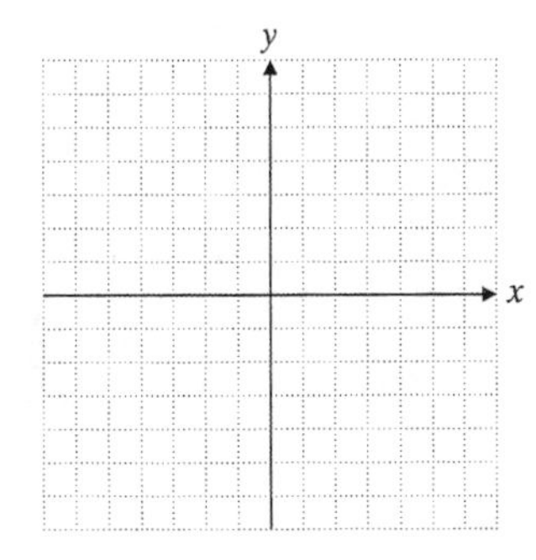

7. $\frac{y^2}{36} - \frac{x^2}{49} = 1$

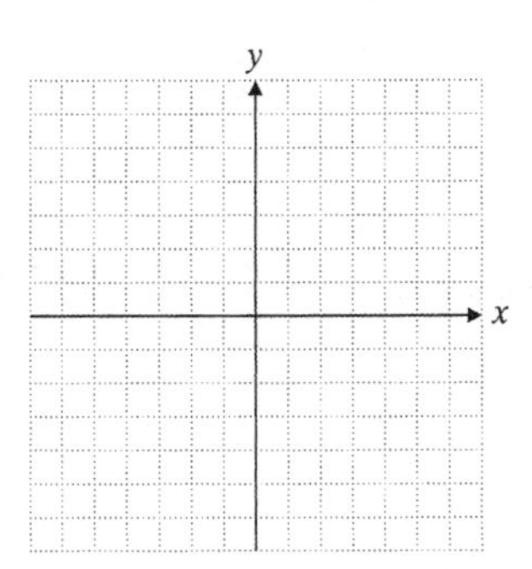

8. $\frac{y^2}{64} - \frac{x^2}{25} = 1$

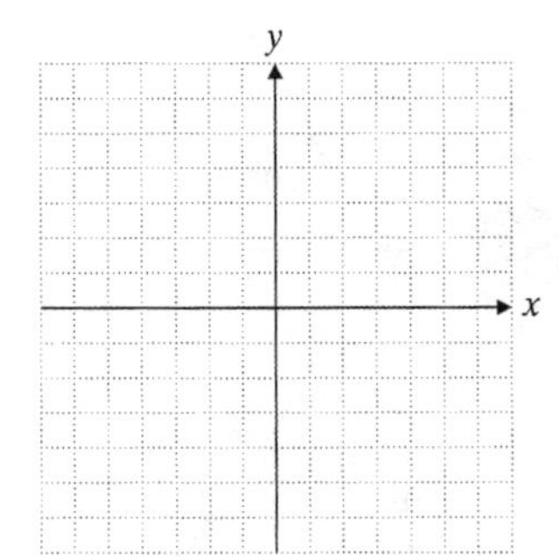

9. $4x^2 - y^2 = 64$

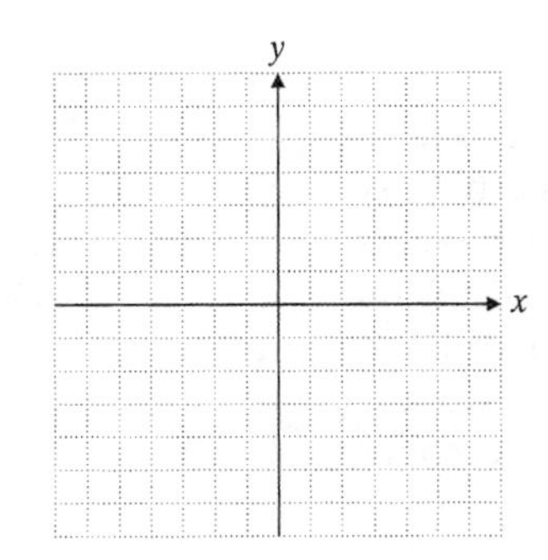

10. $49x^2 - 16y^2 = 196$

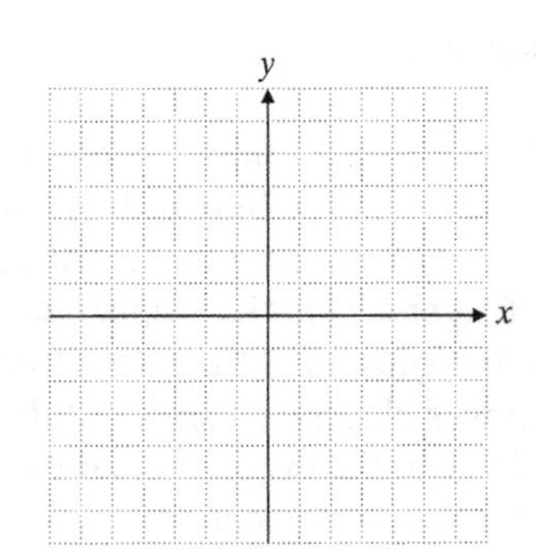

11. $8x^2 - y^2 = 16$

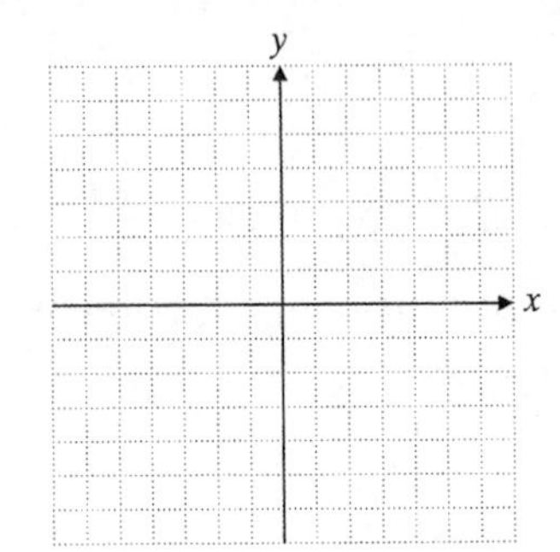

12. $12x^2 - y^2 = 36$

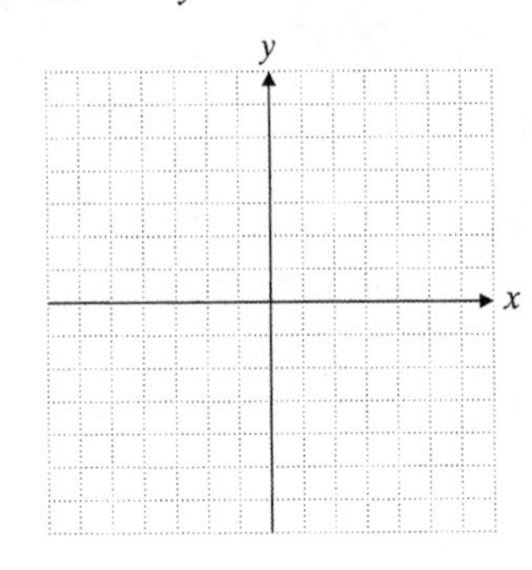

13. $2y^2 - 3x^2 = 54$

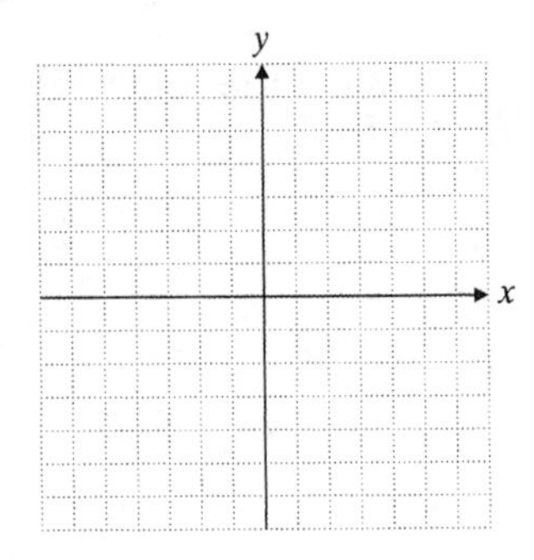

14. $8x^2 - 3y^2 = 24$

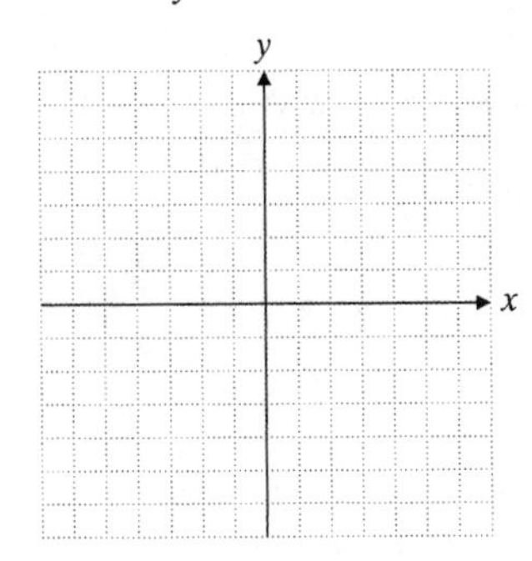

Find the equation of the hyperbola with center at the origin and with the following vertices and asymptotes.

15. Vertices at $(3, 0)$ and $(-3, 0)$; asymptotes $y = \frac{4}{3}x$, $y = -\frac{4}{3}x$

16. Vertices at $(2, 0)$ and $(-2, 0)$; asymptotes $y = \frac{3}{2}x$, $y = -\frac{3}{2}x$

17. Vertices at $(0, 7)$ and $(0, -7)$; asymptotes $y = \frac{7}{3}x$, $y = -\frac{7}{3}x$

18. Vertices at $(0, 6)$ and $(0, -6)$; asymptotes $y = \frac{6}{5}x$, $y = -\frac{6}{5}x$

Applications

19. Some comets have an orbit that is hyperbolic in shape with the Sun at the focus of the hyperbola. A comet is heading toward the Earth but then veers off as shown in the graph. It comes within 120 million miles of the Earth. As it travels into the distance, it moves closer and closer to the line $y = 3x$ with the Earth at the origin. Find the equation that describes the path of the comet.

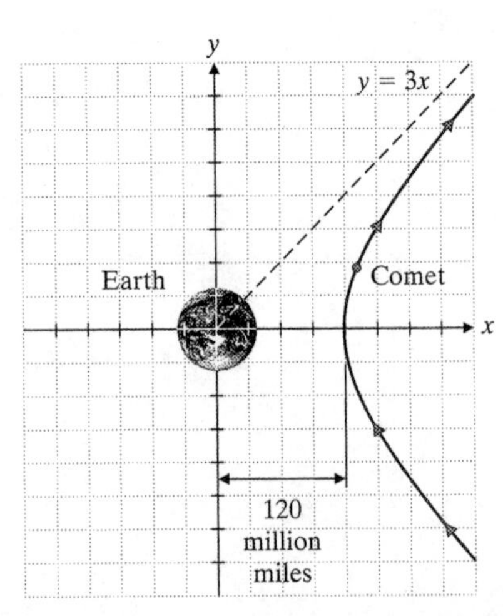

Scale on x axis: each square is 30 million miles.
Scale on y axis: each square is 90 million miles.

20. A rocket following the hyperbolic path shown in the graph turns rapidly at (4, 0) and then moves closer and closer to the line $y = \frac{2}{3}x$ as the rocket gets farther from the tracking station at the origin. Find the equation that describes the path of the rocket if the center of the hyperbola is at (0, 0).

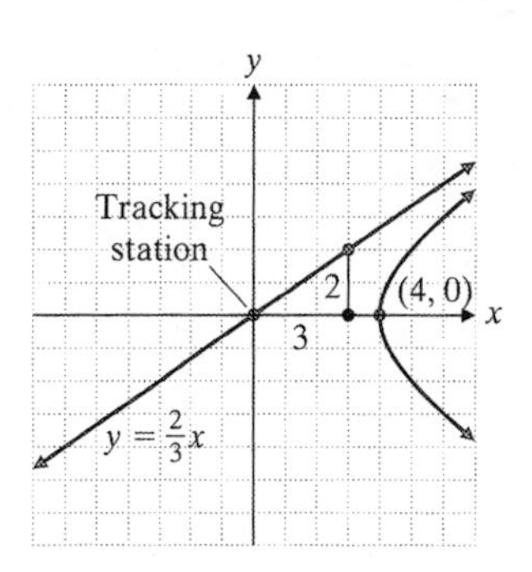

Find the center and then graph each hyperbola. Draw the axes on the grid at a convenient location. You may want to use a scale other than 1 square = 1 unit.

21. $\frac{(x-6)^2}{25} - \frac{(y-4)^2}{49} = 1$

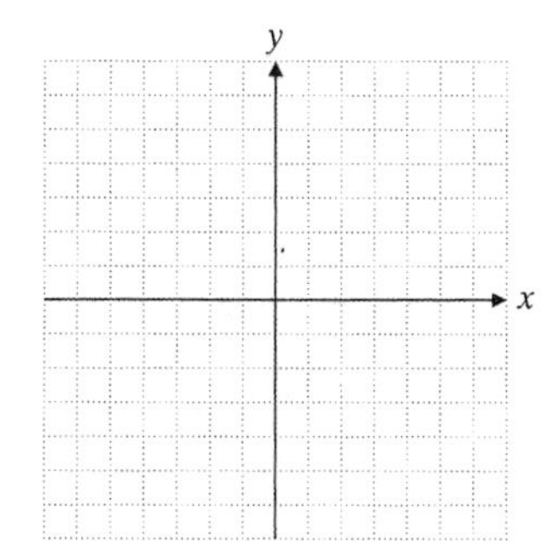

22. $\frac{(x-7)^2}{16} - \frac{(y-5)^2}{25} = 1$

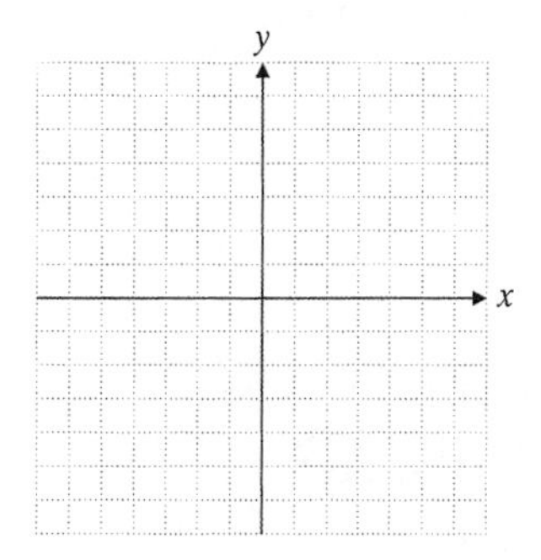

23. $\frac{(y+2)^2}{36} - \frac{(x+1)^2}{81} = 1$

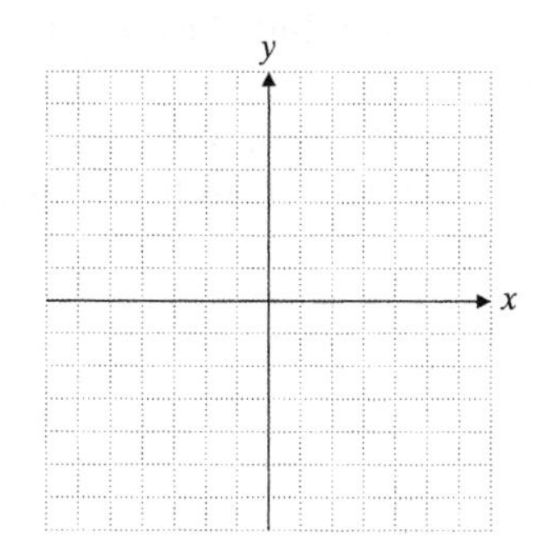

24. $\frac{(y+1)^2}{49} - \frac{(x+3)^2}{81} = 1$

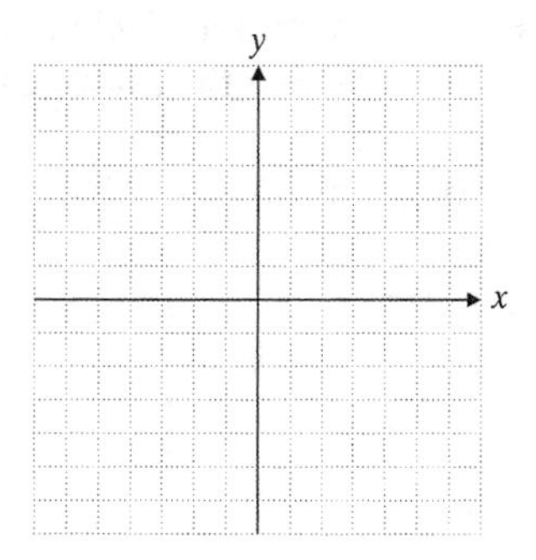

Find the center and the two vertices for each of the following hyperbolas.

25. $\frac{(x+6)^2}{7} - \frac{y^2}{3} = 1$

26. $\frac{x^2}{5} - \frac{(y+3)^2}{10} = 1$

27. A hyperbola's center is not at the origin. Its vertices are (5, 0) and (5, 14); one asymptote is $y = \frac{7}{5}x$. Find the equation of the hyperbola.

28. A hyperbola's center is not at the origin. Its vertices are (4, −14) and (4, 0). One asymptote is $y = -\frac{7}{4}x$. Find the equation of the hyperbola.

Optional Graphing Calculator Problems

29. For the hyperbola $8x^2 - y^2 = 16$, if $x = 3.5$, what are the two values of y?

30. For the hyperbola $x^2 - 12y^2 = 36$, if $x = 8.2$, what are the two values of y?

Cumulative Review Problems

Factor completely.

31. $12x^2 + x - 6$

32. $2x^3 - 54$

Combine.

33. $\dfrac{3}{x^2 - 5x + 6} + \dfrac{2}{x^2 - 4}$

34. $\dfrac{2x}{5x^2 + 9x - 2} - \dfrac{3}{5x - 1}$

35. A Connecticut FM radio station claims that a minimum of 104,755 songs are played every year.

(a) Determine the number of songs played daily. (Assume that it is not a leap year.)

(b) How much time would be left over each day for advertisements, news, sports, interviews, syndicated shows, and DJ chatter if the average song lasts 4 minutes?

(c) What percentage of the airtime is music?

36. A school's hockey team is giving the coach a retirement gift that costs \$240. On the day that the captain of the team was collecting money, four hockey players were absent. He collected an equal amount from each player present and purchased the gift. Later the team captain said that if everyone had been present to chip in, each person would have contributed \$2 less. How many people actually contributed? How many people in total are on the hockey team?

37. In 2000, approximately 2.1 billion pencils were produced in the United States by domestic manufacturers. If you add to this the number of pencils that were imported, then each American used ten pencils during the year. If there were 274 million people in the United States in 2000, how many pencils were imported to the United States in that year? *Source:* U.S. Department of Commerce

38. It is estimated that the number of pencils produced in the United States will increase by 5% from 2000 to 2005. During that time the number of imported pencils will increase by 750 million. If these figures hold true, what percent of all the pencils used in the United States in 2005 will have been imported? *Source:* U.S. Department of Commerce

9.5 Nonlinear Systems of Equations

 Solving a Nonlinear System by the Substitution Method

Student Learning Objectives

After studying this section, you will be able to:

 Solve a nonlinear system by the substitution method.

 Solve a nonlinear system by the addition method.

Any equation that is of second degree or higher is a **nonlinear equation**. In other words, the equation is not a straight line (which is what the word *nonlinear* means) and can't be written in the form $y = mx + b$. A **nonlinear system of equations** includes at least one nonlinear equation.

The most frequently used method for solving a nonlinear system is the method of substitution. This method works especially well when one equation of the system is linear. A sketch can often be used to verify the solution(s).

EXAMPLE 1 Solve the following nonlinear system and verify your answer with a sketch.

$$x + y - 1 = 0 \quad (1)$$
$$y - 1 = x^2 + 2x \quad (2)$$

We'll use the substitution method.

$$y = -x + 1 \quad (3) \qquad \text{Solve for } y \text{ in equation (1).}$$
$$(-x + 1) - 1 = x^2 + 2x \qquad \text{Substitute (3) into equation (2).}$$
$$-x + 1 - 1 = x^2 + 2x$$
$$0 = x^2 + 3x \qquad \text{Solve the resulting quadratic equation.}$$
$$0 = x(x + 3)$$
$$x = 0 \quad \text{or} \quad x = -3$$

Now substitute the values for x in the equation $y = -x + 1$.

For $x = -3$: $\quad y = -(-3) + 1 = +3 + 1 = 4$

For $x = 0$: $\quad y = -(0) + 1 = +1 = 1$

Thus, the solutions of the system are $(-3, 4)$ and $(0, 1)$.

To sketch the system, we see that equation (2) describes a parabola. We can rewrite it in the form

$$y = x^2 + 2x + 1 = (x + 1)^2.$$

This is a parabola opening upward with its vertex at $(-1, 0)$. Equation (1) can be written as $y = -x + 1$, which is a straight line with slope $= -1$ and y-intercept $(0, 1)$.

A sketch shows the two graphs intersecting at $(0, 1)$ and $(-3, 4)$. Thus, the solutions are verified.

Practice Problem 1 Solve the system.

$$\frac{x^2}{4} - \frac{y^2}{4} = 1$$
$$x + y + 1 = 0$$

Graphing Calculator

Solving Nonlinear Systems

Use a graphing calculator to solve the following system. Round your answers to the nearest tenth.

$$30x^2 + 256y^2 = 7680$$
$$3x + y - 40 = 0$$

First we will need to obtain the equations

$$y_1 = \frac{\sqrt{7680 - 30x^2}}{16},$$

$$y_2 = -\frac{\sqrt{7680 - 30x^2}}{16},$$

and

$$y_3 = 40 - 3x$$

and graph them to approximate the solutions. Be sure that your window includes enough of the graphs to find the points of intersection.

EXAMPLE 2 Solve the following nonlinear system and verify your answer with a sketch.

$$y - 2x = 0 \quad (1)$$

$$\frac{x^2}{4} + \frac{y^2}{9} = 1 \quad (2)$$

$$y = 2x \quad (3) \qquad \text{Solve equation (1) for } y.$$

$$\frac{x^2}{4} + \frac{(2x)^2}{9} = 1 \qquad \text{Substitute (3) into equation (2).}$$

$$\frac{x^2}{4} + \frac{4x^2}{9} = 1 \qquad \text{Simplify.}$$

$$36\left(\frac{x^2}{4}\right) + 36\left(\frac{4x^2}{9}\right) = 36(1) \qquad \text{Clear the fractions.}$$

$$9x^2 + 16x^2 = 36$$

$$25x^2 = 36$$

$$x^2 = \frac{36}{25}$$

$$x = \pm\sqrt{\frac{36}{25}}$$

$$x = \pm\frac{6}{5} = \pm 1.2$$

For $x = +1.2$: $\quad y = 2(1.2) = 2.4.$

For $x = -1.2$: $\quad y = 2(-1.2) = -2.4.$

Thus, the solutions are $(1.2, 2.4)$ and $(-1.2, -2.4)$.

We recognize $\frac{x^2}{4} + \frac{y^2}{9} = 1$ as an ellipse with center at the origin and vertices $(0, 3)$, $(0, -3)$, $(2, 0)$, and $(-2, 0)$. When we rewrite $y - 2x = 0$ as $y = 2x$, we recognize it as a straight line with slope 2 passing through the origin. The sketch shows that the points of intersection at $(1.2, 2.4)$ and $(-1.2, -2.4)$ seem reasonable.

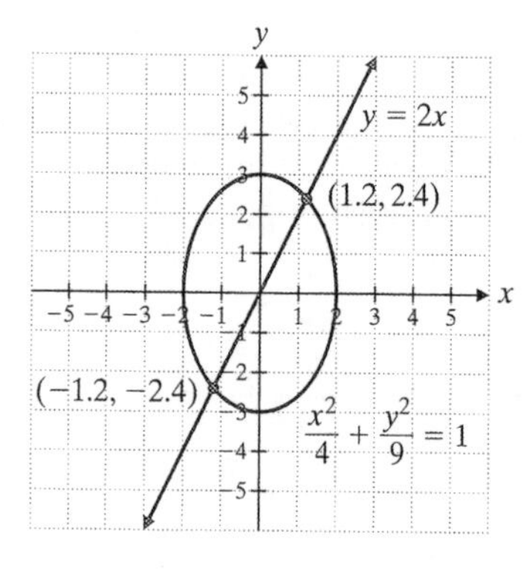

PRACTICE PROBLEM 2

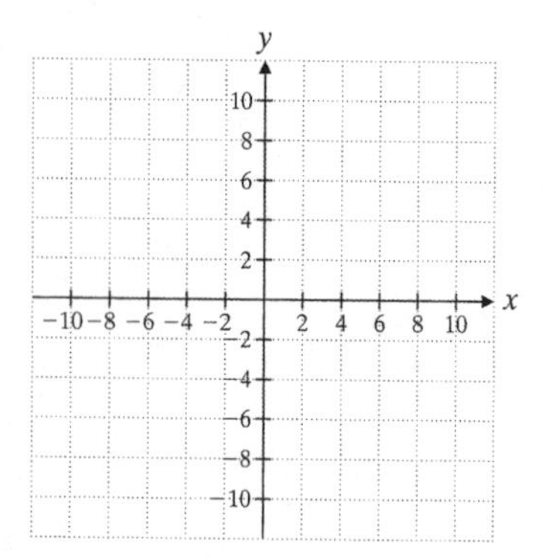

Practice Problem 2 Solve the system. Verify your answer with a sketch.

$$2x - 9 = y$$

$$xy = -4$$

 Solving a Nonlinear System by the Addition Method

Sometimes a system may be solved more readily by adding the equations together. It should be noted that some systems have no solution.

EXAMPLE 3 Solve.

$$4x^2 + y^2 = 1 \quad (1)$$
$$x^2 + 4y^2 = 1 \quad (2)$$

Although we could use the substitution method, it is easier to use the addition method because neither equation is linear.

$$\begin{array}{rl} -16x^2 - 4y^2 &= -4 \\ x^2 + 4y^2 &= 1 \\ \hline -15x^2 &= -3 \end{array}$$

Multiply equation (1) by −4 and add to equation (2).

$$x^2 = \frac{-3}{-15}$$

$$x^2 = \frac{1}{5}$$

$$x = \pm\sqrt{\frac{1}{5}}$$

If $x = +\sqrt{\frac{1}{5}}$, then $x^2 = \frac{1}{5}$. Substituting this value into equation (2) gives

$$\frac{1}{5} + 4y^2 = 1$$

$$4y^2 = \frac{4}{5}$$

$$y^2 = \frac{1}{5}$$

$$y = \pm\sqrt{\frac{1}{5}}$$

Similarly, if $x = -\sqrt{\frac{1}{5}}$, then $y = \pm\sqrt{\frac{1}{5}}$. It is important to determine exactly how many solutions a nonlinear system of equations actually has. In this case, we have four solutions. When x is negative, there are two values for y. When x is positive, there are two values for y. If we rationalize each expression, the four solutions are $\left(\frac{\sqrt{5}}{5}, \frac{\sqrt{5}}{5}\right)$, $\left(\frac{\sqrt{5}}{5}, -\frac{\sqrt{5}}{5}\right)$, $\left(-\frac{\sqrt{5}}{5}, \frac{\sqrt{5}}{5}\right)$, and $\left(-\frac{\sqrt{5}}{5}, -\frac{\sqrt{5}}{5}\right)$.

Practice Problem 3 Solve the system.

$$x^2 + y^2 = 12$$
$$3x^2 - 4y^2 = 8$$

9.5 Exercises

Solve each of the following systems by the substitution method. Graph each equation to verify that the answer seems reasonable.

1. $y^2 = 4x$
$y = x + 1$

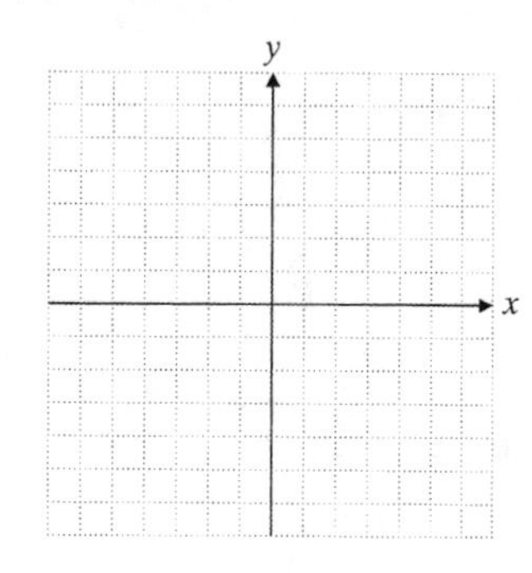

2. $y^2 = 2x$
$y = -2x + 2$

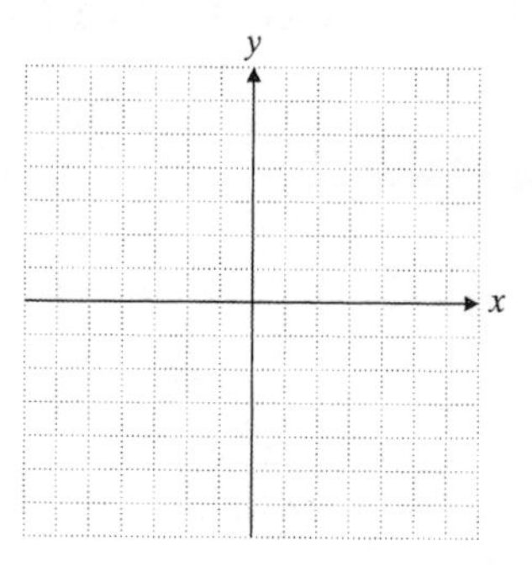

3. $y - 4x = 0$
$4x^2 + y^2 = 20$

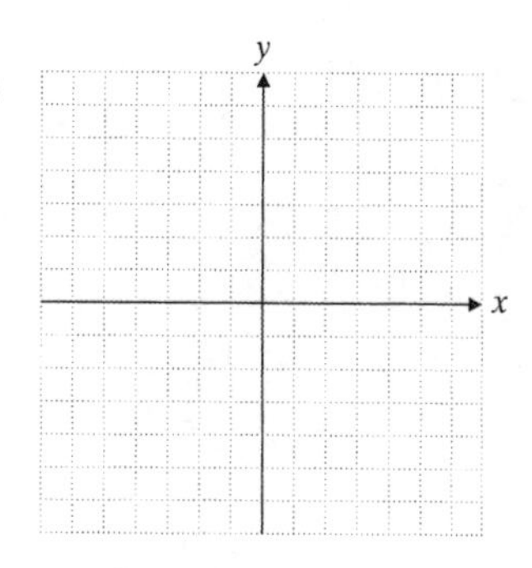

4. $x + 2y = 0$
$x^2 + 4y^2 = 32$

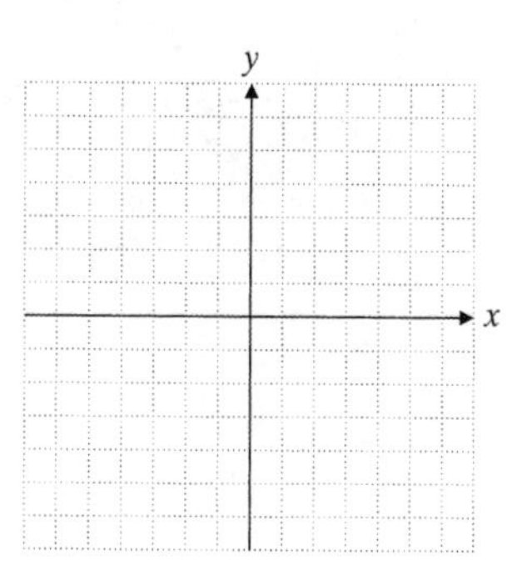

Solve each of the following systems by the substitution method.

5. $\frac{x^2}{1} - \frac{y^2}{3} = 1$
$x + y = 1$

6. $y = (x + 3)^2 - 3$
$2x - y + 2 = 0$

7. $x^2 + y^2 - 25 = 0$
$3y = x + 5$

8. $x^2 + y^2 - 9 = 0$
$2y = 3 - x$

9. $x^2 + 2y^2 = 4$
$y = -x + 2$

10. $2x^2 + 3y^2 = 27$
$y = x + 3$

11. $\dfrac{x^2}{4} - \dfrac{y^2}{4} = 1$
$x + y - 4 = 0$

12. $\dfrac{x^2}{3} - \dfrac{y^2}{12} = 1$
$y = -x$

Solve each of the following systems by the addition method. Graph each equation to verify that the answer seems reasonable.

13. $2x^2 - 5y^2 = -2$
$3x^2 + 2y^2 = 35$

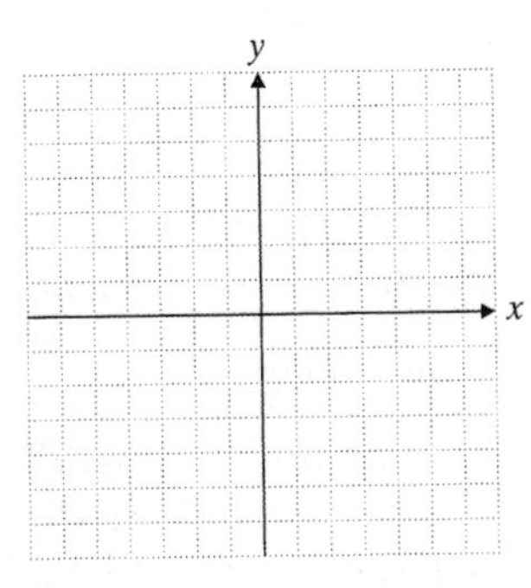

14. $2x^2 - 3y^2 = 5$
$3x^2 + 4y^2 = 16$

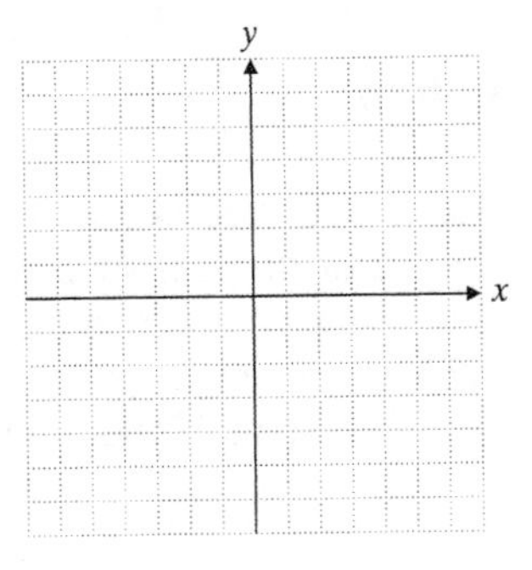

Solve each of the following systems by the addition method.

15. $2x^2 + 5y^2 = 42$
$3x^2 + 4y^2 = 35$

16. $x^2 + 2y^2 = 12$
$2x^2 + 3y^2 = 21$

17. $x^2 + 2y^2 = 8$
$x^2 - y^2 = 1$

18. $x^2 + 4y^2 = 13$
$x^2 - 3y^2 = -8$

Mixed Practice

Solve each of the following systems by any appropriate method. If there is no real number solution, so state.

19. $x^2 + y^2 = 7$
$\dfrac{x^2}{3} - \dfrac{y^2}{9} = 1$

20. $x^2 + 2y^2 = 4$
$x^2 + y^2 = 4$

21. $xy = 3$
$3y = 3x + 6$

22. $xy = 5$
$2y = 2x + 8$

23. $xy = 8$
$y = x + 2$

24. $xy = 1$
$3x - y + 2 = 0$

25. $x + y = 5$
$x^2 + y^2 = 4$

26. $x^2 + y^2 = 0$
$x - y = 6$

Applications

▲ **27.** The area of a rectangle is 540 square meters. The diagonal of the rectangle is 39 meters long. Find the dimensions of the rectangle.
Hint: Let x and y represent the length and width and write a system of two nonlinear equations.

28. In an experiment with a laser beam, the path of a particle orbiting a central object is described by the equation $\frac{x^2}{49} + \frac{y^2}{36} = 1$, where x and y are measured in centimeters from the center of the object. The laser beam follows the path $y = 2x - 6$. Find the coordinates at which the laser will illuminate the particle (that is, when the particle will pass through the beam).

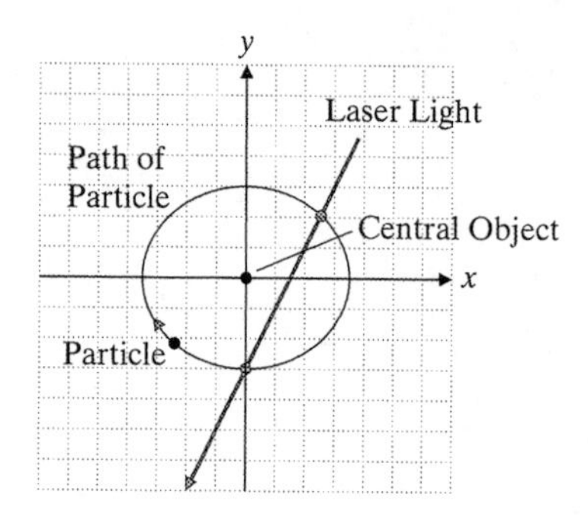

29. The outline of the Earth can be considered a circle with a radius of approximately 4000 miles. Thus, if we say that the center of the Earth is located at $(0, 0)$, then an equation for this circle is $x^2 + y^2 = 16{,}000{,}000$. Suppose that an incoming meteor is approaching the Earth in a hyperbolic path. The equation describing the meteor's path is $25{,}000{,}000x^2 - 9{,}000{,}000y^2 = 2.25 \times 10^{14}$. Will the meteor strike the Earth? Why or why not? If so, locate the point (x, y) where the meteor will strike the Earth. Assume that x and y are both positive. Round your answer to three significant digits.

30. Suppose that a second incoming meteor is approaching the Earth in a hyperbolic path. The equation for this second meteor's path is $16{,}000{,}000x^2 - 25{,}000{,}000y^2 = 4.0 \times 10^{14}$. Will the second meteor strike the Earth? Why or why not? If so, locate the point (x, y) where the meteor will strike the Earth. Assume that x and y are both positive. Round your answer to three significant digits.

Cumulative Review Problems

Simplify.

31. $\dfrac{6x^4 - 24x^3 - 30x^2}{3x^3 - 21x^2 + 30x}$

Divide.

32. $(3x^3 - 8x^2 - 33x - 10) \div (3x + 1)$

33. Highway patrol officers can trap speeders by various methods. Between two certain points on a back country road in a small town in Georgia, a speeding Audi travels 55 miles per hour for 5 seconds. What is the legal speed limit there if at this speed, a car driving between those two points requires 11 seconds?

34. Ricardo is the staff accountant for a CD-ROM factory. He has determined that his monthly profit factor is given by the expression $11.5n - 290{,}000$. Here n represents the number of CD-ROMs manufactured each month. The profit this month was \$1,187,750. How many CD-ROMs were produced this month?

Putting Your Skills to Work

Locating the Center of an Earthquake Mathematically

When an earthquake occurs, it is most important for scientists to locate its center. This location is known as the epicenter. Using a seismograph, scientists can calculate the distance from a recording station to the epicenter of the earthquake. If two recording stations at different locations measure an earthquake, scientists can use this data to narrow the possible locations of the epicenter of two places.

Now let us suppose that there is a scientific recording station for earthquake activity at location A and another at location B. Scientists read their instruments and determine that the epicenter of an earthquake is a miles from station a and b miles from station B. The two possible locations for the epicenter are at L and M on the diagram.

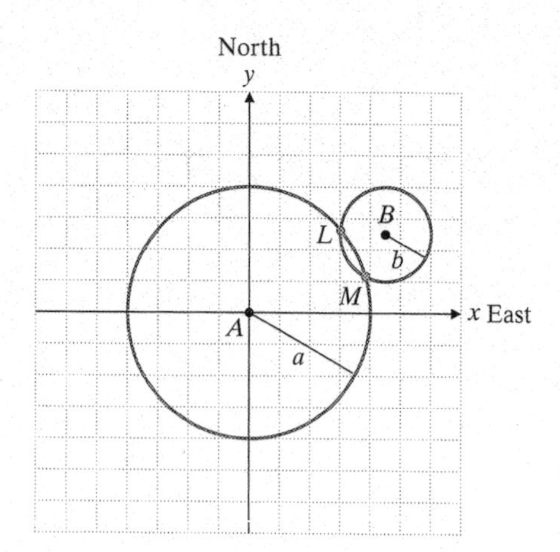

Problems for Individual Investigation and Analysis

1. Scientists determine that the epicenter of a strong earthquake is 40 miles away from station A. Station B is located 50 miles east and 30 miles north of station A. The epicenter is located 20 miles from station B. If station A is located at $(0, 0)$, determine the locations of L and M to the nearest tenth of a mile. Express your answers in terms of how many miles north and how many miles east of station A the possible locations of the epicenter are.

2. A second earthquake is recorded. This time a new recording station B is selected to make measurements. Station B is located 60 miles east and 20 miles north of station A, which is located at $(0, 0)$. The epicenter is located 50 miles from station A and 30 miles from station B. Determine the locations of L and M to the nearest tenth of a mile. Express your answers in terms of how many miles north and how many miles east of station A the possible locations of the epicenter are.

Problems for Group Investigation and Cooperative Learning

3. Station A (located at $(0, 0)$) determines that the epicenter of a strong earthquake is 30 miles away. Station B, located 40 miles east and 30 miles north of station A, determines that the epicenter is located 25 miles away. Station C, 30 miles east and 20 miles south of station A, determines that the epicenter is 27.55 miles away. Determine the location of the epicenter to the nearest tenth of a mile. Express your answer in terms of how many miles north, south, east, and/or west from station A the epicenter is.

4. During the night a stronger earthquake is recorded. Stations A and B from Exercise 3 record the quake. Station C is not operational. A new station D, which is 10 miles east and 15 miles north of station A, is used. This time the epicenter of the quake is recorded as 50 miles from station A, 40 miles from station B, and 45.92 miles from station D. Determine the location of the epicenter to the nearest tenth of a mile. Express your answer in terms of how many miles north, south, east, and/or west from station A the epicenter is.

Internet Connections

Netsite: http://www.prenhall.com/tobey_intermediate

Site: Earthquake Information of USGS

At this site you will find the exact locations of the epicenters of recent earthquakes, measured not only in terms of longitude and latitude but also in terms of depth beneath the Earth's surface. More than 4000 earthquake-measuring stations across the world are now available to record these events.

5. Find the number of major earthquakes (magnitude 7.0 or greater) that have occurred each year for the years 1960 to 1985. Construct a graph where x is the year and y is the number of major earthquakes recorded around the world for the years 1970 to 1985. Is the graph linear or nonlinear? Why? Did the number of major earthquakes around the world increase or decrease during this period?

6. Find the number of major earthquakes (magnitude 7.0 or greater) that have occurred each year for the years 1985 to 2000. Construct a graph where x is the year and y is the number of major earthquakes recorded around the world for the years 1985 to 2000. Is the graph linear or nonlinear? Why? Did the number of major earthquakes around the world increase or decrease during this period?

Math in the Media

Flexible Seating

In the late edition of *The New York Times* September 1999 article "Currents: Stadium; A Dome Where the Seats Move," it was reported that the Saitama Dome, north of Tokyo, will have a section of 10,000 seats, plus accompanying plumbing, lighting, concessions, and ceiling sections, that move on trucklike devices called "bogeys."

The dome will be able to seat 30,000 as a stadium, or 20,000 as an arena, or seat as few as 5,000.

Apply your knowledge from the chapter by taking the role of a design team member and answering the questions that follow.

EXERCISES

Suppose you are the member of the design team for a new stadium with moveable seating. You are doodling on graph paper. You draw a circle with center at (0, 0) and radius R. You want to "stretch" it into an ellipse with a center at (0, 0), with a distance R from the center to the y-intercepts, and with a distance R + M from the center to the x-intercepts. You plot the circle and the ellipse on the same axes and label the appropriate segments as R and M. You know that the area of the circle is $A_{circle} = [\pi]R^2$ *and the area of the ellipse is* $A_{ellipse} = [\pi]R(R + M)$.

1. If you wanted the ellipse to have 3 times the area of the circle, what would the distance M have to be, expressed in terms of R?

2. If you wanted the ellipse to have F times the area of the circle, what would the distance M be, expressed in terms of R?

3. If you drew a square around the circle (touching the circle at four points) and a rectangle around the ellipse (touching the ellipse at four points), how much more area would the rectangle contain than the square, expressed in terms of M and R?

Chapter 9 Organizer

Topic	Procedure	Examples
Distance between two points, p. 489.	The distance d between points (x_1, y_1) and (x_2, y_2) is $d = \sqrt{(x_2 - x_1)^2 + (y_2 - y_1)^2}$.	Find the distance between $(-6, -3)$ and $(5, -2)$. $d = \sqrt{[5 - (-6)]^2 + [-2 - (-3)]^2}$ $= \sqrt{(5 + 6)^2 + (-2 + 3)^2}$ $= \sqrt{121 + 1}$ $= \sqrt{122}$
Standard form of the equation of a circle, p. 490.	The standard form of the equation of a circle with center at (h, k) and radius r is $(x - h)^2 + (y - k)^2 = r^2$.	Graph $(x - 3)^2 + (y + 4)^2 = 16$. Center at $(h, k) = (3, -4)$. Radius $= 4$.
Standard form of the equation of a vertical parabola, p. 497.	The equation of a vertical parabola with its vertex at (h, k) can be written in the form $y = a(x - h)^2 + k$. It opens upward if $a > 0$ and downward if $a < 0$.	Graph $y = \frac{1}{2}(x - 3)^2 + 5$. $a = \frac{1}{2}$, so parabola opens upward. Vertex at $(h, k) = (3, 5)$. If $x = 0$, $y = 9.5$.
Standard form of the equation of a horizontal parabola, p. 499.	The equation of a horizontal parabola with its vertex at (h, k) can be written in the form $x = a(y - k)^2 + h$. It opens to the right if $a > 0$ and to the left if $a < 0$.	Graph $x = \frac{1}{3}(y + 2)^2 - 4$. $a = \frac{1}{3}$, so parabola opens to the right. Vertex at $(h, k) = (-4, -2)$. If $x = 0$, $y = -2 - 2\sqrt{3} \approx -5.5$ and $y = -2 + 2\sqrt{3} \approx 1.5$.

<table>
<tr><th>Topic</th><th>Procedure</th><th>Examples</th></tr>
<tr>
<td>Standard form of the equation of an ellipse with center at (0, 0), p. 507.</td>
<td>An ellipse with center at the origin has the equation

$$\frac{x^2}{a^2} + \frac{y^2}{b^2} = 1,$$

where $a > 0$ and $b > 0$.

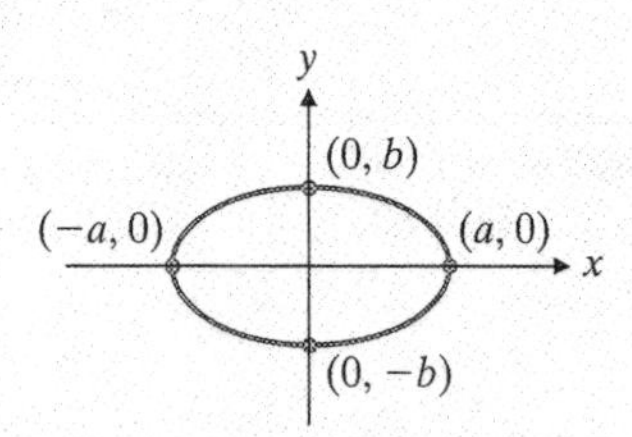

</td>
<td>Graph $\frac{x^2}{16} + \frac{y^2}{4} = 1.$

$a^2 = 16, a = 4; b^2 = 4, b = 2$

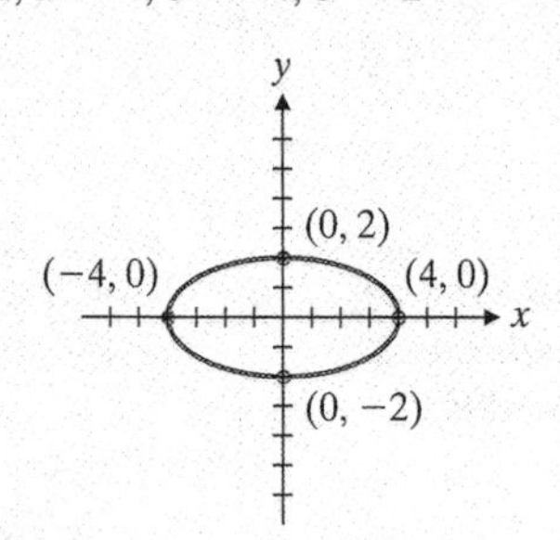

</td>
</tr>
<tr>
<td>Standard form of an ellipse with center at (h, k), p. 509.</td>
<td>An ellipse with center at (h, k) has the equation

$$\frac{(x-h)^2}{a^2} + \frac{(y-k)^2}{b^2} = 1,$$

where $a > 0$ and $b > 0$.

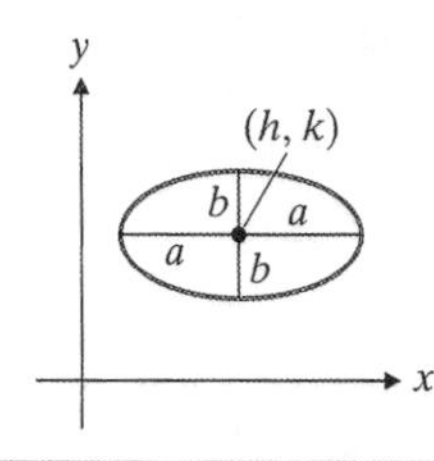

</td>
<td>Graph $\frac{(x+2)^2}{9} + \frac{(y+4)^2}{25} = 1.$

$(h, k) = (-2, -4); a = 3, b = 5$

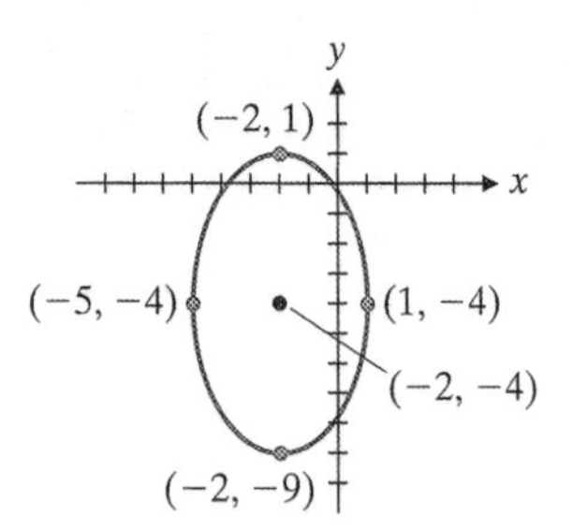

</td>
</tr>
<tr>
<td>Standard form of a horizontal hyperbola with center at (0, 0), p. 515.</td>
<td>Let a and b be positive real numbers. A horizontal hyperbola with center at the origin and vertices $(a, 0)$ and $(-a, 0)$ has the equation

$$\frac{x^2}{a^2} - \frac{y^2}{b^2} = 1$$

and asymptotes

$$y = \pm \frac{b}{a}x.$$

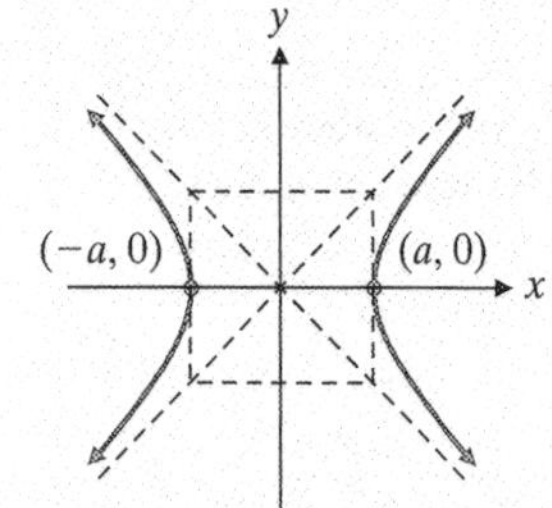

</td>
<td>Graph $\frac{x^2}{25} - \frac{y^2}{9} = 1.$

$a = 5, b = 3$

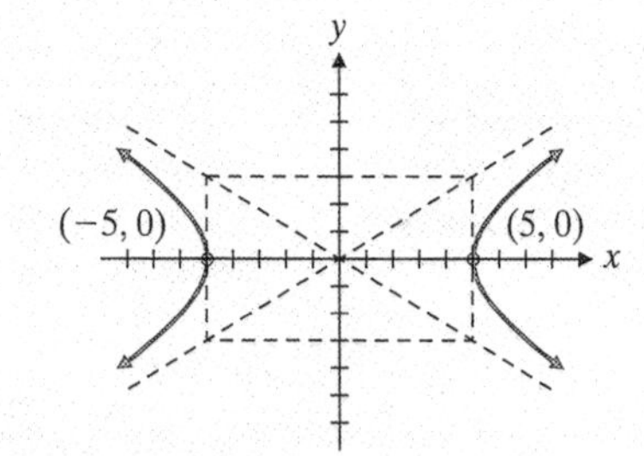

</td>
</tr>
<tr>
<td>Standard form of a vertical hyperbola with center at (0, 0), p. 515.</td>
<td>Let a and b be positive real numbers. A vetical hyperbola with center at the origin and vertices $(0, b)$ and $(0, -b)$ has the equation

$$\frac{y^2}{b^2} - \frac{x^2}{a^2} = 1$$

and asymptotes

$$y = \pm \frac{b}{a}x.$$

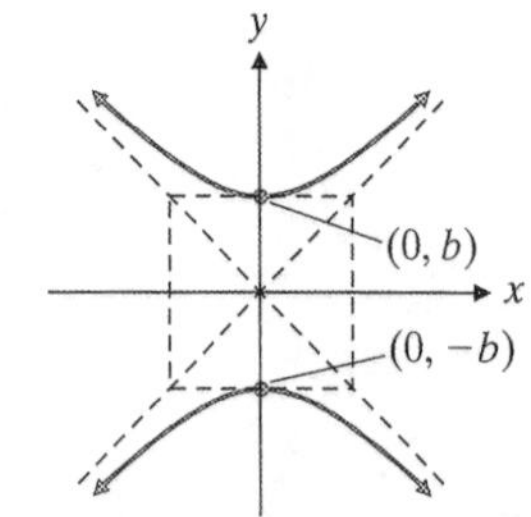

</td>
<td>Graph $\frac{y^2}{9} - \frac{x^2}{4} = 1.$

$b = 3, a = 2$

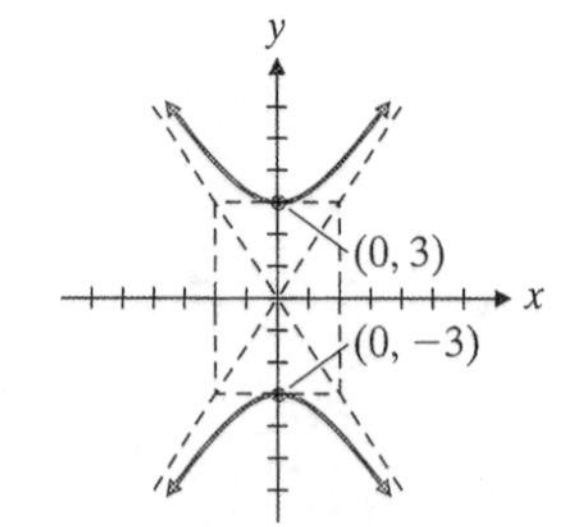

</td>
</tr>
</table>

Topic	Procedure	Examples
Standard form of a horizontal hyperbola with center at (h, k), p. 517.	Let a and b be positive real numbers. A horizontal hyperbola with center at (h, k) and vertices $(h - a, k)$ and $(h + a, k)$ has the equation $\frac{(x-h)^2}{a^2} - \frac{(y-k)^2}{b^2} = 1.$ 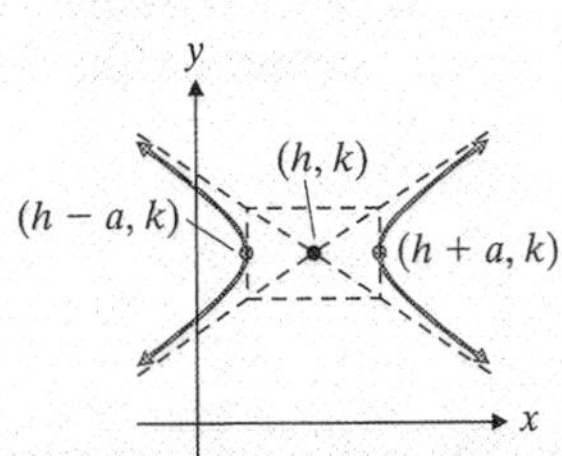	Graph $\frac{(x-2)^2}{4} - \frac{(y-3)^2}{25} = 1.$ Center at $(2, 3)$; $a = 2$, $b = 5$ 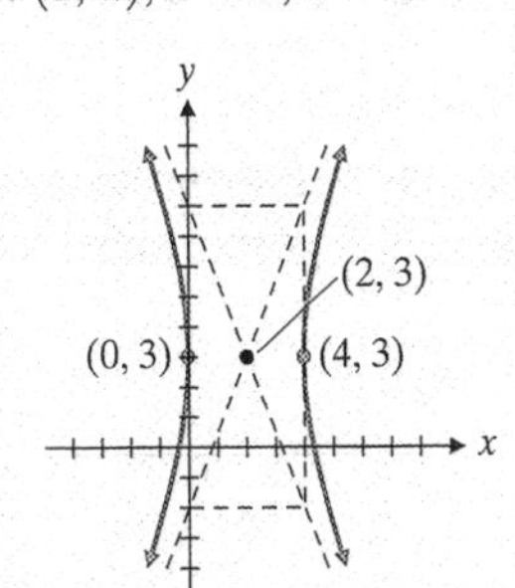
Standard form of a vertical hyperbola with center at (h, k), p. 517.	Let a and b be positive real numbers. A vertical hyperbola with center at (h, k) and vertices $(h, k + b)$ and $(h, k - b)$ has the equation $\frac{(y-k)^2}{b^2} - \frac{(x-h)^2}{a^2} = 1.$ 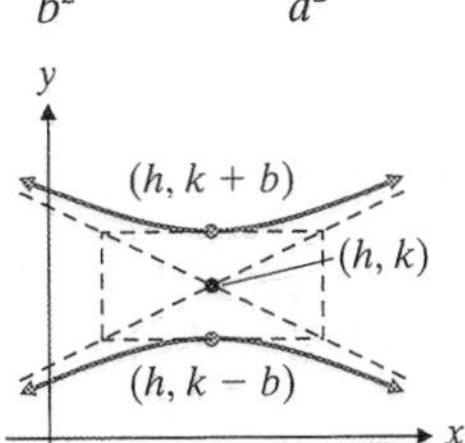	Graph $\frac{(y-5)^2}{9} - \frac{(x-4)^2}{4} = 1.$ Center at $(4, 5)$; $b = 3$, $a = 2$ 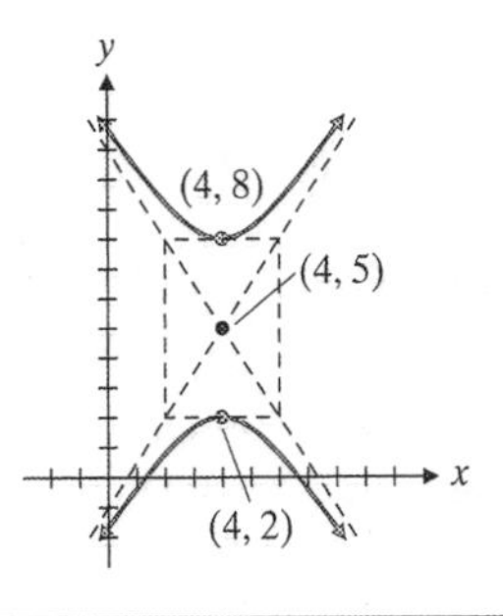
Nonlinear systems of equations, p. 523.	We can solve a nonlinear system by the substitution method or the addition method. In the addition method, we multiply one or more equations by a numerical value and then add them together so that one variable is eliminated. In the substitution method we solve one equation for one variable and substitute that expression into the other equation.	Solve by substitution. $2x^2 + y^2 = 18$ $xy = 4$ Solving the second equation for y, we have $y = \frac{4}{x}$. $2x^2 + \left(\frac{4}{x}\right)^2 = 18$ $2x^2 + \frac{16}{x^2} = 18$ $2x^4 + 16 = 18x^2$ $2x^4 - 18x^2 + 16 = 0$ $x^4 - 9x^2 + 8 = 0$ $(x^2 - 1)(x^2 - 8) = 0$ $x^2 - 1 = 0$ $\quad$ $x^2 - 8 = 0$ $x^2 = 1$ $\quad$ $x^2 = 8$ $x = \pm 1$ $\quad$ $x = \pm 2\sqrt{2}$ Since $xy = 4$, if $x = 1$, then $y = 4$. if $x = -1$, then $y = -4$. if $x = 2\sqrt{2}$, then $y = \sqrt{2}$. if $x = -2\sqrt{2}$, then $y = -\sqrt{2}$. The solutions are $(1, 4)$ $(-1, -4)$, $(2\sqrt{2}, \sqrt{2})$, and $(-2\sqrt{2}, -\sqrt{2})$.

Chapter 9 Review Problems

In Exercises 1 and 2, find the distance between the points.

1. $(10.5, -6)$ and $(7.5, -4)$

2. $(-7, 3)$ and $(-2, -1)$

3. Write in standard form the equation of a circle with center at $(-6, 3)$ and radius $\sqrt{15}$.

4. Write in standard form the equation of a circle with center at $(0, -7)$ and radius 5.

Rewrite each equation in standard form. Find the center and the radius of each circle.

5. $x^2 + y^2 - 6x - 8y + 3 = 0$

6. $x^2 + y^2 - 10x + 12y + 52 = 0$

Graph each parabola. Label its vertex and plot at least one intercept.

7. $x = \frac{1}{3}y^2$

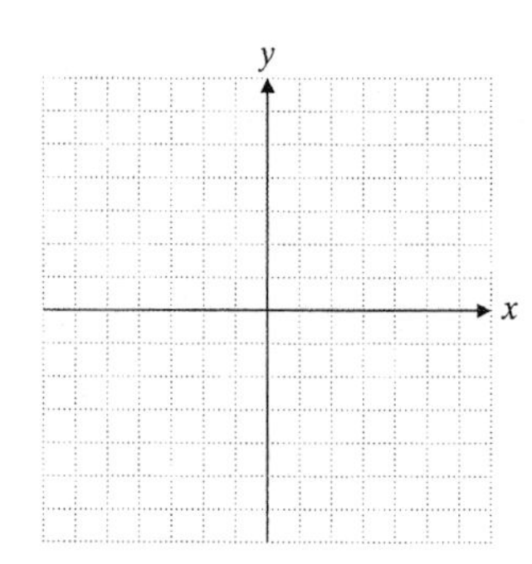

8. $x = \frac{1}{2}(y - 2)^2 + 4$

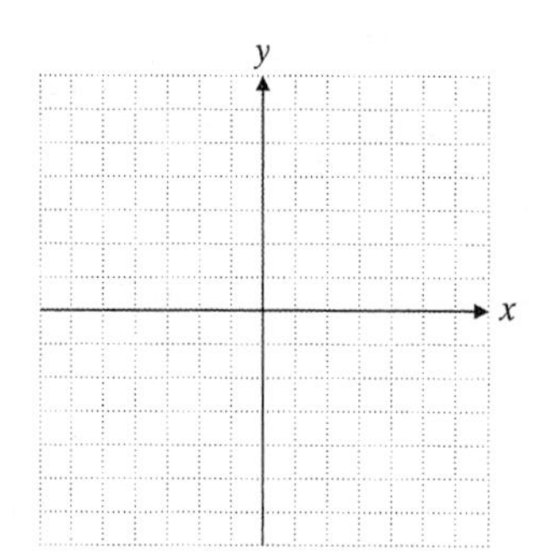

9. $y = -2(x + 1)^2$

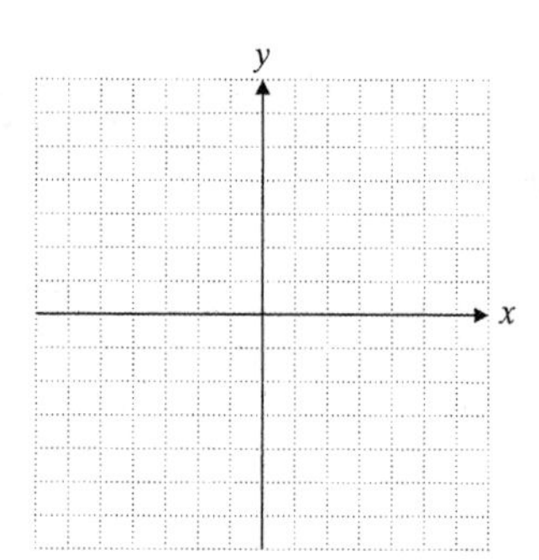

Rewrite each equation in standard form. Find the vertex and determine in which direction the parabola opens.

10. $x + 8y = y^2 + 10$

11. $x^2 + 6x = y - 4$

Graph each ellipse. Label its center and four other points.

12. $\dfrac{x^2}{\frac{1}{4}} + \dfrac{y^2}{1} = 1$

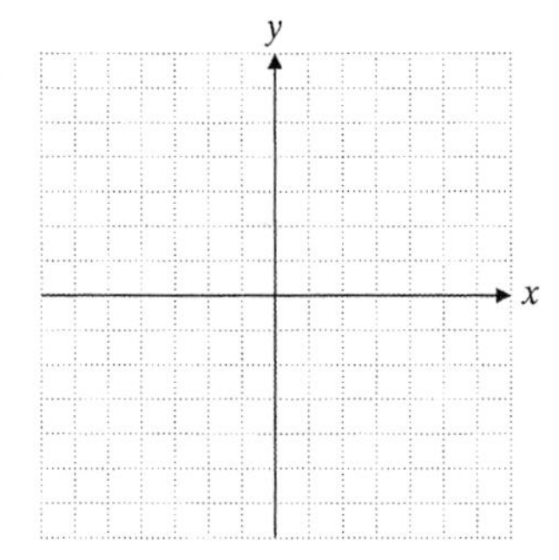

13. $16x^2 + y^2 - 32 = 0$

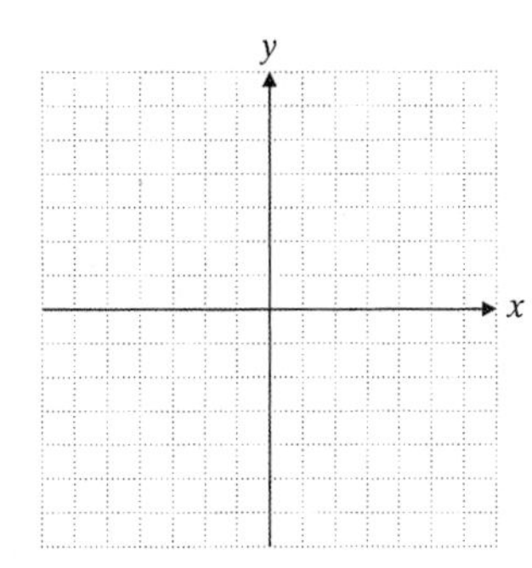

Determine the vertices and the center of each ellipse.

14. $\dfrac{(x+5)^2}{4} + \dfrac{(y+3)^2}{25} = 1$

15. $\dfrac{(x+1)^2}{9} + \dfrac{(y-2)^2}{16} = 1$

Find the center and vertices of each hyperbola and graph it.

16. $x^2 - 4y^2 - 16 = 0$

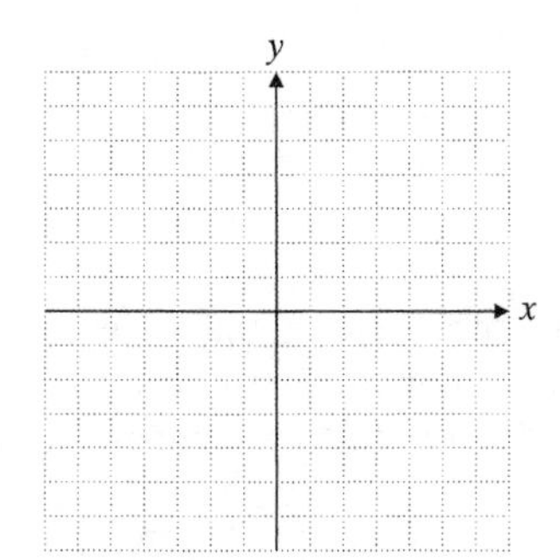

17. $9y^2 - 25x^2 = 225$

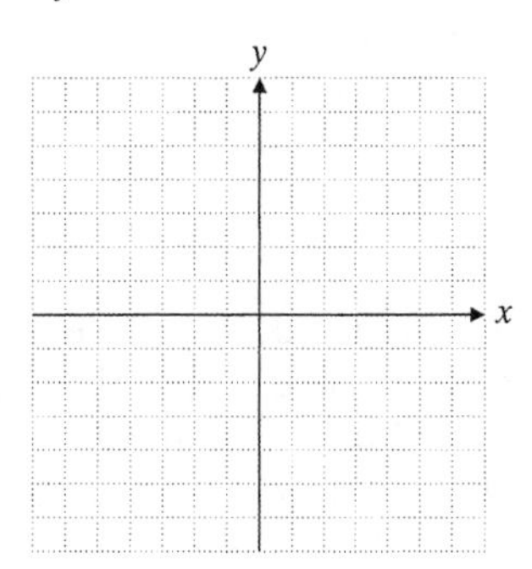

Determine the vertices and the center of each hyperbola.

18. $\dfrac{(x-2)^2}{4} - \dfrac{(y+3)^2}{25} = 1$

19. $9(y-2)^2 - (x+5)^2 - 9 = 0$

Solve each nonlinear system. If there is no real number solution, so state.

20. $x^2 + y = 9$
$y - x = 3$

21. $y^2 + x^2 = 3$
$x - 2y = 1$

22. $2x^2 + y^2 = 17$
$x^2 + 2y^2 = 22$

23. $xy = -2$
$x^2 + y^2 = 5$

24. $3x^2 - 4y^2 = 12$
$7x^2 - y^2 = 8$

25. $y = x^2 + 1$
$x^2 + y^2 - 8y + 7 = 0$

26. $2x^2 + y^2 = 18$
$xy = 4$

27. $y^2 - 2x^2 = 2$
$2y^2 - 3x^2 = 5$

28. $y^2 = \frac{1}{2}x$
$y = x - 1$

29. $y^2 = 2x$
$y = \frac{1}{2}x + 1$

Applications

30. The side view of a satellite dish on Jason and Wendy's house is shaped like a parabola. The signals that come from the satellite hit the surface of the dish and are then reflected to the point where the signal receiver is located. This point is the focus of the parabolic dish. The dish is 10 feet across at its opening and 4 feet deep at its center. How far from the center of the dish should the signal receiver be placed? Round your answer to the nearest hundredth.

31. The side view of an airport searchlight is shaped like a parabola. The center of the light source of the searchlight is located 2 feet from the base along the axis of symmetry, and the opening is 5 feet across. How deep should the searchlight be? Round your answer to the nearest hundredth.

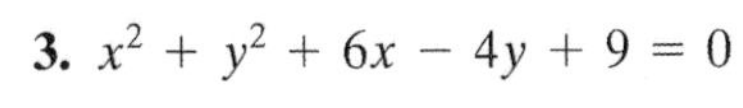

Chapter 9 Test

1. Find the distance between $(-6, -8)$ and $(-2, 5)$.

1. ______

Rewrite the equation in standard form. Find the center or vertex, plot at least one other point, identify the conic, and sketch the curve.

2. $y^2 - 6y - x + 13 = 0.$

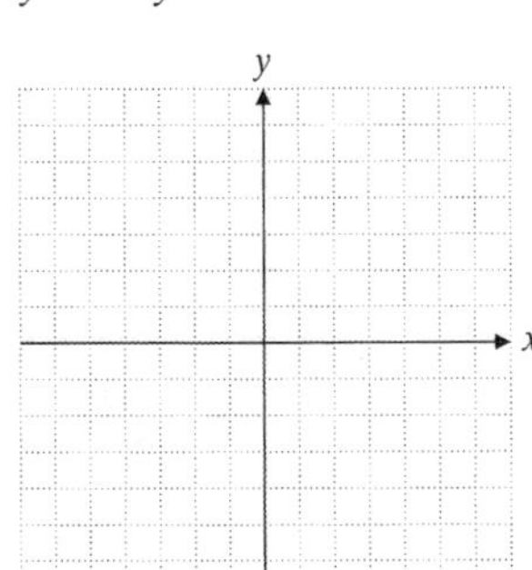

3. $x^2 + y^2 + 6x - 4y + 9 = 0$

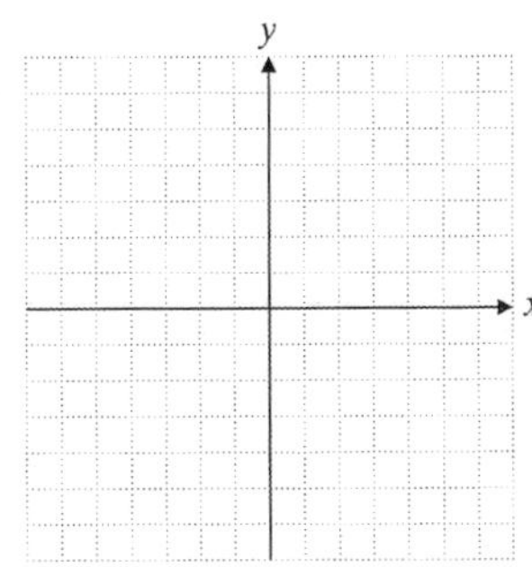

2. ______

3. ______

Identify and graph each conic section. Label the center and/or vertex as appropriate.

4. $\dfrac{x^2}{25} + \dfrac{y^2}{1} = 1$

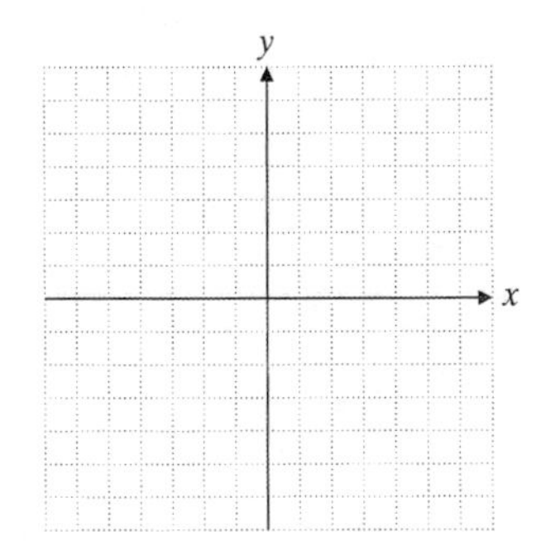

5. $\dfrac{x^2}{10} - \dfrac{y^2}{9} = 1$

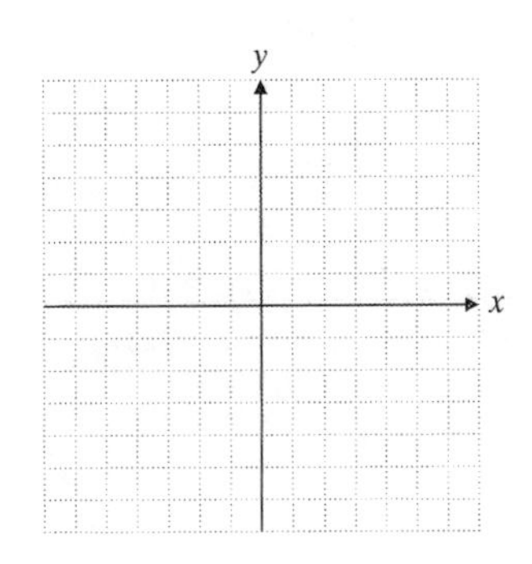

4. ______

5. ______

6. $y = -2(x + 3)^2 + 4$

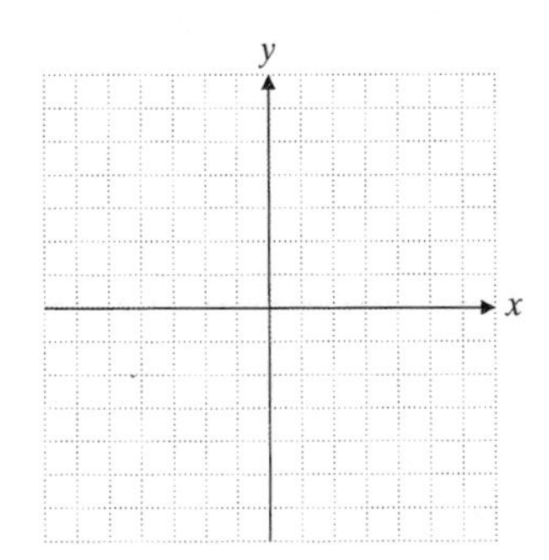

7. $\dfrac{(x + 2)^2}{16} + \dfrac{(y - 5)^2}{4} = 1$

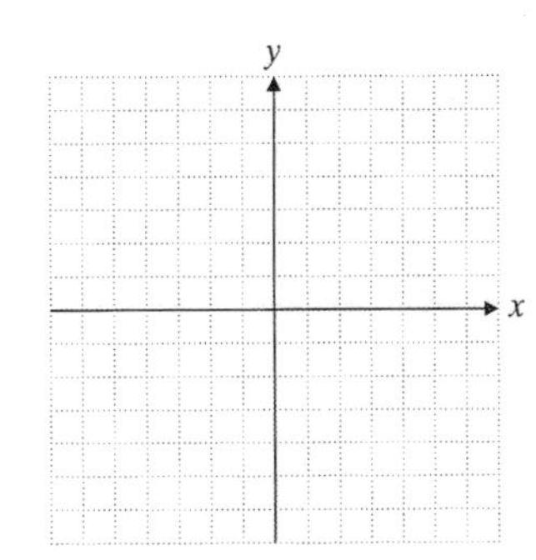

6. ______

7. ______

8. ______

9. ______

10. ______

11. ______

12. ______

13. ______

14. ______

15. ______

16. ______

8. $7y^2 - 7x^2 = 28$

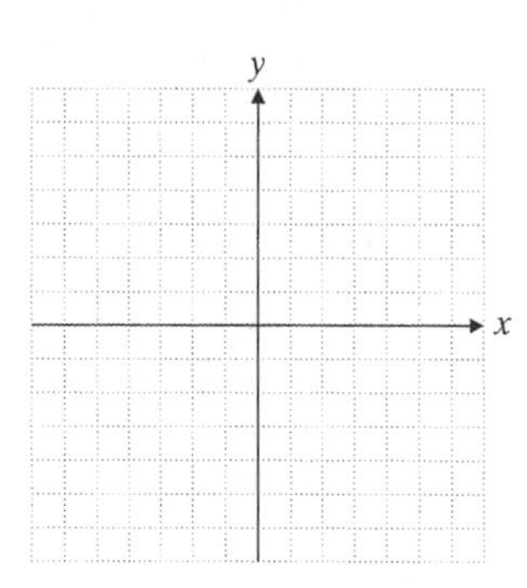

Find the standard form of the equation of each of the following:

9. Circle of radius $\sqrt{8}$ with its center at $(3, -5)$

10. Ellipse with its center at $(-4, -2)$ and vertices at $(-4, 1)$, $(-4, -5)$, $(-5, -2)$, and $(-3, -2)$

11. Parabola with its vertex at $(-7, 3)$ and that opens to the right. This parabola crosses the x-axis at $(2, 0)$. It is of the form $x = (y - k)^2 + h$.

12. Hyperbola with its center at $(6, 7)$ and that is vertical. This hyperbola has vertices of $(6, 14)$ and $(6, 0)$. The value of a for this hyperbola is 3.

Solve each nonlinear system.

13. $-2x + y = 5$
$x^2 + y^2 - 25 = 0$

14. $x^2 + y^2 = 9$
$y = x - 3$

15. $4x^2 + y^2 - 4 = 0$
$9x^2 - 4y^2 - 9 = 0$

16. $2x^2 + y^2 = 9$
$xy = -3$

Cumulative Test for Chapters 1–9

Approximately one-half of this test covers the content of Chapters 1–8. The remainder covers the content of Chapter 9.

1. Identify the property illustrated by the equation $5(-3) = -3(5)$.

2. Simplify: $2\{x - 3[x - 2(x + 1)]\}$

3. Evaluate: $3(4 - 6)^3 + \sqrt{25}$

4. Solve for p: $A = 3bt + prt$

5. Factor: $x^3 + 125$

6. Add: $\dfrac{3}{x - 4} + \dfrac{6}{x^2 - 16}$

7. Solve for x.

$$\frac{3}{2x + 3} = \frac{1}{2x - 3} + \frac{2}{4x^2 - 9}$$

8. Solve for (x, y, z).

$$\begin{aligned} 3x - 2y - 9z &= 9 \\ x - y + z &= 8 \\ 2x + 3y - z &= -2 \end{aligned}$$

9. Multiply and simplify. $(\sqrt{2} + \sqrt{3})(2\sqrt{6} - \sqrt{3})$

10. Simplify: $\sqrt{8x} + 3x\sqrt{50} - 4x\sqrt{32}$

Solve the following inequalities.

11. $2x + (4x - 1) > 6 - x$

12. $\dfrac{6(x - 4)}{5} \geq \dfrac{3(x + 2)}{4}$

13. Find the distance between $(6, -1)$ and $(-3, -4)$.

1. ____________________

2. ____________________

3. ____________________

4. ____________________

5. ____________________

6. ____________________

7. ____________________

8. ____________________

9. ____________________

10. ____________________

11. ____________________

12. ____________________

13. ____________________

14. ______________________

15. ______________________

16. ______________________

17. ______________________

18. ______________________

19. ______________________

20. ______________________

21. ______________________

Identify and graph each equation.

14. $y = -\frac{1}{2}(x + 2)^2 - 3$

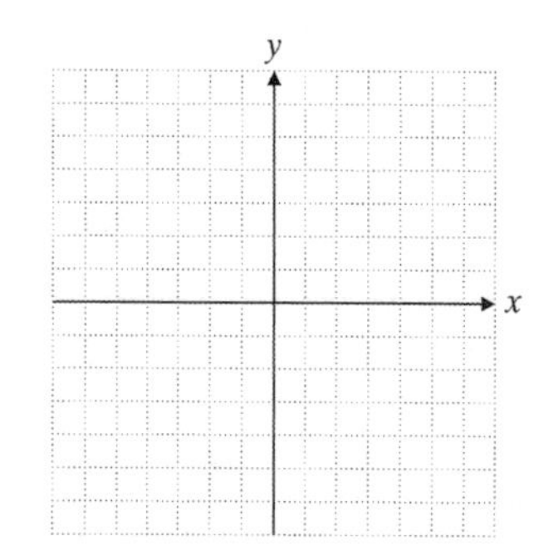

15. $25x^2 + 25y^2 = 125$

y

x

16. $16x^2 - 4y^2 = 64$

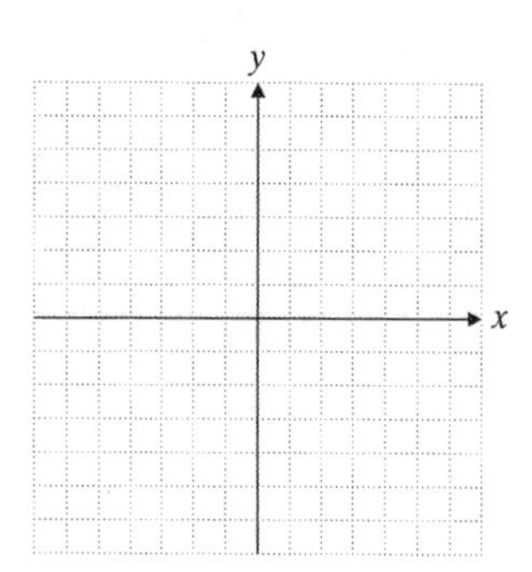

17. $\frac{(x-2)^2}{25} + \frac{(y-3)^2}{16} = 1$

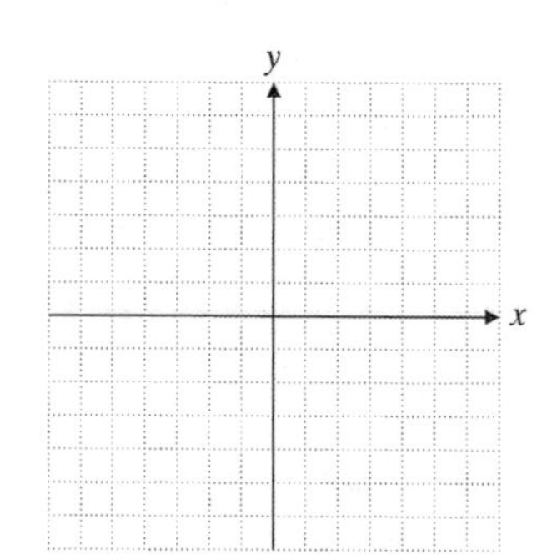

Solve the nonlinear system.

18. $y = 2x^2$
$y = 2x + 4$

19. $x^2 + 2y^2 = 16$
$4x^2 - y^2 = 24$

20. $x^2 + y^2 = 25$
$x - 2y = -5$

21. $xy = -15$
$4x + 3y = 3$

Solutions to Practice Problems

Chapter 5

5.1 Practice Problems

1. (a) $3x^5 - 6x^4 + x^2$

This is a trinomial of degree 5.

(b) $5x^2 + 2$

This is a binomial of degree 2.

(c) $3ab + 5a^2b^2 - 6a^4b$

This is a trinomial of degree 5.

(d) $16x^4y^6$

This is a monomial of degree 10.

2. $p(x) = 2x^4 - 3x^3 + 6x - 8$

(a) $p(-2) = 2(-2)^4 - 3(-2)^3 + 6(-2) - 8$
$= 2(16) - 3(-8) + 6(-2) - 8$
$= 32 + 24 - 12 - 8$
$= 36$

(b) $p(5) = 2(5)^4 - 3(5)^3 + 6(5) - 8$
$= 2(625) - 3(125) + 6(5) - 8$
$= 1250 - 375 + 30 - 8$
$= 897$

3. $(-7x^2 + 5x - 9) + (2x^2 - 3x + 5)$

We remove the parentheses and combine like terms.

$= -7x^2 + 2x^2 + 5x - 3x - 9 + 5$
$= -5x^2 + 2x - 4$

4. $(2x^2 - 14x + 9) - (-3x^2 + 10x + 7)$

We add the opposite of the second polynomial to the first polynomial.

$= (2x^2 - 14x + 9) + (3x^2 - 10x - 7)$
$= 2x^2 + 3x^2 - 14x - 10x + 9 - 7 = 5x^2 - 24x + 2$

5.
$$\begin{array}{r} 2x^2 - 3x + 1 \\ x^2 - 5x \\ \hline -10x^3 + 15x^2 - 5x \\ 2x^4 - 3x^3 + x^2 \\ \hline 2x^4 - 13x^3 + 16x^2 - 5x \end{array}$$

6. $(2x^2 - 3x + 1)(x^2 - 5x)$
$= (2x^2 - 3x + 1)(x^2) + (2x^2 - 3x + 1)(-5x)$
$= 2x^4 - 3x^3 + x^2 - 10x^3 + 15x^2 - 5x$
$= 2x^4 - 3x^3 - 10x^3 + x^2 + 15x^2 - 5x$
$= 2x^4 - 13x^3 + 16x^2 - 5x$

7. $(7x + 3)(2x - 5)$

$14x^2 - 35x + 6x - 15 = 14x^2 - 29x - 15$

8. $(5a - 2b)(3c - 4d)$

$15ac - 20ad - 6bc + 8bd$

9. (a) $(7x - 2y)(7x + 2y) = (7x)^2 - (2y)^2$
$= 49x^2 - 4y^2$

10. (a) $(4u + 5v)^2 = (4u)^2 + 2(4u)(5v) + (5v)^2 = 16u^2 + 40uv + 25v^2$

(b) $(7x^2 - 3y^2)^2 = (7x^2)^2 - 2(7x^2)(3y^2) + (3y^2)^2$
$= 49x^4 - 42x^2y^2 + 9y^4$

5.2 Practice Problems

1. $\dfrac{-16x^4 + 16x^3 + 8x^2 + 64x}{8x}$
$= \dfrac{-16x^4}{8x} + \dfrac{16x^3}{8x} + \dfrac{8x^2}{8x} + \dfrac{64x}{8x}$
$= -2x^3 + 2x^2 + x + 8$

2.
$$\begin{array}{r} 2x + 5 \\ 4x - 3 \overline{)\, 8x^2 + 14x - 14} \\ 8x^2 - 6x \\ \hline 20x - 14 \\ 20x - 15 \\ \hline 1 \end{array}$$

The answer is $2x + 5$ remainder 1 or $2x + 5 + \dfrac{1}{4x - 3}$.

3.
$$\begin{array}{r} 4x^2 - 6x + 9 \\ 2x + 3 \overline{)\, 8x^3 + 0x^2 + 0x + 27} \\ 8x^3 + 12x^2 \\ \hline -12x^2 + 0x \\ -12x^2 - 18x \\ \hline 18x + 27 \\ 18x + 27 \\ \hline 0 \end{array}$$

The answer is $4x^2 - 6x + 9$.

4.
$$\begin{array}{r} x^2 - 3x + 1 \\ x^2 + 0x - 1 \overline{)\, x^4 - 3x^3 + 0x^2 + 3x + 4} \\ x^4 - 0x^3 - x^2 \\ \hline -3x^3 + x^2 + 3x \\ -3x^3 - 0x^2 + 3x \\ \hline x^2 + 0x + 4 \\ x^2 + 0x - 1 \\ \hline 5 \end{array}$$

The answer is $x^2 - 3x + 1 + \dfrac{5}{x^2 - 1}$.

5.3 Practice Problems

1.
$$\begin{array}{r|rrrr} -3 & 1 & -3 & 4 & -5 \\ & & -3 & +18 & -66 \\ \hline & 1 & -6 & 22 & -71 \end{array}$$

The quotient is $x^2 - 6x + 22 + \dfrac{-71}{x + 3}$.

2.
$$\begin{array}{r|rrrrr} 3 & 2 & 0 & -1 & 5 & -12 \\ & & 6 & 18 & 51 & 168 \\ \hline & 2 & 6 & 17 & 56 & 156 \end{array}$$

The quotient is $2x^3 + 6x^2 + 17x + 56 + \dfrac{156}{x - 3}$.

3.
$$\begin{array}{r|rrrrr} 3 & 2 & -9 & 5 & 13 & -3 \\ & & 6 & -9 & -12 & 3 \\ \hline & 2 & -3 & -4 & 1 & 0 \end{array}$$

The quotient is $2x^3 - 3x^2 - 4x + 1$.

5.4 Practice Problems

1. (a) $19x^3 - 38x^2 = 19x^2(x - 2)$

(b) $100a^4 - 50a^2 = 50a^2(2a^2 - 1)$

2. (a) $21x^3 - 18x^2y + 24xy^2 = 3x(7x^2 - 6xy + 8y^2)$

(b) $12xy^2 - 14x^2y + 20x^2y^2 + 36x^3y$
$= 2xy(6y - 7x + 10xy + 18x^2)$

3. $9a^3 - 12a^2b^2 - 15a^4 = 3a^2(3a - 4b^2 - 5a^2)$

To check, we multiply.

$3a^2(3a - 4b^2 - 5a^2) = 9a^3 - 12a^2b^2 - 15a^4$

This is the original polynomial. It checks.

4. $7x(x + 2y) - 8y(x + 2y) - (x + 2y)$
$= (x + 2y)(7x - 8y - 1)$

5. $bx + 5by + 2wx + 10wy = b(x + 5y) + 2w(x + 5y)$
$= (x + 5y)(b + 2w)$

6. To factor $5x^2 - 12y + 4xy - 15x$, rearrange the terms. Then factor.

$5x^2 - 15x + 4xy - 12y$
$= 5x(x - 3) + 4y(x - 3)$
$= (x - 3)(5x + 4y)$

7. To factor $xy - 12 - 4x + 3y$, rearrange the terms. Then factor.

$xy - 4x + 3y - 12$
$= x(y - 4) + 3(y - 4)$
$= (y - 4)(x + 3)$

8. To factor $2x^3 - 15 - 10x + 3x^2$, rearrange the terms. Then factor.

$2x^3 - 10x + 3x^2 - 15$
$= 2x(x^2 - 5) + 3(x^2 - 5)$
$= (x^2 - 5)(2x + 3)$

5.5 Practice Problems

1. $x^2 - 10x + 21 = (x - 7)(x - 3)$

2. $x^2 - 13x - 48 = (x - 16)(x + 3)$

3. $x^4 + 9x^2 + 8 = (x^2 + 8)(x^2 + 1)$

4. (a) $a^2 + 2a - 48 = (a + 8)(a - 6)$
(b) $x^4 + 2x^2 - 15 = (x^2 + 5)(x^2 - 3)$

5. (a) $x^2 - 16xy + 15y^2 = (x - 15y)(x - y)$
(b) $x^2 + xy - 42y^2 = (x + 7y)(x - 6y)$

6. $4x^2 - 44x + 72 = 4(x^2 - 11x + 18) = 4(x - 9)(x - 2)$

7. Factor $3x^2 + 2x - 8$.

The grouping number is -24. Two numbers whose product is -24 and whose sum is 2 are 6 and -4.

$3x^2 + 6x - 4x - 8$
$= 3x(x + 2) - 4(x + 2)$
$= (x + 2)(3x - 4)$

8. Factor $10x^2 - 9x + 2$.

The grouping number is 20. Two numbers whose product is 20 and whose sum is -9 are -5 and -4.

$10x^2 - 5x - 4x + 2$
$= 5x(2x - 1) - 2(2x - 1)$
$= (2x - 1)(5x - 2)$

9. $9x^3 - 15x^2 - 6x = 3x(3x^2 - 5x - 2)$
$= 3x(3x^2 - 6x + x - 2)$
$= 3x[3x(x - 2) + 1(x - 2)]$
$= 3x(x - 2)(3x + 1)$

10. $8x^2 - 6x - 5 = (4x - 5)(2x + 1)$

11. $6x^4 + 13x^2 - 5 = (2x^2 + 5)(3x^2 - 1)$

5.6 Practice Problems

1. $x^2 - 9 = (x + 3)(x - 3)$

2. $64x^2 - 121y^2 = (8x + 11y)(8x - 11y)$

3. $49x^2 - 25y^4 = (7x + 5y^2)(7x - 5y^2)$

4. $7x^2 - 28 = 7(x^2 - 4) = 7(x + 2)(x - 2)$

5. $9x^2 - 30x + 25 = (3x - 5)^2$

6. $25x^2 - 70x + 49 = (5x - 7)^2$

7. $242x^2 + 88x + 8 = 2(121x^2 + 44x + 4)$
$= 2(11x + 2)^2$

8. (a) $49x^4 + 28x^2 + 4 = (7x^2 + 2)^2$
(b) $36x^4 + 84x^2y^2 + 49y^4 = (6x^2 + 7y^2)^2$

9. $8x^3 + 125y^3 = (2x + 5y)(4x^2 - 10xy + 25y^2)$

10. $64x^3 - 125y^3 = (4x - 5y)(16x^2 + 20xy + 25y^2)$

11. $27w^3 - 125z^6 = (3w - 5z^2)(9w^2 + 15wz^2 + 25z^4)$

12. $54x^3 - 16 = 2(27x^3 - 8)$
$= 2(3x - 2)(9x^2 + 6x + 4)$

13. $64a^6 - 1$

Use the difference of two squares first.

$(8a^3 + 1)(8a^3 - 1)$

Now use the formula for the sum and difference of two cubes.

$(2a + 1)(4a^2 - 2a + 1)(2a - 1)(4a^2 + 2a + 1)$

5.7 Practice Problems

1. (a) $7x^5 + 56x^2 = 7x^2(x^3 + 8)$
$= 7x^2(x + 2)(x^2 - 2x + 4)$

(b) $125x^2 + 50xy + 5y^2$
$= 5(25x^2 + 10xy + y^2)$
$= 5(5x + y)^2$

(c) $12x^2 - 75 = 3(4x^2 - 25)$
$= 3(2x + 5)(2x - 5)$

(d) $3x^2 - 39x + 126$
$= 3(x^2 - 13x + 42)$
$= 3(x - 7)(x - 6)$

(e) $6ax + 6ay + 18bx + 18by$
$= 6(ax + ay + 3bx + 3by)$
$= 6[a(x + y) + 3b(x + y)]$
$= 6(x + y)(a + 3b)$

(f) $6x^3 - x^2 - 12x$
$= x(6x^2 - x - 12)$
$= x(6x^2 - 9x + 8x - 12)$
$= x[3x(2x - 3) + 4(2x - 3)]$
$= x(2x - 3)(3x + 4)$

2. $3x^2 - 10x + 4$

Prime. There are no factors of 12 whose sum is -10.

3. $16x^2 + 81$

Prime. Binomials of the form $a^2 + b^2$ cannot be factored.

5.8 Practice Problems

1. $x^2 + x = 56$
$x^2 + x - 56 = 0$
$(x + 8)(x - 7) = 0$
$x + 8 = 0 \qquad x - 7 = 0$
$x = -8 \qquad x = 7$

2. $12x^2 - 11x + 2 = 0$
$(4x - 1)(3x - 2) = 0$
$4x - 1 = 0 \qquad 3x - 2 = 0$
$x = \frac{1}{4} \qquad x = \frac{2}{3}$

3. $7x^2 - 14x = 0$
$7x(x - 2) = 0$
$7x = 0 \qquad x - 2 = 0$
$x = 0 \qquad x = 2$

4.
$$16x(x-2) = 8x - 25$$
$$16x^2 - 32x = 8x - 25$$
$$16x^2 - 32x - 8x + 25 = 0$$
$$16x^2 - 40x + 25 = 0$$
$$(4x-5)^2 = 0$$
$$4x - 5 = 0 \qquad 4x - 5 = 0$$
$x = \frac{5}{4}$ is a double root.

5.
$$3x^3 + 6x^2 = 45x$$
$$3x^3 + 6x^2 - 45x = 0$$
$$3x(x^2 + 2x - 15) = 0$$
$$3x(x+5)(x-3) = 0$$
$$3x = 0 \qquad x + 5 = 0 \qquad x - 3 = 0$$
$$x = 0 \qquad x = -5 \qquad x = 3$$

6. $A = \frac{1}{2}ab$

Let the base $= x$, the altitude $= x + 5$.

$$52 = \frac{1}{2}(x+5)(x)$$
$$104 = (x+5)(x)$$
$$104 = x^2 + 5x$$
$$0 = x^2 + 5x - 104$$
$$0 = x^2 - 8x + 13x - 104$$
$$0 = (x-8)(x+13)$$
$$x - 8 = 0 \qquad x + 13 = 0$$
$$x = 8 \qquad x = -13$$

The base of a triangle must be a positive number, so we disregard -13. Thus,

base $= x = 8$ feet

altitude $= x + 5 = 13$ feet

7. Let $x =$ the length in square feet of last year's garden, then $3x + 2 =$ the length in square feet of this year's garden.

$$(3x+2)^2 = 112 + x^2$$
$$9x^2 + 12x + 4 = 112 + x^2$$
$$8x^2 + 12x - 108 = 0$$
$$4(2x^2 + 3x - 27) = 0$$
$$4(x-3)(2x+9) = 0$$
$$x - 3 = 0 \qquad 2x + 9 = 0$$
$$x = 3 \qquad x = -\frac{9}{2}$$

Length cannot be negative, so we reject the negative answer. We use $x = 3$. Last year's garden is a square with each side measuring 3 feet. This year's garden measures $3x + 2 = 3(3) + 2 = 11$ feet on each side.

Chapter 6

6.1 Practice Problems

1. Solve the equation $x^2 - 9x - 22 = 0$.

$$(x+2)(x-11) = 0$$
$$x + 2 = 0 \qquad x - 11 = 0$$
$$x = -2 \qquad x = 11$$

The domain of $y = f(x)$ is all real numbers except -2 and 11.

2. $$\frac{x^2 - 36y^2}{x^2 - 3xy - 18y^2} = \frac{(x+6y)\cancel{(x-6y)}}{(x+3y)\cancel{(x-6y)}} = \frac{x+6y}{x+3y}$$

3. $$\frac{9x^2y}{3xy^2 + 6x^2y} = \frac{\overset{3}{\cancel{9}}\overset{x}{\cancel{x^2}}\cancel{y}}{\cancel{3xy}(y+2x)} = \frac{3x}{y+2x}$$

4. $$\frac{2x^2 - 8x - 10}{2x^2 - 20x + 50} = \frac{\cancel{2}\cancel{(x-5)}(x+1)}{\cancel{2}\cancel{(x-5)}(x-5)} = \frac{x+1}{x-5}$$

5. $$\frac{-3x + 6y}{x^2 - 7xy + 10y^2} = \frac{-3\cancel{(x-2y)}}{\cancel{(x-2y)}(x-5y)} = \frac{-3}{x-5y}$$

6. $$\frac{7a^2 - 23ab + 6b^2}{4b^2 - 49a^2} = \frac{\cancel{(7a-2b)}(a-3b)}{\cancel{(2b-7a)}(2b+7a)} = -\frac{a-3b}{7a+2b}$$

7. $$\frac{2x^2 + 5xy + 2y^2}{4x^2 - y^2} \cdot \frac{2x^2 + xy - y^2}{x^2 + xy - 2y^2}$$
$$= \frac{\cancel{(2x+y)}\cancel{(x+2y)}}{\cancel{(2x+y)}\cancel{(2x-y)}} \cdot \frac{\cancel{(2x-y)}(x+y)}{\cancel{(x+2y)}(x-y)} = \frac{x+y}{x-y}$$

8. $$\frac{2x^3 - 3x^2}{3x^2 + 3x} \cdot \frac{9x + 36}{10x^2 - 15x}$$
$$= \frac{\cancel{x^2}\cancel{(2x-3)}}{\cancel{3x}(x+1)} \cdot \frac{\overset{3}{\cancel{9}}(x+4)}{5\cancel{x}\cancel{(2x-3)}} = \frac{3(x+4)}{5(x+1)}$$

9. $$\frac{8x^3 + 27}{64x^3 - 1} \div \frac{4x^2 - 9}{16x^2 + 4x + 1}$$
$$= \frac{8x^3 + 27}{64x^3 - 1} \cdot \frac{16x^2 + 4x + 1}{4x^2 - 9}$$
$$= \frac{\cancel{(2x+3)}(4x^2 - 6x + 9)}{(4x-1)\cancel{(16x^2+4x+1)}} \cdot \frac{\cancel{(16x^2+4x+1)}}{\cancel{(2x+3)}(2x-3)}$$
$$= \frac{4x^2 - 6x + 9}{(4x-1)(2x-3)} \text{ or } \frac{4x^2 - 6x + 9}{8x^2 - 14x + 3}$$

10. $$\frac{4x^2 - 9}{2x^2 + 11x + 12} \div (-6x + 9)$$
$$= \frac{4x^2 - 9}{2x^2 + 11x + 12} \cdot \frac{1}{-6x + 9}$$
$$= \frac{\cancel{(2x+3)}\cancel{(2x-3)}}{\cancel{(2x+3)}(x+4)} \cdot \frac{1}{-3\cancel{(2x-3)}} = -\frac{1}{3(x+4)}$$

6.2 Practice Problems

1. Find the LCD. $\frac{8}{x^2 - x - 12}, \frac{3}{x-4}$

Factor each denominator completely.

$x^2 - x - 12 = (x-4)(x+3)$

$x - 4$ cannot be factored.

The LCD is the product of all the different prime factors.

LCD $= (x-4)(x-3)$

2. Find the LCD. $\frac{2}{15x^3y^2}, \frac{13}{25xy^3}$

Factor each denominator.

$$15x^3y^2 = 3 \cdot 5 \cdot x \cdot x \cdot x \cdot y \cdot y$$
$$25xy^3 = 5 \cdot 5 \cdot x \cdot y \cdot y \cdot y$$
$$\text{LCD} = 3 \cdot 5 \cdot 5 \cdot x \cdot x \cdot x \cdot y \cdot y \cdot y$$
$$\text{LCD} = 75x^3y^3$$

3. $$\frac{4x}{(x+6)(2x-1)} - \frac{3x+1}{(x+6)(2x-1)} = \frac{x-1}{(x+6)(2x-1)}$$

4. $\dfrac{8}{(x-4)(x+3)}+\dfrac{3}{x-4}$

LCD $=(x-4)(x+3)$

$=\dfrac{8}{(x-4)(x+3)}+\dfrac{3}{(x-4)}\cdot\dfrac{(x+3)}{(x+3)}$

$=\dfrac{8+3x+9}{(x-4)(x+3)}=\dfrac{3x+17}{(x-4)(x+3)}$

5. $\dfrac{5}{x+4}+\dfrac{3}{4x}$

LCD $=4x(x+4)$

$=\dfrac{5}{x+4}\cdot\dfrac{4x}{4x}+\dfrac{3}{4x}\cdot\dfrac{(x+4)}{(x+4)}$

$=\dfrac{20x+3x+12}{4x(x+4)}=\dfrac{23x+12}{4x(x+4)}$

6. $\dfrac{7}{4ab^3}+\dfrac{1}{3a^3b^2}$

LCD $=12a^3b^3$

$=\dfrac{7}{4ab^3}\cdot\dfrac{(3a^2)}{(3a^2)}+\dfrac{1}{3a^3b^2}\cdot\dfrac{(4b)}{(4b)}=\dfrac{21a^2+4b}{12a^3b^3}$

7. $\dfrac{4x+2}{x^2+x-12}-\dfrac{3x+8}{x^2+6x+8}$

$=\dfrac{4x+2}{(x-3)(x+4)}-\dfrac{3x+8}{(x+2)(x+4)}$

LCD $=(x+2)(x-3)(x+4)$

$=\dfrac{4x+2}{(x+4)(x-3)}\cdot\dfrac{(x+2)}{(x+2)}-\dfrac{3x+8}{(x+2)(x+4)}\cdot\dfrac{(x-3)}{(x-3)}$

$=\dfrac{4x^2+10x+4}{(x+4)(x-3)(x+2)}-\dfrac{3x^2-x-24}{(x+4)(x-3)(x+2)}$

$=\dfrac{x^2+11x+28}{(x+4)(x-3)(x+2)}=\dfrac{(x+4)(x+7)}{(x+4)(x-3)(x+2)}$

$=\dfrac{x+7}{(x-3)(x+2)}$

8. $\dfrac{7x-3}{4x^2+20x+25}-\dfrac{3x}{4x+10}$

$=\dfrac{7x-3}{(2x+5)(2x+5)}-\dfrac{3x}{2(2x+5)}$

LCD $=2(2x+5)(2x+5)$

$=\dfrac{7x-3}{(2x+5)(2x+5)}\cdot\dfrac{2}{2}-\dfrac{3x}{2(2x+5)}\cdot\dfrac{(2x+5)}{(2x+5)}$

$=\dfrac{14x-6-6x^2-15x}{2(2x+5)(2x+5)}=\dfrac{-6x^2-x-6}{2(2x+5)^2}$

6.3 Practice Problems

1. You can use either method 1 or method 2 to simplify a complex fraction.

$$\frac{y+\frac{3}{y}}{\frac{2}{y^2}+\frac{5}{y}}$$

METHOD 1

Simplify the numerator.

$y+\dfrac{3}{y}=\dfrac{y^2}{y}+\dfrac{3}{y}=\dfrac{y^2+3}{y}$

Simplify the denominator.

$\dfrac{2}{y^2}+\dfrac{5}{y}=\dfrac{2}{y^2}+\dfrac{5y}{y^2}=\dfrac{2+5y}{y^2}$

Divide the numerator by the denominator.

$$\frac{\frac{y^2+3}{y}}{\frac{2+5y}{y^2}}$$

$=\dfrac{y^2+3}{y}\cdot\dfrac{y^2}{2+5y}$

$=\dfrac{y(y^2+3)}{2+5y}$

METHOD 2

Find the LCD of all the fractions in the numerator and denominator.

LCD $=y^2$

Multiply the numerator and denominator by the LCD.

$$\frac{y+\frac{3}{y}}{\frac{2}{y^2}+\frac{5}{y}}\cdot\frac{y^2}{y^2}$$

$=\dfrac{y(y^2)+\frac{3}{y}(y^2)}{\frac{2}{y^2}(y^2)+\frac{5}{y}(y^2)}$

$=\dfrac{y^3+3y}{2+5y}$

$=\dfrac{y(y^2+3)}{2+5y}$

2. Simplify.

$$\frac{\frac{4}{16x^2-1}+\frac{3}{4x+1}}{\frac{x}{4x-1}+\frac{5}{4x+1}}$$

METHOD 1

Simplify the numerator.

$\dfrac{4}{(4x+1)(4x-1)}+\dfrac{3(4x-1)}{(4x+1)(4x-1)}=\dfrac{12x+1}{(4x+1)(4x-1)}$

Simplify the denominator.

$\dfrac{x(4x+1)}{(4x-1)(4x+1)}+\dfrac{5(4x-1)}{(4x+1)(4x-1)}=\dfrac{4x^2+21x-5}{(4x-1)(4x+1)}$

To divide the numerator by the denominator, we multiply the numerator by the reciprocal of the denominator.

$\dfrac{12x+1}{(4x+1)(4x-1)}\cdot\dfrac{(4x+1)(4x-1)}{4x^2+21x-5}=\dfrac{12x+1}{4x^2+21x-5}$

METHOD 2

Multiply the numerator and denominator by the LCD of all the rational expressions in the numerator and denominator.

LCD $=(4x+1)(4x-1)$. Notice we factored $16x^2-1$.

$$\frac{\left[\frac{4}{(4x+1)(4x-1)}+\frac{3}{(4x+1)}\right](4x+1)(4x-1)}{\left[\frac{x}{4x-1}+\frac{5}{4x+1}\right](4x+1)(4x-1)}$$

$$= \frac{\frac{4(4x+1)(4x-1)}{(4x+1)(4x-1)} + \frac{3(4x+1)(4x-1)}{4x+1}}{\frac{x}{4x-1}\cdot(4x+1)(4x-1) + \frac{5}{4x+1}\cdot(4x+1)(4x-1)}$$

$$= \frac{4+3(4x-1)}{x(4x+1)+5(4x-1)} = \frac{4+12x-3}{4x^2+x+20x-5} = \frac{12x+1}{4x^2+21x-5}$$

3. Simplify by **METHOD 1**.

$$\frac{4+\frac{1}{x+3}}{\frac{2}{x^2+4x+3}} = \frac{4+\frac{1}{x+3}}{\frac{2}{(x+1)(x+3)}}$$

$$= \frac{4\cdot\frac{(x+3)}{(x+3)} + \frac{1}{x+3}}{\frac{2}{(x+1)(x+3)}} = \frac{\frac{4x+12+1}{x+3}}{\frac{2}{(x+1)(x+3)}}$$

$$= \frac{4x+13}{x+3}\cdot\frac{(x+1)(x+3)}{2}$$

$$= \frac{(4x+13)(x+1)}{2} \text{ or } \frac{4x^2+17x+13}{2}$$

4. Simplify by **METHOD 2**.

LCD $= y(y+3)$

$$\frac{\frac{7}{y+3} - \frac{3}{y}}{\frac{2}{y} + \frac{5}{y+3}} \cdot \frac{y(y+3)}{y(y+3)}$$

$$= \frac{\frac{7}{y+3}\cdot y(y+3) - \frac{3}{y}\cdot y(y+3)}{\frac{2}{y}\cdot y(y+3) + \frac{5}{y+3}\cdot y(y+3)}$$

$$= \frac{7y-3(y+3)}{2(y+3)+5(y)} = \frac{7y-3y-9}{2y+6+5y} = \frac{4y-9}{7y+6}$$

6.4 Practice Problems

1. $\frac{4}{3x} + \frac{x+1}{x} = \frac{1}{2}$

$$6x\left[\frac{4}{3x}\right] + 6x\left[\frac{x+1}{x}\right] = 6x\left[\frac{1}{2}\right]$$

$$8 + 6(x+1) = 3x$$

$$8 + 6x + 6 = 3x$$

$$3x = -14$$

$$x = -\frac{14}{3}$$

Check. $\frac{4}{3\left(\frac{-14}{3}\right)} + \frac{\frac{-14}{3}+1}{-\frac{14}{3}} \stackrel{?}{=} \frac{1}{2}$

$$\frac{4}{-14} + \frac{\frac{-11}{3}}{\frac{-14}{3}} \stackrel{?}{=} \frac{1}{2}$$

$$-\frac{4}{14} + \frac{11}{14} \stackrel{?}{=} \frac{1}{2}$$

$$\frac{7}{14} \stackrel{?}{=} \frac{1}{2}$$

$$\frac{1}{2} = \frac{1}{2} \checkmark$$

2. $\frac{1}{3x-9} = \frac{1}{2x-6} - \frac{5}{6}$

$$\frac{1}{3(x-3)} = \frac{1}{2(x-3)} - \frac{5}{6}$$

$$6(x-3)\left[\frac{1}{3(x-3)}\right] = 6(x-3)\left[\frac{1}{2(x-3)}\right] - 6(x-3)\left(\frac{5}{6}\right)$$

$$2(1) = 3(1) - (x-3)(5)$$

$$2 = 3 - 5x + 15$$

$$2 = 18 - 5x$$

$$-16 = -5x$$

$$\frac{16}{5} = x$$

Check. $\frac{1}{3\left(\frac{16}{5}\right)-9} \stackrel{?}{=} \frac{1}{2\left(\frac{16}{5}\right)-6} - \frac{5}{6}$

$$\frac{1}{\frac{48}{5}-9} \stackrel{?}{=} \frac{1}{\frac{32}{5}-6} - \frac{5}{6}$$

$$\frac{1}{\frac{3}{5}} \stackrel{?}{=} \frac{1}{\frac{2}{5}} - \frac{5}{6}$$

$$\frac{5}{3} = \frac{5}{3} \checkmark$$

3. $\frac{y^2+4y-2}{y^2-2y-8} = 1 + \frac{4}{y-4}$

$$\frac{y^2+4y-2}{(y+2)(y-4)} = 1 + \frac{4}{y-4}$$

$$(y+2)(y-4)\left[\frac{y^2+4y-2}{(y+2)(y-4)}\right]$$

$$= (y+2)(y-4)(1) + (y+2)(y-4)\left(\frac{4}{y-4}\right)$$

$$y^2+4y-2 = y^2-2y-8+4y+8$$

$$4y-2 = 2y$$

$$2y = 2$$

$$y = 1$$

4. $\frac{2x-1}{x^2-7x+10} + \frac{3}{x-5} = \frac{5}{x-2}$

$$\frac{2x-1}{(x-2)(x-5)} + \frac{3}{x-5} = \frac{5}{x-2}$$

$$(x-2)(x-5)\left[\frac{2x-1}{(x-2)(x-5)}\right] + (x-2)(x-5)\left(\frac{3}{x-5}\right)$$

$$= (x-2)(x-5)\left(\frac{5}{x-2}\right)$$

$$2x-1+3(x-2) = 5(x-5)$$

$$2x-1+3x-6 = 5x-25$$

$$5x-7 = 5x-25$$

$$0 = -18$$

Of course $0 \neq -18$. Therefore, no values of x makes the original equation true. Hence the equation has **no solution**.

5. $\frac{y}{y-2} - 3 = 1 + \frac{2}{y-2}$

$$(y-2)\left(\frac{y}{y-2}\right) - (y-2)(3) = (y-2)(1) + (y-2)\left(\frac{2}{y-2}\right)$$

$$y - 3(y-2) = 1(y-2) + 2$$

$$y - 3y + 6 = y - 2 + 2$$

$$-2y + 6 = y$$

$$6 = 3y$$

$$2 = y$$

Check. $\frac{2}{2-2} - 3 \stackrel{?}{=} 1 + \frac{2}{2-2}$

$\frac{2}{0} - 3 \stackrel{?}{=} 1 + \frac{2}{0}$

Division by zero is not defined. The value $y = 2$ is therefore not a solution to the original equation. There is **no solution**.

6.5 Practice Problems

1. Solve for t. $\frac{1}{t} = \frac{1}{c} + \frac{1}{d}$

$$cdt\left[\frac{1}{t}\right] = cdt\left[\frac{1}{c}\right] + cdt\left[\frac{1}{d}\right]$$
$$cd = dt + ct$$
$$cd = t(d + c)$$
$$\frac{cd}{d+c} = t$$

2. Solve for p_1. $C = \frac{Bp_1p_2}{d^2}$

$$Cd^2 = Bp_1p_2$$
$$\frac{Cd^2}{Bp_2} = p_1$$

3. $\frac{21}{2} = \frac{x}{168}$

$$2x = 3528$$
$$x = 1764$$

The number of students enrolled should be 1764 to maintain that ratio.

4. We will draw the picture as two similar triangles.

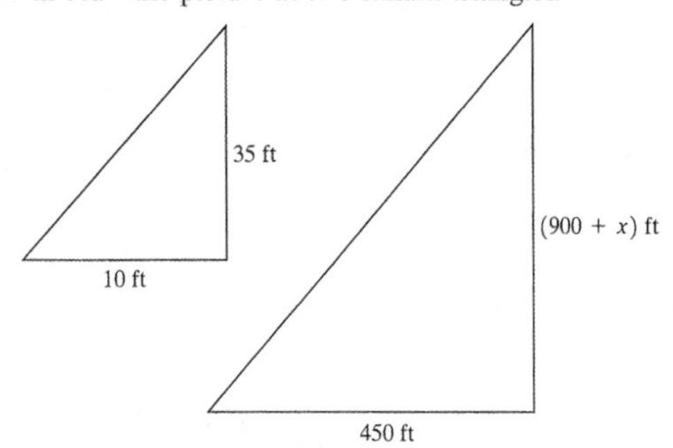

We write a proportion and solve.

$$\frac{10}{35} = \frac{450}{900 + x}$$
$$\text{LCD} = 35(900 + x)$$
$$35(900 + x)\left(\frac{10}{35}\right) = 35(900 + x)\left(\frac{450}{900 + x}\right)$$
$$10(900 + x) = 35(450)$$
$$9000 + 10x = 15{,}750$$
$$10x = 6750$$
$$x = 675$$

The helicopter is about 675 feet over the building.

5. We construct a table for the data.

	Rate of Work per Hour	Time Worked in Hours	Fraction of Task Done
Alfred	$\frac{1}{4}$	x	$\frac{x}{4}$
Son	$\frac{1}{5}$	x	$\frac{x}{5}$

The fraction of work done by Alfred plus the fraction of work done by his son equals 1 completed job.

Write an equation and solve.

$$\frac{x}{4} + \frac{x}{5} = 1$$
$$5x + 4x = 20$$
$$9x = 20$$
$$x = 2.2\overline{2}$$

Alfred and his son can mow the lawn working together in approximately 2.2 hours.

Chapter 7

7.1 Practice Problems

1. $$\left(\frac{3x^{-2}y^4}{2x^{-5}y^2}\right)^{-3} = \frac{(3x^{-2}y^4)^{-3}}{(2x^{-5}y^2)^{-3}}$$
$$= \frac{3^{-3}(x^{-2})^{-3}(y^4)^{-3}}{2^{-3}(x^{-5})^{-3}(y^2)^{-3}}$$
$$= \frac{3^{-3}x^6y^{-12}}{2^{-3}x^{15}y^{-6}}$$
$$= \frac{3^{-3}}{2^{-3}} \cdot \frac{x^6}{x^{15}} \cdot \frac{y^{-12}}{y^{-6}}$$
$$= \frac{2^3}{3^3} \cdot x^{6-15} \cdot y^{-12+6}$$
$$= \frac{8}{27}x^{-9}y^{-6} \text{ or } \frac{8}{27x^9y^6}$$

2. (a) $(x^4)^{3/8} = x^{(4/1)(3/8)} = x^{3/2}$

(b) $\frac{x^{3/7}}{x^{2/7}} = x^{3/7-2/7} = x^{1/7}$

(c) $x^{-7/5} \cdot x^{4/5} = x^{-7/5+4/5} = x^{-3/5}$

3. (a) $(-3x^{1/4})(2x^{1/2}) = -6x^{1/4+1/2} = -6x^{1/4+2/4} = -6x^{3/4}$

(b) $$\frac{13x^{1/12}y^{-1/4}}{26x^{-1/3}y^{1/2}} = \frac{x^{1/12-(-1/3)}y^{-1/4-1/2}}{2}$$
$$= \frac{x^{1/12+4/12}y^{-1/4-2/4}}{2}$$
$$= \frac{x^{5/12}y^{-3/4}}{2}$$
$$= \frac{x^{5/12}}{2y^{3/4}}$$

4. $$-3x^{1/2}(2x^{1/4} + 3x^{-1/2}) = -6x^{1/2+1/4} - 9x^{1/2-1/2}$$
$$= -6x^{2/4+1/4} - 9x^0$$
$$= -6x^{3/4} - 9$$

5. (a) $(4)^{5/2} = (2^2)^{5/2} = 2^{2/1 \cdot 5/2} = 2^5 = 32$

(b) $(27)^{4/3} = (3^3)^{4/3} = 3^{3/1 \cdot 4/3} = 3^4 = 81$

6. $$3x^{1/3} + x^{-1/3} = 3x^{1/3} + \frac{1}{x^{1/3}}$$
$$= \frac{x^{1/3}}{x^{1/3}}(3x^{1/3}) + \frac{1}{x^{1/3}}$$
$$= \frac{3x^{2/3} + 1}{x^{1/3}}$$

7. $4y^{3/2} - 8y^{5/2} = 4y^{2/2+1/2} - 8y^{2/2+3/2}$

$= 4(y^{2/2})(y^{1/2}) - 8(y^{2/2})(y^{3/2})$

$= 4y(y^{1/2} - 2y^{3/2})$

7.2 Practice Problems

1. (a) $\sqrt[3]{216} = \sqrt[3]{(6)^3} = 6$

(b) $\sqrt[5]{32} = \sqrt[5]{(2)^5} = 2$

(c) $\sqrt[3]{-8} = \sqrt[3]{(-2)^3} = -2$

(d) $\sqrt[4]{-81}$ is not a real number.

2. (a) $f(3) = \sqrt{4(3) - 3} = \sqrt{12 - 3} = \sqrt{9} = 3$

(b) $f(4) = \sqrt{4(4) - 3} = \sqrt{16 - 3} = \sqrt{13} \approx 3.6$

(c) $f(7) = \sqrt{4(7) - 3} = \sqrt{28 - 3} = \sqrt{25} = 5$

3. $0.5x + 2 \geq 0$

$0.5x \geq -2$

$x \geq -4$

The domain is all real numbers x where $x \geq -4$.

4.

x	$f(x)$
3	0
4	1.7
5	2.4
6	3
15	6

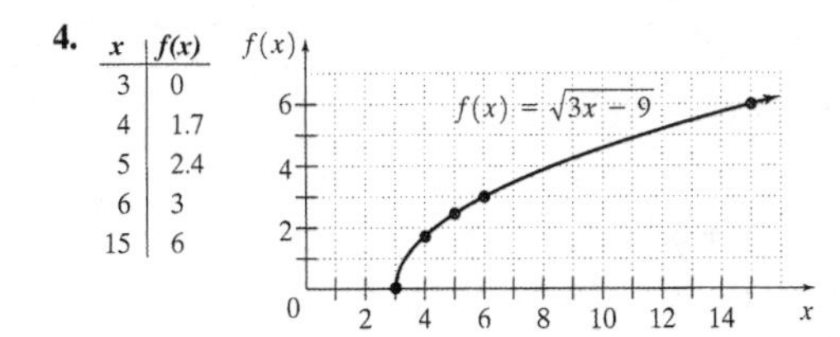

5. (a) $\sqrt[3]{x^3} = (x^3)^{1/3} = x^{3/3} = x^1 = x$

(b) $\sqrt[4]{y^4} = (y^4)^{1/4} = y^{4/4} = y^1 = y$

6. (a) $\sqrt[4]{x^3} = (x^3)^{1/4} = x^{3/4}$

(b) $\sqrt[5]{(xy)^7} = [(xy)^7]^{1/5} = (xy)^{7/5}$

7. (a) $\sqrt[4]{81x^{12}} = (3^4x^{12})^{1/4} = 3x^3$

(b) $\sqrt[3]{27x^6} = [(3)^3x^6]^{1/3} = 3x^2$

(c) $(32x^5)^{3/5} = (2^5x^5)^{3/5} = 2^3x^3 = 8x^3$

8. (a) $x^{3/4} = \sqrt[4]{x^3}$

(b) $y^{-1/3} = \dfrac{1}{y^{1/3}} = \dfrac{1}{\sqrt[3]{y}}$

(c) $(2x)^{4/5} = \sqrt[5]{(2x)^4} = \sqrt[5]{16x^4}$

(d) $2x^{4/5} = 2\sqrt[5]{x^4}$

9. (a) $8^{2/3} = (\sqrt[3]{8})^2 = 2^2 = 4$

(b) $(-8)^{4/3} = (\sqrt[3]{-8})^4 = (-2)^4 = 16$

(c) $100^{-3/2} = \dfrac{1}{100^{3/2}} = \dfrac{1}{(\sqrt{100})^3} = \dfrac{1}{10^3} = \dfrac{1}{1000}$

10. (a) $\sqrt[5]{(-3)^5} = -3$

(b) $\sqrt[4]{(-5)^4} = |-5| = 5$

(c) $\sqrt[4]{w^4} = |w|$

(d) $\sqrt[7]{y^7} = y$

11. (a) $\sqrt{36x^2} = 6|x|$

(b) $\sqrt[3]{125x^3y^6} = \sqrt[3]{(5)^3(x)^3(y^2)^3} = 5xy^2$

(c) $\sqrt[4]{16y^8} = 2|y^2| = 2y^2$

7.3 Practice Problems

1. $\sqrt{20} = \sqrt{4 \cdot 5} = \sqrt{4} \cdot \sqrt{5} = 2\sqrt{5}$

2. $\sqrt{27} = \sqrt{9 \cdot 3} = \sqrt{9} \cdot \sqrt{3} = 3\sqrt{3}$

3. (a) $\sqrt[3]{24} = \sqrt[3]{8} \cdot \sqrt[3]{3} = 2\sqrt[3]{3}$

(b) $\sqrt[3]{-108} = \sqrt[3]{-27} \cdot \sqrt[3]{4} = -3\sqrt[3]{4}$

4. $\sqrt[4]{64} = \sqrt[4]{16} \cdot \sqrt[4]{4} = 2\sqrt[4]{4}$

5. (a) $\sqrt{45x^6y^7} = \sqrt{9 \cdot 5 \cdot x^6 \cdot y^6 \cdot y} = \sqrt{9x^6y^6} \cdot \sqrt{5y}$

$= 3x^3y^3\sqrt{5y}$

(b) $\sqrt{27a^7b^8c^9} = \sqrt{9 \cdot 3a^6 \cdot a \cdot b^8 \cdot c^8 \cdot c}$

$= \sqrt{9a^6b^8c^8} \cdot \sqrt{3ac}$

$= 3a^3b^4c^4\sqrt{3ac}$

6. $19\sqrt{xy} + 5\sqrt{xy} - 10\sqrt{xy} = (19 + 5 - 10)\sqrt{xy} = 14\sqrt{xy}$

7. $4\sqrt{2} - 5\sqrt{50} - 3\sqrt{98}$

$= 4\sqrt{2} - 5\sqrt{25} \cdot \sqrt{2} - 3\sqrt{49} \cdot \sqrt{2}$

$= 4\sqrt{2} - 5(5)\sqrt{2} - 3(7)\sqrt{2}$

$= 4\sqrt{2} - 25\sqrt{2} - 21\sqrt{2}$

$= (4 - 25 - 21)\sqrt{2}$

$= -42\sqrt{2}$

8. $4\sqrt{2x} + \sqrt{18x} - 2\sqrt{125x} - 6\sqrt{20x}$

$= 4\sqrt{2x} + \sqrt{9} \cdot \sqrt{2x} - 2\sqrt{25} \cdot \sqrt{5x} - 6\sqrt{4} \cdot \sqrt{5x}$

$= 4\sqrt{2x} + 3\sqrt{2x} - 2(5)\sqrt{5x} - 6(2)\sqrt{5x}$

$= 4\sqrt{2x} + 3\sqrt{2x} - 10\sqrt{5x} - 12\sqrt{5x}$

$= 7\sqrt{2x} - 22\sqrt{5x}$

9. $3x\sqrt[3]{54x^4} - 3\sqrt[3]{16x^7}$

$= 3x\sqrt[3]{27x^3} \cdot \sqrt[3]{2x} - 3\sqrt[3]{8x^6} \cdot \sqrt[3]{2x}$

$= 3x(3x)\sqrt[3]{2x} - 3(2x^2)\sqrt[3]{2x}$

$= 9x^2\sqrt[3]{2x} - 6x^2\sqrt[3]{2x}$

$= 3x^2\sqrt[3]{2x}$

7.4 Practice Problems

1. $(-4\sqrt{2})(-3\sqrt{13x}) = (-4)(-3)\sqrt{2 \cdot 13x} = 12\sqrt{26x}$

2. $\sqrt{2x}(\sqrt{5} + 2\sqrt{3x} + \sqrt{8})$

$= (\sqrt{2x})(\sqrt{5}) + (\sqrt{2x})(2\sqrt{3x}) + (\sqrt{2x})(\sqrt{8})$

$= \sqrt{10x} + 2\sqrt{6x^2} + \sqrt{16x}$

$= \sqrt{10x} + 2\sqrt{x^2}\sqrt{6} + \sqrt{16}\sqrt{x}$

$= \sqrt{10x} + 2x\sqrt{6} + 4\sqrt{x}$

3. $(\sqrt{7} + 4\sqrt{2})(2\sqrt{7} - 3\sqrt{2})$

$= 2\sqrt{49} - 3\sqrt{14} + 8\sqrt{14} - 12\sqrt{4}$

$= 2(7) + 5\sqrt{14} - 12(2)$

$= 14 + 5\sqrt{14} - 24$

$= -10 + 5\sqrt{14}$

4. $(2 - 5\sqrt{5})(3 - 2\sqrt{2}) = 6 - 4\sqrt{2} - 15\sqrt{5} + 10\sqrt{10}$

5. $(\sqrt{5x} + \sqrt{10})^2 = (\sqrt{5x} + \sqrt{10})(\sqrt{5x} + \sqrt{10})$

$= \sqrt{25x^2} + \sqrt{50x} + \sqrt{50x} + \sqrt{100}$

$= 5x + 2\sqrt{25}\sqrt{2x} + 10$

$= 5x + 2(5)\sqrt{2x} + 10$

$= 5x + 10\sqrt{2x} + 10$

6. (a) $\sqrt[3]{2x}(\sqrt[3]{4x^2} + 3\sqrt[3]{y})$

$= (\sqrt[3]{2x})(\sqrt[3]{4x^2}) + (\sqrt[3]{2x})(3\sqrt[3]{y})$

$= \sqrt[3]{8x^3} + 3\sqrt[3]{2xy}$

$= 2x + 3\sqrt[3]{2xy}$

(b) $(\sqrt[3]{7} + \sqrt[3]{x^2})(2\sqrt[3]{49} - \sqrt[3]{x})$

$= 2\sqrt[3]{343} - \sqrt[3]{7x} + 2\sqrt[3]{49x^2} - \sqrt[3]{x^3}$

$= 2\sqrt[3]{7^3} - \sqrt[3]{7x} + 2\sqrt[3]{49x^2} - x$

$= 2(7) - \sqrt[3]{7x} + 2\sqrt[3]{49x^2} - x$

$= 14 - \sqrt[3]{7x} + 2\sqrt[3]{49x^2} - x$

7. (a) $\dfrac{\sqrt{75}}{\sqrt{3}} = \sqrt{\dfrac{75}{3}} = \sqrt{25} = 5$

(b) $\sqrt[3]{\dfrac{27}{64}} = \dfrac{\sqrt[3]{27}}{\sqrt[3]{64}} = \dfrac{3}{4}$

(c) $\dfrac{\sqrt{54a^3b^7}}{\sqrt{6b^5}} = \sqrt{\dfrac{54a^3b^7}{6b^5}} = \sqrt{9a^3b^2} = 3ab\sqrt{a}$

8. $\dfrac{7}{\sqrt{3}} = \dfrac{7}{\sqrt{3}} \cdot \dfrac{\sqrt{3}}{\sqrt{3}} = \dfrac{7\sqrt{3}}{\sqrt{9}} = \dfrac{7\sqrt{3}}{3}$

9. $\dfrac{8}{\sqrt{20x}} = \dfrac{8}{\sqrt{4}\sqrt{5x}} = \dfrac{8}{2\sqrt{5x}} \cdot \dfrac{\sqrt{5x}}{\sqrt{5x}} = \dfrac{8\sqrt{5x}}{10x} = \dfrac{4\sqrt{5x}}{5x}$

10. $\sqrt[3]{\dfrac{6}{5x}} = \dfrac{\sqrt[3]{6}}{\sqrt[3]{5x}} = \dfrac{\sqrt[3]{6}}{\sqrt[3]{5x}} \cdot \dfrac{\sqrt[3]{25x^2}}{\sqrt[3]{25x^2}} = \dfrac{\sqrt[3]{150x^2}}{\sqrt[3]{125x^3}} = \dfrac{\sqrt[3]{150x^2}}{5x}$

11. $\dfrac{4}{2 + \sqrt{5}} = \dfrac{4}{2 + \sqrt{5}} \cdot \dfrac{2 - \sqrt{5}}{2 - \sqrt{5}}$

$= \dfrac{4(2 - \sqrt{5})}{2^2 - (\sqrt{5})^2}$

$= \dfrac{4(2 - \sqrt{5})}{4 - 5}$

$= \dfrac{4(2 - \sqrt{5})}{-1}$

$= -(8 - 4\sqrt{5})$

$= -8 + 4\sqrt{5}$

12. $\dfrac{\sqrt{11} + \sqrt{2}}{\sqrt{11} - \sqrt{2}} \cdot \dfrac{\sqrt{11} + \sqrt{2}}{\sqrt{11} + \sqrt{2}}$

$= \dfrac{\sqrt{121} + \sqrt{22} + \sqrt{22} + \sqrt{4}}{(\sqrt{11})^2 - (\sqrt{2})^2}$

$= \dfrac{11 + 2\sqrt{22} + 2}{11 - 2} = \dfrac{13 + 2\sqrt{22}}{9}$

7.5 Practice Problems

1. $\sqrt{3x - 8} = x - 2$

$(\sqrt{3x - 8})^2 = (x - 2)^2$

$3x - 8 = x^2 - 4x + 4$

$0 = x^2 - 7x + 12$

$0 = (x - 3)(x - 4)$

$x - 3 = 0$ or $x - 4 = 0$

$x = 3 \qquad x = 4$

Check:

For $x = 3$: $\sqrt{3(3) - 8} \stackrel{?}{=} 3 - 2$

$\sqrt{1} \stackrel{?}{=} 1$

$1 = 1$ ✓

For $x = 4$: $\sqrt{3(4) - 8} \stackrel{?}{=} 4 - 2$

$\sqrt{4} \stackrel{?}{=} 2$

$2 = 2$ ✓

The solutions are 3 and 4.

2. $\sqrt{x + 4} = x + 4$

$(\sqrt{x + 4})^2 = (x + 4)^2$

$x + 4 = x^2 + 8x + 16$

$0 = x^2 + 7x + 12$

$0 = (x + 3)(x + 4)$

$x + 3 = 0$ or $x + 4 = 0$

$x = -3 \qquad x = -4$

Check:

For $x = -3$: $\sqrt{-3 + 4} \stackrel{?}{=} -3 + 4$

$\sqrt{1} \stackrel{?}{=} 1$

$1 = 1$ ✓

For $x = -4$: $\sqrt{-4 + 4} \stackrel{?}{=} -4 + 4$

$\sqrt{0} \stackrel{?}{=} 0$

$0 = 0$ ✓

The solutions are −4 and −3.

3. $\sqrt{2x + 5} - 2\sqrt{2x} = 1$

$\sqrt{2x + 5} = 2\sqrt{2x} + 1$

$(\sqrt{2x + 5})^2 = (2\sqrt{2x} + 1)^2$

$2x + 5 = (2\sqrt{2x} + 1)(2\sqrt{2x} + 1)$

$2x + 5 = 8x + 4\sqrt{2x} + 1$

$-6x + 4 = 4\sqrt{2x}$

$-3x + 2 = 2\sqrt{2x}$

$(-3x + 2)^2 = (2\sqrt{2x})^2$

$9x^2 - 12x + 4 = 8x$

$9x^2 - 20x + 4 = 0$

$(9x - 2)(x - 2) = 0$

$9x - 2 = 0$ or $x - 2 = 0$

$x = \dfrac{2}{9} \qquad x = 2$

Check: For $x = \frac{2}{9}$:

$$\sqrt{2\left(\frac{2}{9}\right) + 5} - 2\sqrt{2\left(\frac{2}{9}\right)} \stackrel{?}{=} 1$$
$$\sqrt{\frac{4}{9} + 5} - 2\sqrt{\frac{4}{9}} \stackrel{?}{=} 1$$
$$\sqrt{\frac{49}{9}} - 2\sqrt{\frac{4}{9}} \stackrel{?}{=} 1$$
$$\frac{7}{3} - \frac{4}{3} \stackrel{?}{=} 1$$
$$\frac{3}{3} \stackrel{?}{=} 1$$
$$1 = 1 \checkmark$$

For $x = 2$:

$$\sqrt{2(2) + 5} - 2\sqrt{2(2)} \stackrel{?}{=} 1$$
$$\sqrt{9} - 2\sqrt{4} \stackrel{?}{=} 1$$
$$3 - 4 \stackrel{?}{=} 1$$
$$-1 \neq 1$$

The only solution is $\frac{2}{9}$.

4.
$$\sqrt{y-1} + \sqrt{y-4} = \sqrt{4y-11}$$
$$\left(\sqrt{y-1} + \sqrt{y-4}\right)^2 = \left(\sqrt{4y-11}\right)^2$$
$$\left(\sqrt{y-1} + \sqrt{y-4}\right)\left(\sqrt{y-1} + \sqrt{y-4}\right) = 4y - 11$$
$$y - 1 + 2\left(\sqrt{y-1}\right)\left(\sqrt{y-4}\right) + y - 4 = 4y - 11$$
$$2y - 5 + 2\left(\sqrt{y-1}\right)\left(\sqrt{y-4}\right) = 4y - 11$$
$$2\left(\sqrt{y-1}\right)\left(\sqrt{y-4}\right) = 2y - 6$$
$$\left(\sqrt{y-1}\right)\left(\sqrt{y-4}\right) = y - 3$$
$$\left(\sqrt{y^2 - 5y + 4}\right)^2 = (y-3)^2$$
$$y^2 - 5y + 4 = y^2 - 6y + 9$$
$$y - 5 = 0$$
$$y = 5$$

Check: $\sqrt{5-1} + \sqrt{5-4} \stackrel{?}{=} \sqrt{4(5) - 11}$
$$2 + 1 \stackrel{?}{=} 3$$
$$3 = 3 \checkmark$$

The solution is 5.

7.6 Practice Problems

1. (a) $\sqrt{-49} = \sqrt{-1}\sqrt{49} = (i)(7) = 7i$

(b) $\sqrt{-31} = \sqrt{-1}\sqrt{31} = i\sqrt{31}$

2. $\sqrt{-98} = \sqrt{-1}\sqrt{98} = i\sqrt{98} = i\sqrt{49}\sqrt{2} = 7i\sqrt{2}$

3. $\sqrt{-8} \cdot \sqrt{-2} = \sqrt{-1}\sqrt{8} \cdot \sqrt{-1}\sqrt{2}$
$$= i\sqrt{8} \cdot i\sqrt{2}$$
$$= i^2\sqrt{16}$$
$$= -1(4) = -4$$

4. $-7 + 2yi\sqrt{3} = x + 6i\sqrt{3}$
$$x = -7 \qquad 2y\sqrt{3} = 6\sqrt{3}$$
$$y = 3$$

5. $(3 - 4i) - (-2 - 18i)$
$$= [3 - (-2)] + [-4 - (-18)]i$$
$$= (3 + 2) + (-4 + 18)i$$
$$= 5 + 14i$$

6. $(4 - 2i)(3 - 7i)$
$$= (4)(3) + (4)(-7i) + (-2i)(3) + (-2i)(-7i)$$
$$= 12 - 28i - 6i + 14i^2$$
$$= 12 - 28i - 6i + 14(-1)$$
$$= 12 - 28i - 6i - 14 = -2 - 34i$$

7. $-2i(5 + 6i)$
$$= (-2)(5)i + (-2)(6)i^2$$
$$= -10i - 12i^2$$
$$= -10i - 12(-1) = 12 - 10i$$

8. (a) $\sqrt{-50} \cdot \sqrt{-4}$
$$= \sqrt{-1}\sqrt{50} \cdot \sqrt{-1}\sqrt{4}$$
$$= i\sqrt{50} \cdot i\sqrt{4}$$
$$= i^2\sqrt{200} = 10i^2\sqrt{2} = 10(-1)\sqrt{2} = -10\sqrt{2}$$

9. (a) $i^{42} = \left(i^{40+2}\right) = \left(i^{40}\right)\left(i^2\right) = \left(i^4\right)^{10}\left(i^2\right) = (1)^{10}(-1) = -1$

(b) $i^{53} = \left(i^{52+1}\right) = \left(i^{52}\right)(i) = \left(i^4\right)^{13}(i) = (1)^{13}(i) = i$

10. $\frac{4 + 2i}{3 + 4i} \cdot \frac{3 - 4i}{3 - 4i} = \frac{12 - 16i + 6i - 8i^2}{9 - 16i^2}$
$$= \frac{12 - 10i - 8(-1)}{9 - 16(-1)}$$
$$= \frac{12 - 10i + 8}{9 + 16} = \frac{20 - 10i}{25}$$
$$= \frac{5(4 - 2i)}{25} = \frac{4 - 2i}{5}$$

11. $\frac{5 - 6i}{-2i} \cdot \frac{2i}{2i}$
$$= \frac{10i - 12i^2}{-4i^2} = \frac{10i - 12(-1)}{-4(-1)}$$
$$= \frac{10i + 12}{4} = \frac{2(5i + 6)}{4} = \frac{6 + 5i}{2}$$

7.7 Practice Problems

1. Let s = speed,

h = horsepower.

$s = k\sqrt{h}$

Substitute $s = 128$ and $h = 256$.

$128 = k\sqrt{256}$

$128 = 16k$

$8 = k$

Now we know the value of k so

$s = 8\sqrt{h}$.

when $h = 225$

$s = 8(\sqrt{225})$

$s = 8(15)$

$s = 120$ miles per hour

2. $y = \dfrac{k}{x}$

Substitute $y = 45$ and $x = 16$.

$45 = \dfrac{k}{16}$

$720 = k$

We now write the equation $y = \dfrac{720}{x}$.

Find the value of y when $x = 36$.

$y = \dfrac{720}{36}$

$y = 20$

3. Let r = resistance,

c = amount of current.

$r = \dfrac{k}{c^2}$

Find the value of k when $r = 800$ ohms and $c = 0.01$ amps.

$800 = \dfrac{k}{(0.01)^2}$

$0.08 = k$

We now write the equation $r = \dfrac{0.08}{c^2}$.

Now substitute $c = 0.04$ and solve for r.

$r = \dfrac{0.08}{(0.04)^2}$

$r = \dfrac{0.08}{0.0016}$

$r = 50$ ohms

4. $y = \dfrac{kzw^2}{x}$

To find the value of k substitute $y = 20$, $z = 3$, $w = 5$ and $x = 4$. Solve for k.

$20 = \dfrac{k(3)(5)^2}{4}$

$20 = \dfrac{75k}{4}$

$\dfrac{80}{75} = k$

$\dfrac{16}{15} = k$

We now substitute $\dfrac{16}{15}$ for k.

$y = \dfrac{16zw^2}{15x}$

We use this equation to find y when $z = 4$, $w = 6$, and $x = 2$.

$y = \dfrac{16(4)(6)^2}{15(2)} = \dfrac{2304}{30}$

$y = \dfrac{384}{5}$

Chapter 8

8.1 Practice Problems

1. $x^2 - 121 = 0$

$x^2 = 121$

$x = \pm 11$

Check:

$(11)^2 - 121 \stackrel{?}{=} 0$ $\qquad$ $(-11)^2 - 121 \stackrel{?}{=} 0$

$121 - 121 \stackrel{?}{=} 0$ $\qquad$ $121 - 121 \stackrel{?}{=} 0$

$0 = 0$ ✓ $\qquad$ $0 = 0$ ✓

2. $x^2 = 18$

$x = \pm\sqrt{18}$

$x = \pm 3\sqrt{2}$

3. $5x^2 + 1 = 46$

$5x^2 = 45$

$x = \pm\sqrt{9}$

$x = \pm 3$

4. $3x^2 = -27$

$x = \pm\sqrt{-9}$

$x = \pm 3i$

Check:

$3(3i)^2 \stackrel{?}{=} -27$ $\qquad$ $3(-3i)^2 \stackrel{?}{=} -27$

$3(9)(-1) \stackrel{?}{=} -27$ $\qquad$ $3(9)(-1) \stackrel{?}{=} -27$

$-27 = -27$ ✓ $\qquad$ $-27 = -27$ ✓

5. $(2x + 3)^2 = 7$

$(2x + 3) = \pm\sqrt{7}$

$2x + 3 = \pm\sqrt{7}$

$2x = -3 \pm \sqrt{7}$

$x = \dfrac{-3 \pm \sqrt{7}}{2}$

6. $x^2 + 8x + 3 = 0$

$x^2 + 8x = -3$

$x^2 + 8x + (4)^2 = -3 + (4)^2$

$(x + 4)^2 = 13$

$x + 4 = \pm\sqrt{13}$

$x = -4 \pm \sqrt{13}$

7. $2x^2 + 4x + 1 = 0$

$x^2 + 2x = \dfrac{-1}{2}$

$x^2 + 2x + (1)^2 = \dfrac{-1}{2} + 1$

$(x + 1)^2 = \dfrac{1}{2}$

$(x + 1) = \pm\sqrt{\dfrac{1}{2}}$

$x + 1 = \pm\dfrac{1}{\sqrt{2}}$

$x = -1 \pm \dfrac{\sqrt{2}}{2}$ or $\dfrac{-2 \pm \sqrt{2}}{2}$

8.2 Practice Problems

1. $x^2 + 5x = -1 + 2x$

$x^2 + 3x + 1 = 0$

$a = 1, b = 3, c = 1$

$x = \dfrac{-3 \pm \sqrt{3^2 - 4(1)(1)}}{2(1)}$

$x = \dfrac{-3 \pm \sqrt{5}}{2}$

2. $2x^2 + 7x + 6 = 0$

$a = 2, b = 7, c = 6$

$x = \dfrac{-7 \pm \sqrt{7^2 - 4(2)(6)}}{2(2)}$

$$x = \frac{-7 \pm \sqrt{49 - 48}}{4}$$

$$x = \frac{-7 \pm \sqrt{1}}{4}$$

$$x = \frac{-7 + 1}{4} \quad \text{or} \quad x = \frac{-7 - 1}{4}$$

$$x = -\frac{6}{4} = -\frac{3}{2} \qquad x = -2$$

3. $2x^2 - 26 = 0$

$a = 2, b = 0, c = -26$

$$x = \frac{-0 \pm \sqrt{0^2 - 4(2)(-26)}}{2(2)}$$

$$x = \frac{\pm\sqrt{208}}{4} = \frac{\pm 4\sqrt{13}}{4} = \pm\sqrt{13}$$

4. $0 = -100x^2 + 4800x - 52{,}559$

$a = -100, b = 4800, c = -52{,}559$

$$x = \frac{-4800 \pm \sqrt{(4800)^2 - 4(-100)(-52{,}559)}}{2(-100)}$$

$$x = \frac{-4800 \pm \sqrt{23{,}040{,}000 - 21{,}023{,}600}}{-200}$$

$$x = \frac{-4800 \pm \sqrt{2{,}016{,}400}}{-200}$$

$$x = \frac{-4800 \pm 1420}{-200}$$

$$x = \frac{-4800 + 1420}{-200} = 16.9 \approx 17$$

or

$$x = \frac{-4800 - 1420}{-200} = 31.1 \approx 31$$

5. $\frac{1}{x} + \frac{1}{x-1} = \frac{5}{6}$ LCD is $6x(x - 1)$.

$$6x(x-1)\left[\frac{1}{x}\right] + 6x(x-1)\left[\frac{1}{x-1}\right] = 6x(x-1)\left[\frac{5}{6}\right]$$

$$6(x - 1) + 6x = 5(x^2 - x)$$

$$6x - 6 + 6x = 5x^2 - 5x$$

$$0 = 5x^2 - 17x + 6$$

$a = 5, b = -17, c = 6$

$$x = \frac{-(-17) \pm \sqrt{(-17)^2 - 4(5)(6)}}{2(5)}$$

$$x = \frac{17 \pm \sqrt{289 - 120}}{10}$$

$$x = \frac{17 \pm \sqrt{169}}{10}$$

$$x = \frac{17 \pm 13}{10}$$

$$x = \frac{17 + 13}{10} = \frac{30}{10} = 3 \qquad x = \frac{17 - 13}{10} = \frac{2}{5}$$

6. $2x^2 - 4x + 5 = 0$

$a = 2, b = -4, c = 5$

$$x = \frac{-(-4) \pm \sqrt{(-4)^2 - 4(2)(5)}}{2(2)}$$

$$x = \frac{4 \pm \sqrt{-24}}{4}$$

$$x = \frac{4 \pm 2i\sqrt{6}}{4} = \frac{2 \pm i\sqrt{6}}{2}$$

7. $9x^2 + 12x + 4 = 0$

$a = 9, b = 12, c = 4$

$b^2 - 4ac = 12^2 - 4(9)(4) = 144 - 144 = 0$

Since the discriminant is 0, there is one rational solution.

8. (a) $x^2 - 4x + 13 = 0$

$a = 1, b = -4, c = 13$

$b^2 - 4ac = (-4)^2 - 4(1)(13) = 16 - 52 = -36$

Since the discriminant is negative, there are two complex solutions containing i.

(b) $9x^2 + 6x + 7 = 0$

$a = 9, b = 6, c = 7$

$b^2 - 4ac = 6^2 - 4(9)(7)$

$= 36 - 252 = -216$

Since the discriminant is negative, there are two complex solutions containing i.

9. $x = -10 \qquad x = -6$

$x + 10 = 0 \qquad x + 6 = 0$

$(x + 10)(x + 6) = 0$

$x^2 + 6x + 10x + 60 = 0$

$x^2 + 16x + 60 = 0$

10. $x = 2i\sqrt{3} \qquad x = -2i\sqrt{3}$

$x - 2i\sqrt{3} = 0 \qquad x + 2i\sqrt{3} = 0$

$(x - 2i\sqrt{3})(x + 2i\sqrt{3}) = 0$

$x^2 - 4i^2(\sqrt{9}) = 0$

$x^2 - 4(-1)(3) = 0$

$x^2 + 12 = 0$

8.3 Practice Problems

1. $x^4 - 5x^2 - 36 = 0$

Let $y = x^2$. Then $y^2 = x^4$.

Thus, our new equation is

$y^2 - 5y - 36 = 0.$

$(y - 9)(y + 4) = 0$

$y - 9 = 0 \qquad y + 4 = 0$

$y = 9 \qquad y = -4$

$x^2 = 9 \qquad x^2 = -4$

$x = \pm\sqrt{9} \qquad x = \pm\sqrt{-4}$

$x = \pm 3 \qquad x = \pm 2i$

2. $x^6 - 5x^3 + 4 = 0$

Let $y = x^3$. Then $y^2 = x^6$.

$y^2 - 5y + 4 = 0$

$(y - 1)(y - 4) = 0$

$y - 1 = 0 \qquad y - 4 = 0$

$y = 1 \qquad y = 4$

$x^3 = 1 \qquad x^3 = 4$

$x = 1 \qquad x = \sqrt[3]{4}$

3. $3x^{4/3} - 5x^{2/3} + 2 = 0$

Let $y = x^{2/3}$ and $y^2 = x^{4/3}$.

$3y^2 - 5y + 2 = 0$

$(3y - 2)(y - 1) = 0$

$3y - 2 = 0 \qquad y - 1 = 0$

$y = \frac{2}{3} \qquad y = 1$

$x^{2/3} = \frac{2}{3} \qquad x^{2/3} = 1$

$(x^{2/3})^3 = \left(\frac{2}{3}\right)^3 \qquad (x^{2/3})^3 = 1^3$

$x^2 = \frac{8}{27} \qquad x^2 = 1$

$x = \pm\sqrt{\frac{8}{27}} \qquad x = \pm\sqrt{1}$

$x = \pm\frac{2\sqrt{2}}{3\sqrt{3}} \qquad x = \pm 1$

$x = \pm\frac{2\sqrt{2}}{3\sqrt{3}} \cdot \frac{\sqrt{3}}{\sqrt{3}}$

$x = \pm\frac{2\sqrt{6}}{9}$

Check: for $x = \frac{2\sqrt{6}}{9}$

$3\left(\frac{2\sqrt{6}}{9}\right)^{4/3} - 5\left(\frac{2\sqrt{6}}{9}\right)^{2/3} + 2 \stackrel{?}{=} 0$

$3\left(\frac{4}{9}\right) - 5\left(\frac{2}{3}\right) + 2 \stackrel{?}{=} 0$

$\frac{4}{3} - \frac{10}{3} + 2 \stackrel{?}{=} 0$

$0 = 0$ ✓

for $x = -\frac{2\sqrt{6}}{9}$

$3\left(-\frac{2\sqrt{6}}{9}\right)^{4/3} - 5\left(-\frac{2\sqrt{6}}{9}\right)^{2/3} + 2 \stackrel{?}{=} 0$

$3\left(\frac{4}{9}\right) - 5\left(\frac{2}{3}\right) + 2 \stackrel{?}{=} 0$

$\frac{4}{3} - \frac{10}{3} + 2 \stackrel{?}{=} 0$

$0 = 0$ ✓

for $x = 1$

$3(1)^{4/3} - 5(1)^{2/3} + 2 \stackrel{?}{=} 0$

$3(1) - 5(1) + 2 \stackrel{?}{=} 0$

$0 = 0$ ✓

for $x = -1$

$3(-1)^{4/3} - 5(-1)^{2/3} + 2 \stackrel{?}{=} 0$

$3(1) - 5(1) + 2 \stackrel{?}{=} 0$

$0 = 0$ ✓

4. $3x^{1/2} = 8x^{1/4} - 4$

$3x^{1/2} - 8x^{1/4} + 4 = 0$

Let $y = x^{1/4}$ and $y^2 = x^{1/2}$.

$3y^2 - 8y + 4 = 0$

$(3y - 2)(y - 2) = 0$

$3y - 2 = 0 \qquad y - 2 = 0$

$y = \frac{2}{3} \qquad y = 2$

$x^{1/4} = \frac{2}{3} \qquad x^{1/4} = 2$

$(x^{1/4})^4 = \left(\frac{2}{3}\right)^4 \qquad (x^{1/4})^4 = (2)^4$

$x = \frac{16}{81} \qquad x = 16$

Check: for $x = \frac{16}{81}$ for $x = 16$

$3\left(\frac{16}{81}\right)^{1/2} \stackrel{?}{=} 8\left(\frac{16}{81}\right)^{1/4} - 4 \qquad 3(16)^{1/2} \stackrel{?}{=} 8(16)^{1/4} - 4$

$3\left(\frac{4}{9}\right) \stackrel{?}{=} 8\left(\frac{2}{3}\right) - 4 \qquad 3(4) \stackrel{?}{=} 8(2) - 4$

$\frac{4}{3} = \frac{4}{3}$ ✓ $\qquad 12 = 12$ ✓

8.4 Practice Problems

1. $V = \frac{1}{3}\pi r^2 h$ Solve for r.

$\frac{3V}{\pi h} = r^2$

$\pm\sqrt{\frac{3V}{\pi h}} = r \qquad r = \sqrt{\frac{3V}{\pi h}}$

2. $2y^2 + 9wy + 7w^2 = 0$ Solve for y.

$(2y + 7w)(y + w) = 0$

$2y + 7w = 0 \qquad y + w = 0$

$2y = -7w \qquad y = -w$

$y = -\frac{7}{2}w$

3. $3y^2 + 2fy - 7g = 0$ Solve for y.

Use the quadratic formula.

$a = 3, b = 2f, c = -7g$

$y = \frac{-2f \pm \sqrt{(2f)^2 - 4(3)(-7g)}}{2(3)}$

$y = \frac{-2f \pm \sqrt{4f^2 + 84g}}{6}$

$y = \frac{-2f \pm \sqrt{4(f^2 + 21g)}}{6}$

$y = \frac{-2f + 2\sqrt{(f^2 + 21g)}}{6}$

$y = \frac{-f \pm \sqrt{f^2 + 21g}}{3}$

4. $d = \frac{n^2 - 3n}{2}$ Solve for n.

Multiply each term by 2.

$2d = n^2 - 3n$

$0 = n^2 - 3n - 2d$

Use the quadratic formula.

$a = 1, b = -3, c = -2d$

$$n = \frac{-(-3) \pm \sqrt{(-3)^2 - 4(1)(-2d)}}{2}$$

$$n = \frac{3 \pm \sqrt{9 + 8d}}{2}$$

5. **(a)** $a^2 + b^2 = c^2$ Solve for b.

$$b^2 = c^2 - a^2$$

$$b = \sqrt{c^2 - a^2}$$

(b) $b = \sqrt{c^2 - a^2}$

$$b = \sqrt{(26)^2 - (24)^2}$$

$$b = \sqrt{676 - 576}$$

$$b = \sqrt{100}$$

$$b = 10$$

6. $x + x - 7 + c = 30$

$$2x - 7 + c = 30$$

$$c = -2x + 37$$

$a = x, b = x - 7, c = -2x + 37$

By the Pythagorean theorem,

$$x^2 + (x - 7)^2 = (-2x + 37)^2$$

$$x^2 + x^2 - 14x + 49 = 4x^2 - 148x + 1369$$

$$-2x^2 + 134x - 1320 = 0$$

$$x^2 - 67x + 660 = 0$$

By the quadratic formula,

$a = 1, b = -67, c = 660$

$$x = \frac{67 \pm \sqrt{(67)^2 - 4(1)(660)}}{2}$$

$$x = \frac{67 \pm \sqrt{4489 - 2640}}{2}$$

$$x = \frac{67 \pm \sqrt{1849}}{2}$$

$$x = \frac{67 \pm 43}{2}$$

$$x = \frac{67 + 43}{2} = 55 \quad \text{or} \quad x = \frac{67 - 43}{2} = 12$$

The only answer that makes sense is $x = 12$; therefore,

$$x = 12$$

$$x - 7 = 5$$

$$-2x + 37 = 13$$

The legs are 5 miles and 12 miles long. The hypotenuse of the triangle is 13 miles long.

7. $A = \pi r^2$

$$A = \pi(6)^2$$

$$= 36\pi$$

Let $x =$ the radius of the new pipe.

(area of new pipe) minus (area of old pipe) $= 45\pi$

$$\pi x^2 - 36\pi = 45\pi$$

$$\pi x^2 = 45\pi + 36\pi$$

$$x^2 = 81$$

$$x = \pm 9$$

Since the radius must be positive, we select $x = 9$. The radius of the new pipe is 9 inches. The radius of the new pipe has been increased by 3 inches.

8. Let $x =$ width. Then $2x - 3 =$ the length.

$$x(2x - 3) = 54$$

$$2x^2 - 3x = 54$$

$$2x^2 - 3x - 54 = 0$$

$$(2x + 9)(x - 6) = 0$$

$$2x + 9 = 0 \qquad x - 6 = 6$$

$$x = -\frac{9}{2} \qquad x = 6$$

We do not use the negative value.

Thus, width $= 6$ feet

length $= 2x - 3 = 2(6) - 3 = 9$ feet

9.

	Distance	Rate	Time
Secondary Road	150	x	$\frac{150}{x}$
Better Road	240	$x + 10$	$\frac{240}{x + 10}$
TOTAL	390	(not used)	7

$$\frac{150}{x} + \frac{240}{x + 10} = 7$$

The LCD of this equation is $x(x + 10)$. Multiply each term by the LCD.

$$x(x + 10)\left[\frac{150}{x}\right] + x(x + 10)\left[\frac{240}{x + 10}\right] = x(x + 10)[7]$$

$$150(x + 10) + 240x = 7x(x + 10)$$

$$150x + 1500 + 240x = 7x^2 + 70x$$

$$7x^2 - 320x - 1500 = 0$$

$$(x - 50)(7x + 30) = 0$$

$$x - 50 = 0 \qquad 7x + 30 = 0$$

$$x = 50 \qquad x = \frac{-30}{7}$$

We disregard the negative answer. Thus, $x = 50$ mph, so Carlos drove 50 mph on the secondary road and 60 mph on the better road.

8.5 Practice Problems

1. $f(x) = x^2 - 6x + 5$

$a = 1, b = -6, c = 15$

Step 1 The vertex occurs at $x = \frac{-b}{2a}$. Thus, $x = \frac{-(-6)}{2(1)} = 3$

The vertex has an x-coordinate of 3.

To find the y-coordinate, we evaluate $f(3)$.

$$f(3) = 3^2 - 6(3) + 5$$

$$= 9 - 18 + 5$$

$$= -4$$

Thus, the vertex is $(3, -4)$.

Step 2 The y-intercept is at $f(0)$.

$$f(0) = 0^2 - 6(0) + 5$$
$$= 5$$

The y-intercept is $(0, 5)$.

Step 3 The x-intercept is at $f(x) = 0$.

$$x^2 - 6x + 5 = 0$$
$$(x - 5)(x - 1) = 0$$
$$x - 5 = 0 \qquad x - 1 = 0$$
$$x = 5 \qquad x = 1$$

Thus, the x-intercepts are $(5, 0)$ and $(1, 0)$.

2. $g(x) = x^2 - 2x - 2$

$a = 1, b = -2, c = -2$

Step 1 The vertex occurs at

$$x = \frac{-b}{2a}$$
$$x = \frac{-(-2)}{2(1)} = \frac{2}{2} = 1$$

The vertex has an x-coordinate of 1. To find the y-coordinate, we evaluate $f(1)$.

$$g(1) = 1^2 - 2(1) - 2$$
$$= 1 - 2 - 2$$
$$= -3$$

Thus, the vertex is $(1, -3)$.

Step 2 The y-intercept is at $g(0)$.

$$g(0) = 0^2 - 2(0) - 2$$
$$= -2$$

The y-intercept is $(0, -2)$.

Step 3 The x-intercepts occur when $g(x) = 0$.

We set $x^2 - 2x - 2 = 0$ and solve for x. The equation does not factor, so we use the quadratic formula.

$$x = \frac{-(-2) \pm \sqrt{12}}{2} = \frac{2 \pm 2\sqrt{3}}{2} = 1 \pm \sqrt{3}$$

The x-intercepts are approximately $(2.7, 0)$ and $(-0.7, 0)$.

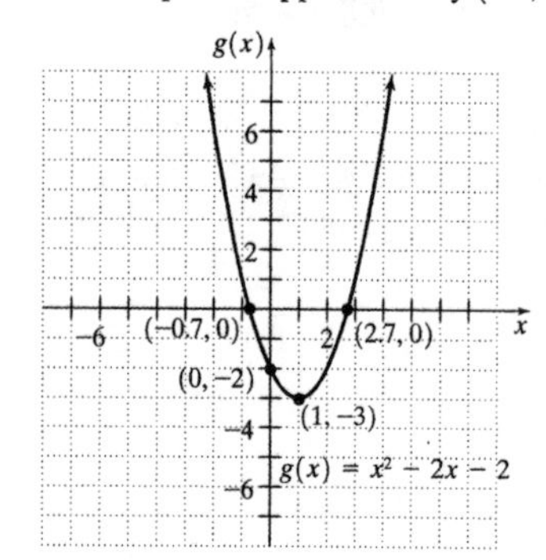

3. $g(x) = -2x^2 - 8x - 6$

$a = -2, b = -8, c = -6$

Since $a < 0$, the parabola opens downward.

The vertex occurs at

$$x = \frac{-b}{2a} = \frac{-(-8)}{2(-2)} = -2.$$

To find the y-coordinate, evaluate $g(-2)$.

$$g(-2) = -2(-2)^2 - 8(-2) - 6$$
$$= -8 + 16 - 6$$
$$= 2$$

Thus, the vertex is $(-2, 2)$.

The y-intercept is at $g(0)$.

$$g(0) = -2(0)^2 - 8(0) - 6$$
$$= -6$$

The y-intercept is $(0, -6)$.

The x-intercepts occur when $g(x) = 0$.

Using the quadratic formula.

$$x = \frac{-(-8) \pm \sqrt{64 - 4(-2)(-6)}}{2(-2)}$$
$$= \frac{8 \pm \sqrt{16}}{-4} = -2 \pm -1$$
$$x = -3, \qquad x = -1$$

The x-intercepts are $(-3, 0)$ and $(-1, 0)$.

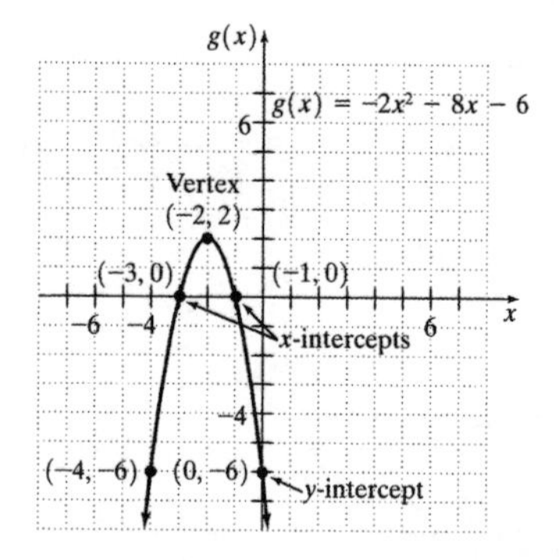

8.6 Practice Problems

1. $x^2 - 2x - 8 < 0$

Replace the inequality by an equal sign and solve.

$(x - 4)(x + 2) = 0$

$x = 4 \qquad x = -2$

Region I	$x < -2$	$(-3)^2 - 2(-3) - 8$
	$x = -3$	$= 9 + 6 - 8 = 7 > 0$
Region II	$-2 < x < 4$	$0^2 - 2(0) - 8 = -8 < 0$
	$x = 0$	
Region III	$x > 4$	$(5)^2 - 2(5) - 8 = 7 > 0$
	$x = 5$	

Thus, $x^2 - 2x - 8 < 0$ when $-2 < x < 4$.

2. $3x^2 - x - 2 \geq 0$

$(3x + 2)(x - 1) = 0$

$3x + 2 = 0 \qquad x - 1 = 0$

$x = -\frac{2}{3} \qquad x = 1$

Region I	$x < -\frac{2}{3}$	
	$x = -1$	$3(-1)^2 + 1 - 2 = 2 > 0$
Region II	$-\frac{2}{3} \leq x \leq 1$	
	$x = 0$	$3(0) - 0 - 2 = -2 < 0$
Region III	$x > 1$	
	$x = 2$	$3(2)^2 - 2 - 2 = 8 > 0$

Thus, $3x^2 - x - 2 \geq 0$ when $x \leq -\frac{2}{3}$ or when $x \geq 1$.

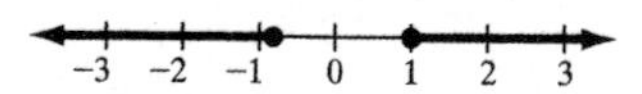

3. $x^2 + 2x < 7$

$x^2 + 2x - 7 < 0$

$x^2 + 2x - 7 = 0$

$x = \dfrac{-2 \pm \sqrt{4 + 28}}{2}$

$x = -1 \pm 2\sqrt{2}$

$x \approx 1.8$ and $x \approx -3.8$

Region I	$x < -3.8$	
	$x = -5$	$(-5)^2 + 2(-5) - 7 = 8 > 0$
Region II	$-3.8 < x < 1.8$	
	$x = 0$	$(0)^2 + 2(0) - 7 = -7 < 0$
Region III	$x > 1.8$	
	$x = 3$	$(3)^2 + 2(3) - 7 = 8 > 0$

Thus, $x^2 + 2x - 7 < 0$ when $-1 - 2\sqrt{2} < x < -1 + 2\sqrt{2}$.

Approximately $-3.8 < x < 1.8$

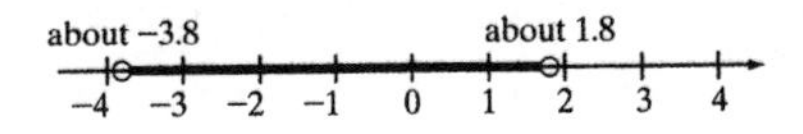

Chapter 9

9.1 Practice Problems

1. Let $(x_1, y_1) = (-6, -2)$ and $(x_2, y_2) = (3, 1)$

$$\begin{aligned} d &= \sqrt{(x_2 - x_1)^2 + (y_2 - y_1)^2} \\ &= \sqrt{[3 - (-6)]^2 + [1 - (-2)]^2} \\ &= \sqrt{(3 + 6)^2 + (1 + 2)^2} \\ &= \sqrt{(9)^2 + (3)^2} \\ &= \sqrt{81 + 9} = \sqrt{90} = 3\sqrt{10} \end{aligned}$$

2. $(x + 1)^2 + (y + 2)^2 = 9$

If we compare this to $(x - h)^2 + (y - k)^2 = r^2$, we can write it in the form

$$[x - (-1)]^2 + [y - (-2)]^2 = 3^2.$$

Thus, we see the center is $(h, k) = (-1, -2)$ and the radius is $r = 3$.

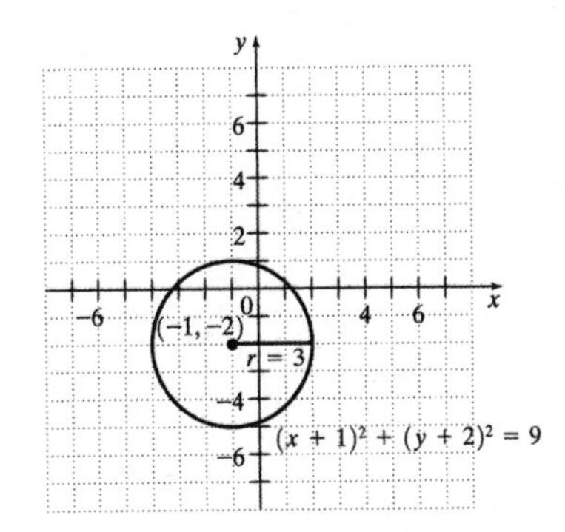

3. We are given that $(h, k) = (-5, 0)$ and $r = \sqrt{3}$. Thus, $(x - h)^2 + (y - k)^2 = r^2$ becomes

$$[x - (-5)]^2 + (y - 0)^2 = (\sqrt{3})^2$$

$$(x + 5)^2 + y^2 = 3$$

4. To write $x^2 + 4x + y^2 + 2y - 20 = 0$ in standard form, we complete the square.

$$x^2 + 4x + \_\_\_\_\_ + y^2 + 2y + \_\_\_\_\_ = 20$$

$$x^2 + 4x + 4 + y^2 + 2y + 1 = 20 + 4 + 1$$

$$x^2 + 4x + 4 + y^2 + 2y + 1 = 25$$

$$(x + 2)^2 + (y + 1)^2 = 25$$

The circle has its center at $(-2, -1)$ and the radius is 5.

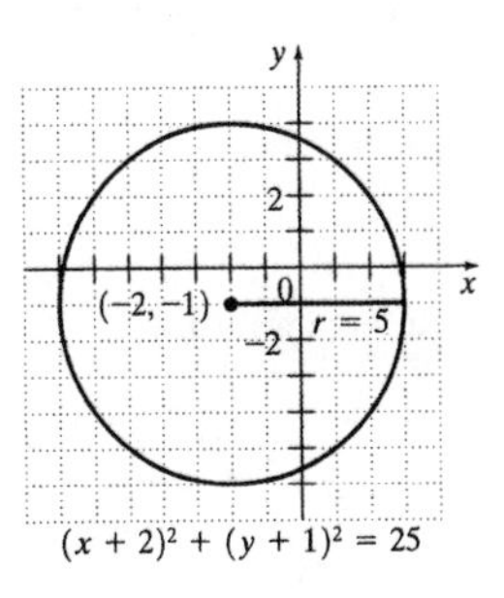

9.2 Practice Problems

1. Make a table of values. Begin with $x = -3$ in the middle of the table because $(-3 + 3) = 0$. Plot the points and draw the graph.

x	y
−5	−4
−4	−1
−3	0
−2	−1
−1	−4
0	−9

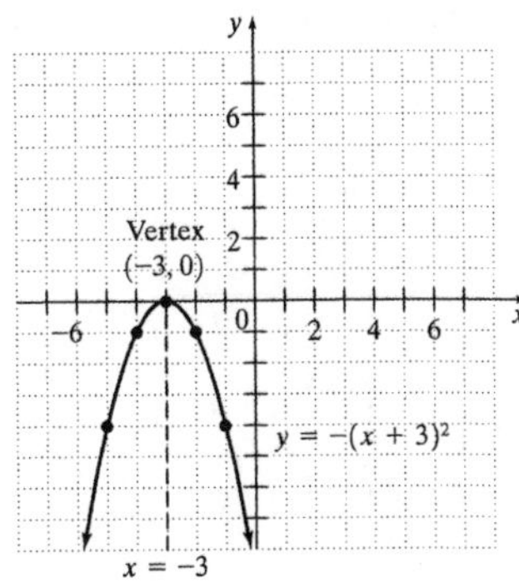

The vertex is $(-3, 0)$, and the axis of symmetry is the line $x = -3$.
$y = -(x + 3)^2$

2. This graph looks like the graph of $y = x^2$, except that it is shifted 6 units to the right and 4 units up.
The vertex is $(6, 4)$. The axis of symmetry is $x = 6$.
If $x = 0$, $y = (0 - 6)^2 + 4 = 36 + 4 = 40$, so the y-intercept is $(0, 40)$.

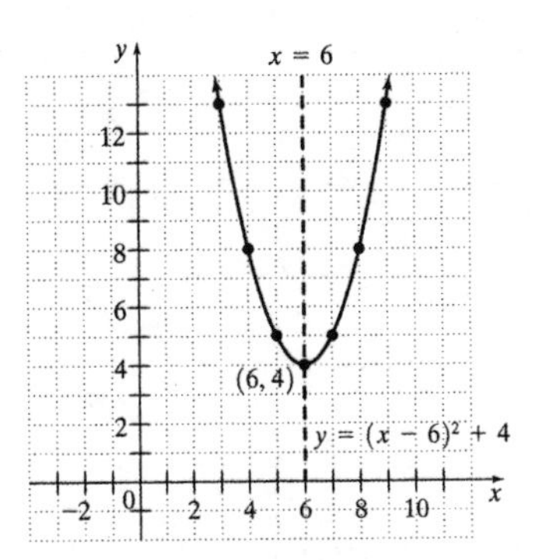

3. Step 1 The equation has the form $y = a(x - h)^2 + k$, where $a = \frac{1}{4}$, $h = 2$, and $k = 3$, so it is a vertical parabola.

Step 2 $a > 0$; so the parabola opens upward.

Step 3 We have $h = 2$ and $k = 3$. Therefore, the vertex is $(2, 3)$.

Step 4 The axis of symmetry is the line $x = 2$. Plot a few points on either side of the axis of symmetry. At $x = 4$, $y = 4$. Thus, the point is $(4, 4)$. The image from symmetry is $(0, 4)$. At $x = 6$, $y = 7$. Thus the point is $(6, 7)$. The image from symmetry is $(-2, 7)$.

At $x = 0$,

$$y = \frac{1}{4}(0 - 2)^2 + 3$$
$$= \frac{1}{4}(4) + 3$$
$$= 1 + 3 = 4.$$

Thus, the y-intercept is $(0, 4)$.

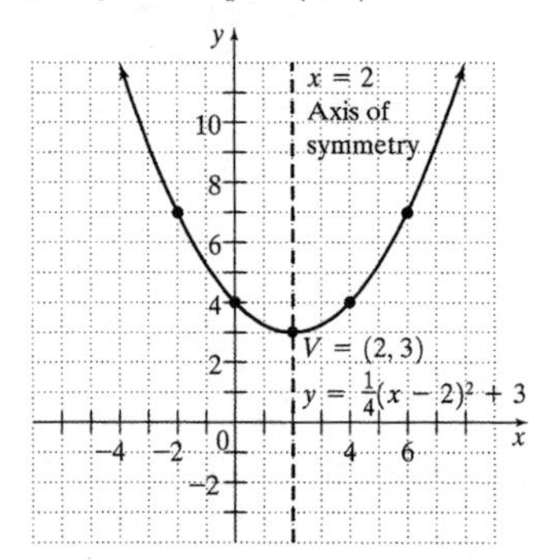

4. Make a table, plot points and draw the graph. Choose values of y and find x. Begin with $y = 0$. $x = -2y^2 + 4$

x	y
−4	2
2	1
4	0
2	−1
−4	−2

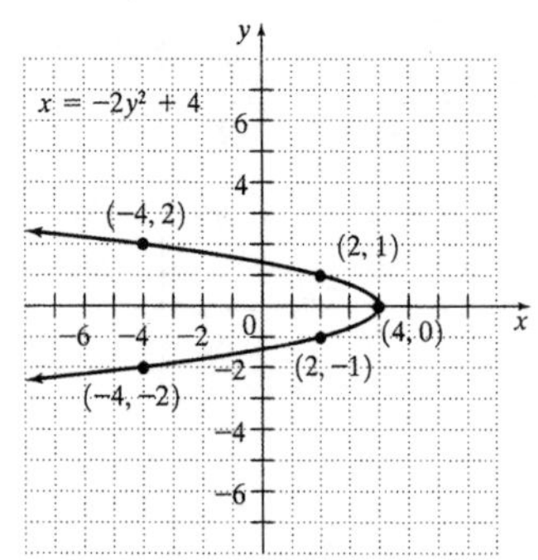

The vertex is at $(4, 0)$. The axis of symmetry is the x-axis.

5. Step 1 The equation has the form $x = a(y - k)^2 + h$, so it is a horizontal parabola.

Step 2 $a < 0$; so the parabola opens to the left.

Step 3 We have $k = -1$ and $h = -3$. Therefore, the vertex is $(-3, -1)$.

Step 4 The line $y = -1$ is the axis of symmetry. At $y = 0$, $x = -4$. Thus, we have the point $(-4, 0)$ and $(-4, -2)$ from symmetry. At $y = 1$, $x = -7$. Thus, we have the point $(-7, 1)$ and $(-7, -3)$ from symmetry.

Step 5 At $y = 0$,

$$x = -(0 + 1)^2 - 3$$
$$= -(1) - 3$$
$$= -1 - 3 = -4$$

Thus, the x-intercept is $(-4, 0)$.

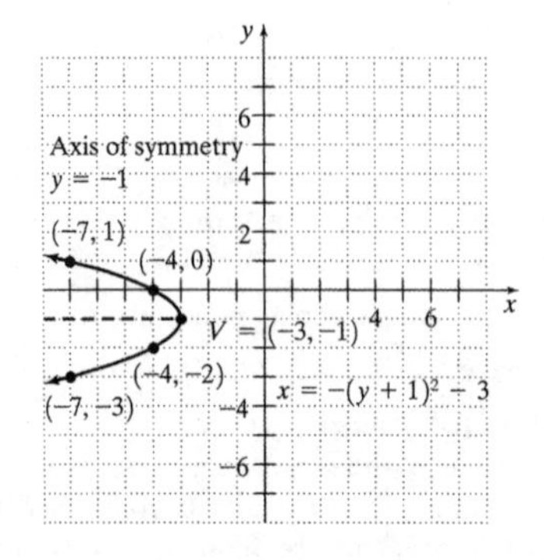

6. Since the y-term is squared, we have a horizontal parabola. The standard form is $x = a(y - k)^2 + h$.

$$x = y^2 - 6y + 13$$
$$= y^2 - 6y + \left(\frac{6}{2}\right)^2 - \left(\frac{6}{2}\right)^2 + 13 \quad \text{Complete the square.}$$
$$= (y^2 - 6y + 9) + 4$$
$$= (y - 3)^2 + 4$$

Therefore, we know that $a = 1, k = 3$, and $h = 4$. The vertex is at $(4, 3)$. The axis of symmetry is $y = 3$. If $y = 0$, $x = (-3)^2 + 4 = 9 + 4 = 13$. So the x-intercept is $(13, 0)$.

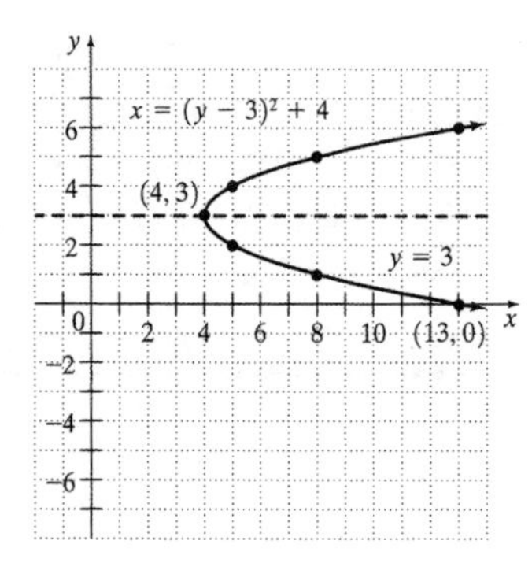

7. $y = 2x^2 + 8x + 9$

Since the x-term is squared, we have a vertical parabola. The standard form is

$$y = a(x - h)^2 + k$$
$$y = 2x^2 + 8x + 9$$
$$= 2(x^2 + 4x + \_\_\_\_) - \_\_\_\_ + 9 \quad \text{Complete the square.}$$
$$= 2(x^2 + 4x + 4) - 2(4) + 9$$
$$= 2(x + 2)^2 + 1$$

The parabola opens upward. The vertex is $(-2, 1)$, and the y-intercept is $(0, 9)$. The axis of symmetry is $x = -2$

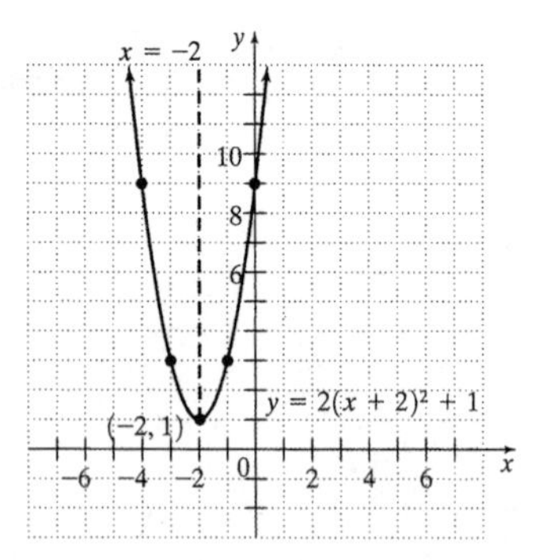

9.3 Practice Problems

1. Write the equation in standard form.

$$4x^2 + y^2 = 16$$
$$\frac{4x^2}{16} + \frac{y^2}{16} = \frac{16}{16}$$
$$\frac{x^2}{4} + \frac{y^2}{16} = 1$$

Thus, we have:

$a^2 = 4$ so $a = 2$

$b^2 = 16$ so $b = 4$

The x-intercepts are $(2, 0)$ and $(-2, 0)$ and the y-intercepts are $(0, 4)$ and $(0, -4)$.

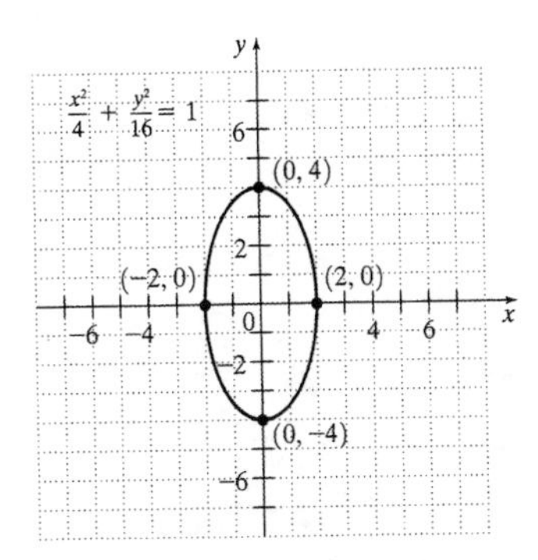

2. $\dfrac{(x-2)^2}{16} + \dfrac{(y+3)^2}{9} = 1$

The center is $(h, k) = (2, -3)$, $a = 4$, and $b = 3$. We start at $(2, -3)$ and measure to the right and to the left 4 units, and up and down 3 units.

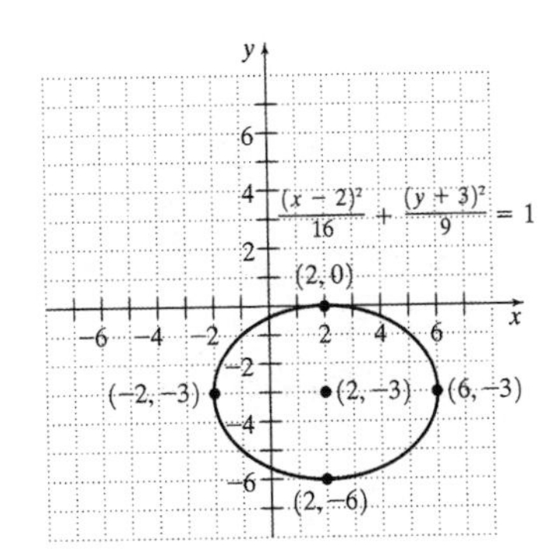

9.4 Practice Problems

1. $\dfrac{x^2}{16} - \dfrac{y^2}{25} = 1$

This is the equation of a horizontal hyperbola with center $(0, 0)$, where $a = 4$ and $b = 5$. The vertices are $(-4, 0)$ and $(4, 0)$.

Construct a fundamental rectangle with corners at $(4, 5)$, $(4, -5)$, $(-4, 5)$, and $(-4, -5)$. Draw extended diagonals as the asymptotes.

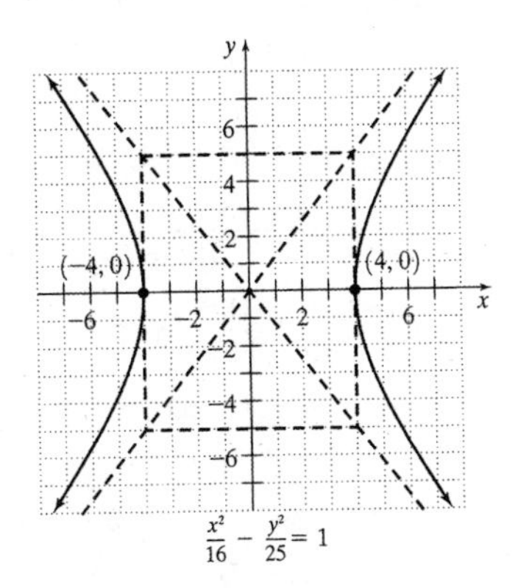

2. Write the equation in standard form.

$$y^2 - 4x^2 = 4$$

$$\frac{y^2}{4} - \frac{4x^2}{4} = \frac{4}{4}$$

$$\frac{y^2}{4} - \frac{x^2}{1} = 1$$

This is the equation of a vertical hyperbola with center $(0, 0)$, where $a = 1$ and $b = 2$. The vertices are $(0, 2)$ and $(0, -2)$.

The fundamental rectangle has corners at $(1, 2)$, $(1, -2)$, $(-1, 2)$, and $(-1, -2)$.

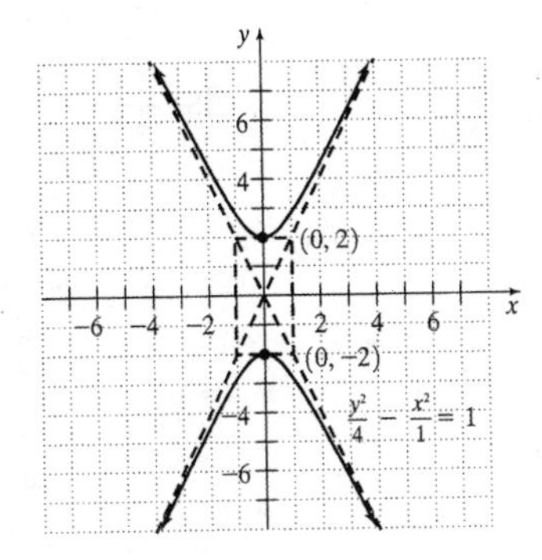

3. $\dfrac{(y+2)^2}{9} - \dfrac{(x-3)^2}{16} = 1$

This is a vertical hyperbola with center at $(3, -2)$, where $a = 4$ and $b = 3$. The vertices are $(3, 1)$ and $(3, -5)$. The fundamental rectangle has corners at $(7, 1)$, $(7, -5)$, $(-1, 1)$, and $(-1, -5)$.

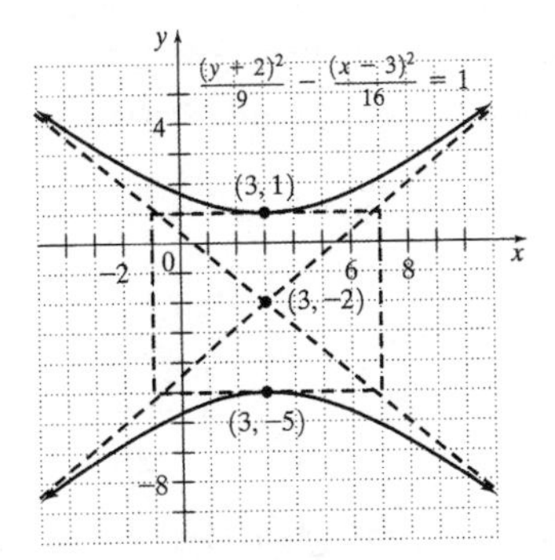

9.5 Practice Problems

1. $\dfrac{x^2}{4} - \dfrac{y^2}{4} = 1$ $\qquad x + y + 1 = 0$

$x^2 - y^2 = 4 \quad (1)$ $\qquad y = -x - 1 \quad (2)$

Substitute (2) into (1).

$$x^2 - (-x - 1)^2 = 4$$

$$x^2 - (x^2 + 2x + 1) = 4$$

$$x^2 - x^2 - 2x - 1 = 4$$

$$-2x - 1 = 4$$

$$-2x = 5$$

$$x = \frac{5}{-2} = -2.5$$

Now substitute the value for x in the equation $y = -x - 1$.

For $x = -2.5$: $y = -(-2.5) - 1 = 2.5 - 1 = 1.5$.

The solution is $(-2.5, 1.5)$.

2. $2x - 9 = y \quad (1)$

$xy = -4 \quad (2)$ $\qquad$ Solve equation (2) for y.

$y = \dfrac{-4}{x} \quad (3)$

Substitute equation (3) into (1) and solve for x.

$$2x - 9 = \frac{-4}{x}$$
$$2x^2 - 9x + 4 = 0$$
$$(2x - 1)(x - 4) = 0$$
$$2x - 1 = 0 \qquad x - 4 = 0$$
$$x = \frac{1}{2} \quad \text{or} \quad x = 4$$

$x = \frac{1}{2}$ and $x = 4$

For $x = \frac{1}{2}$:

$$y = \frac{-4}{\frac{1}{2}} = -8.$$

For $x = 4$:

$$y = \frac{-4}{4} = -1.$$

The solutions are $(4, -1)$ and $\left(\frac{1}{2}, -8\right)$.

The graph of $y = \frac{-4}{x}$ is the graph of $y = \frac{1}{x}$ reflected across the x-axis and stretched by a factor of 4. The graph of $y = 2x - 9$ is a line with slope 2 passing through the point $(0, -9)$, The sketch show that the points $(4, -1)$ and $\left(\frac{1}{2}, -8\right)$ seem reasonable.

3. 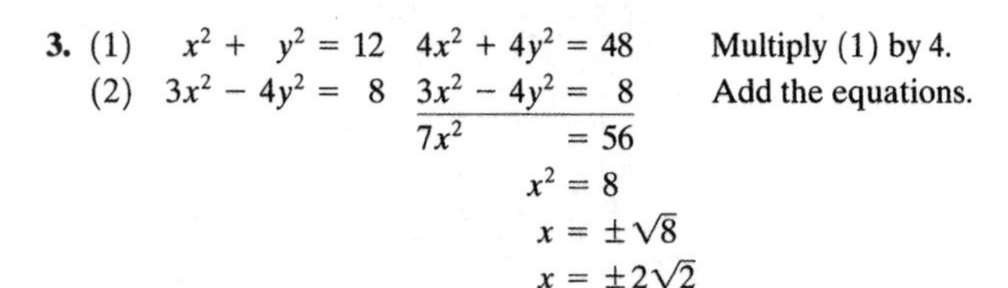

(1) $x^2 + y^2 = 12 \qquad 4x^2 + 4y^2 = 48$ Multiply (1) by 4.

(2) $3x^2 - 4y^2 = 8 \qquad 3x^2 - 4y^2 = 8$ Add the equations.

$$7x^2 = 56$$
$$x^2 = 8$$
$$x = \pm\sqrt{8}$$
$$x = \pm 2\sqrt{2}$$

If $x = 2\sqrt{2}$, then $x^2 = 8$. Substituting this value into equation (1) gives

$$8 + y^2 = 12$$
$$y^2 = 4$$
$$y = \pm\sqrt{4}$$
$$y = \pm 2$$

Similarly, if $x = -2\sqrt{2}$, then $y = \pm 2$.

Thus, the four solutions are $(2\sqrt{2}, 2)$, $(2\sqrt{2}, -2)$, $(-2\sqrt{2}, 2)$, $(-2\sqrt{2}, -2)$.

Chapter 10

10.1 Practice Problems

1. (a) $g(a) = \frac{1}{2}a - 3$

(b) $g(a + 4) = \frac{1}{2}(a + 4) - 3$

$$= \frac{1}{2}a + 2 - 3$$
$$= \frac{1}{2}a - 1$$

(c) $g(a) = \frac{1}{2}a - 3$

$$g(4) = \frac{1}{2}(4) - 3 = 2 - 3 = -1$$

Thus, $g(a) + g(4) = \left(\frac{1}{2}a - 3\right) + (-1)$

$$= \frac{1}{2}a - 3 - 1$$
$$= \frac{1}{2}a - 4$$

2. (a) $p(-3) = -3(-3)^2 + 2(-3) + 4$

$$= -3(9) + 2(-3) + 4$$
$$= -27 - 6 + 4$$
$$= -29$$

(b) $p(a) = -3(a)^2 + 2(a) + 4$

$$= -3a^2 + 2a + 4$$

(c) $p(2a) = -3(2a)^2 + 2(2a) + 4$

$$= -3(4a^2) + 2(2a) + 4$$
$$= -12a^2 + 4a + 4$$

(d) $p(a - 3) = -3(a - 3)^2 + 2(a - 3) + 4$

$$= -3(a - 3)(a - 3) + 2(a - 3) + 4$$
$$= -3(a^2 - 6a + 9) + 2(a - 3) + 4$$
$$= -3a^2 + 18a - 27 + 2a - 6 + 4$$
$$= -3a^2 + 20a - 29$$

3. (a) $r(a + 2) = \frac{-3}{(a + 2) + 1}$

$$= \frac{-3}{a + 3}$$

(b) $r(a) = \frac{-3}{a + 1}$

(c) $r(a + 2) - r(a) = \frac{-3}{a + 3} - \left(\frac{-3}{a + 1}\right)$

$$= \frac{-3}{a + 3} + \frac{3}{a + 1}$$
$$= \frac{(a + 1)(-3)}{(a + 1)(a + 3)} + \frac{3(a + 3)}{(a + 1)(a + 3)}$$
$$= \frac{-3a - 3}{(a + 1)(a + 3)} + \frac{3a + 9}{(a + 1)(a + 3)}$$
$$= \frac{-3a - 3 + 3a + 9}{(a + 1)(a + 3)}$$
$$= \frac{6}{(a + 1)(a + 3)}$$

4. $g(x + h) = 2 - 5(x + h) = 2 - 5x - 5h$

$g(x) = 2 - 5x$

$g(x + h) - g(x) = (2 - 5x - 5h) - (2 - 5x)$

$$= 2 - 5x - 5h - 2 + 5x$$
$$= -5h$$

Therefore, $\frac{g(x + h) - g(x)}{h} = \frac{-5h}{h} = -5.$

5. (a) $S(r) = 16(3.14)r + 2(3.14)r^2 = 50.24r + 6.28r^2$

(b) $S(2) = 50.24(2) + 6.28(2)^2$

$$= 50.24(2) + 6.28(4)$$
$$= 125.6 \text{ square meters}$$